WILLIAM JOSEPH LONG (3 April 1867 – 1952) was an American writer, naturalist and minister. He lived and worked in Stamford, Connecticut as a minister of the First Congregationalist Church.

As a naturalist, he would leave Stamford every March, often with his son, Brian, and two daughters, Lois and Cesca, to travel to "the wilderness" of Maine. There they would stay until the first snows of October, although sometimes he would stay all winter. In the 1920s, he began spending his summers in Nova Scotia, claiming "the wilderness is getting too crowded".

He wrote of these wilderness experiences in the books *Ways of Wood Folk, Wilderness Ways, Wood-folk Comedies, Northern Trails, Wood Folk at School,* and many others. His earlier books were illustrated by Charles Copeland; two later ones were illustrated by Charles Livingston Bull. Long believed that the best way to experience the wild was to "plant yourself and sit for hours on end to let the wild come to you; and they will!"

Long also wrote English Literature which presents the whole splendid history of English Literature from Anglo-Saxon times to the close of the Victorian Era.

AF889218

English Literature

Its History and Its Significance for the Life of the English-Speaking World

WILLIAM J. LONG

Sahitya Sarowar

Published by :
Sahitya Sarowar

Sales Office :
17-A, Prabhoo Nagar, Near Pratap Nagar,
Agra-282002 (U. P.)
Mobile : 9456483713, 9575368775
E-mail : info@sahityasarowar.com
Website : www.sahityasarowar.com
www.facebook.com/sahityasarowar1718
www.twitter.com/sarowarsahitya
www.Instagram.com/sahitya.sarowar
www.amazon.in/sahitya sarowar
www.flipkart.com/sahitya sarowar

ENGLISH LITERATURE by William J. Long

ALL RIGHTS RESERVED. No part of this book may be reproduced in a retrieval system or transmitted in any form or by any means electronics, mechanical, photocopying, recording and or without any permission of the publisher.

Disclaimer

- The author and the publisher have taken every effort to the maximum of their skill, expertise and knowledge to provide correct material in the book. Even then if some mistakes persist in the content of the book, the publisher does not take responsibility for the same. The publisher shall have no liability to any person or entity with respect to any loss or damage caused, or alleged to have been caused directly or indirectly, by the information contained in this book.
- The author has fully tried to follow the copyright law. However, if any work is found to be similar, it is unintentional and the same should not be used as defamatory or to file legal suit against the author.
- If the readers find any mistakes, we shall be grateful to them for pointing out those to us so that these can be corrected in the next edition.
- All disputes are subject to the jurisdiction of Agra courts only.

For more information, visit our **website : www.sahityasarowar.com**
or Download our **Sahitya Sarowar App** from Google Play Store.

ISBN : 978-93-90597-30-7

Printed in India

TO
MY FRIEND
C.H.T.
IN GRATITUDE FOR
HIS CONTINUED HELP IN THE
PREPARATION OF
THIS BOOK

Preface

This book, which presents the whole splendid history of English literature from Anglo-Saxon times to the close of the Victorian Era, has three specific aims. The first is to create or to encourage in every student the desire to read the best books, and to know literature itself rather than what has been written about literature. The second is to interpret literature both personally and historically, that is, to show how a great book generally reflects not only the author's life and thought but also the spirit of the age and the ideals of the nation's history. The third aim is to show, by a study of each successive period, how our literature has steadily developed from its first simple songs and stories to its present complexity in prose and poetry.

To carry out these aims we have introduced the following features:

(1) A brief, accurate summary of historical events and social conditions in each period, and a consideration of the ideals which stirred the whole nation, as in the days of Elizabeth, before they found expression in literature.

(2) A study of the various literary epochs in turn, showing what each gained from the epoch preceding, and how each aided in the development of a national literature.

(3) A readable biography of every important writer, showing how he lived and worked, how he met success or failure, how he influenced his age, and how his age influenced him.

(4) A study and analysis of every author's best works, and of many of the books required for college-entrance examinations.

(5) Selections enough—especially from earlier writers, and from writers not likely to be found in the home or school library—to indicate the spirit of each author's work; and directions as to the best works to read, and where such works may be found in inexpensive editions.

(6) A frank, untechnical discussion of each great writer's work as a whole, and a critical estimate of his relative place and influence in our literature.

(7) A series of helps to students and teachers at the end of each chapter, including summaries, selections for reading, bibliographies, a list of suggestive questions, and a chronological table of important events in the history and literature of each period.

(8) Throughout this book we have remembered Roger Ascham's suggestion, made over three centuries ago and still pertinent, that "'t is a poor way to make a child love study by beginning with the things which he naturally dislikes." We have laid emphasis upon the delights of literature; we have treated books not as mere instruments of research—which is the danger in most of our studies--but rather as instruments of enjoyment and of inspiration; and by making our study as attractive as possible we have sought to encourage the student to read widely for himself, to choose the best books, and to form his own judgment about what our first Anglo-Saxon writers called "the things worthy to be remembered."

To those who may use this book in their homes or in their classrooms, the writer ventures to offer one or two friendly suggestions out of his own experience as a teacher of young people. First, the amount of space here given to different periods and authors is not an index of the relative amount of time to be spent upon the different subjects. Thus, to tell the story of Spenser's life and ideals requires as much space as to tell the story of Tennyson; but the average class will spend its time more pleasantly and profitably with the latter poet than with the former. Second, many authors, who are and ought to be included in this history need not be studied in the classroom.

A textbook is not a catechism but a storehouse, in which one finds what he wants, and some good things beside. Few classes will find time to study Blake or Newman, for instance; but in nearly every class there will be found one or two students who are attracted by the mysticism of Blake or by the profound spirituality of Newman. Such students should be encouraged to follow their own spirits, and to share with their classmates the joy of their discoveries. And they should find in their textbook the material for their own study and reading.

A third suggestion relates to the method of teaching literature; and here it might be well to consider the word of a great poet—that if you would know where the ripest cherries are, ask the boys and the blackbirds. It is surprising how much a young person will get out of the *Merchant of Venice*, and somehow arrive at Shakespeare's opinion of Shylock and Portia, if we do not bother him too much with notes and critical directions as to what he ought to seek and find. Turn a child and a donkey loose in the same field, and the child heads straight for the beautiful spots where brooks are running and birds singing, while the donkey turns as naturally to weeds and thistles. In our study of literature we have perhaps too much sympathy with the latter, and we even insist that the child come back from his own quest of the ideal to join us in our critical companionship. In reading many textbooks of late, and in visiting many class rooms, the writer has received the impression that we lay too much stress on second-hand criticism, passed down from book to book; and we set our pupils to searching for figures of speech and elements of style, as if the great books of the world were subject to chemical analysis. This seems to be a mistake, for two reasons: first, the average young person has no natural interest in such matters; and second, he is unable to appreciate them. He feels unconsciously with Chaucer:

> And as for me, though that my wit be lytë,
> On bookës for to rede I me delytë.

Indeed, many mature persons (including the writer of this history) are often unable to explain at first the charm or the style of an author, who pleases them; and the more profound the impression made by a book, the more difficult it is to give expression to our thought and feeling. To read and enjoy good books is with us, as with Chaucer, the main thing; to analyze the author's style or explain our own enjoyment seems of secondary and small importance. However that may be, we state frankly our own conviction that the detailed study and analysis of a few standard works—which is the only literary pabulum given to many young people in our schools—bears the same relation to true literature that theology bears to religion, or psychology to friendship. One is a more or less unwelcome mental discipline; the other is the joy of life. The writer ventures to suggest, therefore, that, since literature is our subject, we begin and end with good books; and that we stand aside while the great writers speak their own message to our pupils. In studying each successive period, let the student begin by reading the best that the age produced; let him feel in his own way the power and mystery of *Beowulf*, the broad charity of Shakespeare, the sublimity of Milton, the romantic enthusiasm of Scott; and then, when his own taste is pleased and satisfied, a new one will arise—to know something about the author, the times in which he lived, and finally of criticism, which, in its simplicity, is the discovery that the men and women of other ages were very much like ourselves, loving as we love, bearing the same burdens, and following the same ideals:

Lo, with the ancient
Roots of man's nature
Twines the eternal
Passion of song.

Ever Love fans it;
Ever Life feeds it;
Time cannot age it;
Death cannot slay.

To answer the questions which arise naturally between teacher and pupil concerning the books that they read, is one object of this volume. It aims not simply to instruct but also to inspire; to trace the historical development of English literature, and at the same time to allure its readers to the best books and the best writers. And from beginning to end, it is written upon the assumption that the first virtue of such a work is to be accurate, and the second to be interesting.

The author acknowledges, with gratitude and appreciation, his indebtedness to Professor William Lyon Phelps for the use of his literary map of England, and to the keen critics, teachers of literature and history, who have read the proofs of this book, and have improved it by their good suggestions.

WILLIAM J. LONG
STAMFORD, CONNECTICUT

Contents

Full-Page Illustrations

List of Illustrations

William Shakespeare

After the Chandos Portrait in the National Portrait Gallery, London, which is attributed to Richard Burbage or John Taylor. In the catalogue of the National Portrait Gallery the following description is given :

> "The Chandos Shakespeare was the property of John Taylor the player, by whom or by Richard Burbage it was painted. The picture was left by the former in his will to Sir William Davenant. After his death it was bought by Betterton, the actor, upon whose decease Mr. Keck of the Temple purchased it for 40 guineas, from whom it was inherited by Mr. Nicoll of Michenden House, Southgate, Middlesex,whose only daughter married James, Marquess of Caernarvon, afterwards Duke of Chandos, father to Ann Eliza, Duchess of Buckingham."
>
> The above is written on paper attached to the back of the canvas. Its authenticity, however, has been doubted in some quarters.
>
> Purchased at the Stowe Sale, September 1848, by the Earl of Ellesmere, and presented by him to the nation, March 1856.

This reproduction of the portrait was made from a miniature copy on ivory by Caroline King Phillips.

Chapter 1

INTRODUCTION—THE MEANING OF LITERATURE

Hold the hye wey, and lat thy gost thee lede.

Chaucer's *Truth*

On, on, you noblest English, ...
Follow your spirit.

Shakespeare's *Henry V*

The Shell and the Book. A child and a man were one day walking on the seashore when the child found a little shell and held it to his ear. Suddenly he heard sounds,—strange, low, melodious sounds, as if the shell were remembering and repeating to itself the murmurs of its ocean home. The child's face filled with wonder as he listened. Here in the little shell, apparently, was a voice from another world, and he listened with delight to its mystery and music. Then came the man, explaining that the child heard nothing strange; that the pearly curves of the shell simply caught a multitude of sounds too faint for human ears, and filled the glimmering hollows with the murmur of innumerable echoes. It was not a new world, but only the unnoticed harmony of the old that had aroused the child's wonder.

Some such experience as this awaits us when we begin the study of literature, which has always two aspects, one of simple enjoyment and appreciation, the other of analysis and exact description. Let a little song appeal to the ear, or a noble book to the heart, and for the moment, at least, we discover a new world, a world so different from our own that it seems a place of dreams and magic. To enter and enjoy this new world, to love good books for their own sake, is the chief thing; to analyze and explain them is a less joyous but still an important matter. Behind every book is a man; behind the man is the race; and behind the race are the natural and social environments whose influence is unconsciously reflected. These also we must know, if the book is to speak its whole message. In a word, we have now reached a point where we wish to understand as well as to enjoy literature; and the first step, since exact definition is impossible, is to determine some of its essential qualities.

Qualities of Literature. The first significant thing is the essentially artistic quality of all literature. All art is the expression of life in forms of truth and beauty; or rather, it is the reflection of some truth and beauty which are in the world, but which remain unnoticed until brought to our attention by some sensitive human soul, just as the delicate curves of the shell reflect sounds and harmonies too faint to be otherwise noticed. A hundred men may pass a hayfield and see only the sweaty toil and the windrows of dried grass; but here is one who pauses by a Roumanian meadow, where girls are making hay and singing as they work. He looks deeper, sees truth and beauty where we see only dead grass, and he reflects what he sees in a little poem in which the hay tells its own story:

Artistic

Yesterday's flowers am I,
And I have drunk my last sweet draught of dew.
Young maidens came and sang me to my death;
The moon looks down and sees me in my shroud,
The shroud of my last dew.
Yesterday's flowers that are yet in me
Must needs make way for all tomorrow's flowers.
The maidens, too, that sang me to my death
Must even so make way for all the maids
That are to come.

And as my soul, so too their soul will be
Laden with fragrance of the days gone by.
The maidens that tomorrow come this way
Will not remember that I once did bloom,
For they will only see the newborn flowers.
Yet will my perfume-laden soul bring back,
As a sweet memory, to women's hearts
  Their days of maidenhood.
And then they will be sorry that they came
  To sing me to my death;
And all the butterflies will mourn for me.
  I bear away with me
The sunshine's dear remembrance, and the low
  Soft murmurs of the spring.
My breath is sweet as children's prattle is;
I drank in all the whole earth's fruitfulness,
To make of it the fragrance of my soul
  That shall outlive my death.[1]

One who reads only that f irst exquisite line, 'Yesterday's flowers am I', can never again see hay without recalling the beauty that was hidden from his eyes until the poet found it.

In the same pleasing, surprising way, all artistic work must be a kind of revelation. Thus architecture is probably the oldest of the arts; yet we still have many builders but few architects, that is, men whose work in wood or stone suggests some hidden truth and beauty to the human senses. So in literature, which is the art that expresses life in words that appeal to our own sense of the beautiful, we have many writers but few artists. In the broadest sense, perhaps, literature means simply the written records of the race, including all its history and sciences, as well as its poems and novels; in the narrower sense literature is the artistic record of life, and most of our writing is excluded from it, just as the mass of our buildings, mere shelters from storm and from cold, are excluded from architecture. A history or a work of science may be

[1] From *The Bard of the Dimbovitza,* First Series, p. 73.

and sometimes is literature, but only as we forget the subject matter and the presentation of facts in the simple beauty of its expression.

Suggestive

The second quality of literature is its suggestiveness, its appeal to our emotions and imagination rather than to our suggestive intellect. It is not so much what it says as what it awakens in us that constitutes its charm. When Milton makes Satan say, 'Myself am Hell', he does not state any fact, but rather opens up in these three tremendous words a whole world of speculation and imagination. When Faustus in the presence of Helen asks, 'Was this the face that launched a thousand ships?' he does not state a fact or expect an answer. He opens a door through which our imagination enters a new world, a world of music, love, beauty, heroism,—the whole splendid world of Greek literature. Such magic is in words. When Shakespeare describes the young Biron as speaking

> In such apt and gracious words
> That aged ears play truant at his tales,

he has unconsciously given not only an excellent description of himself, but the measure of all literature, which makes us play truant with the present world and run away to live awhile in the pleasant realm of fancy. The province of all art is not to instruct but to delight; and only as literature delights us, causing each reader to build in his own soul that 'lordly pleasure house' of which Tennyson dreamed in his 'Palace of Art', is it worthy of its name.

Permanent

The third characteristic of literature, arising directly from the other two, is its permanence. The world does not live by bread alone. Notwithstanding its hurry and bustle and apparent absorption in material things, it does not willingly let any beautiful thing perish. This is even more true of its songs than of its painting and sculpture; though permanence is a quality we should hardly expect in the present deluge of books and magazines pouring day and night from our presses in the name of literature. But this problem of too many books is not modern, as we suppose. It has been a problem ever since Caxton brought the first printing press from Flanders, four hundred years ago, and in the shadow of Westminster Abbey opened his little shop and advertised his wares as 'good and chepe'. Even earlier, a thousand years before Caxton and his printing press, the busy scholars of the great library of Alexandria found that the number of parchments was much too great for them to handle; and now, when we print more in a week than all the Alexandrian scholars could copy in a century, it would seem impossible that any production could be permanent; that any song or story could live to give delight in future ages. But literature is like a river in flood, which gradually purifies itself in two ways—the mud settles to the bottom, and the scum rises to the top. When we examine the writings that by common consent constitute our literature, the clear stream purified of its dross, we find at least two more qualities, which we call the tests of literature, and which determine its permanence.

Tests of Literature. The first of these is universality, that is, the appeal to the widest human interests and the simplest human emotions. Though we speak of national and race literatures, like the Greek or Teutonic, and though each has certain superficial marks arising out of the peculiarities of its own people, it is nevertheless true that good literature knows no nationality, nor any bounds save those of humanity. It is occupied chiefly with elementary passions and emotions—love and hate, joy and sorrow, fear and faith—which are an essential part of our human nature; and the more it reflects these emotions the more surely does it awaken a response in men of every race. Every father must respond to the parable of the prodigal son; wherever men are heroic, they will acknowledge the mastery of Homer; wherever a man thinks on the strange phenomenon of evil in the world, he will find his own thoughts in the Book of Job; in whatever place men love their children, their hearts must be stirred by the tragic sorrow of *Œdipus* and *King Lear.* All these are but shining examples of the law that only as a book or a little song appeals to universal human interest does it become permanent.

Universality

The second test is a purely personal one, and may be expressed in the indefinite word 'style.' It is only in a mechanical sense that style is 'the adequate expression of thought', or

Style

'the peculiar manner of expressing thought,' or any other of the definitions that are found in the rhetorics. In a deeper sense, style is the man, that is, the unconscious expression of the writer's own personality. It is the very soul of one man reflecting, as in a glass, the thoughts and feelings of humanity. As no glass is colourless, but tinges more or less deeply the reflections from its surface, so no author can interpret human life without unconsciously giving to it the native hue of his own soul. It is this intensely personal element that constitutes style. Every permanent book has more or less of these two elements, the objective and the subjective, the universal and the personal, the deep thought and feeling of the race reflected and coloured by the writer's own life and experience.

The Object in Studying Literature. Aside from the pleasure of reading, of entering into a new world and having our imagination quickened, the study of literature has one definite object, and that is to know men. Now man is ever a dual creature; he has an outward and an inner nature; he is not only a doer of deeds, but a dreamer of dreams; and to know him, the man of any age, we must search deeper than his history. History records his deeds, his outward acts largely; but every great act springs from an ideal, and to understand this we must read his literature, where we find his ideals recorded. When we read a history of the Anglo-Saxons, for instance, we learn that they were sea rovers, pirates, explorers, great eaters and drinkers; and we know something of their hovels and habits, and the lands which they harried and plundered. All that is interesting; but it does not tell us what most we want to know about these old ancestors of ours—not only what they did, but what they thought and felt; how they looked on life and death; what they loved, what they feared, and what they reverenced in God and man. Then we turn from history to the literature which they themselves produced, and instantly we become acquainted. These hardy people were not simply fighters and freebooters; they were men like ourselves; their emotions awaken instant response in the souls of their descendants. At the words of their gleemen we thrill again to their wild love of freedom and the open sea; we grow tender at their love of home, and patriotic at their deathless loyalty to their chief, whom they chose for themselves and hoisted on their shields in symbol of his leadership. Once more we grow respectful in the presence of pure womanhood, or melancholy before the sorrows and problems of life, or humbly confident, looking up to the God whom they dared to call the Allfather. All these and many more intensely real emotions pass through our souls as we read the few shining fragments of verses that the jealous ages have left us.

It is so with any age or people. To understand them we must read not simply their history, which records their deeds, but their literature, which records the dreams that made their deeds possible. So Aristotle was profoundly right when he said that 'poetry is more serious and philosophical than history'; and Goethe, when he explained literature as 'the humanization of the whole world.'

Importance of Literature. It is a curious and prevalent opinion that literature, like all art, is a mere play of imagination, pleasing enough, like a new novel, but without any serious or practical importance. Nothing could be farther from the truth. Literature preserves the ideals of a people; and ideals—love, faith, duty, friendship, freedom, reverence—are the part of human life most worthy of preservation. The Greeks were a marvelous people; yet of all their mighty works we cherish only a few ideals—ideals of beauty in perishable stone, and ideals of truth in imperishable prose and poetry. It was simply the ideals of the Greeks and Hebrews and Romans, preserved in their literature, which made them what they were, and which determined their value to future generations. Our democracy, the boast of all English-speaking nations, is a dream; not the doubtful and sometimes disheartening spectacle presented in our legislative halls, but the lovely and immortal ideal of a free and equal manhood, preserved as a most precious heritage in every great literature from the Greeks to the Anglo-Saxons. All our arts, our sciences, even our inventions are founded squarely upon ideals; for under every invention is still the dream of Beowulf, that man may overcome the forces of nature; and the foundation of all our sciences and discoveries is the immortal dream that men 'shall be as gods, knowing good and evil.'

In a word, our whole civilization, our freedom, our progress, our homes, our religion, rest solidly upon ideals for their foundation. Nothing but an ideal ever endures upon earth. It is therefore impossible to overestimate the practical importance of literature, which preserves these ideals from fathers to sons, while men, cities, governments, civilizations, vanish from the face of the earth. It is only when we remember this that we appreciate the action of the devout Mussulman, who picks up and carefully preserves every scrap of paper on which words are written, because the scrap may perchance contain the name of Allah, and the ideal is too enormously important to be neglected or lost.

Summary of the Subject. We are now ready, if not to define, at least to understand a little more clearly the object of our present study. Literature is the expression of life in words of truth and beauty; it is the written record of man's spirit, of his thoughts, emotions, aspirations; it is the history, and the only history, of the human soul. It is characterized by its artistic, its suggestive, its permanent qualities. Its two tests are its universal interest and its personal style. Its object, aside from the delight it gives us, is to know man, that is, the soul of man rather than his actions; and since it preserves to the race the ideals upon which all our civilization is founded, it is one of the most important and delightful subjects that can occupy the human mind.

Bibliography. (Note. Each chapter in this book includes a special bibliography of historical and literary works, selections for reading, chronology, etc.; and a general bibliography of texts, helps, and reference books will be found at the end. The following books, which are among the best of their kind, are intended to help the student to a better appreciation of literature and to a better knowledge of literary criticism.)

General Works. Woodberry's Appreciation of Literature (Baker & Taylor Co.); Gates's Studies in Appreciation (Macmillan); Bates's Talks on the Study of Literature (Houghton, Mifflin); Worsfold's On the Exercise of Judgment in Literature (Dent); Harrison's The Choice of Books (Macmillan); Ruskin's Sesame and Lilies, Part I; Matthew Arnold's Essays in Criticism.

Essays. Emerson's Books, in Society and Solitude; Dowden's The Interpretation of Literature, in Transcripts and Studies (Kegan Paul & Co.), and The Teaching of English Literature, in New Studies in Literature (Houghton, Mifflin); The Study of Literature, Essays by Morley, Nicolls, and L. Stephen, edited by A.F. Blaisdell (Willard Small).

Criticism. Gayley and Scott's An Introduction to the Methods and Materials of Literary Criticism (Ginn and Company); Winchester's Principles of Literary Criticism (Macmillan); Worsfold's Principles of Criticism (Longmans); Johnson's Elements of Literary Criticism (American Book Company); Saintsbury's History of Criticism (Dodd, Mead).

Poetry. Gummere's Handbook of Poetics (Ginn and Company); Stedman's The Nature and Elements of Poetry (Houghton, Mifflin); Johnson's The Forms of English Poetry (American Book Company); Alden's Specimens of English Verse (Holt); Gummere's The Beginnings of Poetry (Macmillan); Saintsbury's History of English Prosody (Macmillan).

The Drama. Caffin's Appreciation of the Drama (Baker & Taylor Co.).

The Novel. Raleigh's The English Novel (Scribner); Hamilton's The Materials and Methods of Fiction (Baker & Taylor Co.).

Chapter 2

THE ANGLO-SAXON OR OLD-ENGLISH PERIOD (450-1050)

I. OUR FIRST POETRY

Beowulf. Here is the story of Beowulf, the earliest and the greatest epic, or heroic poem, in our literature. It begins with a prologue, which is not an essential part of the story, but which we review gladly for the sake of the splendid poetical conception that produced Scyld, king of the Spear Danes.[1]

At a time when the Spear Danes were without a king, a ship came sailing into their harbour. It was filled with treasures and weapons of war; and in the midst of these warlike things was a baby sleeping. No man sailed the ship; it came of itself, bringing the child, whose name was Scyld.

Now Scyld grew and became a mighty warrior, and led the Spear Danes for many years, and was their king. When his son Beowulf[2] had become strong and wise enough to rule, then Wyrd (Fate), who speaks

[1] There is a mystery about this old hero whch stirs our imagination, but which it never explained. It refers, probably, to some legend of the Anglo-Saxons which we have supplied from other sources, aided by some vague suggestions and glimpses of the past in the poem itself.

[2] This is not the Beowulf who is hero of the poem.

but once to any man, came and stood at hand; and it was time for Scyld to go. This is how they buried him:

Then Scyld departed, at word of Wyrd spoken,
The hero to go to the home of the gods.
Sadly they bore him to brink of the ocean,
Comrades, still heeding his word of command.

There rode in the harbor the prince's ship, ready,
With prow curving proudly and shining sails set.
Shipward they bore him, their hero beloved;
The mighty they laid at the foot of the mast.

Treasures were there from far and near gathered,
Byrnies of battle, armour and swords;
Never a keel sailed out of a harbour
So splendidly tricked with the trappings of war.

They heaped on his bosom a hoard of bright jewels
To fare with him forth on the flood's great breast.
No less gift they gave than the Unknown provided,
When alone, as a child, he came in from the mere.

High o'er his head waved a bright golden standard—
Now let the waves bear their wealth to the holm.
Sad-souled they gave back its gift to the ocean,
Mournful their mood as he sailed out to sea.[1]

'And no man', says the poet, 'neither counselor nor hero, can tell who received that lading.'

One of Scyld's descendants was Hrothgar, king of the Danes; and with him the story of our Beowulf begins. Hrothgar in his old age had built near the sea a mead hall called Heorot, the most splendid hall in the whole world, where the king and his thanes gathered nightly to feast and to listen to the songs of his gleemen. One night, as they were all sleeping, a frightful monster, Grendel, broke into the hall, killed thirty of the sleeping warriors, and carried off their bodies to devour them in his lair under the sea. The appalling visit was speedily repeated, and fear and death reigned

[1]Beowulf, II. 26—50, a free rendering to suggest the alliteration of the original.

in the great hall. The warriors fought at first; but fled when they discovered that no weapon could harm the monster. Heorot was left deserted and silent. For twelve winters Grendel's horrible raids continued, and joy was changed to mourning among the Spear Danes.

At last the rumour of Grendel crossed over the sea to the land of the Geats, where a young hero dwelt in the house of his uncle, King Hygelac. Beowulf was his name, a man of immense strength and courage, and a mighty swimmer who had developed his powers fighting the 'nickers', whales, walruses and seals, in the icebound northern ocean. When he heard the story, Beowulf was stirred to go and fight the monster and free the Danes, who were his father's friends.

With fourteen companions he crosses the sea. There is an excellent bit of ocean poetry here (II. 210-224), and we get a vivid idea of the hospitality of a brave people by following the poet's description of Beowulf's meeting with King Hrothgar and Queen Wealhtheow, and of the joy and feasting and story-telling in Heorot. The picture of Wealhtheow passing the mead cup to the warriors with her own hand is a noble one, and plainly indicates the reverence paid by these strong men to their wives and mothers. Night comes on; the fear of Grendel is again upon the Danes, and all withdraw after the king has warned Beowulf of the frightful danger of sleeping in the hall. But Beowulf lies down with his warriors, saying proudly that, since weapons will not avail against the monster, he will grapple with him bare handed and trust to a warrior's strength.

Forth from the fens, from the misty moorlands,
Grendel came gliding—God's wrath[1] he bore—

---

[1]Grendel, of the Eoten (giant) race, the death shadow, the mark stalker, the shadow ganger, is also variously called god's foe, fiend of hell, Cain's brood, etc. It need hardly be explained that the latter terms are additions to the original poem, made, probably, by monks who copied the manuscript. A belief in Wyrd, the mighty power controlling the distinies of men, is the chief religious motive of the epic. In line 1056 we find a curious blending of pagan and Christian belief, where Wyrd is withstood by the 'wise God'.

Came under clouds, until he saw clearly,
Glittering with gold plates, the mead hall of men.
Down fell the door, though fastened with fire bands;
Open it sprang at the stroke of his paw.
Swollen with rage burst in the bale-bringer;
Flamed in his eyes a fierce light, likest fire.[1]

At the sight of men again sleeping in the hall, Grendel laughs in his heart, thinking of his feast. He seizes the nearest sleeper, crushes his 'bone case' with a bite, tears him limb from limb, and swallows him. Then he creeps to the couch of Beowulf and stretches out a claw, only to find it clutched in a grip of steel. A sudden terror strikes the monster's heart. He roars, struggles, tries to jerk his arm free; but Beowulf leaps to his feet and grapples his enemy barehanded. To and fro they surge. Tables are overturned; golden benches ripped from their fastenings; the whole building quakes, and only its iron bands keep it from falling to pieces. Beowulf's companions are on their feet now, hacking vainly at the monster with swords and battleaxes, adding their shouts to the crashing of furniture and the howling 'war song' of Grendel. Outside in the town the Danes stand shivering at the uproar. Slowly the monster struggles to the door, dragging Beowulf, whose fingers crack with the strain, but who never relaxes his first grip. Suddenly a wide wound opens in the monster's side; the sinews snap; the whole arm is wrenched off at the shoulder; and Grendel escapes shrieking across the moor, and plunges into the sea to die.

Beowulf first exults in his night's work; then he hangs the huge arm with its terrible claws from a cross-beam over the king's seat, as one would hang up a bear's skin after a hunt. At daylight came the Danes; and all day long, in the intervals of singing, storytelling, speech making, and gift giving, they return to wonder at the mighty 'grip of Grendel' and to rejoice in Beowulf's victory.

---

[1] Summary of II. 710-727. We have not indicated in our translation (or in quotations from Garnett, Morley, Brooke, etc.) where parts of the text are omitted.

When night falls a great feast is spread in Heorot, and the Danes sleep once more in the great hall. At midnight comes another monster, a horrible, half-human creature,[1] mother of Grendel, raging to avenge her offspring. She thunders at the door; the Danes leap up and grasp their weapons; but the monster enters, seizes Aeschere, who is friend and adviser of the king, and rushes away with him over the fens.

The old scenes of sorrow are reviewed in the morning; but Beowulf says simply:

Sorrow not, wise man. It is better for each
That his friend he avenge than that he mourn much.
Each of us shall the end await
Of worldly life: let him who may gain
Honor ere death. That is for a warrior,
When he is dead, afterwards best.
Arise, kingdom's guardian! Let us quickly go
To view the track of Grendel's kinsman.
I promise it thee: he will not escape,
Nor in earth's bosom, nor in mountain-wood,
Nor in ocean's depths, go where he will.[2]

Then he girds himself for the new fight and follows the track of the second enemy across the fens. Here is Hrothgar's description of the place where live the monsters, 'spirits of elsewhere,' as he calls them:

They inhabit
The dim land that gives shelter to the wolf,
The windy headlands, perilous fen paths,
Where, under mountain mist, the stream flows down
And floods the ground. Not far hence, but a mile,
The mere stands, over which hang death-chill groves,

---

[1] Grendel's mother belongs also to the Eoten (giant) race. She is called *brimwylf* (sea wolf), merewif (sea woman), *grundwyrgen* (bottom monster), etc.
[2] From Garnett's *Beowulf,* II. 1384-1394.

A wood fast-rooted overshades the flood;
There every night a ghastly miracle
Is seen, fire in the water. No man knows,
Not the most wise, the bottom of that mere.
The firm-horned heath-stalker, the hart, when pressed,
Wearied by hounds, and hunted from afar,
Will rather die of thirst upon its bank
Than bend his head to it. It is unholy.
Dark to the clouds its yeasty waves mount up
When wind stirs hateful tempest, till the air
Grows dreary, and the heavens pour down tears.[1]

Beowulf plunges into the horrible place, while his companions wait for him on the shore. For a long time he sinks through the flood; then, as he reaches bottom, Grendel's mother rushes out upon him and drags him into a cave, where sea monsters swarm at him from behind and gnash his armour with their tusks. The edge of his sword is turned with the mighty blow he deals the *merewif;* but it harms not the monster. Casting the weapon aside, he grips her and tries to hurl her down, while her claws and teeth clash upon his corslet but cannot penetrate the steel rings. She throws her bulk upon him, crushes him down, draws a short sword and plunges it at him; but again his splendid byrnie saves him. He is wearied now, and oppressed. Suddenly, as his eye sweeps the cave, he catches sight of a magic sword, made by the giants long ago, too heavy for warriors to wield. Struggling up he seizes the weapon, whirls it and brings down a crashing blow upon the monster's neck. It smashes through the ring bones; the *merewif* falls, and the fight is won.

The cave is full of treasures; but Beowulf heeds them not, for near him lies Grendel, dead from the wound received the previous night. Again Beowulf swings the great sword and strikes off his enemy's head; and lo, as the venomous blood touches the sword blade, the steel melts like ice before the fire, and only the hilt is left in Beowulf's hand. Taking

[1] From Morley's version, II. 1357-1376.

the hilt and the head, the hero enters the ocean and mounts up to the shore.

Only his own faithful band were waiting there; for the Danes, seeing the ocean bubble with fresh blood, thought it was all over with the hero and had gone home. And there they were, mourning in Heorot, when Beowulf returned with the monstrous head of Grendel carried on a spear shaft by four of his stoutest followers.

In the last part of the poem there is another great fight. Beowulf is now an old man; he has reigned for fifty years, beloved by all his people. He has overcome every enemy but one, a fire dragon keeping watch over an enormous treasure hidden among the mountains. One day a wanderer stumbles upon the enchanted cave and, entering, takes a jeweled cup while the firedrake sleeps heavily. That same night the dragon, in a frightful rage, belching forth fire and smoke, rushes down upon the nearest villages, leaving a trail of death and terror behind him.

Again Beowulf goes forth to champion his people. As he approaches the dragon's cave, he has a presentiment that death lurks within:

> Sat on the headland there the warrior king;
> Farewell he said to hearth-companions true,
> The gold-friend of the Geats; his mind was sad,
> Death-ready, restless. And Wyrd was drawing nigh,
> Who now must meet and touch the aged man,
> To seek the treasure that his soul had saved
> And separate his body from his life.[1]

There is a flash of illumination, like that which comes to a dying man, in which his mind runs back over his long life and sees something of profound meaning in the elemental sorrow moving side by side with magnificent courage. Then follows the fight with the firedrake, in which Beowulf, wrapped in fire and smoke, is helped by the heroism of Wiglaf, one of his companions. The dragon is slain, but the fire has entered

[1] *Beowulf*, II.2417-2423, a free rendering.

Beowulf's lungs and he knows that Wyrd is at hand. This is his thought, while Wiglaf removes his battered armour:

'One deep regret I have: that to a son
I may not give the armour I have worn,
To bear it after me. For fifty years
I ruled these people well, and not a king
Of those who dwell around me, dared oppress
Or meet me with his hosts. At home I waited
For the time that Wyrd controls. Mine own I kept,
Nor quarrels sought, nor ever falsely swore.
Now, wounded sore, I wait for joy to come.'[1]

He sends Wiglaf into the firedrake's cave, who finds it filled with rare treasures and, most wonderful of all, a golden banner from which light proceeds and illumines all the darkness. But Wiglaf cares little for the treasures; his mind is full of his dying chief. He fills his hands with costly ornaments and hurries to throw them at his hero's feet. The old man looks with sorrow at the gold, thanks the 'Lord of all' that by death he has gained more riches for his people, and tells his faithful thane how his body shall be burned on the Whale ness, or headland:

'My life is well paid for this hoard; and now
Care for the people's needs. I may no more
Be with them. Bid the warriors raise a barrow
After the burning, on the ness by the sea,
On Hronesness, which shall rise high and be
For a remembrance to my people. Seafarers
Who from afar over the mists of waters
Drive foamy keels may call it Beowulf's Mount
Hereafter.' Then the hero from his neck
Put off a golden collar; to his thane,
To the young warrior, gave it with his helm,
Armlet and corslet; bade him use them well.

---

[1] Lines 2729-2740, a free rendering.

'Thou art the last Wægmunding of our race,
For fate has swept my kinsmen all away.
Earls in their strength are to their Maker gone,
And I must follow them.'[1]

Beowulf was still living when Wiglaf sent a messenger hurriedly to his people; when they came they found him dead, and the huge dragon dead on the sand beside him.

Then the Goth's people reared a mighty pile
With shields and armour hung, as he had asked,
And in the midst the warriors laid their lord,
Lamenting. Then the warriors on the mount
Kindled a mighty bale fire; the smoke rose
Black from the Swedish pine, the sound of flame
Mingled with sound of weeping; ... while smoke
Spread over heaven. Then upon the hill
The people of the Weders wrought a mound,
High, broad, and to be seen far out at sea.
In ten days they had built and walled it in
As the wise thought most worthy; placed in it
Rings, jewels, other treasures from the hoard.
They left the riches, golden joy of earls,
In dust, for earth to hold; where yet it lies,
Useless as ever. Then about the mound
The warriors rode, and raised a mournful song
For their dead king; exalted his brave deeds,
Holding it fit men honour their liege lord,
Praise him and love him when his soul is fled.
Thus the [Geat's] people, sharers of his hearth,
Mourned their chief's fall, praised him, of kings, of men
The mildest and the kindest, and to all
His people gentlest, yearning for their praise.[2]

[1]Morley's version, II. 2799-2816.

[2]Lines 3156-3182 (Morley's version).

One is tempted to linger over the details of the magnificent ending: the unselfish heroism of Beowulf, the great prototype of King Alfred; the generous grief of his people, ignoring gold and jewels in the thought of the greater treasure they had lost; the memorial mound on the low cliff, which would cause every returning mariner to steer a straight course to harbor in the remembrance of his dead hero; and the pure poetry which marks every noble line. But the epic is great enough and simple enough to speak for itself. Search the literatures of the world, and you will find no other such picture of a brave man's death.

History and Meaning of Beowulf

Concerning the history of Beowulf a whole library has been written, and scholars still differ too radically for us to express History and a positive judgment. This much, however, is clear—that there existed, at the time the poem was composed, various northern legends of Beowa, a half-divine hero, and the monster Grendel. The latter has been interpreted in various ways—sometimes as a bear, and again as the malaria of the marshlands. For those interested in symbols the simplest interpretation of these myths is to regard Beowulf's successive fights with the three dragons as the overcoming, first, of the overwhelming danger of the sea, which was beaten back by the dykes; second, the conquering of the sea itself, when men learned to sail upon it; and third, the conflict with the hostile forces of nature, which are overcome at last by man's indomitable will and perseverance.

All this is purely mythical; but there are historical incidents to reckon with. About the year 520 a certain northern chief, called by the chronicler Chochilaicus (who is generally identified with the Hygelac of the epic), led a huge plundering expedition up the Rhine. After a succession of battles he was overcome by the Franks, but—and now we enter a legendary region once more—not until a gigantic nephew of Hygelac had performed heroic feats of valour, and had saved the remnants of the host by a marvellous feat of swimming. The majority of scholars now hold that these historical events and personages were celebrated in the epic; but some still assert that the events which gave a foundation for *Beowulf* occurred wholly on English soil, where the poem itself was undoubtedly written.

Poetical Form

The rhythm of *Beowulf* and indeed of all our earliest poetry depended upon accent and alliteration; that is, the beginning of two or more words in the same line with the same sound or letter. The lines were made up of two short halves, separated by a pause. No rhme was used; but a musical effect was produced by giving each half line two strongly accented syllables. Each full line, therefore, had four accents, three of which (that is, two in the first half, and one in the second) usually began with the same sound or letter. The musical effect was heightened by the harp with which the gleeman accompanied his singing. The poetical form will be seen clearly in the following selection from the wonderfully realistic description of the fens haunted by Grendel. It will need only one or two readings aloud to show that many of these strange-looking words are practically the same as those we still use, though many of the vowel sounds were pronounced differently by our ancestors.

... Hie dygel lond
Warigeath, wulf-hleothu, windige næssas,
Frecne fen-gelad, thær fyrgen-stream
Under næssa genipu nither gewiteth,
Flod under foldan. Nis thæt feor heonon,
Mil-gemearces, thæt se mere standeth,
Ofer thæm hongiath hrinde bearwas

... They (a) darksome land
Ward (inhabit), wolf cliffs, windy nesses,
Frightful fen paths where mountain stream
Under nesses' mists nether (downward) wanders,
A flood under earth. It is not far hence,
By mile measure, that the mere stands,
Over which hang rimy groves.

Widsith. The poem 'Widsith', the wide goer or wanderer, is in part, at least, probably the oldest in our language. The author and

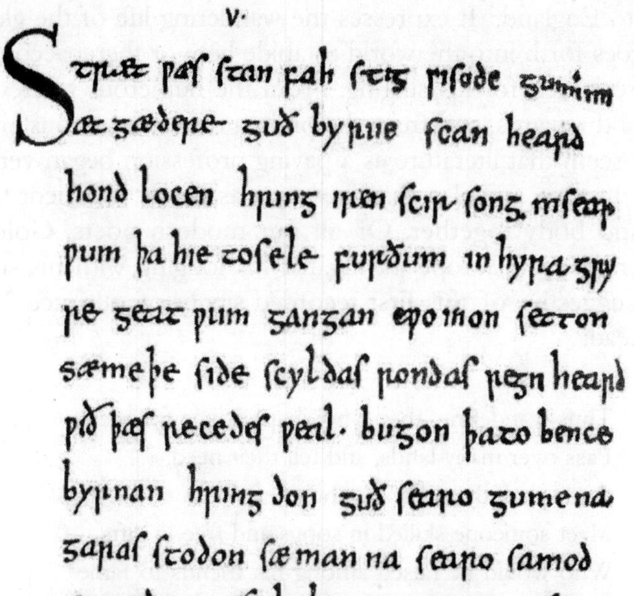

A Page from the Manuscript of Beowulf

the date of its composition are unknown; but the personal account of the minstrel's life belongs to the time before the Saxons first came to England.[1] It expresses the wandering life of the gleeman, who goes forth into the world to abide here or there, according as he is rewarded for his singing. From the numerous references to rings and rewards, and from the praise given to generous givers, it would seem that literature as a paying profession began very early in our history, and also that the pay was barely sufficient to hold soul and body together. Of all our modern poets, Goldsmith wandering over Europe paying for his lodging with his songs is most suggestive of this first recorded singer of our race. His last lines read:

> Thus wandering, they who shape songs for men
> Pass over many lands, and tell their need,
> And speak their thanks, and ever, south or north,
> Meet someone skilled in songs and free in gifts,
> Who would be raised among his friends to fame
> And do brave deeds till light and life are gone.
> He who has thus wrought himself praise shall have
> A settled glory underneath the stars.[2]

Deor's Lament. In 'Deor' we have another picture of the Saxon scop, or minstrel, not in glad wandering, but in manly sorrow. It seems that the scop's living depended entirely upon his power to please his chief, and that at any time he might be supplanted by a better poet. Deor had this experience, and comforts himself in a grim way by recalling various examples of men who have suffered more than himself. The poem is arranged in strophes, each one telling of some afflicted hero and ending with the same refrain:

---

[1] Probably to the fourth century, though some parts of the poem must have been added later. Thus the poet says (II. 88-102) that he visited Eormanric, who died *circa,* 375, and Queen Ealhhild whose father, Eadwin, died cir. 561. The difficulty of fixing a date to the poem is apparent. It contains several references to scenes and characters in *Beowulf.*

[2] Lines 135-143 (Morley's version).

'His sorrow passed away; so will mine'. 'Deor' is much more poetic than 'Widsith,' and is the one perfect lyric[1] of the Anglo-Saxon period.

> Weland for a woman knew too well exile.
> Strong of soul that earl, sorrow sharp he bore;
> To companionship he had care and weary longing,
> Winter-freezing wretchedness. Woe he found again, again,
> After that Nithhad in a need had laid him—
> Staggering sinew-wounds—sorrow-smitten man!
> *That he overwent; this also may I*[2].

The Seafarer. The wonderful poem of 'The Seafarer' seems to be in two distinct parts. The first shows the hardships of ocean life; but stronger than hardships is the subtle call of the sea. The second part is an allegory, in which the troubles of the seaman are symbols of the troubles of this life, and the call of the ocean is the call in the soul to be up and away to its true home with God. Whether the last was added by some monk who saw the allegorical possibilities of the first part, or whether some sea-loving Christian scop wrote both, is uncertain. Following are a few selected lines to show the spirit of the poem:

> The hail flew in showers about me; and there I heard only
> The roar of the sea, ice-cold waves, and the song of the swan;
> For pastime the gannets' cry served me; the kittiwakes' chatter
> For laughter of men; and for mead drink the call of the sea mews.
> When storms on the rocky cliffs beat, then the terns, icy-feathered,
> Made answer; full oft the sea eagle forebodingly screamed,
> The eagle with pinions wave-wet....
> The shadows of night became darker, it snowed from the north;
> The world was enchained by the frost; hail fell upon earth;
> 'Twas the coldest of grain. Yet the thoughts of my heart now
> are throbbing

---

[1] A lyric is a short poem reflecting some personal emotion, like love or grief. Two other Anglo-Saxon poems, 'The Wife's Complaint' and 'The Husband's Message', belong to this class.

[2] First strophe of Brooke's version, *History of Early English Literature.*

To test the high streams, the salt waves in tumultuous play.
Desire in my heart ever urges my spirit to wander,
To seek out the home of the stranger in lands afar off.
There is no one that dwells upon earth, so exalted in mind,
But that he has always a longing, a sea-faring passion
For what the Lord God shall bestow, be it honor or death.
No heart for the harp has he, nor for acceptance of treasure,
No pleasure has he in a wife, no delight in the world,
Nor in aught save the roll of the billows; but always a longing,
A yearning uneasiness, hastens him on to the sea.
The woodlands are captured by blossoms, the *Hamlets* grow fair,
Broad meadows are beautiful, earth again bursts into life,
And all stir the heart of the wanderer eager to journey,
So he meditates going afar on the pathway of tides.
The cuckoo, moreover, gives warning with sorrowful note,
Summer's harbinger sings, and forebodes to the heart bitter sorrow.
Now my spirit uneasily turns in the heart's narrow chamber,
Now wanders forth over the tide, o'er the home of the whale,
To the ends of the earth—and comes back to me.
Eager and greedy,
The lone wanderer screams, and resistlessly drives my soul onward,
Over the whale-path, over the tracts of the sea.[1]

The Fight at Finnsburgh and Waldere. Two other of our oldest poems well deserve mention. The 'Fight at Finnsburgh' is a fragment of fifty lines, discovered on the inside of a piece of parchment drawn over the wooden covers of a book of homilies. It is a magnificent war song, describing with Homeric power the defence of a hall by Hnæf[2] with sixty warriors, against the attack of Finn and his army. At midnight, when Hnæf and his men are sleeping, they are surrounded by an army rushing in with fire and sword.

---

[1] *Seafarer,* Part I, Iddings' version, in *Translations from Old English Poetry.*

[2] It is an open question whether this poem celebrates the fight at which Hnæf, the Danish leader, fell, or a later fight led by Hengist, to avenge Hnæf's death.

Hnæf springs to his feet at the first alarm and wakens his warriors with a call to action that rings like a bugle blast:

> This no eastward dawning is, nor is here a dragon flying,
> Nor of this high hall are the horns a burning;
> But they rush upon us here—now the ravens sing,
> Growling is the gray wolf, grim the war-wood rattles,
> Shield to shaft is answering.[1]

The fight lasts five days, but the fragment ends before we learn the outcome: The same fight is celebrated by Hrothgar's gleeman at the feast in Heorot, after the slaying of Grendel.

'Waldere' is a fragment of two leaves, from which we get only a glimpse of the story of Waldere (Walter of Aquitaine) and his betrothed bride Hildgund, who were hostages at the court of Attila. They escaped with a great treasure, and in crossing the mountains were attacked by Gunther and his warriors, among whom was Walter's former comrade, Hagen. Walter fights them all and escapes. The same story was written in Latin in the tenth century, and is also part of the old German *Nibelungenlied.* Though the saga did not originate with the Anglo-Saxons, their version of it is the oldest that has come down to us. The chief significance of these 'Waldere' fragments lies in the evidence they afford that our ancestors were familiar with the legends and poetry of other Germanic peoples.

II. ANGLO-SAXON LIFE

We have now read some of our earliest records, and have been surprised, perhaps, that men who are generally described in the histories as savage fighters and freebooters could produce such excellent poetry. It is the object of the study of all literature to make us better acquainted with men—not simply with their deeds, which is the function of history, but with the dreams and ideals

---

[1]Brooke's translation, *History of Early English Literature.* For another early battle song see Tennyson's 'Battle of Brunanburh'.

which underlie all their actions. So a reading of this early Anglo-Saxon poetry not only makes us acquainted, but also leads to a profound respect for the men who were our ancestors. Before we study more of their literature it is well to glance briefly at their life and language.

The Name. Originally the name Anglo-Saxon denotes two of the three Germanic tribes—Jutes, Angles, and Saxons—who in the middle of the fifth century left their homes on the shores of the North Sea and the Baltic to conquer and colonize distant Britain. Angeln was the home of one tribe, and the name still clings to the spot whence some of our forefathers sailed on their momentous voyage. The old Saxon word *angul* or *ongul* means a hook, and the English verb *angle* is used invariably by Walton and older writers in the sense of fishing. We may still think, therefore, of the first Angles as hook-men, possibly because of their fishing, more probably because the shore where they lived, at the foot of the peninsula of Jutland, was bent in the shape of a fishhook. The name Saxon from seax, sax, a short sword, means the swordman, and from the name we may judge something of the temper of the hardy fighters who preceded the Angles into Britain. The Angles were the most numerous of the conquering tribes, and from them the new home was called Anglalond. By gradual changes this became first Englelond and then England.

More than five hundred years after the landing of these tribes, and while they called themselves Englishmen, we find the Latin writers of the Middle Ages speaking of the inhabitants of Britain as *Anglisaxones*—that is, Saxons of England—to distinguish them from the Saxons of the Continent. In the Latin charters of King Alfred the same name appears; but it is never seen or heard in his native speech. There he always speaks of his beloved 'Englelond' and of his brave 'Englisc' people. In the sixteenth century, when the old name of Englishmen clung to the new people resulting from the union of Saxon and Norman, the name Anglo-Saxon was first used in the national sense by the scholar Camden[1] in his *History of Britain*; and since then it has been in general use among English writers. In recent years the name has gained a wider significance, until it is now used to denote a spirit rather than a nation, the brave, vigorous, enlarging spirit that characterizes the English-speaking races everywhere, and that has already put a broad belt of English law and English liberty around the whole world.

The Life. If the literature of a people springs directly out of its life, then the stern, barbarous life of our Saxon forefathers would seem, at first glance, to promise little of good literature. Outwardly their life was a constant hardship, a perpetual struggle against savage nature and savage men. Behind them were gloomy forests inhabited by wild beasts and still wilder men, and peopled in their imagination with dragons and evil shapes. In front of them, thundering at the very dykes for entrance, was the treacherous North Sea, with its fogs and storms and ice, but with that indefinable call of the deep that all men hear who live long beneath its influence. Here they lived, a big, blond, powerful race, and hunted and fought and sailed, and drank and feasted when their labour was done. Almost the first thing we notice about these big, fearless, childish men is that they love the sea; and because they love it they hear and answer its call:

> ... No delight has he in the world,
> Nor in aught save the roll of the billows; but always a longing,
> A yearning uneasiness, hastens him on to the sea.[2]

As might be expected, this love of the ocean finds expression in all their poetry. In *Beowulf* alone there are fifteen names for the sea, from the *holm*, that is, the horizon sea, the 'upmounding', to the *brim*, which is the ocean flinging its welter of sand and creamy

[1]William Camden (1551-1623), one of England's earliest and greatest antiquarians. His first work, *Britannia,* a Latin history of England, has been called 'the common sun whereat our modern writers have all kindled their little torches'.
[2] From Idding's version of *The Seafarer.*

foam upon the beach at your feet. And the figures used to describe or glorify it—'the swan road, the whale path, the heaving battle plain'—are almost as numerous. In all their poetry there is a magnificent sense of lordship over the wild sea even in its hour of tempest and fury:

> Often it befalls us, on the ocean's highways,
> In the boats our boatmen, when the storm is roaring,
> Leap the billows over, on our stallions of the foam.[1]

The Inner Life. A man's life is more than his work; his dream is ever greater than his achievement; and literature reflects not so much man's deed as the spirit which animates him; not the poor thing that he does, but rather the splendid thing that he ever hopes to do. In no place is this more evident than in the age we are now studying. Those early sea kings were a marvellous mixture of savagery and sentiment, of rough living and of deep feeling, of splendid courage and the deep melancholy of men who know their limitations and have faced the unanswered problem of death. They were not simply fearless freebooters who harried every coast in their war galleys. If that were all, they would have no more history or literature than the Barbary pirates, of whom the same thing could be said. These strong fathers of ours were men of profound emotions. In all their fighting the love of an untarnished glory was uppermost; and under the warrior's savage exterior was hidden a great love of home and homely virtues, and a reverence for the one woman to whom he would presently return in triumph. So when the wolf hunt was over, or the desperate fight was won, these mighty men would gather in the banquet hall, and lay their weapons aside where the open fire would flash upon them, and there listen to the songs of scop and gleeman—men who could put into adequate words the emotions and aspirations that all men feel but that only a few can ever express:

> Music and song where the heroes sat—

[1]From *Andreas,* II, 511 ff., a free translation. The whole poem thrills with the old Saxon love of the sea and of ships.

The glee-wood rang, a song uprose
When Hrothgar's scop gave the hall good cheer.[1]

It is this great and hidden life of the Anglo-Saxons that finds expression in all their literature. Briefly, it is summed up in five great principles—their love of personal freedom, their responsiveness to nature, their religion, their reverence for womanhood, and their struggle for glory as a ruling motive in every noble life.

Springs of Anglo-Saxon Poetry

In reading Anglo-Saxon poetry it is well to remember these five principles, for they are like the little springs at the head of a great river—clear, pure springs of poetry, and out of them the best of our literature has always flowed. Thus when we read,

Blast of *The Tempest*—it aids our oars;
Rolling of thunder—it hurts us not;
Rush of the hurricane—bending its neck
To speed us whither our wills are bent,

we realize that these sea rovers had the spirit of kinship with the mighty life of nature; and kinship with nature invariably expresses itself in poetry. Again, when we read,

Now hath the man
O'ercome his troubles. No pleasure does he lack,
Nor steeds, nor jewels, nor the joys of mead,
Nor any treasure that the earth can give,
O royal woman, if he have but thee, [2]

---

[1] From *Beowulf,* II. 1063 ff., a free tanslation.
[2] Translated from *The Husband's Message,* written on a piece of bark. With wonderful poetic insight the bark itself is represented as telling its story to the wife, from the time when the birch tree grew beside the sea until the exiled man found it and stripped the bark and carved on its surface a message to the woman he loved. This first of all English love songs deserved to rank with Valentine's description of Silvia:

Why, man, she is mine own,

we know we are dealing with an essentially noble man, not a savage; we are face to face with that profound reverence for womanhood which inspires the greater part of all good poetry, and we begin to honour as well as understand our ancestors. So in the matter of glory or honor; it was, apparently, not the love of fighting, but rather the love of honor resulting from fighting well, which animated our forefathers in every campaign. 'He was a man deserving of remembrance' was the highest thing that could be said of a dead warrior; and 'He is a man deserving of praise' was the highest tribute to the living. The whole secret of Beowulf's mighty life is summed up in the last line, 'Ever yearning for his people's praise.' So every tribe had its scop, or poet, more important than any warrior, who put the deeds of its heroes into the expressive words that constitute literature; and every banquet hall had its gleeman, who sang the scop's poetry in order that the deed and the man might be remembered. Oriental peoples built monuments to perpetuate the memory of their dead; but our ancestors made poems, which should live and stir men's souls long after monuments of brick and stone had crumbled away. It is to this intense love of glory and the desire to be remembered that we are indebted for Anglo-Saxon literature.

Our First Speech. Our first recorded speech begins with the songs of Widsith and Deor, which the Anglo-Saxons may have brought with them when they first conquered Britain. At first glance these songs in their native dress look strange as a foreign tongue; but when we examine them carefully we find many words that have been familiar since childhood. We have seen this in *Beowulf;* but in prose the resemblance of this old speech to our own is even more striking. Here, for instance, is a fragment of the simple story of the conquest of Britain by our Anglo-Saxon ancestors:

And I as rich in having such a jewel
As twenty seas, if all their sand were pearl,
The water nectar and the rocks pure gold.

Two Gentlemen of Verona, II, 4.

Her Hengest and Æsc his sunu gefuhton with Bryttas, on thære stowe the is gecweden Creccanford, and thær ofslogon feower thusenda wera. And tha Bryttas tha forleton Cent-lond, and mid myclum ege flugon to

Stonehenge, on Salisbury Plain

Probably the ruins of a temple of the native Britons

Lundenbyrig. (At this time Hengest and Aesc, his son, fought against the Britons at the place which is called Crayford and there slew four thousand men. And then the Britons forsook Kentland, and with much fear fled to London town.)[1]

The reader who utters these words aloud a few times will speedily recognize his own tongue, not simply in the words but also in the whole structure of the sentences.

From such records we see that our speech is Teutonic in its origin; and when we examine any Teutonic language we learn that it is only a branch of the great Aryan or Indo-European family of languages. In life and language, therefore, we are related first to the Teutonic races, and through them to all the nations of this Indo-European family, which, starting with enormous vigour from their original home (probably in central Europe),[2] spread southward and westward, driving out the native tribes and slowly developing the mighty civilizations of India, Persia, Greece, Rome, and the wilder but more vigorous life of the Celts and Teutons. In all these

[1] From the *Anglo-Saxon Chronicle,* record of the year 457.

[2] According to Sweet the original home of the Aryans is placed in central or northern Europe, rather than in Asia, as was once assumed. See *The History of Language,* p. 103.

languages—Sanskrit, Iranian, Greek, Latin, Celtic, Teutonic—we recognize the same root words for father and mother, for God and man, for the common needs and the common relations of life; and since words are windows through which we see the soul of this old people, we find certain ideals of love, home, faith, heroism, liberty, which seem to have been the very life of our forefathers, and which were inherited by them from their old heroic and conquering ancestors. It was on the borders of the North Sea that our fathers halted for unnumbered centuries on their westward journey, and slowly developed the national life and language which we now call Anglo-Saxon.

Dual Character of our Language

It is this old vigorous Anglo-Saxon language which forms the basis of our modern English. If we read a paragraph from any good English book, and then analyze it, as we would a flower, to see what it contains, we find two distinct classes of words. The first class, containing simple words expressing the common things of life, makes up the strong framework of our language. These words are like the stem and bare branches of a mighty oak, and if we look them up in the dictionary we find that almost invariably they come to us from our Anglo-Saxon ancestors. The second and larger class of words is made up of those that give grace, variety, ornament, to our speech. They are like the leaves and blossoms of the same tree, and when we examine their history we find that they come to us from the Celts, Romans, Normans, and other peoples with whom we have been in contact in the long years of our development. The most prominent characteristic of our present language, therefore, is its dual character. Its best qualities—strength, simplicity, directness—come from Anglo-Saxon sources; its enormous added wealth of expression, its comprehensiveness, its plastic adaptability to new conditions and ideas, are largely the result of additions from other languages, and especially of its gradual absorption of the French language after the Norman Conquest. It is this dual character, this combination of native and foreign, of innate and exotic elements, which accounts for the wealth of our English language and literature. To see it in concrete form, we should read in succession

Beowulf and *Paradise Lost,* the two great epics which show the root and the flower of our literary development.

III. CHRISTIAN WRITERS OF THE ANGLO-SAXON PERIOD

The literature of this period falls naturally into two divisions—pagan and Christian. The former represents the poetry which the Anglo-Saxons probably brought with them in the form of oral sagas—the crude material out of which literature was slowly developed on English soil; the latter represents the writings developed under teaching of the monks, after the old pagan religion had vanished, but while it still retained its hold on the life and language of the people. In reading our earliest poetry it is well to remember that all of it was copied by the monks, and seems to have been more or less altered to give it a religious colouring.

The coming of Christianity meant not simply a new life and leader for England; it meant also the wealth of a new language. The scop is now replaced by the literary monk; and that monk, though he lives among common people and speaks with the English tongue, has behind him all the culture and literary resources of the Latin language. The effect is seen instantly in our early prose and poetry.

Northumbrian Literature. In general, two great schools of Christian influence came into England, and speedily put an end to the frightful wars that had waged continually among the various petty kingdoms of the Anglo-Saxons. The first of these, under the leadership of Augustine, came from Rome. It spread in the south and centre of England, especially in the kingdom of Essex. It founded schools and partially educated the rough people, but it produced no lasting literature.

The other, under the leadership of the saintly Aidan, came from Ireland, which country had been for centuries a centre of religion and education for all western Europe. The monks of this school laboured chiefly in Northumbria, and to their influence we owe all that is best in Anglo-Saxon literature. It is called the

From a Copley Print. Copyright, 1899, Curtis and Cameron

The Manuscript Book

After the painting in the Congressional Library, by John W. Alexander

Northumbrian School; its centre was the monasteries and abbeys, such as Jarrow and Whitby, and its three greatest names are Bede, Cædmon, and Cynewulf.

BEDE (673-735)

Initial Letter of a Ms. Copy of St. Luke's Gospel, Circa. 700 A.D.

The Venerable Bede, as he is generally called, our first great scholar and 'the father of our English learning', wrote almost exclusively in Latin, his last work, the translation of the Gospel of John into Anglo-Saxon, having been unfortunately lost. Much to our regret, therefore, his books and the story of his gentle, heroic life must be excluded from this history of our literature. His works, over forty in number, covered the whole field of human knowledge in his day, and were so admirably written that they were widely copied as textbooks, or rather manuscripts, in nearly all the monastery schools of Europe.

The First History of England

The work most important to us is the *Ecclesiastical History of the English People.* It is a fascinating history to read even now, with its curious combination of accurate scholarship and immense credulity. In all strictly historical matters Bede is a model. Every known authority on the subject, from Pliny to Gildas, was carefully considered; every learned pilgrim to Rome was commissioned by Bede to ransack the archives and to make copies of papal decrees and royal letters; and to these were added the testimony of abbots who could speak from personal knowledge of events or repeat the traditions of their several monasteries.

Side by side with this historical exactness are marvelous stories of saints and missionaries. It was an age of credulity, and miracles were in men's minds continually. The men of whom he wrote lived

Ruins at Whitby

lives more wonderful than any romance, and their courage and gentleness made a tremendous impression on the rough, warlike people to whom they came with open hands and hearts. It is the natural way of all primitive peoples to magnify the works of their heroes, and so deeds of heroism and kindness, which were part of the daily life of the Irish missionaries, were soon transformed into the miracles of the saints. Bede believed these things, as all other men did, and records them with charming simplicity, just as he received them from bishop or abbot. Notwithstanding its errors, we owe to this work nearly all our knowledge of the eight centuries of our history following the landing of Cæsar in Britain.

CÆDMON (SEVENTH CENTURY)

Now must we hymn the Master of heaven,
The might of the Maker, the deeds of the Father,
The thought of His heart. He, Lord everlasting,
Established of old the source of all wonders:
Creator all-holy, He hung the bright heaven,

A roof high upreared, o'er the children of men;
The King of mankind then created for mortals
The world in its beauty, the earth spread beneath them,
He, Lord everlasting, omnipotent God.[1]

If *Beowulf* and the fragments of our earliest poetry were brought into England, then the hymn given above is the first verse of all native English song that has come down to us, and Cædmon is the first poet to whom we can give a definite name and date. The words were written about 665 A.D. and are found copied at the end of a manuscript of Bede's *Ecclesiastical History.*

Life of Cædmon. What little we know of Cædmon, the Anglo-Saxon Milton, as he is properly called, is taken from Bede's account[2] of the Abbess Hilda and of her monastery at Whitby. Here is a free and condensed translation of Bede's story:

There was, in the monastery of the Abbess Hilda, a brother distinguished by the grace of God, for that he could make poems treating of goodness and religion. Whatever was translated to him (for he could not read) of Sacred Scripture he shortly reproduced in poetic form of great sweetness and beauty. None of all the English poets could equal him, for he learned not the art of song from men, nor sang by the arts of men. Rather did he receive all his poetry as a free gift from God, and for this reason he did never compose poetry of a vain or worldly kind.

Until of mature age he lived as a layman and had never learned any poetry. Indeed, so ignorant of singing was he that sometimes, at a feast, where it was the custom that for the pleasure of all each guest should sing in turn, he would rise from the table when he saw the harp coming to him and go home ashamed. Now it happened once that he did this thing at a certain festivity, and went out to the stall to care for the horses, this duty being assigned to him for that night. As he slept at the usual time, one stood by him saying: 'Cædmon, sing me something.' 'I cannot sing,' he answered, 'and that is why I came hither from the feast.' But he who spake unto him said again, 'Cædmon, sing to me.' And he said, 'What

[1] Cædmon's Hymn', Cook's version, in *Translation from Old English Poetry.*
[2] *Ecclesiastical History,* IV, xxiv.

shall I sing?' and he said, 'Sing the beginning of created things.' Thereupon Cædmon began to sing verses that he had never heard before, of this import: 'Now should we praise the power and wisdom of the Creator, the works of the Father.' This is the sense but not the form of the hymn that he sang while sleeping.

When he awakened, Cædmon remembered the words of the hymn and added to them many more. In the morning he went to the steward of the monastery lands and showed him the gift he had received in sleep. The steward brought him to Hilda, who made him repeat to the monks the hymn he had composed, and all agreed that the grace of God was upon Cædmon. To test him they expounded to him a bit of Scripture from the Latin and bade him, if he could, to turn it into poetry. He went away humbly and returned in the morning with an excellent poem. Thereupon Hilda received him and his family into the monastery, made him one of the brethren, and commanded that the whole course of Bible history be expounded to him. He in turn, reflecting upon what he had heard, transformed it into most delightful poetry, and by echoing it back to the monks in more melodious sounds made his teachers his listeners. In all this his aim was to turn men from wickedness and to help them to the love and practice of well doing.

[Then follows a brief record of Cædmon's life and an exquisite picture of his death amidst the brethren.] And so it came to pass [says the simple record] that as he served God while living in purity of mind and serenity of spirit, so by a peaceful death he left the world and went to look upon His face.

Cædmon's Works. The greatest work attributed to Cædmon is the so-called *Paraphrase.* It is the story of Genesis, Exodus, and a part of Daniel, told in glowing, poetic language, with a power of insight and imagination which often raises it from paraphrase into the realm of true poetry. Though we have Bede's assurance that Cædmon 'transformed the whole course of Bible history into most delightful poetry', no work known certainly to have been composed by him has come down to us. In the seventeenth century this Anglo-Saxon *Paraphrase* was discovered and attributed to Cædmon, and his name is still associated with it, though it is now almost certain that the *Paraphrase* is the work of more than one writer.

Aside from the doubtful question of authorship, even a casual reading of the poem brings us into the presence of a poet rude indeed, but with a genius strongly suggestive at times of the matchless Milton. The book opens with a hymn of praise, and then tells of the fall of Satan and his rebel angels from heaven, which is familiar to us in Milton's *Paradise Lost*. Then follows the creation of the world, and the *Paraphrase* begins to thrill with the old Anglo-Saxon love of nature.

> Here first the Eternal Father, guard of all,
> Of heaven and earth, raisèd up the firmament,
> The Almighty Lord set firm by His strong power
> This roomy land; grass greened not yet the plain,
> Ocean far spread hid the wan ways in gloom.
> Then was the Spirit gloriously bright
> Of Heaven's Keeper borne over the deep
> Swiftly. The Life-giver, the Angel's Lord,
> Over the ample ground bade come forth Light.
> Quickly the High King's bidding was obeyed,
> Over the waste there shone light's holy ray.
> Then parted He, Lord of triumphant might,
> Shadow from shining, darkness from the light.
> Light, by the Word of God, was first named day.[1]

After recounting the story of Paradise, the Fall, and the Deluge, the *Paraphrase* is continued in the Exodus, of which the poet makes a noble epic, rushing on with the sweep of a Saxon army to battle. A single selection is given here to show how the poet adapted the story to his hearers:

> Then they saw,
> Forth and forward faring, Pharaoh's war array
> Gliding on, a grove of spears;—glittering the hosts!
> Fluttered there the banners, there the folk the march trod.
> Onwards surged the war, strode the spears along,

[1]Genesis, 112-131 (Morley).

Blickered the broad shields; blew aloud the trumpets....
Wheeling round in gyres, yelled the fowls of war,
Of the battle greedy; hoarsely barked the raven,
Dew upon his feathers, o'er the fallen corpses—
Swart that chooser of the slain! Sang aloud the wolves
At eve their horrid song, hoping for the carrion.[1]

Besides the *Paraphrase* we have a few fragments of the same general character which are attributed to the school of Cædmon. The longest of these is *Judith*, in which the story of an apocryphal book of the Old Testament is done into vigorous poetry. Holofernes is represented as a savage and cruel Viking, revelling in his mead hall; and when the heroic Judith cuts off his head with his own sword and throws it down before the warriors of her people, rousing them to battle and victory, we reach perhaps the most dramatic and brilliant point of Anglo-Saxon literature.

Cynewulf (Eighth Century)

Of Cynewulf, greatest of the Anglo-Saxon poets, excepting only the unknown author of *Beowulf*, we know very little. Indeed, it was not till 1840, more than a thousand years after his death, that even his name became known. Though he is the only one of our early poets who signed his works, the name was never plainly written, but woven into the verses in the form of secret runes,[2]

---

[1] Exodus, 155 ff. (Brooke).

[2] Runes were primitive letters of the old northern alphabet. In a few passages Cynewulf used each rune to represent not only a letter but a word beginning with that letter. Thus the rune-equivalent of C stands for *cene* (keen, courageous), Y for *yfel* (evil, in the sense of wretched), N for *nyd* (need), W for *wyn* (joy), U for *ur* (our), L for *lagu* (lake), F for *feoh* (fee, wealth). Using the runes equivalent to these seven letters, Cynewulf hides and at the same time reveals his name in certain verses of *The Christ,* for instance :

Then the Courage-hearted quakes, when the King (Lord) he hears
Speak to those who once on earth but obeyed Him weakly.
While as yet their Yearning pain and their Need most easily

suggesting a modern charade, but more difficult of interpretation until one has found the key to the poet's signature.

Works of Cynewulf. The only signed poems of Cynewulf are *The Christ, Juliana, The Fates of the Apostles, and Elene*. Unsigned poems attributed to him or his school are *Andreas,* the *Phœnix,* the *Dream of the Rood*, the *Descent into Hell, Guthlac,* the *Wanderer,* and some of the Riddles. The last are simply literary conundrums in which some well-known object, like the bow or drinking horn, is described in poetic language, and the hearer must guess the name. Some of them, like 'The Swan'[1] and 'The Storm Spirit', are unusually beautiful.

The Christ

Of all these works the most characteristic is undoubtedly *The Christ,* a didactic poem in three parts: the first celebrating the Nativity; the second, the Ascension; and the third, 'Doomsday', telling the torments of the wicked and the unending joy of the redeemed. Cynewulf takes his subject matter partly from the Church liturgy, but more largely from the homilies of Gregory the Great. The whole is well woven together, and contains some hymns of great beauty and many passages of intense dramatic force. Throughout the poem a deep love for Christ and a reverence for

---

Comfort might discover... Gone is then the *Winsomeness*
Of the earth's adornments! What to Us as men belonged
Of the joys of life was locked, long ago, in *Lake-flood.*
All the *Fee* on earth.

See Brooke's *History of Early English Literature, pp. 377-379,* or *The Christ of Cynewulf,* ed. by Cook, also by Gollancz.

[1]My robe is noiseless while I tread the earth,
Or tarry 'neath the banks, or stir the shallows;
But when these shining wings, this depth of air,
Bear me aloft above the bending shores
Where men abide, and far the welkin's strength
Over the multitudes conveys me, then
With rushing whir and clear melodious sound
My raiment sings. And like a wandering spirit
I float unweariedly o'er flood and field.

(Brougham's version, in *Translations from Old English Poetry.*)

the Virgin Mary are manifest. More than any other poem in any language, *The Christ* reflects the spirit of early Latin Christianity.

Here is a fragment comparing life to a sea voyage—a comparison which occurs sooner or later to every thoughtful person, and which finds perfect expression in Tennyson's 'Crossing the Bar'.

> Now 'tis most like as if we fare in ships
> On the ocean flood, over the water cold,
> Driving our vessels through the spacious seas
> With horses of the deep. A perilous way is this
> Of boundless waves, and there are stormy seas
> On which we toss here in this (reeling) world
> O'er the deep paths. Ours was a sorry plight
> Until at last we sailed unto the land,
> Over the troubled main. Help came to us
> That brought us to the haven of salvation,
> God's Spirit-Son, and granted grace to us
> That we might know e'en from the vessel's deck
> Where we must bind with anchorage secure
> Our ocean steeds, old stallions of the waves.

Andreas and Elene

In the two epic poems of *Andreas* and *Elene* Cynewulf (if he be the author) reaches the very summit of his poetical art. *Andreas*, an unsigned poem, records the story of St. Andrew, who crosses the sea to rescue his comrade St. Matthew from the cannibals. A young shipmaster who sails the boat turns out to be Christ in disguise, Matthew is set free, and the savages are converted by a miracle.[1] It is a spirited poem, full of rush and incident, and the descriptions of the sea are the best in Anglo-Saxon poetry.

Elene has for its subject-matter the finding of the true cross. It tells of Constantine's vision of the Rood, on the eve of battle. After his victory under the new emblem he sends his mother Helena

[1] The source of *Andreas* is an early Greek legend of St. Andrew that found its way to England and was probably known to Cynewulf in some brief Latin form, now lost.

(Elene) to Jerusalem in search of the original cross and the nails. The poem, which is of very uneven quality, might properly be put at the end of Cynewulf's works. He adds to the poem a personal note, signing his name in runes; and, if we accept the wonderful 'Vision of the Rood' as Cynewulf's work, we learn how he found the cross at last in his own heart. There is a suggestion here of the future Sir Launfal and the search for the Holy Grail.

Decline of Northumbrian Literature. The same northern energy which had built up learning and literature so rapidly in Northumbria was instrumental in pulling it down again. Toward the end of the century in which Cynewulf lived, the Danes swept down on the English coasts and overwhelmed Northumbria. Monasteries and schools were destroyed; scholars and teachers alike were put to the sword, and libraries that had been gathered leaf by leaf with the toil of centuries were scattered to the four winds. So all true Northumbrian literature perished, with the exception of a few fragments, and that which we now possess[1] is largely a translation in the dialect of the West Saxons. This translation was made by Alfred's scholars, after he had driven back the Danes in an effort to preserve the ideals and the civilization that had been so hardly won. With the conquest of Northumbria ends the poetic period of Anglo-Saxon literature. With Alfred the Great of Wessex our prose literature makes a beginning.

---

[1]Our two chief sources are the famous Exeter Book, in Exeter Cathedral, a collection of Anglo-Saxon poems presented by Bishop Leofric (*circa* 1050), and the Vercelli Book, discovered in the monastery of Vercelli, Italy, in 1822. The only known manuscript of Beowulf was discovered *circa* 1600, and is now in the Cotton Library of the British Museum. All these are fragmentary copies, and show the marks of fire and of hard usage. The Exeter Book contains *the Christ, Guthlac, the Phœnix, Juliana, Widsith, The Seafarer, Deor*'s *Lament, The Wife*'s *Complaint, The Lover's Message,* ninety-five *Riddles,* and many short hymns and fragments an—astonishing variety for a single manuscript.

Alfred (848-901)

'Every craft and every power soon grows old and is passed over and forgotten, if it be without wisdom.... This is now to be said, that whilst I live I wish to live nobly, and after life to leave to the men who come after me a memory of good works'.[1]

Cædmon Cross at Whitby Abbey

So wrote the great Alfred, looking back over his heroic life. That he lived nobly none can doubt who reads the history of the greatest of Anglo-Saxon kings; and his good works include, among others, the education of half a country, the salvage of a noble native literature, and the creation of the first English prose.

Life and Times of Alfred. For the history of Alfred's times, and details of the terrific struggle with the Northmen, the reader must be referred to the histories. The struggle ended with the Treaty of Wedmore, in 878, with the establishment of Alfred not only as king of Wessex, but as overlord of the whole northern country. Then the hero laid down his sword, and set himself as a little child to learn to read and write Latin, so that he might lead his people in peace as he had led them in war. It is then that Alfred began to be the heroic figure in literature that he had formerly been in the wars against the Northmen.

With the same patience and heroism that had marked the long struggle for freedom, Alfred set himself to the task of educating his people. First he gave them laws, beginning with the Ten Commandments and ending with the Golden Rule, and then established courts where laws could be

[1] From Alfred's *Boethius.*

faithfully administered. Safe from the Danes by land, he created a navy, almost the first of the English fleets, to drive them from the coast. Then, with peace and justice established within his borders, he sent to Europe for scholars and teachers, and set them over schools that he established. Hitherto all education had been in Latin; now he set himself the task, first, of teaching every freeborn Englishman to read and write his own language, and second, of translating into English the best books for their instruction. Every poor scholar was honoured at his court and was speedily set to work at teaching or translating; every wanderer bringing a book or a leaf of manuscript from the pillaged monasteries of Northumbria was sure of his reward. In this way the few fragments of native Northumbrian literature, which we have been studying, were saved to the world. Alfred and his scholars treasured the rare fragments and copied them in the West Saxon dialect. With the exception of Cædmon's Hymn, we have hardly a single leaf from the great literature of Northumbria in the dialect in which it was first written.

Works of Alfred. Aside from his educational work, Alfred is known chiefly as a translator. After fighting his country's battles, and at a time when most men were content with military honour, he began to learn Latin, that he might translate the works that would be most helpful to his people. His important translations are four in number: Orosius's *Universal History* and *Geography*, the leading work in general history for several centuries; Bede's *History*,[1] the first great historical work written on English soil; Pope Gregory's *Shepherds' Book*, intended especially for the clergy; and Boethius's *Consolations of Philosophy,* the favourite philosophical work of the Middle Ages.

The Saxon Chronicle

More important than any translation is the English or *Saxon Chronicle.* This was probably at first a dry record, especially of important births and deaths in the West Saxon kingdom. Alfred enlarged this scant record, beginning the story with Cæsar's conquest. When it touches his own reign the dry chronicle becomes an interesting and connected story, the oldest history belonging to any modern nation in its own language.

[1] It is not certain that the translation of Bede is the work of Alfred.

The record of Alfred's reign, probably by himself, is a splendid bit of writing and shows clearly his claim to a place in literature as well as in history. The *Chronicle* was continued after Alfred's death, and is the best monument of early English prose that is left to us. Here and there stirring songs are included in the narrative, like 'The Battle of Brunanburh' and 'The Battle of Maldon'.[1] The last, entered 991, seventy-five years before the Norman Conquest, is the swansong of Anglo-Saxon poetry. The *Chronicle* was continued for a century after the Norman Conquest, and is extremely valuable not only as a record of events but as a literary monument showing the development of our language.

Close of the Anglo-Saxon Period. After Alfred's death there is little to record, except the loss of the two supreme objects of his heroic struggle, namely, a national life and a national literature. It was at once the strength and the weakness of the Saxon that he lived apart as a free man and never joined efforts willingly with any large body of his fellows. The tribe was his largest idea of nationality, and, with all our admiration, we must confess as we first meet him that he has not enough sense of unity to make a great nation, nor enough culture to produce a great literature. A few noble political ideals repeated in a score of petty kingdoms, and a few literary ideals copied but never increased—that is the summary of his literary history. For a full century after Alfred literature was practically at a standstill, having produced the best of which it was capable, and England waited for the national impulse and for the culture necessary for a new and greater art. Both of these came speedily, by way of the sea, in the Norman Conquest.

Summary of the Anglo-Saxon Period. Our literature begins with songs and stories of a time when our Teutonic ancestors were living on the borders of the North Sea. Three tribes of these ancestors, the Jutes, Angles, and Saxons, conquered Britain in the latter half of the fifth century, and laid the foundation of the English nation. The first landing was

---

[1] See *Translations from Old English Poetry.* Only a brief account of the fight is given in the Chronicle. The song known as 'The Battle of Maldon', or 'Byrhtnoth's Death', is recorded in another manuscript.

probably by a tribe of Jutes, under chiefs called by the chronicle Hengist and Horsa. The date is doubtful; but the year 449 is accepted by most historians.

These old ancestors were hardy warriors and sea rovers, yet were capable of profound and noble emotions. Their poetry reflects this double nature. Its subjects were chiefly the sea and the plunging boats, battles, adventure, brave deeds, the glory of warriors, and the love of home. Accent, alliteration, and an abrupt break in the middle of each line gave their poetry a kind of martial rhythm. In general the poetry is earnest and somber, and pervaded by fatalism and religious feeling. A careful reading of the few remaining fragments of Anglo-Saxon literature reveals five striking characteristics: the love of freedom; responsiveness to nature, especially in her sterner moods; strong religious convictions, and a belief in Wyrd, or Fate; reverence for womanhood; and a devotion to glory as the ruling motive in every warrior's life.

In our study we have noted: (1) the great epic or heroic poem *Beowulf,* and a few fragments of our first poetry, such as 'Widsith', 'Deor's Lament', and 'The Seafarer'. (2) Characteristics of Anglo-Saxon life; the form of our first speech. (3) The Northumbrian school of writers. Bede, our first historian, belongs to this school; but all his extant works are in Latin. The two great poets are Cædmon and Cynewulf. Northumbrian literature flourished between 650 and 850. In the year 867 Northumbria was conquered by the Danes, who destroyed the monasteries and the libraries containing our earliest literature. (4) The beginnings of English prose writing under Alfred (848-901). Our most important prose work of this age is the Anglo-Saxon Chronicle, which was revised and enlarged by Alfred, and which was continued for more than two centuries. It is the oldest historical record known to any European nation in its own tongue.

Selections for Reading. *Miscellaneous Poetry:* The Seafarer, Love Letter (Husband's Message), Battle of Brunanburh, Deor's Lament, Riddles, Exodus, The Christ, Andreas, Dream of the Rood, extracts in Cook and Tinker's Translations from Old English Poetry[1] (Ginn and Company);

[1] This is an admirable little book, containing the cream of Anglo-Saxon poetry, in free translations, with notes. Translations from *Old English Prose* is a companion volume.

Judith, translation by A.S. Cook. Good selections are found also in Brooke's History of Early English Literature, and Morley's English Writers, vols. 1 and 2.

Beowulf. J.R.C. Hall's prose translation; Child's Beowulf (Riverside Literature Series); Morris and Wyatt's The Tale of Beowulf; Earle's The Deeds of Beowulf; Metrical versions by Garnett, J.L. Hall, Lumsden, etc.

Prose. A few paragraphs of the Anglo-Saxon Chronicle in Manly's English Prose; translations in Cook and Tinker's Old English Prose.

Bibliography.[1] ***History.*** For the facts of the Anglo-Saxon conquest of England consult first a good textbook: Montgomery, pp. 31--57, or Cheyney, pp. 36-84. For fuller treatment see Green, ch. 1; Traill, vol. 1; Ramsey's Foundations of England; Turner's History of the Anglo-Saxons; Freeman's Old English History; Allen's Anglo-Saxon England; Cook's Life of Alfred; Asser's Life of King Alfred, edited by W.H. Stevenson; C. Plummer's Life and Times of Alfred the Great; E. Dale's National Life and Character in the Mirror of Early English Literature; Rhys's Celtic Britain.

Literature. *Anglo-Saxon* Texts. Library of Anglo-Saxon Poetry, and Albion Series of Anglo-Saxon and Middle English Poetry (Ginn and Company); Belles Lettres Series of English Classics, sec. 1 (Heath & Co.); J.W. Bright's Anglo-Saxon Reader; Sweet's Anglo-Saxon Primer, and Anglo-Saxon Reader.

General Works. Jusserand, Ten Brink, Cambridge History, Morley (full titles and publishers in General Bibliography).

Special Works. Brooke's History of Early English Literature; Earle's Anglo-Saxon Literature; Lewis's Beginnings of English Literature; Arnold's Celtic Literature (for relations of Saxon and Celt); Longfellow's Poets and Poetry of Europe; Hall's Old English Idyls; Gayley's Classic Myths, or Guerber's Myths of the Northlands (for Norse Mythology); Brother Azarias's Development of Old English Thought.

Beowulf, prose translations by Tinker, Hall, Earle, Morris and Wyatt; metrical versions by Garnett, J.L. Hall, Lumsden, etc. The Exeter Book (a collection of Anglo-Saxon texts), edited and translated by Gollancz. The

---

[1] For full titles and publishers of general reference books, and for a list of inexpensive texts and helps, see General Bibliography at the end of this book.

Christ of Cynewulf, prose translation by Whitman; the same poem, text and translation, by Gollancz; text by Cook. Cædmon's Paraphrase, text and translation, by Thorpe. Garnett's Elene, Judith, and other Anglo-Saxon Poems. Translations of Andreas and the Phœnix, in Gollancz's Exeter Book. Bede's History, in Temple Classics; the same with the Anglo-Saxon Chronicle (one volume) in Bohn's Antiquarian Library.

Suggestive Questions.[1] 1. What is the relation of history and literature? Why should both subjects be studied together? Explain the qualities that characterize all great literature. Has any textbook in history ever appealed to you as a work of literature? What literary qualities have you noticed in standard historical works, such as those of Macaulay, Prescott, Gibbon, Green, Motley, Parkman, and John Fiske?

2. Why did the Anglo-Saxons come to England? What induced them to remain? Did any change occur in their ideals, or in their manner of life? Do you know any social or political institutions which they brought, and which we still cherish?

3. From the literature you have read, what do you know about our Anglo-Saxon ancestors? What virtues did they admire in men? How was woman regarded? Can you compare the Anglo-Saxon ideal of woman with that of other nations, the Romans for instance?

4. Tell in your own words the general qualities of Anglo-Saxon poetry. How did it differ in its metrical form from modern poetry? What passages seem to you worth learning and remembering? Can you explain why poetry is more abundant and more interesting than prose in the earliest literature of all nations?

5. Tell the story of Beowulf. What appeals to you most in the poem? Why is it a work for all time, or, as the Anglo-Saxons would say, why is it worthy to be remembered? Note the permanent quality of literature, and the ideals and emotions which are emphasized in Beowulf). Describe

[1] The chief object of these questions is not to serve as a review, or to prepare for examination, but rather to set the student thinking for himself about what he has read. A few questions of an advanced nature are inserted, which call for special study and research in interesting fields.

the burials of Scyld and of Beowulf. Does the poem teach any moral lesson? Explain the Christian elements in this pagan epic.

6. Name some other of our earliest poems, and describe the one you like best. How does the sea figure in our first poetry? How is nature regarded? What poem reveals the life of the scop or poet? How do you account for the serious character of Anglo-Saxon poetry? Compare the Saxon and the Celt with regard to the gladsomeness of life as shown in their literature.

7. What useful purpose did poetry serve among our ancestors? What purpose did the harp serve in reciting their poems? Would the harp add anything to our modern poetry?

8. What is meant by Northumbrian literature? Who are the great Northumbrian writers? What besides the Danish conquest caused the decline of Northumbrian literature?

9. For what is Bede worthy to be remembered? Tell the story of Cædmon, as recorded in Bede's History. What new element is introduced in Cædmon's poems? What effect did Christianity have upon Anglo-Saxon literature? Can you quote any passages from Cædmon to show that Anglo-Saxon character was not changed but given a new direction? If you have read Milton's *Paradise Lost*, what resemblances are there between that poem and Cædmon's *Paraphrase*?

10. What are the Cynewulf poems? Describe any that you have read. How do they compare in spirit and in expression with *Beowulf*? with Cædmon? Read The Phænix (which is a translation from the Latin) in Brooke's History of Early English Literature, or in Gollancz's Exeter Book, or in Cook's Translations from Old English Poetry, and tell what elements you find to show that the poem is not of Anglo-Saxon origin. Compare the views of nature in Beowulf and in the Cynewulf poems.

11. Describe the Anglo-Saxon Chronicle. What is its value in our language, literature, and history? Give an account of Alfred's life and of his work for literature. How does Anglo-Saxon prose compare in interest with the poetry?

CHRONOLOGY

History	Literature
449(?). Landing of Hengist and Horsa in Britain	
477. Landing of South Saxons	
547. Angles settle Northumbria	547. Gildas's History
597. Landing of Augustine and his monks. Conversion of Kent	
617. Eadwine, king of Northumbria	
635-665. Coming of St. Aidan. Conversion of Northumbria	664. Cædmon at Whitby
	673-735. Bede
	750(cir.). Cynewulf poems
867. Danes conquer Northumbria	
871. Alfred, king of Wessex	860. Anglo-Saxon Chronicle begun
878. Defeat of Danes. Peace of Wedmore	
901. Death of Alfred	991. Last known poem of the Anglo-Saxon period, The Battle of Maldon, otherwise called Byrhtnoth's Death
1013-1042. Danish period	
1016. Cnut, king	
1042. Edward the Confessor. Saxon period restored	
1049. Westminster Abbey begun	
1066. Harold, last of Saxon kings. Norman Conquest	

CHAPTER 3

THE ANGLO-NORMAN PERIOD (1066-1350)

I. HISTORICAL INTRODUCTION

The Normans. The name Norman, which is a softened form of Northman, tells its own story. The men who bore the name came originally from Scandinavia—bands of big, blond, fearless men cruising after plunder and adventure in their Viking ships, and bringing terror wherever they appeared. It was these same 'Children of Woden' who, under the Danes' raven flag, had blotted out Northumbrian civilization in the ninth century. Later the same race of men came plundering along the French coast and conquered the whole northern country; but here the results were altogether different. Instead of blotting out a superior civilization, as the Danes had done, they promptly abandoned their own. Their name of Normandy still clings to the new home; but all else that was Norse disappeared as the conquerors intermarried with the native Franks and accepted French ideals and spoke the French language. So rapidly did they adopt and improve the Roman civilization of the natives that, from a rude tribe of heathen Vikings, they had developed within a single century into the most polished and intellectual people in all Europe. The union of Norse and French (that is Roman-Gallic) blood had here produced a race having the best qualities of both—the willpower and energy of the one, the eager curiosity and vivid imagination of the other. When these Norman-French people appeared in Anglo-Saxon England they brought with them three noteworthy things: a lively Celtic disposition, a vigorous and progressive Latin civilization, and a Romance language.[1] We are to think of the conquerors, therefore, as they thought and spoke of themselves in the Domesday Book and all their contemporary literature, not as Normans but as Franci, that is, Frenchmen.

The Conquest. At the battle of Hastings (1066) the power of Harold, last of the Saxon kings, was broken, and William, duke of Normandy, became master of England. Of the completion of that stupendous Conquest which began at Hastings, and which changed the civilization of a whole nation, this is not the place to speak. We simply point out three great results of the Conquest which have a direct bearing on our literature. First, notwithstanding Cæsar's legions and Augustine's monks, the Normans were the first to bring the culture and the practical ideals of Roman civilization home to the English people; and this at a critical time, when England had produced her best, and her own literature and civilization had already begun to decay. Second, they forced upon England the national idea, that is, a strong, centralized government

Leif Ericson's Vessel

[1] A Romance language is one whose basis is Latin—not the classic language of literature, but a vulgar or popular Latin spoken in the military camps and provinces. Thus Italian, Spanish, and French were originally different dialects of the vulgar Latin, slightly modified by the mingling of the Roman soldiers with the natives of the conquered provinces.

to replace the loose authority of a Saxon chief over his tribesmen. And the world's history shows that without a great nationality a great literature is impossible. Third, they brought to England the wealth of a new language and literature, and our English gradually absorbed both. For three centuries after Hastings French was the language of the upper classes, of courts and schools and literature; yet so tenaciously did the common people cling to their own strong speech that in the end English absorbed almost the whole body of French words and became the language of the land. It was the welding of Saxon and French into one speech that produced the wealth of our modern English.

Naturally such momentous changes in a nation were not brought about suddenly. At first Normans and Saxons lived apart in the relation of masters and servants, with more or less contempt on one side and hatred on the other; but in an astonishingly short time these two races were drawn powerfully together, like two men of different dispositions who are often led into a steadfast friendship by the attraction of opposite qualities, each supplying what the other lacks. The *Anglo-Saxon Chronicle*, which was continued for a century after Hastings, finds much to praise in the conquerors; on the other hand the Normans, even before the Conquest, had no great love for the French nation. After conquering England they began to regard it as home and speedily developed a new sense of nationality. Geoffrey's popular *History,*[1] written less than a century after the Conquest, made conquerors and conquered alike proud of their country by its stories of heroes who, curiously enough, were neither Norman nor Saxon, but creations of the native Celts. Thus does literature, whether in a battle song or a history, often play the chief role in the development of nationality.[2] Once the mutual distrust was overcome the two

[1] See P. 51.

[2] It is interesting to note that all the chroniclers of the period, whether of English or Norman birth, unite in admiration of the great figures of English history, as it was then understood. Brutus, Arthur, Hengist, Horsa, Edward the Confessor, and William of Normandy are all alike set down as English heroes.

races gradually united, and out of this union of Saxons and Normans came the new English life and literature.

Literary Ideals of the Normans. The change in the life of the conquerors from Norsemen to Normans, from Vikings to Frenchmen, is shown most clearly in the literature which they brought with them to England. The old Norse strength and grandeur, the magnificent sagas telling of the tragic struggles of men and gods, which still stir us profoundly—these have all disappeared. In their place is a bright, varied, talkative literature, which runs to endless verses, and which makes a wonderful romance out of every subject it touches. The theme may be religion or love or chivalry or history, the deeds of Alexander or the misdeeds of a monk; but the author's purpose never varies. He must tell a romantic story and amuse his audience; and the more wonders and impossibilities he relates, the more surely is he believed. We are reminded, in reading, of the native Gauls, who would stop every traveller and compel him to tell a story ere he passed on. There was more of the Gaul than of the Norseman in the conquerors, and far more of fancy than of thought or feeling in their literature. If you would see this in concrete form, read the *Chanson de Roland*, the French national epic (which the Normans first put into literary form), in contrast with Beowulf, which voices the Saxon's thought and feeling before the profound mystery of human life. It is not our purpose to discuss the evident merits or the serious defects of Norman-French literature, but only to point out two facts which impress the student, namely, that Anglo-Saxon literature was at one time enormously superior to the French, and

---

In a French poem of the thirteenth century, for instance, we read that 'there is no land in the world where so many good kings and saints have lived as in the isle of the English...such as the strong and brave Arthur, Edmund, and Cnut.' This national poem, celebrating the English Edward, was written in French by a Norman monk of Westminster Abbey, and its first heroes are a Celt, a Saxon, and a Dane. (See Jusserand, *Literary History of the English People,* I, 112 ff.)

that the latter, with its evident inferiority, absolutely replaced the former. 'The fact is too often ignored', says Professor Schofield,[1] 'that before 1066 the Anglo-Saxons had a body of native literature distinctly superior to any which the Normans or French could boast at that time; their prose especially was unparalleled for extent and power in any European vernacular'. Why, then, does this superior literature disappear and for nearly three centuries French remain supreme, so much so that writers on English soil, even when they do not use the French language, still slavishly copy the French models?

To understand this curious phenomenon it is necessary only to remember the relative conditions of the two races who lived side by side in England. On the one hand the Anglo-Saxons were a conquered people, and without liberty a great literature is impossible. The inroads of the Danes and their own tribal wars had already destroyed much of their writings, and in their new condition of servitude they could hardly preserve what remained. The conquering Normans, on the other hand, represented the civilization of France, which country, during the early Middle Ages, was the literary and educational center of all Europe. They came to England at a time when the idea of nationality was dead, when culture had almost vanished, when Englishmen lived apart in narrow isolation; and they brought with them law, culture, the prestige of success, and above all the strong impulse to share in the great world's work and to join in the moving currents of the world's history. Small wonder, then, that the young Anglo-Saxons felt the quickening of this new life and turned naturally to the cultured and progressive Normans as their literary models.

II. LITERATURE OF THE NORMAN PERIOD

In the Advocates' Library at Edinburgh there is a beautifully illuminated manuscript, written about 1330, which gives us an excellent picture of the literature of the Norman period. In

[1] *English Literature from the Norman Conquest to Chaucer.*

examining it we are to remember that literature was in the hands of the clergy and nobles; that the common people could not read, and had only a few songs and ballads for their literary portion. We are to remember also that parchments were scarce and very expensive, and that a single manuscript often contained all the reading matter of a castle or a village. Hence this old manuscript is as suggestive as a modern library. It contains over forty distinct

Canterbury Cathedral as it was Completed Long after the Conquest

works, the great bulk of them being romances. There are metrical or verse romances of French and Celtic and English heroes, like Roland, Arthur and Tristram, and Bevis of Hampton. There are stories of Alexander, the Greek romance of 'Flores and Blanchefleur', and a collection of Oriental tales called 'The Seven Wise Masters'. There are legends of the Virgin and the saints, a paraphrase of Scripture, a treatise on the seven deadly sins, some Bible history, a dispute among birds concerning women, a love song or two, a vision of Purgatory, a vulgar story with a Gallic flavor, a chronicle of English kings and Norman barons, and a political satire. There are a few other works, similarly incongruous, crowded together in this typical manuscript, which now gives mute testimony to the literary taste of the times.

Obviously it is impossible to classify such a variety. We note simply that it is mediæval in spirit, and French in style and expression; and that sums up the age. All the scholarly works of the period, like William of Malmesbury's *History,* and Anselm's[1] *Cur Deus Homo*, and Roger Bacon's *Opus Majus*, the beginning of modern experimental science, were written in Latin; while nearly all other works were written in French, or else were English copies or translations of French originals. Except for the advanced student, therefore, they hardly belong to the story of English literature. We shall note here only one or two marked literary types, like the Riming Chronicle (or verse history) and the Metrical Romance, and a few writers whose work has especial significance.

Geoffrey of Monmouth. (d. 1154). Geoffrey's *Historia Regum Britanniae* is noteworthy, not as literature, but rather as a source book from which many later writers drew their literary materials. Among the native Celtic tribes an immense number of legends, many of them of exquisite beauty, had been preserved through four successive conquests of Britain. Geoffrey, a Welsh monk, collected some of these legends and, aided chiefly by his imagination, wrote a complete history of the Britons. His alleged authority was an ancient manuscript in the native Welsh tongue containing the lives and deeds of all their kings, from Brutus, the alleged founder of Britain, down to the coming of *Julius Cæsar.*[2] From this Geoffrey wrote his history, down to the death of Cadwalader in 689.

The 'History' is a curious medley of pagan and Christian legends, of chronicle, comment, and pure invention—all recorded in minute detail and with a gravity which makes it clear that Geoffrey had no conscience, or else was a great joker. As history

[1] Anselm was an Italian by birth, but wrote his famous work while holding the see of Canterbury.

[2] During the Roman occupancy of Britain occurred a curious mingling of Celtic and Roman traditions. The Welsh began to associate their national hero Arthur with Roman ancestors; hence the story of Brutus, great-grandson of Æneas, the first king of Britain, as related by Geoffrey and Layamon.

the whole thing is rubbish; but it was extraordinarily successful at the time and made all who heard it, whether Normans or Saxons, proud of their own country. It is interesting to us because it gave a new direction to the literature of England by showing the wealth of poetry and romance that lay in its own traditions of Arthur and his knights. Shakespeare's *King Lear,* Malory's *Morte d'Arthur,* and Tennyson's *Idylls of the King* were founded on the work of this monk, who had the genius to put unwritten Celtic tradition in the enduring form of Latin prose.

Work of the French Writers. The French literature of the Norman period is interesting chiefly because of the avidity with which foreign writers seized upon the native legends and made them popular in England. Until Geoffrey's preposterous chronicle appeared, these legends had not been used to any extent as literary material. Indeed, they were scarcely known in England, though familiar to French and Italian minstrels. Legends of Arthur and his court were probably first taken to Brittany by Welsh emigrants in the fifth and sixth centuries. They became immensely popular wherever they were told, and they were slowly carried by minstrels and storytellers all over Europe. That they had never received literary form or recognition was due to a peculiarity of mediæval literature, which required that every tale should have some ancient authority behind it. Geoffrey met this demand by creating an historical manuscript of Welsh history. That was enough for the age. With Geoffrey and his alleged manuscript to rest upon, the Norman-French writers were free to use the fascinating stories which had been for centuries in the possession of their wandering minstrels. Geoffrey's Latin history was put into French verse by Gaimar (*circa* 1150) and by Wace (*circa* 1155), and from these French versions the work was first translated into English. From about 1200 onward Arthur and Guinevere and the matchless band of Celtic heroes that we meet later (1470) in Malory's *Morte d' Arthur* became the permanent possession of our literature.

Layamon's Brut (*circa* 120). This is the most important of the English rhyming chronicles, that is, history related in the form of doggerel verse, probably because poetry is more easily memorized than prose. We give here a free rendering of selected lines at the beginning of the poem, which tell us all we know of Layamon, the first who ever wrote as an Englishman for Englishmen, including in the term all who loved England and called it home, no matter where their ancestors were born.

Now there was a priest in the land named Layamon. He was son of Leovenath—may God be gracious unto him. He dwelt at Ernley, at a noble church on Severn's bank. He read many books, and it came to his mind to tell the noble deeds of the English. Then he began to journey far and wide over the land to procure noble books for authority. He took the English book that Saint Bede made, another in Latin that Saint Albin made,[1] and a third book that a French clerk made, named Wace.[2] Layamon laid these works before him and turned the leaves; lovingly he beheld them. Pen he took, and wrote on book-skin, and made the three books into one.

The poem begins with the destruction of Troy and the flight of 'Æneas the duke' into Italy. Brutus, a great-grandson of Æneas, gathers his people and sets out to find a new land in the West. Then follows the founding of the Briton kingdom, and the last third of the poem, which is over thirty thousand lines in length, is taken up with the history of Arthur and his knights. If the *Brut* had no merits of its own, it would still interest us, for it marks the first appearance of the Arthurian legends in our own tongue. A single selection is given here from Arthur's dying speech, familiar to us in Tennyson's *Morte d'Arthur*. The reader will notice here two things: first, that though the poem is almost pure Anglo-Saxon,[3] our first speech has already dropped many inflections and is more easily

---

[1] Probably a Latin copy of Bede.

[2] Wace's translation of Geoffrey.

[3] Only one word in about three hundred and fifty is of French origin. A century later Robert Mannyng uses one French word in eighty, while Chaucer has one in six or seven. This includes repetitions, and is a fair estimate rather than an exact computation.

read than *Beowulf;* second, that French influence is already at work in Layamon's rhymes and assonances, that is, the harmony resulting from using the same vowel sound in several successive lines:

And ich wulle varen to Avalun:	And I will fare to Avalun,
To vairest alre maidene,	To fairest of all maidens,
To Argante there quene,	To Argante the queen,
Alven swithe sceone.	An elf very beautiful.
And heo seal mine wunden	And she shall my wounds
Makien alle isunde,	Make all sound;
Al hal me makien	All whole me make
Mid haleweiye drenchen.	With healing drinks.
And seothe ich cumen wulle	And again will I come
To mine kiueriche	To my kingdom
And wunien mid Brutten	And dwell with Britons
Mid muchelere wunne.	With mickle joy.
Æfne than worden	Even (with) these words
Ther com of se wenden	There came from the sea
That wes an sceort bat lithen,	A short little boat gliding,
Sceoven mid uthen,	Shoved by the waves;
And twa wimmen ther inne,	And two women therein,
Wunderliche idihte.	Wondrously attired.
And heo nomen Arthur anan	And they took Arthur anon
And an eovste hine vereden	And bore him hurriedly
And softe hine adun leiden,	And softly laid him down,
And forth gunnen lithen.	And forth gan glide.

Metrical Romances. Love, chivalry, and religion, all pervaded by the spirit of romance—these are the three great literary ideals which find expression in the metrical romances. Read these romances now, with their knights and fair ladies, their perilous adventures and tender lovemaking, their minstrelsy and tournaments and gorgeous cavalcades—as if humanity were on parade, and life itself were one tumultuous holiday in the open air—and you have an epitome of the whole childish, credulous soul of the Middle Ages. The Normans first brought this type of romance into England, and so popular did it become, so thoroughly did it express the romantic spirit of the time, that it speedily overshadowed all other forms of literary expression.

Form

Though the metrical romances varied much in form and subject matter, the general type remains the same—a long rambling poem or series of poems treating of love or knightly adventure or both. Its hero is a knight; its characters are fair ladies in distress, warriors in armour, giants, dragons, enchanters, and various enemies of Church and State; and its emphasis is almost invariably on love, religion, and duty as defined by chivalry. In the French originals of these romances the lines were a definite length, the metre exact, and rhymes and assonances were both used to give melody. In England this metrical system came in contact with the uneven lines, the strong accent and alliteration of the native songs; and it is due to the gradual union of the two systems, French and Saxon, that our English became capable of the melody and amazing variety of verse forms which first find expression in Chaucer's poetry.

Cycles of romances

In the enormous number of these verse romances we note three main divisions, according to subject, into the romances (or the so-called matter) of France, Rome, and Britain.[1] The matter of France deals largely with the exploits of Charlemagne and his peers, and the chief of these Carlovingian cycles is the *Chanson de Roland*, the national epic, which celebrates the heroism of Roland in his last fight against the Saracens at Ronceval. Originally these romances were called *Chansons de Geste;* and the name is significant as indicating that the poems were originally short songs[2] celebrating the deeds (*gesta*) of

[1] The matter of Britain refers strictly to the Arthurian, that is, the Welsh romances; and so another division, the matter of England, may be noted. This includes tales of popular English heroes, like Bevis of Hampton, Guy of Warwick, Horn Child, etc.

[2] According to mediæval literary custom these songs were rarely signed. Later, when many songs were made over into a long poem, the author signed his name to the entire work, without indicating what he had borrowed.

well-known heroes. Later the various songs concerning one hero were gathered together and the *Geste* became an epic, like the *Chanson de Roland*, or a kind of continued ballad story, hardly deserving the name of epic, like the *Geste of Robin Hood.*[1]

The matter of Rome consisted largely of tales from Greek and Roman sources; and the two great cycles of these romances deal with the deeds of Alexander, a favorite hero, and the siege of Troy, with which the Britons thought they had some historic connection. To these were added a large number of tales from Oriental sources; and in the exuberant imagination of the latter we see the influence which the Saracens—those nimble wits who gave us our first modern sciences and who still reveled in the *Arabian Nights*—had begun to exercise on the literature of Europe.

The Matter of Britain

To the English reader, at least, the most interesting of the romances are those which deal with the exploits of Arthur The Matter and his Knights of the Round Table—the richest storehouse of romance which our literature has ever found. There were many cycles of Arthurian romances, chief of which are those of Gawain, Launcelot, Merlin, the Quest of the Holy Grail, and the Death of Arthur. In preceding sections we have seen how these fascinating romances were used by Geoffrey and the French writers, and how, through the French, they found their way into English, appearing first in our speech in Layamon's *Brut.* The point to remember is that, while the legends are Celtic in origin, their literary form is due to French poets, who originated the metrical romance. All our early English romances are either copies or translations of the French; and this is true not only of

[1] An English book in which such romances were written was called a Gest or Jest Book. So also at the beginning of *Cursor Mundi (circa* 1320) we read:

Men yernen jestis for to here
And romaunce rede in diverse manere,

and then follows a summary of the great cycles of romance, which we are considering.

the matter of France and Rome, but of Celtic heroes like Arthur, and English heroes like Guy of Warwick and Robin Hood.

The most interesting of all Arthurian romances are those of the Gawain cycle,[1] and of these the story of *Sir Gawain and the Green Knight* is best worth reading, for many reasons. First, though the material is taken from French sources,[2] the English workmanship is the finest of our early romances. Second, the unknown author of this romance probably wrote also 'The Pearl', and is the greatest English poet of the Norman period. Third, the poem itself with its dramatic interest, its vivid descriptions, and its moral purity, is one of the most delightful old romances in any language.

Sir Gawain and the Green Knight

In form *Sir Gawain* is an interesting combination of French and Saxon elements. It is written in an elabourate stanza combining metre and alliteration. At the end of each stanza is a rhymed refrain, called by the French a 'tail rhyme.' We give here a brief outline of the story; but if the reader desires the poem itself, he is advised to begin with a modern version, as the original is in the West Midland dialect and is exceedingly difficult to follow.

On New Year's day, while Arthur and his knights are keeping the Yuletide feast at Camelot, a gigantic knight in green enters the banquet hall on horseback and challenges the bravest knight present to an exchange of blows; that is, he will expose his neck to a blow of his own big battleaxe, if any knight will agree to abide a blow in return. After some natural consternation and a fine speech by Arthur, Gawain accepts the challenge, takes the battleaxe, and with one blow sends the giant's head rolling through the hall. The Green Knight, who is evidently a terrible magician, picks up his head and mounts his horse. He holds out his head and the ghastly lips speak, warning Gawain to be faithful to his promise

---

[1] Tennyson goes farther than Malory in making Gawain false and irreverent. That seems to be a mistake; for in all the earliest romances Gawain is, next to Arthur, the noblest of knights, the most loved and honoured of all the heroes of the Round Table.

[2] There were various French versions of the story; but it came originally from the Irish, where the hero was called Cuchulinn.

and to seek through the world till he finds the Green Chapel. There, on next New Year's day, the Green Knight will meet him and return the blow.

The second canto of the poem describes Gawain's long journey through the wilderness on his steed Gringolet, and his adventures with storm and cold, with, wild beasts and monsters, as he seeks in vain for the Green Chapel. On Christmas eve, in the midst of a vast forest, he offers a prayer to 'Mary, mildest mother so dear', and is rewarded by sight of a great castle. He enters and is royally entertained by the host, an aged hero, and by his wife, who is the most beautiful woman the knight ever beheld. Gawain learns that he is at last near the Green Chapel, and settles down for a little comfort after his long quest.

The next canto shows the life in the castle, and describes a curious compact between the host, who goes hunting daily, and the knight, who remains in the castle to entertain the young wife. The compact is that at night each man shall give the other whatever good thing he obtains during the day. While the host is hunting, the young woman tries in vain to induce Gawain to make love to her, and ends by giving him a kiss. When the host returns and gives his guest the game he has killed Gawain returns the kiss. On the third day, her temptations having twice failed, the lady offers Gawain a ring, which he refuses; but when she offers a magic green girdle that will preserve the wearer from death, Gawain, who remembers the giant's axe so soon to fall on his neck, accepts the girdle as a 'jewel for the jeopardy' and promises the lady to keep the gift secret. Here, then, are two conflicting compacts. When the host returns and offers his game, Gawain returns the kiss but says nothing of the green girdle.

The last canto brings our knight to the Green Chapel, after he is repeatedly warned to turn back in the face of certain death. The Chapel is a terrible place in the midst of desolation; and as Gawain approaches he hears a terrifying sound, the grating of steel on stone, where the giant is sharpening a new battle axe. The Green Knight appears, and Gawain, true to his compact, offers his neck for the blow. Twice the axe swings harmlessly; the third time it falls on his shoulder and wounds him. Whereupon Gawain jumps for his armour, draws his sword, and warns the giant that the compact calls for only one blow, and that, if another is offered, he will defend himself.

Then the Green Knight explains things. He is lord of the castle where Gawain has been entertained for days past. The first two swings of the axe were harmless because Gawain had been true to his compact and twice returned the kiss. The last blow had wounded him because he concealed the gift of the green girdle, which belongs to the Green Knight and was woven by his wife. Moreover, the whole thing has been arranged by Morgain the fay-woman (an enemy of Queen Guinevere, who appears often in the Arthurian romances). Full of shame, Gawain throws back the gift and is ready to atone for his deception; but the Green Knight thinks he has already atoned, and presents the green girdle as a free gift. Gawain returns to Arthur's court, tells the whole story frankly, and ever after that the knights of the Round Table wear a green girdle in his honour.[1]

The Pearl. In the same manuscript with 'Sir Gawain' are found three other remarkable poems, written about 1350, and known to us, in order, as 'The Pearl', 'Cleanness', and 'Patience'. The first is the most beautiful, and received its name from the translator and editor, Richard Morris, in 1864. 'Patience' is a paraphrase of the book of Jonah; 'Cleanness' moralizes on the basis of Bible stories; but 'The Pearl' is an intensely human and realistic picture of a father's grief for his little daughter Margaret, 'My precious perle wythouten spot.' It is the saddest of all our early poems.

On the grave of his little one, covered over with flowers, the father pours out his love and grief till, in the summer stillness, he falls asleep, while we hear in the sunshine the drowsy hum of insects and the faraway sound of the reapers' sickles. He dreams there, and the dream grows into a vision beautiful. His body lies still upon the grave while his spirit goes to a land, exquisite beyond all words, where he comes suddenly upon a stream that he cannot cross. As he wanders along the bank, seeking in vain for a ford, a marvel rises before his eyes, a crystal cliff, and seated beneath it a little maiden who raises a happy, shining face—the face of his little Margaret.

---

[1] It is often alleged that in this romance we have a very poetical foundation for the Order of the Garter, which was instituted by *Edward III,* in 1349; but the history of the order makes this extremely doubtful. The reader will be chiefly interested in comparing this romance with *Beowulf,* for instance, to see what new ideals have taken root to England.

More then me lyste my drede aros,
I stod full stylle and dorste not calle;
Wyth yghen open and mouth ful clos,
I stod as hende as hawk in halle.

He dares not speak for fear of breaking the spell; but sweet as a lily she comes down the crystal stream's bank to meet and speak with him, and tell him of the happy life of heaven and how to live to be worthy of it. In his joy he listens, forgetting all his grief; then the heart of the man cries out for its own, and he struggles to cross the stream to join her. In the struggle the dream vanishes; he wakens to find his eyes wet and his head on the little mound that marks the spot where his heart is buried.

From the ideals of these three poems, and from peculiarities of style and metre, it is probable that their author wrote also Sir Gawain and the *Green Knight.* If so, the unknown author is the one genius of the age whose poetry of itself has power to interest us, and who stands between Cynewulf and Chaucer as a worthy follower of the one and forerunner of the other.

Miscellaneous Literature of the Norman Period. It is well-nigh impossible to classify the remaining literature of this period, and very little of it is now read, except by advanced students. Those interested in the development of 'transition' English will find in the *Ancren Riwle, that is* 'Rule of the Anchoresses' (*circa* 1225), the most beautiful bit of old English prose ever written. It is a book of excellent religious advice and comfort, written for three ladies who wished to live a religious life, without, however, becoming nuns or entering any religious orders. The author was Bishop Poore of Salisbury, according to Morton, who first edited this old classic in 1853. Orm's *Ormulum*, written soon after the *Brut*, is a paraphrase of the gospel lessons for the year, somewhat after the manner of Cædmon's *Paraphrase*, but without any of Cædmon's poetic fire and originality. *Cursor Mundi* (*circa* 1320) is a very long poem which makes a kind of metrical romance out of Bible history and shows the whole dealing of God with man from Creation to Domesday. It is interesting as showing a parallel to the cycles of miracle plays, which attempt to cover the same vast ground. They were forming in this age; but we will study them later, when we try to understand the rise of the drama in England.

Besides these greater works, an enormous number of fables and satires appeared in this age, copied or translated from the French, like the metrical romances. The most famous of these are 'The Owl and the Nightingale'—a long debate between the two birds, one representing the gay side of life, the other the sterner side of law and morals—and 'Land of Cockaygne', 'Luxury Land', a keen satire on monks and monastic religion.[1]

Ballads

While most of the literature of the time was a copy of the French and was intended only for the upper classes, here and there were singers who made ballads for the common people; and these, next to the metrical romances, are the most interesting and significant of all the works of the Norman period. On account of its obscure origin and its oral transmission, the ballad is always the most difficult of literary subjects.[2] We make here only three suggestions, which may well be borne in mind: that ballads were produced continually in England from Anglo-Saxon times until the seventeenth century; that for centuries they were the only really popular literature; and that in the ballads alone one is able to understand the common people. Read, for instance, the ballads of the 'merrie greenwood men', which gradually collected into the *Geste of Robin Hood*, and you will understand

---

[1] Originally 'Cockaygne' (variously spelled) was intended to ridicule the mythical country of Avalon, somewhat as Cervantes' *Don Quixote* later ridicules the romances of chivalry. In 'Luxury Land' everything was good to eat; houses were built of dainties and shingled with cakes; buttered larks fell instead of rain; the streams ran with good wine; and roast geese passed slowly down the streets, turning themselves as they went.

[2] Child's *English and Scottish Popular Ballads* is the most scholarly and complete collection in our language. Gummere's *Old English Ballads* is a good short work. Professor Kittredge's Introduction to the Cambridge edition of Child's *Ballads* is the best summary of a very difficult subject. For an extended discussion of the literary character of the ballad, see Gummere's *The Popular Ballad*.

better, perhaps, than from reading many histories what the common people of England felt and thought while their lords and masters were busy with impossible metrical romances.

In these songs speaks the heart of the English folk. There is lawlessness indeed; but this seems justified by the oppression of the times and by the barbarous severity of the game laws. An intense hatred of shams and injustice lurks in every song; but the hatred is saved from bitterness by the humour with which captives, especially rich churchmen, are solemnly lectured by the bandits, while they squirm at sight of devilish tortures prepared before their eyes in order to make them give up their golden purses; and the scene generally ends in a bit of wild horseplay. There is fighting enough, and ambush and sudden death lurk at every turn of the lonely roads; but there is also a rough, honest chivalry for women, and a generous sharing of plunder with the poor and needy. All literature is but a dream expressed, and 'Robin Hood' is the dream of an ignorant and oppressed but essentially noble people, struggling and determined to be free.

Remains of the Scriptorium of Fountains Abbey
(Fourteenth century)

Far more poetical than the ballads, and more interesting even than the romances, are the little lyrics of the period—those tears and smiles of long ago that crystallized into poems, to tell us that the hearts of men are alike in all ages. Of these, the best known are the 'Luve Ron' (love rune or letter) of Thomas de Hales (*circa,* 1250); 'Springtime' (*circa,* 1300), beginning 'Lenten (spring) ys come with luve to toune'; and the melodious love song 'Alysoun', written at the end of the thirteenth century by some unknown poet who heralds the coming of Chaucer:

Lyrics

Bytuene Mersh and Averil,
When spray biginneth to springe
The lutel foul[1] hath hire wyl
On hyre lud[2] to synge.
Ich libbe[3] in love longinge
For semlokest[4] of all thinge.
She may me blisse bringe;
Icham[5] in hire baundoun.[6]
An hendy hap ichabbe yhent,[7]
Ichot[8] from hevene it is me sent,
From alle wymmen mi love is lent[9]
And lyht[10] on Alysoun.

Summary of the Anglo-Norman Period. The Normans were originally a hardy race of sea rovers inhabiting Scandinavia. In the tenth century they conquered a part of northern France, which is still called Normandy, and rapidly adopted French civilization and the French language. Their conquest of Anglo-Saxon England under William, Duke of Normandy, began with the battle of Hastings in 1066. The literature which they brought to England is remarkable for its bright, romantic tales of love and adventure, in marked contrast with the strength and sombreness of Anglo-Saxon poetry. During the three centuries following Hastings, Normans and Saxons gradually united. The Anglo-Saxon speech simplified itself by dropping most of its Teutonic inflections, absorbed eventually a large part of the French vocabulary, and became our English language. English literature is also a combination of French and Saxon

[1] little bird. [2] in her language [3] I live. [4] fairest. [5] I am. [6] power, bondage
[7] a pleasant fate I have attained. [8] I know. [9] gone. [10] lit, alighted.

elements. The three chief effects of the conquest were (1) the bringing of Roman civilization to England; (2) the growth of nationality, that is a strong centralized government, instead of the loose union of Saxon tribes; (3) the new language and literature, which were proclaimed in Chaucer.

At first the new literature was remarkably varied, but of small intrinsic worth; and very little of it is now read. In our study we have noted: (1) Geoffrey's History, which is valuable as a source book of literature, since it contains the native Celtic legends of Arthur. (2) The work of the French writers, who made the Arthurian legends popular. (3) Riming Chronicles, that is history in doggerel verse, like Layamon's *Brut.* (4) Metrical Romances, or tales in verse. These were numerous, and of four classes: (a) the Matter of France, tales centreing about Charlemagne and his peers, chief of which is the Chanson de Roland; (b) Matter of Greece and Rome, an endless series of fabulous tales about Alexander, and about the Fall of Troy; (c) Matter of England, stories of Bevis of Hampton, Guy of Warwick, Robin Hood, etc.; (d) Matter of Britain, tales having for their heroes Arthur and his knights of the Round Table. The best of these romances is Sir Gawain and the Green Knight. (5) Miscellaneous literature—the Ancren Riwle, our best piece of early English prose; Orm's Ormulum; Cursor Mundi, with its suggestive parallel to the Miracle plays; and ballads, like King Horn and the Robin Hood songs, which were the only poetry of the common people.

Selections for Reading. For advanced students, and as a study of language, a few selections as given in Manly's English Poetry and in Manly's English Prose; or selections from the Ormulum, Brut, Ancren Riwle, and King Horn, etc., in Morris and Skeat's Specimens of Early English. The ordinary student will get a better idea of the literature of the period by using the following: Sir Gawain, modernized by J. L. Weston, in Arthurian Romances Series (Nutt); The Nun's Rule (Ancren Riwle), modern version by J. Morton, in King's Classics; Aucassin and Nicolete, translated by A. Lang (Crowell & Co.); Tristan and Iseult, in Arthurian Romances; Evans's The High History of the Holy Grail, in Temple Classics; The Pearl, various modern versions in prose and verse; one of the best is Jewett's metrical version (Crowell & Co.); The Song of Roland, in King's Classics, and in Riverside Literature Series; Evans's translation of Geoffrey's History, in Temple Classics; Guest's The Mabinogion, in Everyman's Library, or S.

Lanier's Boy's Mabinogion (that is Welsh fairy tales and romances); Selected Ballads, in Athenæum Press Series, and in Pocket Classics; Gayley and Flaherty's Poetry of the People; Bates's A Ballad Book.

Bibliography.[1] ***History.*** *Textbook,* Montgomery, pp. 58-86, or Cheyney, pp. 88-144. For fuller treatment, Green, ch. 2; Traill; Gardiner, etc. Jewett's Story of the Normans (Stories of the Nations Series); Freeman's Short History of the Norman Conquest; Hutton's King and Baronage (Oxford Manuals of English History).

Literature. *General Works.* Jusserand; Ten Brink; Mitchell, vol. I, From Celt to Tudor; The Cambridge History of English Literature.

Special Works. Schofield's English Literature from the Norman Conquest to Chaucer; Lewis's Beginnings of English Literature; Ker's Epic and Romance; Saintsbury's The Flourishing of Romance and the Rise of Allegory; Newell's King Arthur and the Round Table; Maynadier, The Arthur of the English Poets; Rhys's Studies in the Arthurian Legends.

Ballads. Child's English and Scottish Popular Ballads; Gummere's Old English Ballads (one volume); Hazlitt's Early Popular Poetry of England; Gayley and Flaherty's Poetry of the People; Percy's Reliques of Ancient English Poetry, in Everyman's Library.

Texts, Translations, etc. Morris and Skeat's Specimens of Early English; Morris's Sir Gawain and the Green Knight, in Early English Text Series; Madden's Layamon's Brut, text and translation (a standard work, but rare); The Pearl, text and translation, by Gollancz; the same poem, prose version, by Osgood, metrical versions by Jewett, Weir Mitchell, and Mead; Geoffrey's History, translation, in Giles's Six Old English Chronicles (Bohn's Antiquarian Library); Morley's Early English Prose Romances; Joyce's Old Celtic Romances; Guest's The Mabinogion; Lanier's Boy's Mabinogion; Arthurian Romances Series (translations). The Belles Lettres Series, sec. 2 (announced), will contain the texts of a large number of works of this period, with notes and introductions.

Language. Marsh's Lectures on the English Language; Bradley's Making of English; Lounsbury's History of the English Language; Emerson's Brief History of the English Language; Greenough and Kittredge's Words and their Ways in English Speech; Welsh's Development of English Literature and Language.

---

[1] For titles and publishers of reference books see General Bibliography at the end of this book.

Suggestive Questions. 1. What did the Northmen originally have in common with the Anglo-Saxons and the Danes? What brought about the remarkable change from Northmen to Normans? Tell briefly the story of the Norman Conquest. How did the Conquest affect the life and literature of England?

2. What types of literature were produced after the Conquest? How do they compare with Anglo-Saxon literature? What works of this period are considered worthy of a permanent place in our literature?

3. What is meant by the Riming Chronicles? What part did they play in developing the idea of nationality? What led historians of this period to write in verse? Describe Geoffrey's History. What was its most valuable element from the viewpoint of literature?

4. What is Layamon's Brut? Why did Layamon choose this name for his Chronicle? What special literary interest attaches to the poem?

5. What were the Metrical Romances? What reasons led to the great interest in three classes of romances, that is Matters of France, Rome, and Britain? What new and important element enters our literature in this type? Read one of the Metrical Romances in English and comment freely upon it, as to interest, structure, ideas, and literary quality.

6. Tell the story of *Sir Gawain and the Green Knight.* What French and what Saxon elements are found in the poem? Compare it with *Beowulf* to show the points of inferiority and superiority. Compare Beowulf's fight with Grendel or the Fire Drake and Sir Gawain's encounter with the Green Knight, having in mind (1) the virtues of the hero, (2) the qualities of the enemy, (3) the methods of warfare, (4) the purpose of the struggle. Read selections from 'The Pearl' and compare with *Deor's Lament.* What are the personal and the universal interests in each poem?

7. Tell some typical story from the Mabinogion. Where did the Arthurian legends originate, and how did they become known to English readers? What modern writers have used these legends? What fine elements do you find in them that are not found in Anglo-Saxon poetry?

8. What part did Arthur play in the early history of Britain? How long did the struggle between Britons and Saxons last? What Celtic names and elements entered into English language and literature?

9. What is a ballad, and what distinguishes it from other forms of poetry? Describe the ballad which you like best. Why did the ballad,

more than any other form of literature, appeal to the common people? What modern poems suggest the old popular ballad? How do these compare in form and subject matter with the Robin Hood ballads?

CHRONOLOGY

HISTORY	LITERATURE
912. Northmen settle in Normandy	
1066. Battle of Hastings. William, King of England	
	1086. Domesday Book completed
1087. William Rufus	
1093. Anselm, archbishop of Canterbury	1094(*cir.*). Anselm's Cur Deus Homo
1096. First Crusade	
1100. Henry I	1110. First recorded Miracle play in England (see chapter on the Drama)
1135. Stephen	
1147. Second Crusade	1137(*cir.*). Geoffrey's History
1154. Henry II	
1189. Richard I. Third Crusade	
1199. John	1200 (*cir.*). Layamon's Brut
1215. Magna Charta	
1216. Henry III	1225 (*cir.*). Ancren Riwle
1230 (*cir.*) University of Cambridge chartered	
1265. Beginning of House of Commons. Simon de Montfort	1267. Roger Bacon's Opus Majus
1272. Edward I	
1295. First complete Parliament	1300-1400. York and Wakefield. Miracle plays
1307. Edward II	1320 (*cir.*). Cursor Mundi
1327. Edward III	
1338. Beginning of Hundred Years' War with France	1340 (?). Birth of Chaucer
	1350 (*cir.*). Sir Gawain. The Pearl

Geoffrey Chaucer
After the Rawlinson Pastel Portrait in the Bodleian Library, Oxford

CHAPTER 4

THE AGE OF CHAUCER (1350-1400)

THE NEW NATIONAL LIFE AND LITERATURE

History of the Period. Two great movements may be noted in the complex life of England during the fourteenth century. The first is political, and culminates in the reign of *Edward* III. It shows the growth of the English national spirit following the victories of Edward and the Black Prince on French soil, during the Hundred Years' War. In the rush of this great national movement, separating England from the political ties of France and, to a less degree, from ecclesiastical bondage to Rome, the mutual distrust and jealousy which had divided nobles and commons were momentarily swept aside by a wave of patriotic enthusiasm. The French language lost its official prestige, and English became the speech not only of the common people but of courts and Parliament as well.

The second movement is social; it falls largely within the reign of Edward's successor, *Richard II*, and marks the growing discontent with the contrast between luxury and poverty, between the idle wealthy classes and the overtaxed peasants. Sometimes this movement is quiet and strong, as when Wyclif arouses the conscience of England; again it has the portentous rumble of an approaching tempest, as when John Ball harangues a multitude of discontented peasants on Black Heath commons, using the famous text:

When Adam delved and Eve span
Who was then the gentleman?

and again it breaks out into the violent rebellion of Wat Tyler. All these things show the same Saxon spirit that had won its freedom in a thousand years' struggle against foreign enemies, and that now felt itself oppressed by a social and industrial tyranny in its own midst.

Aside from these two movements, the age was one of unusual stir and progress. Chivalry, that mediæval institution of mixed good and evil, was in its Indian summer—a sentiment rather than a practical system. Trade, and its resultant wealth and luxury, were increasing enormously. Following trade, as the Vikings had followed glory, the English began to be a conquering and colonizing people, like the Anglo-Saxons. The native shed something of his insularity and became a traveller, going first to view the places where trade had opened the way, and returning with wider interests and a larger horizon. Above all, the first dawn of the Renaissance is heralded in England, as in Spain and Italy, by the appearance of a national literature.

Five Writers of the Age. The literary movement of the age clearly reflects the stirring life of the times. There is Langland, voicing the social discontent, preaching the equality of men and the dignity of labour; Wyclif, greatest of English religious reformers, giving the Gospel to the people in their own tongue, and the freedom of the Gospel in unnumbered tracts and addresses; Gower, the scholar and literary man, criticising this vigorous life and plainly afraid of its consequences; and Mandeville, the traveller, romancing about the wonders to be seen abroad. Above all there is Chaucer—scholar, traveller, business man, courtier, sharing in all the stirring life of his times, and reflecting it in literature as no other but Shakespeare has ever done. Outside of England the greatest literary influence of the age was that of Dante, Petrarch, and Boccaccio, whose works, then at the summit of their influence in Italy, profoundly affected the literature of all Europe.

CHAUCER (1340?-1400)

> 'What man artow?' quod he;
> 'Thou lokest as thou woldest finde an hare,
> For ever upon the ground I see thee stare.
> Approchë neer, and loke up merily....
> He semeth elvish by his contenaunce.'
>
> (The Host's description of Chaucer,
> Prologue, *Sir Thopas*)

On reading Chaucer. The difficulties of reading Chaucer are more apparent than real, being due largely to obsolete spelling, and there is small necessity for using any modern versions of the poet's work, which seem to miss the quiet charm and dry humour of the original. If the reader will observe the following general rules (which of necessity ignore many differences in pronunciation of fourteenth-century English), he may, in an hour or two, learn to read Chaucer almost as easily as Shakespeare: (1) Get the lilt of the lines, and let the metre itself decide how final syllables are to be pronounced. Remember that Chaucer is among the most musical of poets, and that there is melody in nearly every line. If the verse seems rough, it is because we do not read it correctly. (2) Vowels in Chaucer have much the same value as in modern German; consonants are practically the same as in modern English. (3) Pronounce aloud any strange-looking words. Where the eye fails, the ear will often recognize the meaning. If eye and ear both fail, then consult the glossary found in every good edition of the poet's works. (4) Final *e* is usually sounded (like *a* in Virginia) except where the following word begins with a vowel or with *h*. In the latter case the final syllable of one word and the first of the word following are run together, as in reading Virgil. At the end of a line the *e*, if lightly pronounced, adds melody to the verse.[1]

---

[1] The reader may perhaps be more interested in these final letters, which are sometimes sounded and again silent, if he remembers that they represent the decaying inflections of our old Anglo-Saxon speech.

In dealing with Chaucer's masterpiece, the reader is urged to read widely at first, for the simple pleasure of the stories, and to remember that poetry and romance are more interesting and important than Middle English. When we like and appreciate Chaucer—his poetry, his humour, his good stories, his kind heart—it will be time enough to study his language.

Life of Chaucer. For our convenience the life of Chaucer is divided into three periods. The first, of thirty years, includes his youth and early manhood, in which time he was influenced almost exclusively by French literary models. The second period, of fifteen years, covers Chaucer's active life as diplomat and man of affairs; and in this the Italian influence seems stronger than the French. The third, of fifteen years, generally known as the English period, is the time of Chaucer's richest development. He lives at home, observes life closely but kindly, and while the French influence is still strong, as shown in the *Canterbury Tales*, he seems to grow more independent of foreign models and is dominated chiefly by the vigorous life of his own English people.

Chaucer's boyhood was spent in London, on Thames Street near the river, where the world's commerce was continually coming

First Period

and going. There he saw daily the shipman of the *Canterbury Tales* just home in his good ship Maudelayne, with the fascination of unknown lands in his clothes and conversation. Of his education we know nothing, except that he was a great reader. His father was a wine merchant, purveyor to the royal household, and from this accidental relation between trade and royalty may have arisen the fact that at seventeen years Chaucer was made page to the Princess Elizabeth. This was the beginning of his connection with the brilliant court, which in the next forty years, under three kings, he was to know so intimately.

At nineteen he went with the king on one of the many expeditions of the Hundred Years' War, and here he saw chivalry and all the pageantry of mediæval war at the height of their outward splendour. Taken prisoner at the unsuccessful siege of Rheims, he is said to have been ransomed by money out of the royal purse.

Returning to England, he became after a few years squire of the royal household, the personal attendant and confidant of the king. It was during this first period that he married a maid of honour to the queen. This was probably Philippa Roet, sister to the wife of John of Gaunt, the famous Duke of Lancaster. From numerous whimsical references in his early poems, it has been thought that this marriage into a noble family was not a happy one; but this is purely a matter of supposition or of doubtful inference.

In 1370 Chaucer was sent abroad on the first of those diplomatic missions that were to occupy the greater part of the next fifteen years. Two years later he made his first official visit to Italy, to arrange a commercial treaty with Genoa, and from this time is noticeable a rapid development in his literary powers and the prominence of Italian literary influences. During the intervals between his different missions he filled various offices at home, chief of which was Comptroller of Customs at the port of London. An enormous amount of personal labour was involved; but Chaucer seems to have found time to follow his spirit into the new fields of Italian literature:

Second Period

> For whan thy labour doon al is,
> And hast y-maad thy rekeninges,
> In stede of reste and newe thinges,
> Thou gost hoom to thy hous anoon,
> And, also domb as any stoon,
> Thou sittest at another boke
> Til fully daswed is thy loke,
> And livest thus as an hermyte.[1]

In 1386 Chaucer was elected member of Parliament from Kent, and the distinctly English period of his life and work begins. Though exceedingly busy in public affairs and

Third Period

[1] *House of Fame,* II, 652 ff. The passage is more or less autobiographical.

as receiver of customs, his heart was still with his books, from which only nature could win him:

> And as for me, though that my wit be lyte,
> On bokes for to rede I me delyte,
> And to hem yeve I feyth and ful credence,
> And in myn herte have hem in reverence
> So hertely, that ther is game noon
> That fro my bokes maketh me to goon,
> But hit be seldom, on the holyday;
> Save, certeynly, whan that the month of May
> Is comen, and that I here the foules singe,
> And that the floures ginnen for to springe—
> Farwel my book and my devocioun![1]

In the fourteenth century politics seems to have been, for honest men, a very uncertain business. Chaucer naturally adhered to the party of John of Gaunt, and his fortunes rose or fell with those of his leader. From this time until his death he is up and down on the political ladder; to-day with money and good prospects, tomorrow in poverty and neglect, writing his 'Complaint to His Empty Purs', which he humorously calls his 'saveour doun in this werlde here.' This poem called the king's attention to the poet's need and increased his pension; but he had but few months to enjoy the effect of this unusual 'Complaint'. For he died the next year, 1400, and was buried with honor in Westminster Abbey. The last period of his life, though outwardly most troubled, was the most fruitful of all. His 'Truth', or 'Good Counsel', reveals the quiet, beautiful spirit of his life, unspoiled either by the greed of trade or the trickery of politics:

> Flee fro the prees, and dwelle with sothfastnesse,
> Suffyce unto thy good, though hit be smal;
> For hord[2] hath hate, and climbing tikelnesse,

---

[1] *Legend of Good Women,* Prologue, II. 29 ff.

[2] wealth.

Prees[1] hath envye, and wele[2] blent[3] overal;
Savour no more than thee bihovë shal;
Werk[4] wel thyself, that other folk canst rede;
And trouthe shal delivere, hit is no drede.

Tempest[5] thee noght al croked to redresse,
In trust of hir[6] that turneth as a bal:
Gret reste stant in litel besinesse;
And eek be war to sporne[7] ageyn an al[8];
Stryve noght, as doth the crokke with the wal.
Daunte[9] thyself, that dauntest otheres dede;
And trouthe shal delivere, hit is no drede.

That thee is sent, receyve in buxumnesse,
The wrastling for this worlde axeth a fal.
Her nis non hoom, her nis but wildernesse:
Forth, pilgrim, forth! Forth, beste, out of thy stal!
Know thy contree, look up, thank God of al;
Hold the hye wey, and lat thy gost thee lede:
And trouthe shal delivere, hit is no drede.

Works of Chaucer, First Period. The works of Chaucer are roughly divided into three classes, corresponding to the three periods of his life. It should be remembered, however, that it is impossible to fix exact dates for most of his works. Some of his *Canterbury Tales* were written earlier than the English period, and were only grouped with the others in his final arrangement.

The best known, though not the best, poem of the first period is the *Romaunt of the Rose*,[10] a translation from the French *Roman de la Rose*, the most popular poem of the Middle Ages—a graceful but exceedingly tiresome allegory of the whole course of love.

---

[1] the crowd. [2] success. [3] blinds. [4] act. [5] trouble. [6] that is, the goddess Fortune. [7] kick [8] awl. [9] judge.

[10] For the typography of titles the author has adopted the plan of putting the titles of all books, and of all important works generally regarded as single books, in italics. Individual poems, essays, etc., are in Roman letters with quotation marks. Thus we have the 'Knight's Tale', or the story of 'Palamon and Arcite', in the *Canterbury Tales.* This system seems on the whole the best, though it may result in some inconsistencies.

The Rose growing in its mystic garden is typical of the lady Beauty. Gathering the Rose represents the lover's attempt to win his lady's favour; and the different feelings aroused—Love, Hate, Envy, Jealousy, Idleness, Sweet Looks—are the allegorical persons of the poet's drama. Chaucer translated this universal favourite, putting in some original English touches; but of the present *Romaunt* only the first seventeen hundred lines are believed to be Chaucer's own work.

Perhaps the best poem of this period is the 'Dethe of Blanche the Duchesse', better known, as the 'Boke of the Duchesse', a poem of considerable dramatic and emotional power, written after the death of Blanche, wife of Chaucer's patron, John of Gaunt. Additional poems are the 'Compleynte to Pite', a graceful love poem; the 'ABC', a prayer to the Virgin, translated from the French of a Cistercian monk, its verses beginning with the successive letters of the alphabet; and a number of what Chaucer calls 'ballads, roundels, and virelays', with which, says his friend Gower, 'the land was filled.' The latter were imitations of the prevailing French love ditties.

Second Period. The chief work of the second or Italian period is *Troilus and Criseyde*, a poem of eight thousand lines. The original story was a favourite of many authors during the Middle Ages, and Shakespeare makes use of it in his *Troilus and Cressida*. The immediate source of Chaucer's poem is Boccaccio's *Il Filostrato*, 'the love-smitten one'; but he uses his material very freely, to reflect the ideals of his own age and society, and so gives to the whole story a dramatic force and beauty which it had never known before.

The 'Hous of Fame' is one of Chaucer's unfinished poems, having the rare combination of lofty thought and simple, homely language, showing the influence of the great Italian master. In the poem the author is carried away in a dream by a great eagle from the brittle temple of Venus, in a sandy wilderness, up to the hall of fame. To this house come all rumours of earth, as the sparks fly upward. The house stands on a rock of ice

writen ful of names
Of folk that hadden grete fames.

Many of these have disappeared as the ice melted; but the older names are clear as when first written. For many of his ideas Chaucer is indebted to Dante, Ovid, and Virgil; but the unusual conception and the splendid workmanship are all his own.

The third great poem of the period is the *Legende of Goode Wimmen.* As he is resting in the fields among the daisies, he falls asleep and a gay procession draws near. First comes the love god, leading by the hand Alcestis, model of all wifely virtues, whose emblem is the daisy; and behind them follow a troupe of glorious women, all of whom have been faithful in love. They gather about the poet; the god upbraids him for having translated the *Romance of the Rose*, and for his early poems reflecting on the vanity and fickleness of women. Alcestis intercedes for him, and offers pardon if he will atone for his errors by writing a 'glorious legend of good women'. Chaucer promises, and as soon as he awakes sets himself to the task. Nine legends were written, of which 'Thisbe' is perhaps the best. It is probable that Chaucer intended to make this his masterpiece, devoting many years to stories of famous women who were true to love; but either because he wearied of his theme, or because the plan of the *Canterbury Tales* was growing in his mind, he abandoned the task in the middle of his ninth legend—fortunately, perhaps, for the reader will find the Prologue more interesting than any of the legends.

Third Period. Chaucer's masterpiece, the *Canterbury Tales*, one of the most famous works in all literature, fills the third or English period of his life. The plan of the work is magnificent: to represent the wide sweep of English life by gathering a motley company together and letting each class of society tell its own favourite stories. Though the great work was never finished, Chaucer succeeded in his purpose so well that in the *Canterbury Tales* he has given us a picture of contemporary English life, its work and play, its deeds and dreams, its fun and sympathy and hearty joy of living, such as no other single work of literature has ever equalled.

Plan of the Canterbury Tales. Opposite old London, at the southern end of London Bridge, once stood the Tabard Inn of Southwark, a quarter made famous not only by the *Canterbury Tales*,

Tabard Inn

but also by the first playhouses where Shakespeare had his training. This Southwark was the point of departure of all travel to the south of England, especially of those mediæval pilgrimages to the shrine of Thomas Becket in Canterbury. On a spring evening, at the inspiring time of the year when 'longen folk to goon on pilgrimages', Chaucer alights at the Tabard Inn, and finds it occupied by a various company of people bent on a pilgrimage. Chance alone had brought them together; for it was the custom of pilgrims to wait at some friendly inn until a sufficient company were gathered to make the journey pleasant and safe from robbers that might be encountered on the way. Chaucer joins this company, which includes all classes of English society, from the Oxford scholar to the drunken miller, and accepts gladly their invitation to go with them on the morrow.

At supper the jovial host of the Tabard Inn suggests that, to enliven the journey, each of the company shall tell four tales, two going and two coming, on whatever subject shall suit him best. The host will travel with them as master of ceremonies, and whoever tells the best story shall be given a fine supper at the general expense when they all come back again—a shrewd bit of business and a fine idea, as the pilgrims all agree.

When they draw lots for the first story the chance falls to the Knight, who tells one of the best of the *Canterbury Tales*, the chivalric story of 'Palamon and Arcite'. Then the tales follow rapidly, each with its prologue and epilogue, telling how the story came about, and its effects on the merry company. Interruptions are numerous; the narrative is full of life and movement, as when the miller gets drunk and insists on telling his tale out of season, or when they stop at a friendly inn for the night, or when the poet with sly humour starts his story of 'Sir Thopas', in dreary imitation of the metrical romances of the day, and is roared at by the host for his 'drasty ryming'. With Chaucer we laugh at his own expense, and are ready for the next tale.

From the number of persons in the company, thirty-two in all, it is evident that Chaucer meditated an immense work of one hundred and twenty-eight tales, which should cover the whole life of England. Only twenty-four were written; some of these are incomplete, and others are taken from his earlier work to fill out the general plan of the *Canterbury Tales*. Incomplete as they are, they cover a wide range, including stories of love and chivalry, of saints and legends, travels, adventures, animal fables, allegory, satires, and the coarse humour of the common people. Though all but two are written in verse and abound in exquisite poetical touches, they are stories as well as poems, and Chaucer is to be regarded as our first short-storyteller as well as our first modern poet. The work ends with a kindly farewell from the poet to his reader, and so 'here taketh the makere of this book his leve'.

Prologue to the Canterbury Tales. In the famous 'Prologue' the poet makes us acquainted with the various characters of his drama. Until Chaucer's day popular literature had been busy chiefly with the gods and heroes of a golden age; it had been essentially romantic, and so had never attempted to study men and women as they are, or to describe them so that the reader recognizes them, not as ideal heroes, but as his own neighbours. Chaucer not only attempted this new realistic task, but accomplished it so well that his characters were instantly recognized as true to life, and they have since become the permanent possession of our literature. Beowulf and Roland are ideal heroes, essentially creatures of the imagination; but the merry host of the Tabard Inn, Madame Eglantyne, the fat monk, the parish priest, the kindly ploughman, the poor scholar with his 'bookes black and red',—all seem more like personal acquaintances than characters in a book. Says Dryden: 'I see all the pilgrims, their humours, their features and their very dress, as distinctly as if I had supped with them at the Tabard in Southwark'. Chaucer is the first English writer to bring the atmosphere of romantic interest about the men and women and the daily work of one's own world—which is the aim of nearly all modern literature.

The historian of our literature is tempted to linger over this 'Prologue' and to quote from it passage after passage to show how keenly and yet kindly our first modern poet observed his fellow-men. The characters, too, attract one like a good play: the 'verray parfit gentil knight' and his manly son, the modest prioress, model of sweet piety and society manners, the sporting monk and the fat friar, the discreet man of law, the well-fed country squire, the sailor just home from sea, the canny doctor, the lovable parish priest who taught true religion to his flock, but 'first he folwed it himselve'; the coarse but good-hearted Wyf of Bath, the thieving miller leading the pilgrims to the music of his bagpipe—all these and many others from every walk of English life, and all described with a quiet, kindly humour which seeks instinctively the best in human nature, and which has an ample garment of charity to cover even its faults and failings. 'Here', indeed, as Dryden says, 'is God's plenty'. Probably no keener or kinder critic ever described his fellows; and in this immortal 'Prologue' Chaucer is a model for all those who would put our human life into writing. The student should read it entire, as an introduction not only to the poet but to all our modern literature.

The Knight's Tale. As a story, 'Palamon and Arcite' is, in many respects, the best of the *Canterbury Tales*, reflecting as it does the ideals of the time in regard to romantic love and knightly duty. Though its dialogues and descriptions are somewhat too long and interrupt the story, yet it shows Chaucer at his best in his dramatic power, his exquisite appreciation of nature, and his tender yet profound philosophy of living, which could overlook much of human frailty in the thought that

> Infinite been the sorwes and the teres
> Of olde folk, and folk of tendre yeres.

The idea of the story was borrowed from Boccaccio; but parts of the original tale were much older and belonged to the common literary stock of the Middle Ages. Like Shakespeare, Chaucer took the material for his poems wherever he found it, and his originality consists in giving to an old story some present human interest, making it express the life and ideals of his own age. In this respect the 'Knight's Tale' is remarkable. Its names are those of an ancient civilization, but its characters are men and women of the English nobility as Chaucer knew them. In consequence the story has many anachronisms, such as the mediæval tournament before the temple of Mars; but the reader scarcely notices these things, being absorbed in the dramatic interest of the narrative.

Briefly, the 'Knight's Tale' is the story of two young men, fast friends, who are found wounded on the battlefield and taken prisoners to Athens. There from their dungeon window they behold the fair maid Emily; both fall desperately in love with her, and their friendship turns to strenuous rivalry. One is pardoned; the other escapes; and then knights, empires, nature—the whole universe follows their desperate efforts to win one small maiden, who prays meanwhile to be delivered from both her bothersome suitors. As the best of the *Canterbury Tales* are now easily accessible, we omit here all quotations. The story must be read entire, with the Prioress' tale of Hugh of Lincoln, the Clerk's tale of Patient Griselda, and the Nun's Priest's merry tale of Chanticleer and the Fox, if the reader would appreciate the variety and charm of our first modern poet and storyteller.

Form of Chaucer's Poetry. There are three principal metres to be found in Chaucer's verse. In the Canterbury Tales he uses lines of ten syllables and five accents each, and the lines run in couplets:

> His eyen twinkled in his heed aright
> As doon the sterres in the frosty night.

The same musical measure, arranged in seven-line stanzas, but with a different rhyme, called the Rime Royal, is found in its most perfect form in *Troilus.*

> O blisful light, of whiche the bemes clere
> Adorneth al the thridde hevene faire!
> O sonnes leef, O Joves doughter dere,
> Plesaunce of love, O goodly debonaire,
> In gentil hertes ay redy to repaire!
> O verray cause of hele and of gladnesse,
> Y-heried be thy might and thy goodnesse!
> In hevene and helle, in erthe and salte see
> Is felt thy might, if that I wel descerne;
> As man, brid, best, fish, herbe and grene tree
> Thee fete in tymes with vapour eterne.
> God loveth, and to love wol nought werne;
> And in this world no lyves creature,
> With-outen love, is worth, or may endure.[1]

The third metre is the eight-syllable line with four accents, the lines rhyming in couplets, as in the 'Boke of the Duchesse':

[1] *Troilus and Criseyde,* III.

Thereto she coude so wel pleye,
Whan that hir liste, that I dar seye
That she was lyk to torche bright,
That every man may take-of light
Ynough, and hit hath never the lesse.

Besides these principal metres, Chaucer in his short poems used many other poetical forms modelled after the French, who in the fourteenth century were cunning workers in every form of verse. Chief among these are the difficult but exquisite rondel, 'Now welcom Somer with thy sonne softe', which closes the 'Parliament of Fowls', and the ballad, 'Flee fro the prees', which has been already quoted. In the 'Monk's Tale' there is a melodious measure which may have furnished the model for Spenser's famous stanza.[1] Chaucer's poetry is extremely musical and must be judged by the ear rather than by the eye. To the modern reader the lines appear broken and uneven; but if one reads them over a few times, he soon catches the perfect swing of the measure, and finds that he is in the hands of a master whose ear is delicately sensitive to the smallest accent. There is a lilt in all his lines which is marvellous when we consider that he is the first to show us the poetic possibilities of the language. His claim upon our gratitude is twofold:[2] first, for discovering the music that is in our English speech; and second, for his influence in fixing the Midland dialect as the literary language of England.

CHAUCER'S CONTEMPORARIES

William Langland (1332? — ?)

Life. Very little is known of Langland. He was born probably near Malvern, in Worcestershire, the son of a poor freeman, and in his early life lived in the fields as a shepherd. Later he went to London with his wife and children, getting a hungry living as clerk in the

[1] See p. 107.
[2] For a summary of Chaucer's work and place in our literature, see the Comparison with Spenser, p. III.

church. His real life meanwhile was that of a seer, a prophet after Isaiah's own heart, if we may judge by the prophecy which soon found a voice in *Piers Ploughman*. In 1399, after the success of his great work, he was possibly writing another poem called *Richard the Redeless*, a protest against *Richard II*; but we are not certain of the authorship of this poem, which was left unfinished by the assassination of the king. After 1399 Langland disappears utterly, and the date of his death is unknown.

Piers Plowman. 'The voice of him that crieth in the wilderness, Prepare ye the way of the Lord', might well be written at the beginning of this remarkable poem. Truth, sincerity, a direct and practical appeal to conscience, and a vision of right triumphant over wrong—these are the elements of all prophecy; and it was undoubtedly these elements in *Piers Plowman* that produced such an impression on the people of England. For centuries literature had been busy in pleasing the upper classes chiefly; but here at last was a great poem which appealed directly to the common people, and its success was enormous. The whole poem is traditionally attributed to Langland; but it is now known to be the work of several different writers. It first appeared in 1362 as a poem of eighteen hundred lines, and this may have been Langland's work. In the next thirty years, during the desperate social conditions which led to Tyler's Rebellion, it was repeatedly revised and enlarged by different hands till it reached its final form of about fifteen thousand lines.

The poem as we read it now is in two distinct parts, the first containing the vision of Piers, the second a series of visions called 'The Search for Dowel, Dobet, Dobest' (do well, better, best). The entire poem is in strongly accented, alliterative lines, something like *Beowulf*, and its immense popularity shows that the common people still cherished this easily memorized form of Saxon poetry. Its tremendous appeal to justice and common honesty, its clarion call to every man, whether king, priest, noble, or laborer, to do his Christian duty, takes from it any trace of prejudice or bigotry with which such works usually abound. Its loyalty to the Church, while denouncing abuses that had crept into it in that period, was one of the great influences which led to the Reformation in England. Its two great principles, the equality of men before God and the dignity of honest labour, roused a whole nation of freemen. Altogether it is one of the world's great works, partly because of its national influence, partly because it is the very best picture we possess of the social life of the fourteenth century:

Briefly, *Piers Plowman* is an allegory of life. In the first vision, that of the 'Field Full of Folk', the poet lies down on the Malvern Hills on a May morning, and a vision comes to him in sleep. On the plain beneath him gather a multitude of folk, a vast crowd expressing the varied life of the world. All classes and conditions are there; workingmen are toiling that others may seize all the first fruits of their labour and live high on the proceeds; and the genius of the throng is Lady Bribery, a powerfully drawn figure, expressing the corrupt social life of the times.

The next visions are those of the Seven Deadly Sins, allegorical figures, but powerful as those of *Pilgrim's Progress,* making the allegories of the Romaunt of the Rose seem like shadows in comparison. These all came to Piers asking the way to Truth; but Piers is ploughing his half acre and refuses to leave his work and lead them. He sets them all to honest toil as the best possible remedy for their vices, and preaches the gospel of work as a preparation for salvation. Throughout the poem Piers bears strong resemblance to John the Baptist preaching to the crowds in the wilderness. The later visions are proclamations of the moral and spiritual life of man. The poem grows dramatic in its intensity, rising to its highest power in Piers's triumph over Death. And then the poet wakes from his vision with the sound of Easter bells ringing in his ears.

Here are a few lines to illustrate the style and language; but the whole poem must be read if one is to understand its crude strength and prophetic spirit:

In a somer sesun, whon softe was the sonne,
I schop[1] me into a shroud, as I a scheep were,
In habite as an heremite, unholy of werkes,
Went wyde in this world, wondres to here.
Bote in a Mayes mornynge, on Malverne hulles,
Me byfel a ferly,[2] of fairie me thoughte.
I was wery, forwandred, and went me to reste
Undur a brod banke, bi a bourne[3] side;
And as I lay and lened, and loked on the watres,
I slumbred in a slepyng—hit swyed[4] so murie....

JOHN WYCLIF (1324? – 1384)

Life. Wyclif, as a man, is by far the most powerful English figure of the fourteenth century. The immense influence of his preaching in the native tongue, and the power of his Lollards to stir the souls of the common folk, are too well known historically to need repetition. Though a university man and a profound scholar, he sides with Langland, and his interests are with the people rather than with the privileged classes, for whom Chaucer writes. His great work, which earned him his title of 'father of English prose', is the translation of the Bible. Wyclif himself translated the gospels, and much more of the New Testament; the rest was finished by his followers, especially by Nicholas of Hereford. These translations were made from the Latin Vulgate, not from the original Greek and Hebrew, and the whole work was revised in 1388 by John Purvey, a disciple of Wyclif. It is impossible to overestimate the influence of this work, both on our English prose and on the lives of the English people.

Though Wyclif's works are now unread, except by occasional scholars, he still occupies a very high place in our literature. His translation of the Bible was slowly copied all over England, and so fixed a national standard of English prose to replace the various dialects. Portions of this translation, in the form of favourite passages from Scripture, were copied by thousands, and for the first time in

---

[1] clad. [2] wonder. [3] brook. [4] sounded.

our history a standard of pure English was established in the homes of the common people.

As a suggestion of the language of that day, we quote a few familiar sentences from the Sermon on the Mount, as given in the later version of Wyclif's Gospel:

John Wyclif

And he openyde his mouth, and taughte hem, and seide, Blessid ben pore men in spirit, for the kyngdom of hevenes is herne.[1] Blessid ben mylde men, for thei schulen welde[2] the erthe. Blessid ben thei that mornen, for thei schulen be coumfortid. Blessid ben thei that hungren and thristen rightwisnesse,[3] for thei schulen be fulfillid. Blessid ben merciful men, for thei schulen gete merci. Blessid ben thei that ben of clene herte, for thei schulen se God. Blessid ben pesible men, for thei schulen be clepid[4] Goddis children. Blessid ben thei that suffren persecusioun for rightfulnesse, for the kyngdom of hevenes is herne....

Eftsoone ye han herd, that it was seid to elde men, Thou schalt not forswere, but thou schalt yelde[5] thin othis to the Lord. But Y seie[6] to you, that ye swere not for ony thing;... but be youre worde, yhe, yhe; nay, nay; and that that is more than these, is of yvel....

Ye han herd that it was seid, Thou schalt love thi neighboure, and hate thin enemye. But Y seie to you, love ye youre enemyes, do ye wel to hem[7] that hatiden[8] you, and preye ye for hem that pursuen[9] and sclaundren[10] you; that ye be the sones of youre Fadir that is in hevenes, that makith his sunne to rise upon goode and yvele men, and reyneth[11] on just men and unjuste.... Therefore be ye parfit, as youre hevenli Fadir is parfit.

---

[1] theirs [2] rule [3] righteousness [4] called [5] yield [6] say [7] them [8] hate [9] persecute [10] slander [11] rains

JOHN MANDEVILLE

Life. About the year 1356 there appeared in England an extraordinary book called the *Voyage and Travail of Sir John Maundeville*, written in excellent style in the Midland dialect, which was then becoming the literary language of England. For years this interesting work and its unknown author were subjects of endless dispute; but it is now fairly certain that this collection of travellers' tales is simply a compilation from Odoric, Marco Polo, and various other sources. The original work was probably in French, which was speedily translated into Latin, then into English and other languages; and wherever it appeared it became extremely popular, its marvellous stories of foreign lands being exactly suited to the credulous spirit of the age.[1] At the present time there are said to be three hundred copied manuscripts of 'Mandeville' in various languages—more, probably, than of any other work save the gospels. In the prologue of the English version the author calls himself John Maundeville and gives an outline of his wide travels during thirty years; but the name is probably a 'blind', the prologue more or less spurious, and the real compiler is still to be discovered.

The modern reader may spend an hour or two very pleasantly in this old wonderland. On its literary side the book is remarkable,

[1]In its English form the alleged Mandeville describes the lands and customs he has seen, and brings in all the wonders he has heard about. Many things he has seen himself, he tells us, and these are certainly true; but others he has heard in his travels, and of these the reader must judge for himself. Then he incidentally mentions a desert where he saw devils as thick as grasshoppers. As for things that he has been told by devout travellers, here are the dog-faced men, and birds that carry off elephants, and giants twenty-eight feet tall, and dangerous women who have bright jewels in their heads instead of eyes, 'and if they behold any man in wrath, they slay him with a look, as doth the basilisk.' Here also are the folk of Ethiopia, who have only one leg, but who hop about with extraordinary rapidity. Their one foot is so big that, when they lie in the sun, they raise it to shade their bodies; in rainy weather it is as good as an umbrella. At the close of this interesting book of travel, which is a guide for pilgrims, the author promises to all those who say a prayer for him a share in whatever heavenly grace he may himself obtain for all his holy pilgrimages.

though a translation, as being the first prose work in modern English having a distinctly literary style and flavour. Otherwise it is a most interesting commentary on the general culture and credulity of the fourteenth century.

Summary of the Age of Chaucer. The fourteenth century is remarkable historically for the decline of feudalism (organized by the Normans), for the growth of the English national spirit during the wars with France, for the prominence of the House of Commons, and for the growing power of the labouring classes, who had heretofore been in a condition hardly above that of slavery.

The age produced five writers of note, one of whom, Geoffrey Chaucer, is one of the greatest of English writers. His poetry is remarkable for its variety, its story interest, and its wonderful melody. Chaucer's work and Wyclif's translation of the Bible developed the Midland dialect into the national language of England.

In our study we have noted: (1) Chaucer, his life and work; his early or French period, in which he translated 'The Romance of the Rose' and wrote many minor poems; his middle or Italian period, of which the chief poems are 'Troilus and Cressida' and 'The Legend of Good Women'; his late or English period, in which he worked at his masterpiece, the famous *Canterbury Tales.* (2) Langland, the poet and prophet of social reforms. His chief work is *Piers Plowman.* (3) Wyclif, the religious reformer, who first translated the gospels into English, and by his translation fixed a common standard of English speech. (4) Mandeville, the alleged traveller, who represents the new English interest in distant lands following the development of foreign trade. He is famous for *Mandeville's Travels,* a book which romances about the wonders to be seen abroad. The fifth writer of the age is Gower, who wrote in three languages, French, Latin, and English. His chief English work is the *Confessio Amantis,* a long poem containing one hundred and twelve tales. Of these only the 'Knight Florent' and two or three others are interesting to a modern reader.

Selections for Reading. Chaucer's Prologue, the Knight's Tale, Nun's Priest's Tale, Prioress' Tale, Clerk's Tale. These are found, more or less complete, in Standard English Classics, King's Classics, Riverside Literature Series, etc. Skeat's school edition of the Prologue, Knight's Tale, etc., is especially good, and includes a study of fourteenth-century English. Miscellaneous poems of Chaucer in Manly's English Poetry or Ward's

English Poets. Piers Plowman, in King's Classics. Mandeville's Travels, modernized, in English Classics, and in Cassell's National Library.

For the advanced student, and as a study of language, compare selections from Wyclif, Chaucer's prose work, Mandeville, etc., in Manly's English Prose, or Morris and Skeat's Specimens of Early English, or Craik's English Prose Selections. Selections from Wyclif's Bible in English Classics Series.

Bibliography.[1] **History.** *Textbook*, Montgomery, pp. 115-149, or Cheyney, pp. 186-263. For fuller treatment, Green, ch. 5; Traill; Gardiner.

Special Works. Hutton's King and Baronage (Oxford Manuals); Jusserand's Wayfaring Life in the Fourteenth Century; Coulton's Chaucer and his England; Pauli's Pictures from Old England; Wright's History of Domestic Manners and Sentiments in England during the Middle Ages; Trevelyan's England in the Age of Wyclif; Jenks's In the Days of Chaucer; Froissart's Chronicle, in Everyman's Library; the same, new edition, 1895 (Macmillan); Lanier's Boys' Froissart (that is Froissart's Chronicle of Historical Events, 1325-1400); Newbolt's Stories from Froissart; Bulfinch's Age of Chivalry may be read in connection with this and the preceding periods.

Literature. *General Works.* Jusserand; Ten Brink; Mitchell; Minto's Characteristics of English Poets; Courthope's History of English Poetry.

Chaucer. (1) Life: by Lounsbury, in Studies in Chaucer, vol. I; by Ward, in English Men of Letters Series; Pollard's Chaucer Primer. (2) Aids to study: F.J. Snell's The Age of Chaucer; Lounsbury's Studies in Chaucer (3 vols.); Root's The Poetry of Chaucer; Lowell's Essay, in My Study Windows; Hammond's Chaucer: a Biographical Manual; Hempl's Chaucer's Pronunciation; Introductions to school editions of Chaucer, by Skeat, Liddell, and Mather. (3) Texts and selections: The Oxford Chaucer, 6 vols., edited by Skeat, is the standard; Skeat's Student's Chaucer; The Globe Chaucer (Macmillan); Works of Chaucer, edited by Lounsbury (Crowell); Pollard's The Canterbury Tales, Eversley edition; Skeat's Selections from Chaucer (Clarendon Press); Chaucer's Prologue, and various tales, in Standard English Classics (Ginn and Company), and in other school series.

---

[1] For titles and publishers of reference works see General Bibliography at the end of this book.

Minor Writers. Morris and Skeat's Specimens of Early English Prose. Jusserand's Piers Plowman; Skeat's Piers Plowman (text, glossary and notes); Warren's Piers Plowman in Modern Prose. Arnold's Wyclif's Select English Works; Sergeant's Wyclif (Heroes of the Nation Series); Le Bas's Life of John Wyclif. Travels of Sir John Mandeville (modern spelling), in Library of English Classics; Macaulay's Gower's English Works.

Suggestive Questions. 1. What are the chief historical events of the fourteenth century? What social movement is noticeable? What writers reflect political and social conditions?

2. Tell briefly the story of Chaucer's life. What foreign influences are noticeable? Name a few poems illustrating his three periods of work. What qualities have you noticed in his poetry? Why is he called our first national poet?

3. Give the plan of the Canterbury Tales. For what is the Prologue remarkable? What light does it throw upon English life of the fourteenth century? Quote or read some passages that have impressed you. Which character do you like best? Are any of the characters like certain men and women whom you know? What classes of society are introduced? Is Chaucer's attitude sympathetic or merely critical?

4. Tell in your own words the tale you like best. Which tale seems truest to life as you know it? Mention any other poets who tell stories in verse.

5. Quote or read passages which show Chaucer's keenness of observation, his humour, his kindness in judgment, his delight in nature. What side of human nature does he emphasize? Make a little comparison between Chaucer and Shakespeare, having in mind (1) the characters described by both poets, (2) their knowledge of human nature, (3) the sources of their plots, (4) the interest of their works.

6. Describe briefly Piers Plowman and its author. Why is the poem called 'the gospel of the poor'? What message does it contain for daily labour? Does it apply to any modern conditions? Note any resemblance in ideas between Piers Plowman and such modern works as Carlyle's Past and Present, Kingsley's *Alton Locke, Morris's Dream of John Ball,* etc.

7. For what is Wyclif remarkable in literature? How did his work affect our language? Note resemblances and differences between Wyclif and the Puritans.

8. What is *Mandeville's Travels?* What light does it throw on the mental condition of the age? What essential difference do you note between this book and *Gulliver's Travels?*

CHRONOLOGY

Fourteenth Century

HISTORY	LITERATURE
1327. *Edward III*	
1338. Beginning of Hundred Years' War with France	1340(?). Birth of Chaucer
1347. Capture of Calais	
1348-1349. Black Death	1356. Mandeville's Travels
	1359. Chaucer in French War
	1360-1370. Chaucer's early or French period
1373. Winchester College, first great public school	1370-1385. Chaucer's Middle or Italian period
1377. *Richard II.* Wyclif and the Lollards begin Reformation in England	1362-1395. Piers Plowman
1381. Peasant Rebellion. Wat Tyler	1385-1400. Canterbury Tales
	1382. First complete Bible in English
1399. Deposition of *Richard II.* Henry IV chosen by Parliament	1400. Death of Chaucer (Dante's Divina Commedia, *c.* 1310; Petrarch's *Sonnets* and poems, 1325-1374; Boccaccio's tales, *c.* 1350.)

Chapter 5

THE REVIVAL OF LEARNING (1400-1550)

I. HISTORY OF THE PERIOD

Political Changes. The century and a half following the death of Chaucer (1400-1550) is the most volcanic period of English history. The land is swept by vast changes, inseparable from the rapid accumulation of national power; but since power is the most dangerous of gifts until men have learned to control it, these changes seem at first to have no specific aim or direction. Henry V—whose erratic yet vigorous life, as depicted by Shakespeare, was typical of the life of his times—first let Europe feel the might of the new national spirit. To divert that growing and unruly spirit from rebellion at home, Henry led his army abroad, in the apparently impossible attempt to gain for himself three things: a French wife, a French revenue, and the French crown itself. The battle of Agincourt was fought in 1415, and five years later, by the Treaty of Troyes, France acknowledged his right to all his outrageous demands.

The uselessness of the terrific struggle on French soil is shown by the rapidity with which all its results were swept away. When Henry died in 1422, leaving his son heir to the crowns of France and England, a magnificent recumbent statue with head of pure silver was placed in Westminster Abbey to commemorate his victories. The silver head was presently stolen, and the loss is typical of all that he had struggled for. His son, Henry VI, was but the shadow of a king, a puppet in the hands of powerful nobles, who seized the power of England and turned it to self-destruction. Meanwhile all his foreign possessions were won back by the French under the magic leadership of Joan of Arc. Cade's Rebellion (1450) and the bloody Wars of the Roses (1455-1485) are names to show how the energy of England was violently destroying itself, like a great engine that has lost its balance wheel. The frightful reign of Richard III followed, which had, however, this redeeming quality, that it marked the end of civil wars and the self-destruction of feudalism, and made possible a new growth of English national sentiment under the popular Tudors.

In the long reign of Henry VIII the changes are less violent, but have more purpose and significance. His age is marked by a steady increase in the national power at home and abroad, by the entrance of the Reformation 'by a side door', and by the final separation of England from all ecclesiastical bondage in Parliament's famous Act of Supremacy. In previous reigns chivalry and the old feudal system had practically been banished; now monasticism, the third mediæval institution with its mixed evil and good, received its death-blow in the wholesale suppression of the monasteries and the removal of abbots from the House of Lords. Notwithstanding the evil character of the king and the hypocrisy of proclaiming such a creature the head of any church or the defender of any faith, we acquiesce silently in

¶ Fynysshed and translated out of frensshe in to englysshe the viij day of Juyn the yere of our lord M iiij C lxxxvj / and the first yere of the regne of kyng harry the vij / And enprynted the xj day of Maye after / &c

Laus deo

Specimen of Caxton's Printing in the Year 1486

Stubb's declaration[1] that 'the world owes some of its greatest debts to men from whose memory the world recoils'.

While England during this period was in constant political strife, yet rising slowly, like the spiral flight of an eagle, to heights of national greatness, intellectually it moved forward with bewildering rapidity. Printing was brought to England by Caxton (*circa* 1476), and for the first time in history it was possible for a book or an idea to reach the whole nation. Schools and universities were established in place of the old monasteries; Greek ideas and Greek culture came to England in the Renaissance, and man's spiritual freedom was proclaimed in the Reformation. The great names of the period are numerous and significant, but literature is strangely silent. Probably the very turmoil of the age prevented any literary development, for literature is one of the arts of peace; it requires quiet and meditation rather than activity, and the stirring life of the Renaissance had first to be lived before it could express itself in the new literature of the Elizabethan period.

The Revival of Learning. The Revival of Learning denotes, in its broadest sense, that gradual enlightenment of the human mind after the darkness of the Middle Ages. The names Renaissance and Humanism, which are often applied to the same movement, have properly a narrower significance. The term Renaissance, though used by many writers 'to denote the whole transition from the Middle Ages to the modern world',[2] is more correctly applied to the revival of art resulting from the discovery and imitation of classic models in the fourteenth and fifteenth centuries. Humanism applies to the revival of classic literature, and was so called by its leaders, following the example of Petrarch, because they held that the study of the classics, *literæ humaniores*—that is the 'more human writings', rather than the old theology—was the best means of promoting the largest human interests. We use the term Revival of Learning to cover the whole movement, whose essence was,

[1] *Constitutional History of England.*
[2] Symonds, *Revival of Learning.*

according to Lamartine, that 'man discovered himself and the universe', and, according to Taine, that man, so long blinded, 'had suddenly opened his eyes and seen'.

We shall understand this better if we remember that in the Middle Ages man's whole world consisted of the narrow Mediterranean and the nations that clustered about it; and that this little world seemed bounded by impassable barriers, as if God had said to their sailors, 'Hitherto shalt thou come, but no farther'. Man's mind also was bounded by the same narrow lines. His culture as measured by the great deductive system of Scholasticism consisted not in discovery, but rather in accepting certain principles and traditions established by divine and ecclesiastical authority as the basis of all truth. These were his Pillars of Hercules, his mental and spiritual bounds that he must not pass, and within these, like a child playing with lettered blocks, he proceeded to build his intellectual system. Only as we remember their limitations can we appreciate the heroism of these toilers of the Middle Ages, giants in intellect, yet playing with children's toys; ignorant of the laws and forces of the universe, while debating the essence and locomotion of angels; eager to learn, yet forbidden to enter fresh fields in the right of free exploration and the joy of individual discovery.

The World

The Revival stirred these men as the voyages of Da Gama and Columbus stirred the mariners of the Mediterranean. First came the sciences and inventions of the Arabs, making their way slowly against the prejudice of the authorities, and opening men's eyes to the unexplored realms of nature. Then came the flood of Greek literature which the new art of printing carried swiftly to every school in Europe, revealing a new world of poetry and philosophy. Scholars flocked to the universities, as adventurers to the new world of America, and there the old authority received a death-blow. Truth only was authority; to search for truth everywhere, as men sought for new lands and gold and the fountain of youth—that was the new spirit which awoke in Europe with the Revival of Learning.

II. LITERATURE OF THE REVIVAL

The hundred and fifty years of the Revival period are singularly destitute of good literature. Men's minds were too much occupied with religious and political changes and with the rapid enlargement of the mental horizon to find time for that peace and leisure which are essential for literary results. Perhaps, also, the floods of newly discovered classics, which occupied scholars and the new printing presses alike, were by their very power and abundance a discouragement of native talent. Roger Ascham (1515-1568), a famous classical scholar, who published a book called Toxophilus (School of Shooting) in 1545, expresses in his preface, or 'apology', a very widespread dissatisfaction over the neglect of native literature when he says, 'And as for ye Latin or greke tongue, every thing is so excellently done in them, that none can do better: In the Englysh tonge contrary, every thinge in a maner so meanly, both for the matter and handelynge, that no man can do worse.'

On the Continent, also, this new interest in the classics served to check the growth of native literatures. In Italy especially, for a full century after the brilliant age of Dante and Petrarch, no great literature was produced, and the Italian language itself seemed to go backward.[1] The truth is that these great writers were, like Chaucer, far in advance of their age, and that the mediæval mind was too narrow, too scantily furnished with ideas to produce a varied literature. The fifteenth century was an age of preparation, of learning the beginnings of science, and of getting acquainted with the great ideals—the stern law, the profound philosophy, the suggestive mythology, and the noble poetry of the Greeks and Romans. So the mind was furnished with ideas for a new literature.

With the exception of Malory's *Morte d'Arthur* (which is still mediæval in spirit) the student will find little of interest in the literature of this period. We give here a brief summary of the men

---

[1] Sismondi attributes this to two causes: first, the lack of general culture; and second, the absorption of the schools in the new study of antiquity. See *Literature of the South of Europe,* II, 400 ff.

and the books most 'worthy of remembrance'; but for the real literature of the Renaissance one must go forward a century and a half to the age of Elizabeth.

Praise of Folly

The two greatest books which appeared in England during this period are undoubtedly Erasmus's[1] *Praise of Folly* (*Encomium Moriæ*) and More's *Utopia*, the famous 'Kingdom of Nowhere'. Both were written in Latin, but were speedily translated into all European languages. The *Praise of Folly* is like a song of victory for the New Learning, which had driven away vice, ignorance, and superstition, the three foes of humanity. It was published in 1511 after the accession of Henry VIII. Folly is represented as donning cap and bells and mounting a pulpit, where the vice and cruelty of kings, the selfishness and ignorance of the clergy, and the foolish standards of education are satirized without mercy.

Utopia

More's *Utopia*, published in 1516, is a powerful and original study of social conditions, unlike anything which had ever appeared in any literature.[2] In our own day we have seen its influence in Bellamy's *Looking Backward*, an enormously successful book, which recently set people to thinking of the unnecessary cruelty of modern social conditions. More learns from a sailor, one of Amerigo Vespucci's companions, of a wonderful Kingdom of Nowhere, in which all questions of labour, government, society, and religion have been easily settled by simple justice and common sense. In this *Utopia* we find for the first time, as the foundations of civilized society, the three great words, Liberty, Fraternity, Equality, which retained their inspiration through all the violence

---

[1] Erasmus, the greatest scholar of the Renaissance, was not an Englishman, but seems to belong to every nation. He as born at Rotterdam (*circa* 1466), but lived the greater part of his life in France, Switzerland, England, and Italy. His *Encomium Moriæ* was sketched on a journey from Italy (1509) and written while he was the guest of Sir Thomas More in London.

[2] Unless, perchance, the reader finds some points of resemblance in Plato's 'Republic'.

of the French Revolution and which are still the unrealized ideal of every free government. As he hears of this wonderful country. More wonders why, after fifteen centuries of Christianity, his own land is so little civilized; and as we read the book today we ask ourselves the same question. The splendid dream is still far from being realized; yet it seems as if any nation could become Utopia in a single generation, so simple and just are the requirements.

Tyndale's New Testament

Greater than either of these books, in its influence upon the common people, is Tyndale's translation of the New Testament (1525), which fixed a standard of good English, and at the same time brought that standard not only to scholars but to the homes of the common people. Tyndale made his translation from the original Greek, and later translated parts of the Old Testament from the Hebrew. Much of Tyndale's work was included in Cranmer's Bible, known also as the Great Bible, in 1539, and was read in every parish church in England. It was the foundation for the Authorized Version, which appeared nearly a century later and became the standard for the whole English-speaking race.

Wyatt and Surrey. In 1557 appeared probably the first printed collection of miscellaneous English poems, known as *Tottel"s Miscellany.* It contained the work of the so-called courtly makers, or poets, which had hitherto circulated in manuscript form for the benefit of the court. About half of these poems were the work of Sir Thomas Wyatt (1503?-1542) and of Henry Howard, Earl of Surrey (1517?-1547). Both together wrote amorous *Sonnets* modelled after the Italians, introducing a new verse form which, although very difficult, has been a favourite ever since with our English poets.[1] Surrey is noted, not for any especial worth or originality of his own poems, but rather for his translation of two books of Virgil 'in strange metre'. The strange metre was the blank verse, which had never before appeared in English. The chief literary work of these two men, therefore, is to introduce the sonnet and the blank verse—one the most dainty, the other the most

[1] See Wordsworth's sonnet, *On the Sonnet.* For a detailed study of this most perfect verse form, see Tomlinson's *The Sonnet, Its Origin, Structure, and Place in Poetry.*

flexible and characteristic form of English poetry—which in the hands of Shakespeare and Milton were used to make the world's masterpieces.

Malory's Morte d'Arthur. The greatest English work of this period, measured by its effect on subsequent literature, is undoubtedly the *Morte d'Arthur*, a collection of the Arthurian romances told in simple and vivid prose. Of Sir Thomas Malory, the author, Caxton[1] in his introduction says that he was a knight, and completed his work in 1470, fifteen years before Caxton printed it. The record adds that 'he was the servant of Jesu both by day and night'. Beyond that we know little[2] except what may be inferred from the splendid work itself.

Malory groups the legends about the central idea of the search for the Holy Grail. Though many of the stories, like Tristram and Isolde, are purely pagan, Malory treats them all in such a way as to preserve the whole spirit of mediæval Christianity as it has been preserved in no other work. It was to Malory rather than to Layamon or to the early French writers that Shakespeare and his contemporaries turned for their material; and in our own age he has supplied Tennyson and Matthew Arnold and Swinburne and Morris with the inspiration for the 'Idylls of the King' and the 'Death of Tristram' and the other exquisite poems which centre about Arthur and the knights of his Round Table.

In subject-matter the book belongs to the mediæval age; but Malory himself, with his desire to preserve the literary monuments of the past, belongs to the Renaissance; and he deserves our lasting gratitude for attempting to preserve the legends and poetry of Britain at a time when scholars were chiefly busy with the classics of Greece and Rome. As the Arthurian legends are one of the great recurring motives of English literature, Malory's work should

---

[1] William Caxton (*circa* 1422-1491) was the first English printer. He learned the art abroad, probably at Cologne or Bruges, and about the year 1476 set up the first wooden printing press in England. His influence in fixing a national language to supersede the various dialects, and in preparing the way for the literary renaissance of the Elizabethan age, is beyond calculation.

[2] Malory has, in our own day, been identified with an English country gentleman and soldier, who was member of Parliament for Warwickshire in 1445.

be better known. His stories may be and should be told to every child as part of his literary inheritance. Then Malory may be read for his style and his English prose and his expression of the mediæval spirit. And then the stories may be read again, in Tennyson's 'Idylls', to show how those exquisite old fancies appeal to the minds of our modern poets.

Summary of the Revival of Learning Period. This transition period is at first one of decline from the Age of Chaucer, and then of intellectual preparation for the Age of Elizabeth. For a century and a half after Chaucer not a single great English work appeared, and the general standard of literature was very low. There are three chief causes to account for this: (1) the long war with France and the civil Wars of the Roses distracted attention from books and poetry, and destroyed or ruined many noble English families who had been friends and patrons of literature; (2) the Reformation in the latter part of the period filled men's minds with religious questions; (3) the Revival of Learning set scholars and literary men to an eager study of the classics, rather than to the creation of native literature. Historically the age is noticeable for its intellectual progress, for the introduction of printing, for the discovery of America, for the beginning of the Reformation, and for the growth of political power among the common people.

In our study we have noted: (1) the Revival of Learning, what it was, and the significance of the terms Humanism and Renaissance; (2) three influential literary works—Erasmus's *Praise of Folly*, More's *Utopia*, and Tyndale's translation of the New Testament; (3) Wyatt and Surrey, and the so-called courtly makers or poets; (4) Malory's *Morte d'Arthur*, a collection of the Arthurian legends in English prose. The Miracle and Mystery Plays were the most popular form of entertainment in this age; but we have reserved them for special study in connection with the Rise of the Drama, in the following chapter.

Selections for Reading. Malory's *Morte d'Arthur*, selections, in Athenæum Press Series, etc. (It is interesting to read Tennyson's Passing of Arthur in connection with Malory's account.) Utopia, in Arber's Reprints, Temple Classics, King's Classics, etc. Selections from Wyatt, Surrey, etc., in Manly's English Poetry or Ward's English Poets; Tottel's Miscellany, in Arber's

Reprints. Morris and Skeat's Specimens of Early English, vol. 3, has good selections from this period.

Bibliography.[1] ***History.*** *Textbook,* Montgomery, pp. 150-208, or Cheyney, pp. 264-328. Greene, ch. 6; Traill; Gardiner; Froude; etc.

Special Works. Denton's England in the Fifteenth Century; Flower's The Century of Sir Thomas More; The Household of Sir Thomas More, in King's Classics; Green's Town Life in the Fifteenth Century; Field's Introduction to the Study of the Renaissance; Einstein's The Italian Renaissance in England; Seebohm's The Oxford Reformers (Erasmus, More, etc.).

Literature. *General Works.* Jusserand; Ten Brink; Minto's Characteristics of English Poets.

Special Works. Saintsbury's Elizabethan Literature; Malory's Morte d'Arthur, edited by Sommer; the same by Gollancz (Temple Classics); Lanier's The Boy's King Arthur; More's Utopia, in Temple Classics, King's Classics, etc.; Roper's Life of Sir Thomas More, in King's Classics, Temple Classics, etc.; Ascham's Schoolmaster, in Arber's English Reprints; Poems of Wyatt and Surrey, in English Reprints and Bell's Aldine Poets; Simonds's Sir Thomas Wyatt and His Poems; Allen's Selections from Erasmus; Jusserand's Romance of a King's Life (James I of Scotland) contains extracts and an admirable criticism of the King's Quair.

Suggestive Questions. 1. The fifteenth century in English literature is sometimes called "the age of arrest." Can you explain why? What causes account for the lack of great literature in this period? Why should the ruin of noble families at this time seriously affect our literature? Can you recall anything from the Anglo-Saxon period to justify your opinion?

2. What is meant by Humanism? What was the first effect of the study of Greek and Latin classics upon our literature? What excellent literary purposes did the classics serve in later periods?

3. What are the chief benefits to literature of the discovery of printing? What effect on civilization has the multiplication of books?

4. Describe More's *Utopia.* Do you know any modern books like it? Why should any impractical scheme of progress be still called Utopian?

5. What work of this period had the greatest effect on the English language? Explain why.

---

[1] For titles and publishers of general works see General Bibliography at the end of this book.

6. What was the chief literary influence exerted by Wyatt and Surrey? Do you know any later poets who made use of the verse forms which they introduced?

7. Which of Malory's stories do you like best? Where did these stories originate? Have they any historical foundation? What two great elements did Malory combine in his work? What is the importance of his book to later English literature? Compare Tennyson's 'Idylls of the King' and Malory's stories with regard to material, expression, and interest. Note the marked resemblances and differences between the *Morte d'Arthur* and the *Nibelungen Lied.*

CHRONOLOGY

HISTORY	LITERATURE
1413. Henry V	
1415. Battle of Agincourt	
1422. Henry VI	1470. Malory's Morte d' Arthur
1428. Siege of Orleans. Joan of Arc	1474. circa Caxton, at Bruges, prints the first book in English, the Recuyell of the Histories of Troye
1453. End of Hundred Year's War	
1455-1485. War of Roses	
1461. Edward IV	
1483. *Richard III*	1477. First book printed in England
1485. Henry VII	1485. Morte d'Arthur printed by Caxton
1492. Columbus discovers America	1499. Colet, Erasmus, and More bring the New Learning to Oxford
1509. Henry VIII	
	1509. Erasmus's Praise of Folly
	1516. More's Utopia
	1525. Tydale's New Testament
1534. Act of Supremacy. The Reformation accomplished	1530(*c.*) Introduction of the sonnet and blank verse by Wyatt and Surrey
	1539. The Great Bible
1547. Edward VI	
1553. Mary	1557. Tottel's Miscellany
1558. Elizabeth	

Chapter 6

THE AGE OF ELIZABETH (1550-1620)

I. HISTORY OF THE PERIOD

Political Summary. In the Age of Elizabeth all doubt seems to vanish from English history. After the reigns of Edward and Mary, with defeat and humiliation abroad and persecutions and rebellion at home, the accession of a popular sovereign was like the sunrise after a long night, and, in Milton's words, we suddenly see England, 'a noble and puissant nation, rousing herself, like a strong man after sleep, and shaking her invincible locks'. With the queen's character, a strange mingling of frivolity and strength which reminds one of that iron image with feet of clay, we have nothing whatever to do. It is the national life that concerns the literary student, since even a beginner must notice that any great development of the national life is invariably associated with a development of the national literature. It is enough for our purpose, therefore, to point out two facts: that Elizabeth, with all her vanity and inconsistency, steadily loved England and England's greatness; and that she inspired all her people with the unbounded patriotism which exults in Shakespeare, and with the personal devotion which finds a voice in the *Faery Queen*. Under her administration the English national life progressed by gigantic leaps rather than by slow historical process, and English literature reached the very highest point of its development. It is possible to indicate only a few general characteristics of this great age which had a direct bearing upon its literature.

Characteristics of the Elizabethan Age. 1. The most characteristic feature of the age was the comparative religious tolerance, which was due largely to the queen's influence. The frightful excesses of the religious war known as the Thirty Years' War on the Continent found no parallel in England. Upon her accession Elizabeth found the whole kingdom divided against itself; the North was largely Catholic, while the southern counties were as strongly Protestant. Scotland had followed the Reformation in its own intense way, while Ireland remained true to its old religious traditions, and both countries were openly rebellious. The court, made up of both parties, witnessed the rival intrigues of those who sought to gain the royal favour. It was due partly to the intense absorption of men's minds in religious questions that the preceding century, though an age of advancing learning, produced scarcely any literature worthy of the name. Elizabeth favoured both religious parties, and presently the world saw with amazement Catholics and Protestants acting together as trusted counsellors of a great sovereign. The defeat of the Spanish Armada established the Reformation as a fact in England, and at the same time united all Englishmen in a magnificent national enthusiasm. For the first time since the Reformation began, the fundamental question of religious toleration seemed to be settled, and the mind of man, freed from religious fears and persecutions, turned with a great creative impulse to other forms of activity. It is partly from this new freedom of the mind that the Age of Elizabeth received its great literary stimulus.

Religious Toleration

2. It was an age of comparative social contentment, in strong contrast with the days of Langland. The rapid increase of manufacturing towns gave employment to thousands who had before been idle and discontented. Increasing trade brought enormous wealth to England, and this wealth was shared to this extent, at least, that for the first time some systematic care for the needy was attempted. Parishes were made responsible for their own poor, and the wealthy were taxed

Social Contentment

to support them or give them employment. The increase of wealth, the improvement in living, the opportunities for labour, the new social content—these also are factors which help to account for the new literary activity.

Enthusiasm

3. It is an age of dreams, of adventure, of unbounded enthusiasm springing from the new lands of fabulous riches revealed by English explorers. Drake sails around the world, shaping the mighty course which English colonizers shall follow through the centuries; and presently the young philosopher Bacon is saying confidently, 'I have taken all knowledge for my province'. The mind must search farther than the eye; with new, rich lands opened to the sight, the imagination must create new forms to people the new worlds. Hakluyt's famous *Collection of Voyages,* and *Purchas, His Pilgrimage,* were even more stimulating to the English imagination than to the English acquisitiveness. While her explorers search the new world for the Fountain of Youth, her poets are creating literary works that are young forever. Marston writes:[1] 'Why, man, all their dripping pans are pure gold. The prisoners they take are fettered in gold; and as for rubies and diamonds, they goe forth on holydayes and gather 'hem by the seashore to hang on their children's coates'. This comes nearer to being a description of Shakespeare's poetry than of the Indians in Virginia. Prospero, in *The Tempest*, with his control over the mighty powers and harmonies of nature, is only the literary dream of that science which had just begun to grapple with the forces of the universe. Cabot, Drake, Frobisher, Gilbert, Raleigh, Willoughby, Hawkins—a score of explorers reveal a new earth to men's eyes, and instantly literature creates a new heaven to match it. So dreams and deeds increase side by side, and the dream is ever greater than the deed. That is the meaning of literature.

---

[1] *Eastward Ho!* a play given in Blackfriars Theatre about 1603. The play was written by Marston and two collabourators.

4. To sum up, the Age of Elizabeth was a time of intellectual liberty, of growing intelligence and comfort among all classes, of unbounded patriotism, and of peace at home and abroad. For a parallel we must go back to the Age of *Pericles* in Athens, or of Augustus in Rome, or go forward a little to the magnificent court of Louis XIV, when Corneille, Racine, and Molière brought the drama in France to the point where Marlowe, Shakespeare, and Jonson had left it in England half a century earlier. Such an age of great thought and great action, appealing to the eyes as well as to the imagination and intellect, finds but one adequate literary expression; neither poetry nor the story can express the whole man—his thought, feeling, action, and the resulting character; hence in the Age of Elizabeth literature turned instinctively to the drama and brought it rapidly to the highest stage of its development.

The Drama

II. THE NON-DRAMATIC POETS OF THE ELIZABETHAN AGE

Edmund Spenser (1552-1599)

(*Cuddie*)

'Piers, I have pipéd erst so long with pain
That all mine oaten reeds been rent and wore,
And my poor Muse hath spent her sparéd store,
Yet little good hath got, and much less gain.
Such pleasaunce makes the grasshopper so poor,
And ligge so layd[1] when winter doth her strain.

The dapper ditties that I wont devise,
To feed youth's fancy, and the flocking fry
Delighten much—what I the bet forthy?
They han the pleasure, I a slender prize:
I beat the bush, the birds to them do fly:
What good thereof to Cuddie can arise?

[1] Lie so faint.

(*Piers*)

Cuddie, the praise is better than the price,
The glory eke much greater than the gain:...'

Shepherd's Calendar, October

In these words, with their sorrowful suggestion of Deor, Spenser reveals his own heart, unconsciously perhaps, as no biographer could possibly do. His life and work seem to centre about three great influences, summed up in three names: Cambridge, where he grew acquainted with the classics and the Italian poets; London, where he experienced the glamour and the disappointment of court life; and Ireland, which steeped him in the beauty and imagery of old Celtic poetry and first gave him leisure to write his masterpiece.

Edmund Spenser

Life. Of Spenser's early life and parentage we know little, except that he was born in East Smithfield, near the Tower of London, and was poor. His education began at the Merchant Tailors' School in London and was continued in Cambridge, where as a poor sizar and fag for wealthy students he earned a scant living. Here in the glorious world that only a poor scholar knows how to create for himself he read the classics, made acquaintance with the great Italian poets, and wrote numberless little poems of his own. Though Chaucer was his beloved master, his ambition was not to rival the Canterbury *Tales*, but rather to express the dream of English chivalry, much as Ariosto had done for Italy in *Orlando Furioso.*

After leaving Cambridge (1576) Spenser went to the north of England, on some unknown work or quest. Here his chief occupation was to fall in love and to record his melancholy over the lost Rosalind in the *Shepherd's Calendar.* Upon his friend Harvey's advice he came to London, bringing his poems; and here he met Leicester, then at the height of royal favour, and the latter took him to live at Leicester House. Here he finished the *Shepherd's Calendar*, and here he met Sidney and all the queen's favourites.

The court was full of intrigues, lying and flattery, and Spenser's opinion of his own uncomfortable position is best expressed in a few lines from 'Mother Hubbard's Tale':

> Full little knowest thou, that has not tried,
> What hell it is, in suing long to bide:
> To lose good days, that might be better spent;
> To waste long nights in pensive discontent;
> ....
> To fret thy soul with crosses and with cares;
> To eat thy heart through comfortless despairs;
> To fawn, to crouch, to wait, to ride, to run,
> To spend, to give, to want, to be undone.

In 1580, through Leicester's influence, Spenser, who was utterly weary of his dependent position, was made secretary to Lord Grey, the queen's deputy in Ireland, and the third period of his life began. He accompanied his chief through one campaign of savage brutality in putting down an Irish rebellion, and was given an immense estate with the castle of Kilcolman, in Munster, which had been confiscated from Earl Desmond, one of the Irish leaders. His life here, where according to the terms of his grant he must reside as an English settler, he regarded as lonely exile:

> My luckless lot,
> That banished had myself, like wight forlore,
> Into that waste, where I was quite forgot.

It is interesting to note here a gentle poet's view of the 'unhappy island'. After nearly sixteen years' residence he wrote his *View of the State of Ireland* (1596),[1] his only prose work, in which he submits a plan for 'pacifying the oppressed and rebellious people'. This was to bring a huge force of cavalry and infantry into the country, give the Irish a brief time to submit, and after that to hunt them down like wild beasts. He calculated that cold, famine, and sickness would help the work of the sword, and that after the rebels had been well hounded for two winters the following summer would find the country peaceful. This plan, from the poet of harmony and beauty, was somewhat milder than the usual treatment of a brave people whose offence was that they loved liberty and religion.

[1] The View as not published till 1633.

Strange as it may seem, the *View* was considered most statesmanlike, and was excellently well received in England.

In Kilcolman, surrounded by great natural beauty, Spenser finished the first three books of the *Faery Queen.* In 1589 Raleigh visited him, heard the poem with enthusiasm, hurried the poet off to London, and presented him to Elizabeth. The first three books met with instant success when published and were acclaimed as the greatest work in the English language. A yearly pension of fifty pounds was conferred by Elizabeth, but rarely paid, and the poet turned back to exile, that is, to Ireland again.

Soon after his return, Spenser fell in love with his beautiful Elizabeth, an Irish girl; wrote his *Amoretti*, or Sonnets, in her honour; and afterwards represented her, in the *Faery Queen*, as the beautiful woman dancing among the Graces. In 1594 he married Elizabeth, celebrating his wedding with his 'Epithalamion', one of the most beautiful wedding hymns in any language.

Spenser's next visit to London was in 1595, when he published 'Astrophel', an elegy on the death of his friend Sidney, and three more books of the *Faery Queen.* On this visit he lived again at Leicester House, now occupied by the new favourite Essex, where he probably met Shakespeare and the other literary lights of the Elizabethan Age. Soon after his return to Ireland, Spenser was appointed Sheriff of Cork, a queer office for a poet, which probably brought about his undoing. The same year Tyrone's Rebellion broke out in Munster. Kilcolman, the ancient house of Desmond, was one of the first places attacked by the rebels, and Spenser barely escaped with his wife and two children. It is supposed that some unfinished parts of the *Faery Queen* were burned in the castle.

From the shock of this frightful experience Spenser never recovered. He returned to England heartbroken, and in the following year (1599) he died in an inn at Westminster. According to Ben Jonson he died 'for want of bread'; but whether that is a poetic way of saying that he had lost his property or that he actually died of destitution, will probably never be known. He was buried beside his master Chaucer in Westminster Abbey, the poets of that age thronging to his funeral and, according to Camden, 'casting their elegies and the pens that had written them into his tomb'.

Spenser's Works. The *Faery Queen* is the great work upon which the poet's fame chiefly rests. The original plan of the poem included twenty-four books, each of which was to recount the adventure and triumph of a knight who represented a moral virtue. Spenser's purpose, as indicated in a letter to Raleigh which introduces the poem, is as follows:

To pourtraict in Arthure, before he was king, the image of a brave Knight, perfected in the twelve private Morall Vertues, as Aristotle hath devised; which is the purpose of these first twelve books: which if I finde to be well accepted, I may be perhaps encoraged to frame the other part of Polliticke Vertues in his person, after that hee came to be king.

Each of the Virtues appears as a knight, fighting his opposing Vice, and the poem tells the story of the conflicts. It is therefore purely allegorical, not only in its personified virtues but also in its representation of life as a struggle between good and evil. In its strong moral element the poem differs radically from *Orlando Furioso*, upon which it was modelled. Spenser completed only six books, celebrating Holiness, Temperance, Chastity, Friendship, Justice, and Courtesy. We have also a fragment of the seventh, treating of Constancy; but the rest of this book was not written, or else was lost in the fire at Kilcolman. The first three books are by far the best; and judging by the way the interest lags and the allegory grows incomprehensible, it is perhaps as well for Spenser's reputation that the other eighteen books remained a dream.

Argument of the Faery Queen. From the introductory letter we learn that the hero visits the queen's court in Fairy Land, while she is holding a twelve-days festival. On each day some distressed person appears unexpectedly, tells a woeful story of dragons, of enchantresses, or of distressed beauty or virtue, and asks for a champion to right the wrong and to let the oppressed go free. Sometimes a knight volunteers or begs for the dangerous mission; again the duty is assigned by the queen; and the journeys and adventures of these knights are the subjects of the several books. The first recounts the adventures of the Redcross Knight, representing Holiness, and the lady Una, representing Religion. Their contests are symbolical of the worldwide struggle between virtue and faith on the one hand, and sin and heresy on the other.

The second book tells the story of Sir Guyon, or Temperance; the third, of Britomartis, representing Chastity; the fourth, fifth, and sixth, of Cambel and Triamond (Friendship), Artegall (Justice), and Sir Calidore (Courtesy). Spenser's plan was a very elastic one and he filled up the measure of his narrative with everything that caught his fancy—historical events and personages under allegorical masks, beautiful ladies, chivalrous knights, giants, monsters, dragons, sirens, enchanters, and adventures enough to stock a library of fiction. If you read Homer or Virgil, you know his subject in the first strong line; if you read Cædmon's *Paraphrase* or Milton's epic, the introduction gives you the theme; but Spenser's great poem—with the exception of a single line in the prologue, "Fierce warres and faithfull loves shall moralize my song'—gives hardly a hint of what is coming.

As to the meaning of the allegorical figures, one is generally in doubt. In the first three books the shadowy *Faery Queen* sometimes represents the glory of God and sometimes Elizabeth, who was naturally flattered by the parallel. Britomartis is also Elizabeth. The Redcross Knight is Sidney, the model Englishman. Arthur, who always appears to rescue the oppressed, is Leicester, which is another outrageous flattery. Una is sometimes religion and sometimes the Protestant Church; while Duessa represents Mary Queen of Scots, or general Catholicism. In the last three books Elizabeth appears again as Mercilla; Henry IV of France as Bourbon; the war in the Netherlands as the story of Lady Beige; Raleigh as Timias; the earls of Northumberland and Westmoreland (lovers of Mary or Duessa) as Blandamour and Paridell; and so on through the wide range of contemporary characters and events, till the allegory becomes as difficult to follow as the second part of Goethe's *Faust.*

Poetical Form. For the *Faery Queen* Spenser invented a new verse form, which has been called since his day the Spenserian stanza. Because of its rare beauty it has been much used by nearly all our poets in their best work. The new stanza was an improved form of Ariosto's *ottava rima* (*i.e.* eight-line stanza) and bears a close resemblance to one of Chaucer's most musical verse forms in the 'Monk's Tale'. Spenser's stanza is in nine lines, eight of five feet each and the last of six feet, rhyming *ababbcbcc*. A few selections from the first book, which is best worth reading, are reproduced here to show the style and melody of the verse.

A Gentle Knight was pricking on the plaine,
Ycladd[1] in mightie armes and silver shielde,
Wherein old dints of deepe woundes did remaine.
The cruell markes of many a bloody fielde;
Yet armes till that time did he never wield:
His angry steede did chide his foming bitt,
As much disdayning to the curbe to yield:
Full iolly[2] knight he seemd, and faire did sitt,
As one for knightly giusts[3] and fierce encounters fitt.

And on his brest a bloodie crosse he bore,
The deare remembrance of his dying Lord,
For whose sweete sake that glorious badge he wore,
And dead, as living ever, him ador'd:
Upon his shield the like was also scor'd,
For soveraine hope, which in his helpe he had,
Right faithfull true he was in deede and word;
But of his cheere[4] did seeme too solemne sad;
Yet nothing did he dread, but ever was ydrad.[5]

This sleepy bit, from the dwelling of Morpheus, invites us to linger:

And, more to lulle him in his slumber soft,
A trickling streame from high rock tumbling downe,
And ever-drizling raine upon the loft,
Mixt with a murmuring winde, much like the sowne
Of swarming bees, did cast him in a swowne.

---

[1] clad. [2] handsome. [3] jousts, tournaments. [4] countenance. [5] dreaded

No other noyse, nor peoples troublous cryes,
As still are wont t'annoy the walled towne,
Might there be heard: but carelesse Quiet lyes,
Wrapt in eternall silence farre from enimyes.

The description of Una shows the poet's sense of ideal beauty:

One day, nigh wearie of the yrkesome way,
From her unhastie beast she did alight;
And on the grasse her dainty limbs did lay
In secrete shadow, far from all mens sight;
From her fayre head her fillet she undight,[1]
And layd her stole aside; Her angels face,
As the great eye of heaven, shynéd bright,
And made a sunshine in the shady place;
Did never mortall eye behold such heavenly grace.

It fortunéd, out of the thickest wood
A ramping lyon rushéd suddeinly,
Hunting full greedy after salvage blood:
Soone as the royall Virgin he did spy,
With gaping mouth at her ran greedily,
To have at once devourd her tender corse:
But to the pray whenas he drew more ny,
His bloody rage aswaged with remorse,[2]
And, with the sight amazd, forgat his furious forse.

Instead thereof he kist her wearie feet,
And lickt her lilly hands with fawning tong;
As he her wrongéd innocence did weet.[3]
O how can beautie maister the most strong,
And simple truth subdue avenging wrong!

---

[1] took off. [2] pity. [3] know.

Minor Poems. Next to his masterpiece, the *Shepherd's Calendar* (1579) is the best known of Spenser's poems; though, as his first work, it is below many others in melody. It consists of twelve pastoral poems, or eclogues, one for each month of the year. The themes are generally rural life, nature, love in the fields; and the speakers are shepherds and shepherdesses. To increase the rustic effect Spenser uses strange forms of speech and obsolete words, to such an extent that Jonson complained his works are not English or any other language. Some are melancholy poems on his lost Rosalind; some are satires on the clergy; one, 'The Briar and the Oak', is an allegory; one flatters Elizabeth, and others are pure fables touched with the Puritan spirit. They are written in various styles and metres, and show plainly that Spenser was practicing and preparing himself for greater work.

Other noteworthy poems are 'Mother Hubbard's Tale', a satire on society; 'Astrophel', an elegy on the death of Sidney; *Amoretti,* or Sonnets, to his Elizabeth; the marriage hymn, 'Epithalamion', and four "Hymns', on Love, Beauty, Heavenly Love, and Heavenly Beauty. There are numerous other poems and collections of poems, but these show the scope of his work and are best worth reading.

Importance of the Shepherd's Calendar. The publication of this work, in 1579, by an unknown writer who signed himself modestly 'Immerito', marks an important epoch in our literature. We shall appreciate this better if we remember the long years during which England had been without a great poet. Chaucer and Spenser are often studied together as poets of the Renaissance period, and the idea prevails that they were almost contemporary. In fact, nearly two centuries passed after Chaucer's death—years of enormous political and intellectual development—and not only did Chaucer have no successor but our language had changed so rapidly that Englishmen had lost the ability to read his lines correctly.[1]

[1] In the nineteenth century men learned again to appreciate Chaucer.

This first published work of Spenser is noteworthy in at least four respects: first, it marks the appearance of the first national poet in two centuries; second, it shows again the variety and melody of English verse, which had been largely a tradition since Chaucer; third, it was our first pastoral, the beginning of a long series of English pastoral compositions modelled on Spenser, and as such exerted a strong influence on subsequent literature; and fourth, it marks the real beginning of the outburst of great Elizabethan poetry.

Characteristics of Spenser's Poetry. The five main qualities of Spenser's poetry are (1) a perfect melody; (2) a rare sense of beauty; (3) a splendid imagination, which could gather into one poem heroes, knights, ladies, dwarfs, demons and dragons, classic mythology, stories of chivalry, and the thronging ideals of the Renaissance—all passing in gorgeous procession across an ever-changing and ever-beautiful landscape; (4) a lofty moral purity and seriousness; (5) a delicate idealism, which could make all nature and every common thing beautiful. In contrast with these excellent qualities the reader will probably note the strange appearance of his lines due to his fondness for obsolete words, like *eyne* (*eyes*) and shend (shame), and his tendency to coin others, like *mercify,* to suit his own purposes.

It is Spenser's idealism, his love of beauty, and his exquisite melody which have caused him to be known as 'the poets' poet'. Nearly all our subsequent singers acknowledge their delight in him and their indebtedness. Macaulay alone among critics voices a fault which all who are not poets quickly feel, namely that, with all Spenser's excellences, he is difficult to read. The modern man loses himself in the confused allegory of the *Faery Queen,* skips all but the marked passages, and softly closes the book in gentle weariness. Even the best of his longer poems, while of exquisite workmanship and delightfully melodious, generally fail to hold the reader's attention. The movement is languid; there is little dramatic interest, and only a suggestion of humour. The very melody of his verses sometimes grows monotonous, like a Strauss waltz too long continued. We shall best appreciate Spenser by reading at first only a few well-chosen selections from the *Faery Queen* and the

Shepherd's Calendar, and a few of the minor poems which exemplify his wonderful melody.

Comparison between Chaucer and Spenser. At the outset it is well to remember that, though Spenser regarded Chaucer as his master, two centuries intervene between them, and that their writings have almost nothing in common. We shall appreciate this better by a brief comparison between our first two modern poets.

Chaucer was a combined poet and man of affairs, with the latter predominating. Though dealing largely with ancient or mediæval material, he has a curiously modern way of looking at life. Indeed, he is our only author preceding Shakespeare with whom we feel thoroughly at home. He threw aside the outgrown metrical romance, which was practically the only form of narrative in his day, invented the art of storytelling in verse, and brought it to a degree of perfection which has probably never since been equalled. Though a student of the classics, he lived wholly in the present, studied the men and women of his own time, painted them as they were, but added always a touch of kindly humour or romance to make them more interesting. So his mission appears to be simply to amuse himself and his readers. His mastery of various and melodious verse was marvellous and has never been surpassed in our language; but the English of his day was changing rapidly, and in a very few years men were unable to appreciate his art, so that even to Spenser and Dryden, for example, he seemed deficient in metrical skill. On this account his influence on our literature has been much less than we should expect from the quality of his work and from his position as one of the greatest of English poets.

Like Chaucer, Spenser was a busy man of affairs, but in him the poet and the scholar always predominates. He writes as the idealist, describing men not as they are but as he thinks they should be; he has no humour, and his mission is not to amuse but to reform. Like Chaucer he studies the classics and contemporary French and Italian writers; but instead of adapting his material to present-day conditions, he makes poetry, as in his Eclogues for instance, more artificial even than his foreign models. Where

Chaucer looks about him and describes life as he sees it, Spenser always looks backward for his inspiration; he lives dreamily in the past, in a realm of purely imaginary emotions and adventures. His first quality is imagination, not observation, and he is the first of our poets to create a world of dreams, fancies, and illusions. His second quality is a wonderful sensitiveness to beauty, which shows itself not only in his subject matter but also in the manner of his poetry. Like Chaucer, he is an almost perfect workman; but in reading Chaucer we think chiefly of his natural characters or his ideas, while in reading Spenser we think of the beauty of expression. The exquisite Spenserian stanza and the rich melody of Spenser's verse have made him the model of all our modern poets.

Minor Poets

Though Spenser is the one great non-dramatic poet of the Elizabethan Age, a multitude of minor poets demand attention of the student who would understand the tremendous literary activity of the period. One needs only to read *The Paradyse of Daynty Devises* (1576), or *A Gorgeous Gallery of Gallant Inventions* (1578), or any other of the miscellaneous collections to find hundreds of songs, many of them of exquisite workmanship, by poets whose names now awaken no response. A glance is enough to assure one that over all England 'the sweet spirit of song had arisen, like the first chirping of birds after a storm'. Nearly two hundred poets are recorded in the short period from 1558 to 1625, and many of them were prolific writers. In a work like this, we can hardly do more than mention a few of the best known writers, and spend a moment at least with the works that suggest Marlowe's description of 'infinite riches in a little room'. The reader will note for himself the interesting union of action and thought in these men, so characteristic of the Elizabethan Age; for most of them were engaged chiefly in business or war or politics, and literature was to them a pleasant recreation rather than an absorbing profession.

Thomas Sackville (1536-1608). Sir Thomas Sackville, Earl of Dorset and Lord High Treasurer of England, is generally classed with Wyatt and Surrey among the predecessors of the Elizabethan Age. In imitation of Dante's *Inferno*, Sackville formed the design of a great poem called The Mirror for Magistrates. Under guidance of an allegorical personage called Sorrow, he meets the spirits of all the important actors in English history. The idea was to follow Lydgate's Fall of Princes and let each character tell his own story; so that the poem would be a mirror in which present rulers might see themselves and read this warning: 'Who reckless rules right soon may hope to rue'. Sackville finished only the 'Induction' and the 'Complaint of the Duke of Buckingham'. These are written in the rhyme royal, and are marked by strong poetic feeling and expression. Unfortunately Sackville turned from poetry to politics, and the poem was carried on by two inferior poets, William Baldwin and George Ferrers.

Sackville wrote also, in connection with Thomas Norton, the first English tragedy, *Ferrex and Porrex*, called also *Gorboduc*, which will be considered in the following section[1] on the Rise of the Drama.

Philip Sidney (1554-1586). Sidney, the ideal gentleman, the Sir Calidore of Spenser's 'Legend of Courtesy', is vastly more interesting as a man than as a writer, and the student is recommended to read his biography rather than his books. His life expresses, better than any single literary work, the two ideals of the age—personal honour and national greatness.

As a writer he is known by three principal works, all published after his death, showing how little importance he attached to his own writing, even while he was encouraging Spenser. The *Arcadia* is a pastoral romance, interspersed with eclogues, in which shepherds and shepherdesses sing of the delights of rural life. Though the work was taken up idly as a summer's pastime, it became immensely popular and was imitated by a hundred poets. The *Apologie for Poetrie* (1595), generally called the *Defense of Poesie*, appeared in answer to a pamphlet by Stephen Gosson called *The*

[1] See p. 125.

School of Abuse (1579), in which the poetry of the age and its unbridled pleasure were denounced with Puritan thoroughness and conviction. The *Apologie* is one of the first critical essays in English; and though its style now seems laboured and unnatural—the pernicious result of Euphues and his school—it is still one of the best expressions of the place and meaning of poetry in any language. *Astrophel and Stella* is a collection of songs and *Sonnets* addressed to Lady Penelope Devereux, to whom Sidney had once been betrothed. They abound in exquisite lines and passages, containing more poetic feeling and expression than the songs of any other minor writer of the age.

George Chapman (1559?-1634). Chapman spent his long, quiet life among the dramatists, and wrote chiefly for the stage. His plays, which were for the most part merely poems in dialogue, fell far below the high dramatic standard of his time and are now almost unread. His most famous work is the metrical translation of the *Iliad* (1611) and of the *Odyssey* (1614). Chapman's *Homer*, though lacking the simplicity and dignity of the original, has a force and rapidity of movement which makes it superior in many respects to Pope's more familiar translation. Chapman is remembered also as the finisher of Marlowe's *Hero and Leander*, in which, apart from the drama, the Renaissance movement is seen at perhaps its highest point in English poetry. Out of scores of long poems of the period, Hero and Leander and the *Faery Queen* are the only two which are even slightly known to modern readers.

Michael Drayton (1563-1631). Drayton is the most voluminous and, to antiquarians at least, the most interesting of the minor poets. He is the Layamon of the Elizabethan Age, and vastly more scholarly than his predecessor. His chief work is *Polyolbion,* an enormous poem of many thousand couplets, describing the towns, mountains, and rivers of Britain, with the interesting legends connected with each. It is an extremely valuable work and represents a lifetime of study and research. Two other long works are the *Barons' Wars* and the *Heroic Epistle of England*; and besides these were many minor poems. One of the best of these is the 'Battle of

Agincourt', a ballad written in the lively metre which Tennyson used with some variations in the 'Charge of the Light Brigade', and which shows the old English love of brave deeds and of the songs that stir a people's heart in memory of noble ancestors.

III. THE FIRST ENGLISH DRAMATISTS

The Origin of the Drama. First the deed, then the story, then the play; that seems to be the natural development of the drama in its simplest form. The great deeds of a people are treasured in its literature, and later generations represent in play or pantomime certain parts of the story which appeal most powerfully to the imagination. Among primitive races the deeds of their gods and heroes are often represented at the yearly festivals; and among children, whose instincts are not yet blunted by artificial habits, one sees the story that was heard at bedtime repeated next day in vigorous action, when our boys turn scouts and our girls princesses, precisely as our first dramatists turned to the old legends and heroes of Britain for their first stage productions. To act a part seems as natural to humanity as to tell a story; and originally the drama is but an old story retold to the eye, a story put into action by living performers, who for the moment 'make believe' or imagine themselves to be the old heroes.

To illustrate the matter simply, there was a great life lived by him who was called the Christ. Inevitably the life found its way into literature, and we have the Gospels. Around the life and literature sprang up a great religion. Its worship was at first simple—the common prayer, the evening meal together, the remembered words of the Master, and the closing hymn. Gradually a ritual was established, which grew more elabourate and impressive as the centuries went by. Scenes from the Master's life began to be represented in the churches, especially at Christmas time, when the story of Christ's birth was made more effective, to the eyes of a people, who could not read, by a babe in a manger surrounded by magi and shepherds, with a choir of angels chanting the *Gloria in Excelsis.*[1] Other impressive scenes from the Gospel followed; then the Old Testament was called upon, until a complete cycle of plays from the Creation to the Final Judgment was established, and we have the Mysteries and Miracle plays of the Middle Ages. Out of these came directly the drama of the Elizabethan Age.

Periods in the Development of the Drama

1. The Religious Period. In Europe, as in Greece, the drama had a distinctly religious origin.[2] The first characters were drawn from the New Testament, and the object of the first plays was to make the church service more impressive, or to emphasize moral lessons by showing the reward of the good and the punishment of the evil doer. In the latter days of the Roman Empire the Church found the stage possessed by frightful plays, which debased the morals of a people already fallen too low. Reform seemed impossible; the corrupt drama was driven from the stage, and plays of every kind were forbidden. But mankind loves a spectacle, and soon the Church itself provided a substitute for the forbidden plays in the famous Mysteries and Miracles.

---

[1] The most dramatic part of the early ritual centred about Christ's death and resurrection, On Good Fridays and Easter days. An exquisite account of this most impressive service is preserved in St. Ethelwold's Latin manual of church services, written about 965. The Latin and English versions are found in Chamber's *Mediæval Stage,* Vol. II. For a brief, interesting description, see Gayley, *Plays of Our Forefathers,* pp. 14 ff.

[2] How much we are indebted to the Norman love of pageantry for the development of the drama in England is an unanswered question. During the Middle Ages it was customary, in welcoming a monarch or in celebrating a royal wedding, to represent allegorical and mythological scenes, line the combat of St. George and the dragon, for instance, on a stage constructed for the purpose. These pageants were popular all over Europe and developed during the Renaissance into the dramatic form known as the Masque. Though the drama was of religious origin, we must not overlook these secular pageants as an important factor in the development of dramatic art.

Miracle and Mystery Plays. In France the name miracle was given to any play representing the lives of the saints, while the mystère represented scenes from the life of Christ or stories from the Old Testament associated with the coming of Messiah. In England this distinction was almost unknown; the name Miracle was used indiscriminately for all plays having their origin in the Bible or in the lives of the saints; and the name Mystery, to distinguish a certain class of plays, was not used until long after the religious drama had passed away.

The earliest Miracle of which we have any record in England is the *Ludus de Sancta Katharina*, which was performed in Dunstable about the year 1110.[1] It is not known who wrote the original play of St. Catherine, but our first version was prepared by Geoffrey of St. Albans, a French schoolteacher of Dunstable. Whether or not the play was given in English is not known, but it was customary in the earliest plays for the chief actors to speak in Latin or French, to show their importance, while minor and comic parts of the same play were given in English.

For four centuries after this first recorded play the Miracles increased steadily in number and popularity in England. They were given first very simply and impressively in the churches; then, as the actors increased in number and the plays in liveliness, they overflowed to the churchyards; but when fun and hilarity began to predominate even in the most sacred representations, the scandalized priests forbade plays altogether on church grounds. By the year 1300 the Miracles were out of ecclesiastical hands and adopted eagerly by the town guilds; and in the following two centuries we find the Church preaching against the abuse of the religious drama which it had itself introduced, and which at first

[1] Miracles were acted on the Continent earlier than this. The Normans undoubtedly brought religious plays with them, but it is probable that they began in England before the Conquest (1066). See Manly, *Specimens of the Pre- Shakespearean Drama,* I, xix.

had served a purely religious purpose.[1] But by this time the Miracles had taken strong hold upon the English people, and they continued to be immensely popular until, in the sixteenth century, they were replaced by the Elizabethan drama.

Cycles of Plays

The early Miracle plays of England were divided into two classes: the first, given at Christmas, included all plays connected with the birth of Christ; the second, at Easter, included the plays relating to his death and triumph. By the beginning of the fourteenth century all these plays were, in various localities, united in single cycles beginning with the Creation and ending with the Final Judgment. The complete cycle was presented every spring, beginning on Corpus Christi day; and as the presentation of so many plays meant a continuous outdoor festival of a week or more, this day was looked forward to as the happiest of the whole year.

Probably every important town in England had its own cycle of plays for its own guilds to perform, but nearly all have been lost. At the present day only four cycles exist (except in the most fragmentary condition), and these, though they furnish an interesting commentary on the times, add very little to our literature. The four cycles are the Chester and York plays, so called from the towns in which they were given; the Towneley or Wakefield plays, named for the Towneley family, which for a long time owned the manuscript; and the Coventry plays, which on doubtful evidence have been associated with the Grey Friars (Franciscans) of Coventry. The Chester cycle has twenty-five plays, the Wakefield thirty, the Coventry forty-two, and the York forty-eight. It is impossible to fix either the date or the authorship of any of these plays; we only know certainly that they were in great favour from the twelfth to the sixteenth century. The York plays are generally considered to be the best; but those of Wakefield show more humour and variety, and better workmanship. The former cycle especially shows a certain unity resulting from its aim to represent

[1] See Jusserand, *A Literary History of the English People,* I, III, vi. For our earliest plays and their authors see Gayley, *Plays of Our Forefathers.*

the whole of man's life from birth to death. The same thing is noticeable in Cursor Mundi, which, with the York and Wakefield cycles, belongs to the fourteenth century.

The Stage and the Actors

At first the actors as well as the authors of the Miracles were the priests and their chosen assistants. Later, when The town guilds took up the plays and each guild became responsible for one or more of the series, the actors were carefully selected and trained. By four o'clock on the morning of Corpus Christi all the players had to be in their places in the movable theatres, which were scattered throughout the town in the squares and open places. Each of these theatres consisted of a two-storey platform, set on wheels. The lower story was a dressing room for the actors; the upper storey was the stage proper, and was reached by a trapdoor from below. When the play was over the platform was dragged away, and the next play in the cycle took its place. So in a single square several plays would be presented in rapid sequence to the same audience. Meanwhile the first play moved on to another square, where another audience was waiting to hear it.

Though the plays were distinctly religious in character, there is hardly one without its humorous element. In the play of Noah, for instance, Noah's shrewish wife makes fun for the audience by wrangling with her husband. In the Crucifixion play Herod is a prankish kind of tyrant who leaves the stage to rant among the audience; so that to 'out-herod Herod' became a common proverb. In all the plays the devil is a favourite character and the butt of every joke. He also leaves the stage to play pranks or frighten the wondering children. On the side of the stage was often seen a huge dragon's head with gaping red jaws, belching forth fire and smoke, out of which poured a tumultuous troop of devils with clubs and pitchforks and gridirons to punish the wicked characters and to drag them away at last, howling and shrieking, into hell-mouth, as the dragon's head was called. So the fear of hell was ingrained into an ignorant people for four centuries. Alternating with these horrors were bits of rough horseplay and domestic scenes of peace and kindliness, representing the life of the English fields and homes. With these were songs and carols, like that of the Nativity, for instance:

As I out rode this enderes (last) night,
Of three jolly shepherds I saw a sight,
And all about their fold a star shone bright;
They sang *terli terlow,*
So merryly the shepherds their pipes can blow.

Down from heaven, from heaven so high,
Of angels there came a great companye
With mirth, and joy, and great solemnitye;
They sang *terli terlow,*
So merryly the shepherds their pipes can blow.

Such songs were taken home by the audience and sung for a season, as a popular tune is now caught from the stage and sung on the streets; and at times the whole audience would very likely join in the chorus.

After these plays were written according to the general outline of the Bible stories, no change was tolerated, the audience insisting, like children at 'Punch and Judy', upon seeing the same things year after year. No originality in plot or treatment was possible, therefore; the only variety was in new songs and jokes, and in the pranks of the devil. Childish as such plays seem to us, they are part of the religious development of all uneducated people. Even now the Persian play of the 'Martyrdom of Ali' is celebrated yearly, and the famous 'Passion Play', a true Miracle, is given every ten years at Oberammergau.

2. The Moral Period of the Drama.[1] The second or moral period of the drama is shown by the increasing prevalence of the Morality

[1] These three periods are not historically accurate. The author uses them to emphasize three different views of our earliest plays rather than to suggest that there was any orderly or chronological devleopment from Miracle to Morality and thence to the Interludes. The latter is a prevalent opinion, but it seems hardly warranted by the facts. Thus, though the Miracles precede the Moralities by two centuries (the first known Morality, 'The Play of the, Lord's Prayer', mentioned by

plays. In these the characters were allegorical personages—Life, Death, Repentance, Goodness, Love, Greed, and other virtues and vices. The Moralities may be regarded, therefore, as the dramatic counterpart of the once popular allegorical poetry exemplified by the *Romance of the Rose.* It did not occur to our first, unknown dramatists to portray men and women as they are until they had first made characters of abstract human qualities. Nevertheless, the Morality marks a distinct advance over the Miracle in that it gave free scope to the imagination for new plots and incidents. In Spain and Portugal these plays, under the name *auto,* were wonderfully developed by the genius of Calderon and Gil Vicente; but in England the Morality was a dreary kind of performance, like the allegorical poetry which preceded it.

To enliven the audience the devil of the Miracle plays was introduced; and another lively personage called the Vice was the predecessor of our modern clown and jester. His business was to torment the 'virtues' by mischievous pranks, and especially to make the devil's life a burden by beating him with a bladder or a wooden sword at every opportunity. The Morality generally ended in the triumph of virtue, the devil leaping into hell-mouth with Vice on his back.

The best known of the Moralities is 'Everyman', which has recently been revived in England and America. The subject of the play is the summoning of every man by Death; and the moral is that nothing can take away the terror of the inevitable summons but an honest life and the comforts of religion. In its dramatic unity it suggests the pure Greek drama; there is no change of time or scene, and the stage is never empty from the beginning to the end of the performance. Other well-known

---

Wyclif, was given probably about 1375), some of the best known Moralities, like 'Pride of Life', precede many of the later York Miracles. And the term Interlude, which is often used as symbolical of the transition from the moral to the artistic period of the drama, was occasionally used in England (fourteenth century) as synonymous with Miracle and again (sisteenth century) as synonymous with Comedy. That the drama had these three stages seems reasonably certain; but it is impossible to fix the limits of any one of them, and all three are sometimes seen together in one of the later Miracles of the Wakefield cycle.

Moralities are the 'Pride of Life', 'Hyckescorner', and 'Castell of Perseverance.' In the latter, man is represented as shut up in a castle garrisoned by the virtues and besieged by the vices.

Like the Miracle plays, most of the old Moralities are of unknown date and origin. Of the known authors of Moralities, two of the best are John Skelton, who wrote 'Magnificence', and probably also 'The Necromancer'; and Sir David Lindsay (1490-1555), 'the poet of the Scotch Reformation', whose religious business it was to make rulers uncomfortable by telling them unpleasant truths in the form of poetry. With these men a new element enters into the Moralities. They satirize or denounce abuses of Church and State, and introduce living personages thinly disguised as allegories; so that the stage first becomes a power in shaping events and correcting abuses.

The Interludes. It is impossible to draw any accurate line of distinction between the Moralities and Interludes. In general we may think of the latter as dramatic scenes, sometimes given by themselves (usually with music and singing) at banquets and entertainments where a little fun was wanted; and again slipped into a Miracle play to enliven the audience after a solemn scene. Thus on the margin of a page of one of the old Chester plays we read, 'The boye and pigge when the kinges are gone'. Certainly this was no part of the original scene between Herod and the three kings. So also the quarrel between Noah and his wife is probably a late addition to an old play. The Interludes originated, undoubtedly, in a sense of humour; and to John Heywood (1497?-1580?), a favourite retainer and jester at the court of Mary, is due the credit for raising the Interlude to the distinct dramatic form known as comedy.

Heywood's Interludes were written between 1520 and 1540. His most famous is 'The Four P's', a contest of wit between a 'Pardoner, a Palmer, a Pedlar and a Poticary'. The characters here strongly suggest those of Chaucer.[1] Another interesting Interlude is called 'The Play of the

[1] 'In fact, Heywood 'cribbed' from Chaucer's Tales in another Interlude called 'The Pardoner and the Frere'.

Weather'. In this Jupiter and the gods assemble to listen to complaints about the weather and to reform abuses. Naturally everybody wants his own kind of weather. The climax is reached by a boy who announces that a boy's pleasure consists in two things, catching birds and throwing snowballs, and begs for the weather to be such that he can always do both. Jupiter decides that he will do just as he pleases about the weather, and everybody goes home satisfied.

All these early plays were written, for the most part, in a mingling of prose and wretched doggerel, and add nothing to our literature. Their great work was to train actors, to keep alive the dramatic spirit, and to prepare the way for the true drama.

3. The Artistic Period of the Drama. The artistic is the final stage in the development of the English drama. It differs radically from the other two in that its chief purpose is not to point a moral but to represent human life as it is. The artistic drama may have purpose, no less than the Miracle play, but the motive is always subordinate to the chief end of representing life itself.

The first true play in English, with a regular plot, divided into acts and scenes, is probably the comedy, 'Ralph Royster Doyster'.

The First Comedy

It was written by Nicholas Udall, master of Eton, and later of Westminster school, and was first acted by his schoolboys some time before 1556. The story is that of a conceited fop in love with a widow, who is already engaged to another man. The play is an adaptation of the Miles Gloriosus, a classic comedy by Plautus, and the English characters are more or less artificial; but as furnishing a model of a clear plot and natural dialogue, the influence of this first comedy, with its mixture of classic and English elements, can hardly be overestimated.

The next play, 'Gammer Gurton's Needle' (*circa.* 1562), is a domestic comedy, a true bit of English realism, representing the life of the peasant class.

Gammer Gurton is patching the leather breeches of her man Hodge, when Gib, the cat, gets into the milk pan. While Gammer chases the cat the family needle is lost, a veritable calamity in those days. The whole household is turned upside down, and the neighbours are dragged into the affair. Various comical situations are brought about by Diccon, a thieving vagabond, who tells Gammer that her neighbour, Dame Chatte, has taken her needle, and who then hurries to tell Dame Chatte that she is accused by Gammer of stealing a favourite rooster. Naturally there is a terrible row when the two irate old women meet and misunderstand each other. Diccon also drags Doctor Rat, the curate, into the quarrel by telling him that, if he will but creep into Dame Chatte's cottage by a hidden way, he will find her using the stolen needle. Then Diccon secretly warns Dame Chatte that Gammer Gurton's man Hodge is coming to steal her chickens; and the old woman hides in the dark passage and cudgels the curate soundly with the door bar. All the parties are finally brought before the justice, when Hodge suddenly and painfully finds the lost needle—which is all the while stuck in his leather breeches—and the scene ends uproariously for both audience and actors.

This first wholly English comedy is full of fun and coarse humour, and is wonderfully true to the life it represents. It was long attributed to John Still, afterwards bishop of Bath; but the authorship is now definitely assigned to William Stevenson.[1] Our earliest edition of the play was printed in 1575; but a similar play called 'Dyccon of Bedlam' was licensed in 1552, twelve years before Shakespeare's birth.

To show the spirit and the metrical form of the play we give a fragment of the boy's description of the dullard Hodge trying to light a fire on the hearth from the cat's eyes, and another fragment of the old drinking song at the beginning of the second act.

At last in a dark corner two sparkes he thought he sees
Which were, indede, nought els but Gyb our cat's two eyes.
'Puffe!' quod Hodge, thinking therby to have fyre without doubt;
With that Gyb shut her two eyes, and so the fyre was out.
And by-and-by them opened, even as they were before;
With that the sparkes appeared, even as they had done of yore.
And, even as Hodge blew the fire, as he did thincke,
Gyb, as she felt the blast, strayght-way began to wyncke,

[1] Schelling, *Elizabethan Drama,* I, 86.

Tyll Hodge fell of swering, as came best to his turne,
The fier was sure bewicht, and therfore wold not burne.
At last Gyb up the stayers, among the old postes and pinnes,
And Hodge he hied him after till broke were both his shinnes,
Cursynge and swering othes, were never of his makyng,
That Gyb wold fyre the house if that shee were not taken.

Fyrste a Songe:
Backe and syde, go bare, go bare;
Booth foote and hande, go colde;
But, bellye, God sende thee good ale ynoughe,
Whether it be newe or olde!
I can not eate but lytle meate,
My stomacke is not good;
But sure I thinke that I can dryncke
With him that weares a hood.
Thoughe I go bare, take ye no care,
I am nothinge a-colde,
I stuffe my skyn so full within
Of ioly good ale and olde.

Backe and syde, go bare, etc.

The First Tragedy

Our first tragedy, 'Gorboduc', was written by Thomas Sackville and Thomas Norton, and was acted in 1562, only two years before the birth of Shakespeare. It is remarkable not only as our first tragedy, but as the first play to be written in blank verse, the latter being most significant, since it started the drama into the style of verse best suited to the genius of English playwrights.

The story of 'Gorboduc' is taken from the early annals of Britain and recalls the story used by Shakespeare in *King Lear.* Gorboduc, king of Britain, divides his kingdom between his sons Ferrex and Porrex. The sons quarrel, and Porrex, the younger, slays his brother, who is the queen's favourite. Videna, the queen, slays Porrex in revenge; the people rebel and slay Videna and Gorboduc; then the nobles kill the rebels, and in turn fall to fighting each other. The line of Brutus being extinct with the death of Gorboduc, the country falls into anarchy, with rebels, nobles, and a Scottish invader all fighting for the right of succession. The curtain falls upon a scene of bloodshed and utter confusion.

The artistic finish of this first tragedy is marred by the authors' evident purpose to persuade Elizabeth to marry. It aims to show the danger to which England is exposed by the uncertainty of succession. Otherwise the plan of the play follows the classical rule of Seneca. There is very little action on the stage; bloodshed and battle are announced by a messenger; and the chorus, of four old men of Britain, sums up the situation with a few moral observations at the end of each of the first four acts.

Classical Influence upon the Drama. The revival of Latin literature had a decided influence upon the English drama as it developed from the Miracle plays. In the fifteenth century English teachers, in order to increase the interest in Latin, began to let their boys act the plays which they had read as literature, precisely as our colleges now present Greek or German plays at the yearly festivals. Seneca was the favourite Latin author, and all his tragedies were translated into English between 1559 and 1581. This was the exact period in which the first English playwrights were shaping their own ideas; but the severe simplicity of the classical drama seemed at first only to hamper the exuberant English spirit. To understand this, one has only to compare a tragedy of Seneca or of Euripides with one of Shakespeare, and see how widely the two masters differ in methods.

Dramatic Unities

In the classic play the so-called dramatic unities of time, place, and action were strictly observed. Time and place must remain the same; the play could represent a period of only a few hours, and whatever action was introduced must take place at the spot where the play began. The characters, therefore, must remain unchanged throughout; there was no possibility of the child becoming a man, or of the man's growth with changing circumstances. As the play was within doors, all vigorous action was deemed out of place on the stage, and battles and important events were simply announced by a messenger. The classic drama also drew a sharp line between tragedy and comedy, all fun being rigorously excluded from serious representations.

The English drama, on the other hand, strove to represent the whole sweep of life in a single play. The scene changed rapidly; the same actors appeared now at home, now at court, now on the battlefield; and vigorous action filled the stage before the eyes of the spectators. The child of one act appeared as the man of the next, and the imagination of the spectator was called upon to bridge the gaps from place to place and from year to year. So the dramatist had free scope to present all life in a single place and a single hour. Moreover, since the world is always laughing and always crying at the same moment, tragedy and comedy were presented side by side, as they are in life itself. As *Hamlet* sings, after the play that amused the court but struck the king with deadly fear:

> Why, let the stricken deer go weep,
> The hart ungalled play;
> For some must watch, while some must sleep:
> So runs the world away.

Two Schools of Drama

Naturally, with these two ideals struggling to master the English drama, two schools of writers arose. The University Wits, as men of learning were called, generally upheld the classical ideal, and ridiculed the crudeness of the new English plays. Sackville and Norton were of this class, and 'Gorboduc' was classic in its construction. In the 'Defense of Poesie' Sidney upholds the classics and ridicules the too ambitious scope of the English drama. Against these were the popular playwrights, Lyly, Peele, Greene, Marlowe, and many others, who recognized the English love of action and disregarded the dramatic unities in their endeavour to present life as it is. In the end the native drama prevailed, aided by the popular taste which had been trained by four centuries of Miracles. Our first plays, especially of the romantic type, were extremely crude and often led to ridiculously extravagant scenes; and here is where the classic drama exercised an immense influence for good, by insisting upon beauty of form and definiteness of structure at a time when the tendency was to satisfy a taste for stage spectacles without regard to either.

The Theatre

In the year 1574 a royal permit to Lord Leicester's actors allowed them 'to give plays anywhere throughout our realm of England', and this must be regarded as the beginning of the regular drama. Two years later the first playhouse, known as 'The Theatre', was built for these actors by James Burbage in Finsbury Fields, just north of London. It was in this theatre that Shakespeare probably found employment when he first came to the city. The success of this venture was immediate, and the next thirty years saw a score of theatrical companies, at least seven regular theatres, and a dozen or more inn yards permanently fitted for the giving of plays—all established in the city and its immediate suburbs. The growth seems all the more remarkable when we remember that the London of those days would now be considered a small city, having (in 1600) only about a hundred thousand inhabitants.

A Dutch traveller, Johannes de Witt, who visited London in 1596, has given us the only contemporary drawing we possess of the interior of one of these theatres. They were built of stone and wood, round or octagonal in shape, and without a roof, being simply an enclosed courtyard. At one side was the stage, and before it on the bare ground, or pit, stood that large part of the audience who could afford to pay only an admission fee. The players and these groundlings were exposed to the weather; those that paid for seats were in galleries sheltered by a narrow porch-roof projecting inwards from the encircling walls; while the young nobles and gallants, who came to be seen and who could afford the extra fee, took seats on the stage itself, and smoked and chaffed the actors and threw nuts at the groundlings.[1] The whole idea of these first

---

[1] That these gallants were an unmitigated nuisance, and had frequently to be silenced by the common people who came to enjoy the play, seems certain. Dekker's *Gulls Hornbook* (1609) has an interesting chapter on 'How a Gallant should behave Himself in a Playhouse'.

theatres, according to De Witt, was like that of the Roman amphitheater; and the resemblance was heightened by the fact that, when no play was on the boards, the stage might be taken away and the pit given over to bull and bear baiting.

In all these theatres, probably, the stage consisted of a bare platform, with a curtain or 'traverse' across the middle, separating the front from the rear stage. On the latter unexpected scenes or characters were 'discovered' by simply drawing the curtain aside. At first little or no scenery was used, a gilded sign being the only announcement of a change of scene; and this very lack of scenery led to better acting, since the actors must be realistic enough to make the audience forget its shabby surroundings.[1] By Shakespeare's day, however, painted scenery had appeared, first at university plays, and then in the regular theatres.[2] In all our first plays female parts were taken by boy actors, who evidently were more distressing than the crude scenery, for contemporary literature has many satirical references to their acting,[3] and even the tolerant Shakespeare writes:

The Stage

> Some squeaking Cleopatra boy my greatness.

However that may be, the stage was deemed unfit for women, and actresses were unknown in England until after the Restoration.

---

[1] The first actors were classed wtih thieves and vagabonds; but they speedily raised their profession to an art and won a reputation which extended far abroad. Thus a contemporary, Fynes Moryson, writes in his *Itinerary;* 'So I remember that when some of our cast despised stage players came...........into Germany and played at Franckford.........having neither a complete number of actors, nor any good aparell, nor any ornament of the stage, yet the Germans, not understanding a worde they sayde, both men and women, flocked wonderfully to see their gesture and action'.

[2] Schelling, *Elizabethan Drama.*

[3] Baker, in his *Development of Shakespeare as a Dramatist,* pp. 57-62, takes a different view, and shows how carefully many of the boy actors were trained. It would require, however, a vigorous use of the imagination to be satisfied with a boy's presentation of Portia, Juliet, Cordelia, Rosalind, or any other of Shakespeare's wonderful women.

Shakespeare's Predecessors in the Drama. The English drama as it developed from the Miracle plays has an interesting history. It began with schoolmasters, like Udall, who translated and adapted Latin plays for their boys to act, and who were naturally governed by classic ideals. It was continued by the choirmasters of St. Paul and the Royal and the Queen's Chapel, whose companies of choirboy actors were famous in London and rivalled the players of the regular theatres.[1] These choirmasters were our first stage managers. They began with masques and interludes and the dramatic presentation of classic myths modelled after the Italians; but some of them, like Richard Edwards (choirmaster of the Queen's Chapel in 1561), soon added farces from English country life and dramatized some of Chaucer's stories. Finally, the regular playwrights, Kyd, Nash, Lyly, Peele, Greene, and Marlowe, brought the English drama to the point where Shakespeare began to experiment upon it.

Each of these playwrights added or emphasized some essential element in the drama, which appeared later in the work of Shakespeare. Thus John Lyly (1554?-1606), who is now known chiefly as having developed the pernicious literary style called euphuism,[2] is one of the most influential of the early dramatists. His court comedies are remarkable for their witty dialogue and for being our first plays to aim definitely at unity and artistic finish. Thomas Kyd's *Spanish Tragedy* (*circa* 1585) first gives us the drama, or rather the melodrama, of passion, copied by Marlowe and

[1] There choir masters had royal permits to take boys of good voice, wherever found, and train them as singers and actors. The boys were taken from their parents and were often half starved and most brutally treated. The abuse of this unnatural privilege led to the final withdrawal of all such permits.

[2] So called from Euphues, the hero of Lyly's two prose works, *Euphues, the Anatomy of Wit* (1579), and *Euphues and his England* (1580). The style is affected and over-elegant, abounds in odd conceits, and uses hopelessly involved sentences. It is found in nearly all Elizabethan prose writers, and partially accounts for their general tendency to artificiality. Shakespeare satirizes euphuism in the character of Don Adriano of *Love's Labour's Lost,* but is himself tiresomely euphuistic at times, especially in his early or 'Lylian' comedies. Lyly, by the way, did not invent the style, but did more than any other to diffuse it.

Shakespeare. This was the most popular of the early Elizabethan plays; it was revised again and again, and Ben Jonson is said to have written one version and to have acted the chief part of Hieronimo.[1] And Robert Greene (1558?-1592) plays the chief part in the early development of romantic comedy, and gives us some excellent scenes of English country life in plays like *Friar Bacon* and *Friar Bungay.*

Methods of the Early Dramatists

Even a brief glance at the life and work of these first playwrights shows three noteworthy things which have a bearing on Shakespeare's career: (1) These men were usually actors as well as dramatists. They knew the stage and the audience, and in writing their plays they remembered not only the actor's part but also the audience's love for stories and brave spectacles. 'Will it act well, and will it please our audience', were the questions of chief concern to our early dramatists. (2) Their training began as actors; then they revised old plays, and finally became independent writers. In this their work shows an exact parallel with that of Shakespeare. (3) They often worked together, probably as Shakespeare worked with Marlowe and Fletcher, either in revising old plays or in creating new ones. They had a common store of material from which they derived their stories and characters, hence their frequent repetition of names; and they often produced two or more plays on the same subject. Much of Shakespeare's work depends, as we shall see, on previous plays; and even his *Hamlet* uses the material of an earlier play of the same name, probably by Kyd, which was well known to the London stage in 1589, some twelve years before Shakespeare's great work was written.

All these things are significant, if we are to understand the Elizabethan drama and the man who brought it to perfection. Shakespeare was not simply a great genius; he was also a great worker, and he developed in exactly the same way as did all his fellow craftsmen. And, contrary to the prevalent opinion, the Elizabethan drama is not a Minervalike creation, springing full

---

[1] See Schelling, I, 211

grown from the head of one man; it is rather an orderly though rapid development, in which many men bore a part. All our early dramatists are worthy of study for the part they played in the development of the drama; but we can here consider only one, the most typical of all, whose best work is often ranked with that of Shakespeare.

CHRISTOPHER MARLOWE (1564-1593)

Marlowe is one of the most suggestive figures of the English Renaissance, and the greatest of Shakespeare's predecessors. The glory of the Elizabethan drama dates from his *Tamburlaine* (1587), wherein the whole restless temper of the age finds expression:

> Nature, that framed us of four elements
> Warring within our breasts for regiment,
> Doth teach us all to have aspiring minds:
> Our souls—whose faculties can comprehend
> The wondrous architecture of the world,
> And measure every wandering planet's course,
> Still climbing after knowledge infinite,
> And always moving as the restless spheres—
> Will us to wear ourselves and never rest.
>
> *Tamburlaine,* Pt. I, II, vii.

Life. Marlowe was born in Canterbury, only a few months before Shakespeare. He was the son of a poor shoemaker, but through the kindness of a patron was educated at the town grammar school and then at Cambridge. When he came to London (*circa.* 1584), his soul was surging with the ideals of the Renaissance, which later found expression in *Faustus*, the scholar longing for unlimited knowledge and for power to grasp the universe. Unfortunately, Marlowe had also the unbridled passions which mark the early, or Pagan Renaissance, as Taine calls it, and the conceit of a young man just entering the realms of knowledge. He became an actor and lived in a low-tavern atmosphere of excess and wretchedness. In 1587, when but twenty-three years old, he produced *Tamburlaine*, which brought him instant recognition. Thereafter, notwithstanding his wretched life, he holds steadily to a high literary purpose. Though all his plays abound in violence, no doubt reflecting many of the violent scenes in which he lived, he develops his 'mighty line' and depicts great scenes in magnificent bursts of poetry, such as the stage had never heard before. In five years, while Shakespeare was serving his apprenticeship, Marlowe produced all his great work. Then he was stabbed in a drunken brawl and died wretchedly, as he had lived. The Epilogue of Faustus might be written across his tombstone:

> Cut is the branch that might have grown full straight,
> And burned is Apollo's laurel bough
> That sometime grew within this learnéd man.

Marlowe's Works. In addition to the poem 'Hero and Leander,' to which we have referred,[1] Marlowe is famous for four dramas, now known as the Marlowesque or one-man type of tragedy, each revolving about one central personality who is consumed by the lust of power. The first of these is *Tamburlaine*, the story of Timur the Tartar. Timur begins as a shepherd chief, who first rebels and then triumphs over the Persian king. Intoxicated by his success, Timur rushes like a tempest over the whole East. Seated on his chariot drawn by captive kings, with a caged emperor before him, he boasts of his power which overrides all things. Then, afflicted with disease, he raves against the gods and would overthrow them as he has overthrown earthly rulers. *Tamburlaine* is an epic rather than a drama; but one can understand its instant success with a people only half civilized, fond of military glory, and the instant adoption of its 'mighty line' as the instrument of all dramatic expression.

Faustus

Faustus, the second play, is one of the best of Marlowe's works.[2] The story is that of a scholar who longs for infinite knowledge, and who turns from Theology, Philosophy, Medicine, and Law, the four sciences of the time, to the study of magic, much as a child might turn from jewels to tinsel and colored paper. In order to learn magic he sells himself to the devil, on condition that he shall have twenty-four years of absolute power and knowledge. The play is the story of those twenty-four years. Like

[1] See p. 114.

[2] In 1587 the first history of Johann Faust, a half-legendary German necromancer, apeared in Frankfurt. Where Marlowe found the story is unknown; but he used it, as Goethe did two centuries later, for the basis of his great tragedy.

Tamburlaine, it is lacking in dramatic construction,[1] but has an unusual number of passages of rare poetic beauty. Milton's Satan suggests strongly that the author of Paradise Lost had access to *Faustus* and used it, as he may also have used *Tamburlaine*, for the magnificent panorama displayed by Satan in *Paradise Regained.* For instance, more than fifty years before Milton's hero says, 'Which way I turn is hell, myself am hell', Marlowe had written:

Faust.

How comes it then that thou art out of hell?

Mephisto.

Why this is hell, nor am I out of it.

....

Hell hath no limits, nor is circumscribed
In one self place; for where we are is hell,
And where hell is there must we ever be.

Marlowe's third play is *The Jew of Malta*, a study of the lust for wealth, which centres about Barabas, a terrible old moneylender, strongly suggestive of Shylock in *The Merchant of Venice.* The first part of the play is well constructed, showing a decided advance, but the last part is an accumulation of melodramatic horrors. Barabas is checked in his murderous career by falling into a boiling cauldron which he had prepared for another, and dies blaspheming, his only regret being that he has not done more evil in his life.

Marlowe's last play is *Edward II*, a tragic study of a king's weakness and misery. In point of style and dramatic construction, it is by far the best of Marlowe's plays, and is a worthy predecessor of Shakespeare's historical drama.

Marlowe is the only dramatist of the time who is ever compared with Shakespeare.[2] When we remember that he died at twenty-

---

[1] We must remember, however, that our present version of *Faustus* is very much mutilated, and does not preserve the play as Marlowe wrote it.

[2] The two dramatists may have worked together in such doubtful plays as *Richard III,* the hero of which is like Timur in an English dress, and *Titus Andronicus,* with its violence and horror. In many strong scenes in Shakespeare's works Marlowe's influence is manifest.

nine, probably before Shakespeare had produced a single great play, we must wonder what he might have done had he outlived his wretched youth and become a man. Here and there his work is remarkable for its splendid imagination, for the stateliness of its verse, and for its rare bits of poetic beauty; but in dramatic instinct, in wide knowledge of human life, in humour, in delineation of woman's character, in the delicate fancy which presents an Ariel as perfectly as a *Macbeth*—in a word, in all that makes a dramatic genius, Shakespeare stands alone. Marlowe simply prepared the way for the master who was to follow.

Marlowe and Shakespeare

Variety of the Early Drama. The thirty years between our first regular English plays and Shakespeare's first comedy[1] witnessed a development of the drama which astonishes us both by its rapidity and variety. We shall better appreciate Shakespeare's work if we glance for a moment at the plays that preceded him, and note how he covers the whole field and writes almost every form and variety of the drama known to his age.

First in importance, or at least in popular interest, are the new Chronicle plays, founded upon historical events and characters. They show the strong national spirit of the Elizabethan Age, and their popularity was due largely to the fact that audiences came to the theatres partly to gratify their awakened national spirit and to get their first knowledge of national history. Some of the Moralities, like Bayle's *King Johan* (1538), are crude Chronicle plays, and the early Robin Hood plays and the first tragedy, *Gorboduc*, show the same awakened popular interest in English history. During the reign of Elizabeth the popular Chronicle plays increased till we have the record of over two hundred and twenty, half of which are still extant, dealing with almost every important character, real or legendary, in English history. Of Shakespeare's thirty-seven dramas, ten are true Chronicle plays of English kings; three are from the legendary

Types of Drama

---

[1] *Gammer Gurton's Needle* appeared *circa.* 1562; *Love's Labour's Lost, circa.* 1591.

annals of Britain; and three more are from the history of other nations.

Other types of the early drama are less clearly defined, but we may sum them up under a few general heads: (1) The Domestic Drama began with crude home scenes introduced into the Miracles and developed in a score of different ways, from the coarse humour of *Gammer Gurton's Needle* to the Comedy of Manners of Jonson and the later dramatists. Shakespeare's *Taming of the Shrew* and *Merry Wives of Windsor* belong to this class. (2) The so-called Court Comedy is the opposite of the former in that it represented a different kind of life and was intended for a different audience. It was marked by elaborate dialogue, by jests, retorts, and endless plays on words, rather than by action. It was made popular by Lyly's success, and was imitated in Shakespeare's first or 'Lylian' comedies, such as *Love's Labour's Lost*, and the complicated *Two Gentlemen of Verona.* (3) Romantic Comedy and Romantic Tragedy suggest the most artistic and finished types of the drama, which were experimented upon by Peele, Greene, and Marlowe, and were brought to perfection in *The Merchant of Venice, Romeo and Juliet,* and *The Tempest.* (4) In addition to the above types were several others—the Classical Plays, modelled upon Seneca and favoured by cultivated audiences; the Melodrama, favourite of the groundlings, which depended not on plot or characters but upon a variety of striking scenes and incidents; and the Tragedy of Blood, always more or less melodramatic, like Kyd's *Spanish Tragedy*, which grew more blood-and-thundery in Marlowe and reached a climax of horrors in Shakespeare's *Titus Andronicus*. It is noteworthy that *Hamlet, Lear,* and *Macbeth* all belong to this class, but the developed genius of the author raised them to a height such as the Tragedy of Blood had never known before.

These varied types are quite enough to show with what doubtful and unguided experiments our first dramatists were engaged, like men first setting out in rafts and dugouts on an unknown sea. They are the more interesting when we remember that Shakespeare tried them all; that he is the only dramatist whose plays cover the whole range of the drama from its beginning to its decline. From the stage spectacle he developed the drama of human life; and instead of the doggerel and bombast of our first plays he gives us the poetry of *Romeo and Juliet* and *Midsummer Night's Dream.* In a word, Shakespeare brought order out of dramatic chaos. In a few short years he raised the drama from a blundering experiment to a perfection of form and expression which has never since been rivaled.

IV. Shakespeare (1564–1616)

The Wonder of Shakespeare

One who reads a few of Shakespeare's great plays and then the meagre story of his life is generally filled with a vague wonder. Here is an unknown country boy, poor and poorly educated according to the standards of his age, who arrives at the great city of London and goes to work at odd jobs in a theatre. In a year or two he is associated with scholars and dramatists, the masters of their age, writing plays of kings and clowns, of gentlemen and heroes and noble women, all of whose lives he seems to know by intimate association. In a few years more he leads all that brilliant group of poets and dramatists who have given undying glory to the Age of Elizabeth. Play after play runs from his pen, mighty dramas of human life and character following one another so rapidly that good work seems impossible; yet they stand the test of time, and their poetry is still unrivalled in any language. For all this great work the author apparently cares little, since he makes no attempt to collect or

William Shakespeare

preserve his writings. A thousand scholars have ever since been busy collecting, identifying, classifying the works which this magnificent workman tossed aside so carelessly when he abandoned the drama and retired to his native village. He has a marvellously imaginative and creative mind; but he invents few, if any, new plots or stories. He simply takes an old play or an old poem, makes it over quickly, and lo! this old familiar material glows with the deepest thoughts and the tenderest feelings that ennoble our humanity; and each new generation of men finds it more wonderful than the last. How did he do it? That is still an unanswered question and the source of our wonder.

Genius or Training

There are, in general, two theories to account for Shakespeare. The romantic school of writers have always held that in him 'all came from within'; that his genius was his sufficient guide; and that to the overmastering power of his genius alone we owe all his great works. Practical, unimaginative men, on the other hand, assert that in Shakespeare 'all came from without', and that we must study his environment rather than his genius, if we are to understand him. He lived in a play-loving age; he studied the crowds, gave them what they wanted, and simply reflected their own thoughts and feelings. In reflecting the English crowd about him he unconsciously reflected all crowds, which are alike in all ages; hence his continued popularity. And in being guided by public sentiment he was not singular, but followed the plain path that every good dramatist has always followed to success.

Probably the truth of the matter is to be found somewhere between these two extremes. Of his great genius there can be no question; but there are other things to consider. As we have already noticed, Shakespeare was trained, like his fellow workmen, first as an actor, second as a reviser of old plays, and last as an independent dramatist. He worked with other playwrights and learned their secret. Like them, he studied and followed the public taste, and his work indicates at least three stages, from his first somewhat crude experiments to his finished masterpieces. So it would seem that in Shakespeare we have the result of hard work and of orderly human development, quite as much as of transcendent genius.

Life (1564-1616). Two outward influences were powerful; developing the genius of Shakespeare—the little village of Stratford, centre of the most beautiful and romantic district in rural England, and the great city of London, the centre of the world's political activity. In one he learned to know the natural man in his natural environment; in the other, the social, the artificial man in the most unnatural of surroundings.

From the register of the little parish church at Stratford-on-Avon we learn that William Shakespeare was baptized there on the twenty-sixth of April, 1564 (old style). As it was customary to baptize children on the third day after birth, the twenty-third of April (3 May, according to our present calendar) is generally accepted as the poet's birthday.

His father, John Shakespeare, was a farmer's son from the neighbouring village of Snitterfield, who came to Stratford about 1551, and began to prosper as a trader in corn, meat, leather, and other agricultural products. His mother, Mary Arden, was the daughter of a prosperous farmer, descended from an old Warwickshire family of mixed Anglo-Saxon and Norman blood. In 1559 this married couple sold a piece of land, and the document is signed, 'The marke + of John Shacksper. The marke + of Mary Shacksper'; and from this it has been generally inferred that, like the vast majority of their countrymen, neither of the poet's parents could read or write. This was probably true of his mother; but the evidence from Stratford documents now indicates that his father could write, and that he also audited the town accounts; though in attesting documents he sometimes made a mark, leaving his name to be filled in by the one who drew up the document.

Of Shakespeare's education we know little, except that for a few years he probably attended the endowed grammar school at Stratford, where he picked up the 'small Latin and less Greek' to which his learned friend Ben Jonson refers. His real teachers, meanwhile, were the men and women and the natural influences which surrounded him. Stratford is a charming little village in beautiful Warwickshire, and near at hand were the Forest of Arden, the old castles of Warwick and Kenilworth, and the old Roman camps and military roads, to appeal powerfully to the boy's lively imagination. Every phase of the natural beauty of this exquisite region is reflected in Shakespeare's poetry; just as his characters reflect the nobility and the littleness, the gossip, vices, emotions, prejudices, and traditions of the people about him.

I saw a smith stand with his hammer, thus,
The whilst his iron did on the anvil cool,
With open mouth swallowing a tailor's news;
Who, with his shears and measure in his hand,
Standing on slippers, which his nimble haste
Had falsely thrust upon contrary feet,
Told of a many thousand warlike French
That were embattailed and ranked in Kent.[1]

Such passages suggest not only genius but also a keen, sympathetic observer, whose eyes see every significant detail. So with the nurse in *Romeo and Juliet,* whose endless gossip and vulgarity cannot quite hide a kind heart. She is simply the reflection of some forgotten nurse with whom Shakespeare had talked by the wayside.

Not only the gossip but also the dreams, the unconscious poetry that sleeps in the heart of the common people, appeal tremendously to Shakespeare's imagination and are reflected in his greatest plays. *Othello* tries to tell a curt soldier's story of his love; but the account is like a bit of Mandeville's famous travels, teeming with the fancies that filled men's heads when the great round world was first brought to their attention by daring explorers. Here is a bit of folklore, touched by Shakespeare's exquisite fancy, which shows what one boy listened to before the fire at Halloween:

She comes
In shape no bigger than an agate-stone
On the fore-finger of an alderman,
Drawn with a team of little atomies
Athwart men's noses as they lie asleep;
Her waggon-spokes made of long spinners' legs,
The cover of the wings of grasshoppers,
The traces of the smallest spider's web,
The collars of the moonshine's watery beams,

[1] *King John,* IV, 2

Her whip of cricket's bone, the lash of film,
Her waggoner a small grey-coated gnat,

....

Her chariot is an empty hazel nut
Made by the joiner squirrel, or old grub,
Time out o' mind the fairies' coachmakers.
And in this state she gallops night by night
Through lovers' brains, and then they dream of love;

....

O'er lawyers' fingers, who straight dream on fees,
O'er ladies' lips, who straight on kisses dream.[1]

So with Shakespeare's education at the hands of Nature, which came from keeping his heart as well as his eyes wide open to the beauty of the world. He speaks of a horse, and we know the fine points of a thoroughbred; he mentions the duke's hounds, and we hear them clamouring on a fox trail, their voices matched like bells in the frosty air; he stops for an instant in the sweep of a tragedy to note a flower, a star, a moonlit bank, a hilltop touched by the sunrise, and instantly we know what our own hearts felt but could not quite express when we saw the same thing. Because he notes and remembers every significant thing in the changing panorama of earth and sky, no other writer has ever approached him in the perfect natural setting of his characters.

When Shakespeare was about fourteen years old his father lost his little property and fell into debt, and the boy probably left school to help support the family of younger children. What occupation he followed for the next eight years is a matter of conjecture. From evidence found in his plays, it is alleged with some show of authority that he was a country schoolmaster and a lawyer's clerk, the character of Holofernes, in *Love's Labour's Lost,* being the warrant for one, and Shakespeare's knowledge of law terms for the other. But if we take such evidence, then Shakespeare must have been a botanist, because of his knowledge of wild flowers; a sailor, because he knows the ropes; a courtier, because of his extraordinary facility in quips and compliments and courtly language; a clown, because none other is so dull and foolish; a king, because Richard and Henry are true to life; a woman, because he has sounded the depths of a woman's

[1] Queen Mab, in *Rumeo and Juliet*

feelings; and surely a Roman, because in *Coriolanus* and *Julius Cæsar* he has shown us the Roman spirit better than have the Roman writers themselves. He was everything, in his imagination, and it is impossible from a study of his scenes and characters to form a definite opinion as to his early occupation.

Anne Hathaway's Cottage

In 1582 Shakespeare was married to Anne Hathaway, the daughter of a peasant family of Shottery, who was eight years older than her boy husband. From numerous sarcastic references to marriage made by the characters in his plays, and from the fact that he soon left his wife and family and went to London, it is generally alleged that the marriage was a hasty and unhappy one; but here again the evidence is entirely untrustworthy. In many Miracles as well as in later plays it was customary to depict the seamy side of domestic life for the amusement of the crowd; and Shakespeare may have followed the public taste in this as he did in other things. The references to love and home and quiet joys in Shakespeare's plays are enough, if we take such evidence, to establish firmly the opposite supposition, that his love was a very happy one. And the fact that, after his enormous success in London, he retired to Stratford to live quietly with his wife and daughters, tends to the same conclusion.

About the year 1587 Shakespeare left his family and went to London and joined himself to Burbage's company of players. A persistent tradition says that he had incurred the anger of Sir Thomas Lucy, first by poaching deer in that nobleman's park, and then, when haled before a magistrate, by writing a scurrilous ballad about Sir Thomas, which so aroused the old gentleman's ire that Shakespeare was obliged to flee the country. An old record[1] says that the poet 'was much given to all unluckiness in stealing venison and rabbits', the unluckiness probably consisting in getting caught himself, and not in any lack of luck in catching the rabbits. The ridicule heaped upon the Lucy family in Henry IV and the *Merry Wives of Windsor* gives some weight to this tradition. Nicholas Rowe, who published the first life of Shakespeare,[2] is the authority for this story; but there is some reason to doubt whether, at the time when Shakespeare is said to have poached in the deer park of Sir Thomas Lucy at Charlescote, there were any deer or park at the place referred to. The subject is worthy of some scant attention, if only to show how worthless is the attempt to construct out of rumour the story of a great life which, fortunately perhaps, had no contemporary biographer.

Of his life in London from 1587 to 1611, the period of his greatest literary activity, we know nothing definitely. We can judge only from his plays, and from these it is evident that he entered into the stirring life of England's capital with the same perfect sympathy and understanding that marked him among the plain people of his native Warwickshire. The first authentic reference to him is in 1592, when Greene's[3] bitter attack appeared, showing plainly that Shakespeare had in five years assumed an important position among playwrights. Then appeared the apology of the publishers of Greene's pamphlet, with their tribute to the poet's sterling character, and occasional literary references which show that he was known among his fellows as 'the gentle Shakespeare'. Ben Jonson says of him: 'I loved the man and do honor his memory, on this side idolatry, as much as any. He was indeed honest, and of an open and free nature'. To judge from only three of his earliest plays[4] it would seem reasonably evident that in the first five years of his London life he had gained entrance to the society of gentlemen and scholars, had caught their characteristic mannerisms and expressions, and so was ready by knowledge and observation as well as by genius to weave into his dramas the whole stirring life of the

[1] By Archdeacon Davies, in the seventeenth century.

[2] In 1709, nearly a century after the poet's death.

[3] Robert Greene, one of the popular playwrights of the time, who attacked Shakespeare in a pamphlet called 'A Groat's Worth of Wit Bought with a Million of Repentance'. The pamphlet, aside from its jealousy of Shakespeare, is a sad picture of a man of genius dying of dissipation, and contains a warning to other playwrights of the time, whose lives were apparently almost as bad as that of Greene.

[4] *Love's Labout's Lost, Comedy of Errors, Two Gentlemen of Verona.*

English people. The plays themselves, with the testimony of contemporaries and his business success, are strong evidence against the tradition that his life in London was wild and dissolute, like that of the typical actor and playwright of his time.

Shakespeare's first work may well have been that of a general helper, an odd-job man, about the theatre; but he soon became an actor, and the records of the old London theatres show that in the next ten years he gained a prominent place, though there is little reason to believe that he was counted among the 'stars'. Within two years he was at work on plays, and his course here was exactly like that of other playwrights of his time. He worked with other men, and he revised old plays before writing his own, and so gained a practical knowledge of his art. *Henry VI* (*circa.*

Birthplace of Shakespeare

1590-1591) is an example of this tinkering work, in which, however, his native power is unmistakably manifest. The three parts of *Henry VI* (and *Richard III*, which belongs with them) are a succession of scenes from English Chronicle history strung together very loosely; and only in the last is there any definite attempt at unity. That he soon fell under Marlowe's influence is evident from the atrocities and bombast of *Titus Andronicus* and *Richard III*. The former may have been written by both playwrights in collabouration, or may be one of Marlowe's horrors left unfinished by his early death and brought to an end by Shakespeare. He soon broke away from this apprentice work, and then appeared in rapid succession

Love's Labour's Lost, Comedy of Errors, Two Gentlemen of Verona, the first English Chronicle plays,[1] *A Midsummer Nights' Dream*, and *Romeo and Juliet*. This order is more or less conjectural; but the wide variety of these plays, as well as their unevenness and frequent crudities, marks the first or experimental stage of Shakespeare's work. It is as if the author were trying his power, or more likely trying the temper of his audience. For it must be remembered that to please his audience was probably the ruling motive of Shakespeare, as of the other early dramatists, during the most vigorous and prolific period of his career.

Shakespeare's poems, rather than his dramatic work, mark the beginning of his success. '*Venus and Adonis*' became immensely popular in London, and its dedication to the Earl of Southampton brought, according to tradition, a substantial money gift, which may have laid the foundation for Shakespeare's business success. He appears to have shrewdly invested his money, and soon became part owner of the Globe and Blackfriars theatres, in which his plays were presented by his own companies. His success and popularity grew amazingly. Within a decade of his unnoticed arrival in London he was one of the most famous actors and literary men in England.

Following his experimental work there came a succession of wonderful plays—*Merchant of Venice, As You Like It, Twelfth Night, Julius Cæsar, Hamlet, Macbeth, Othello, King Lear, Antony and Cleopatra*. The great tragedies of this period are associated with a period of gloom and sorrow in the poet's life; but of its cause we have no knowledge. It may have been this unknown sorrow which turned his thoughts back to Stratford and caused, apparently, a dissatisfaction with his work and profession; but the latter is generally attributed to other causes. Actors and playwrights were in his day generally looked upon with suspicion or contempt; and Shakespeare, even in the midst of success, seems to have looked forward

---

[1] *Henry VI, Richard III, Richard II, King John*. Prior to 1588 only three true Chronicle plays are known to have been acted. The defeat of the Armada in that year led to an outburst of national feeling which found one outlet in the theatres, and in the next ten years over eighty Chronicle plays appeared. Of these Shakespeare furnished nine or ten. It was the great popular success of *Henry VI*, a revision of an old play, in 1593 that probably led to Greene's jealous attack.

to the time when he could retire to Stratford to live the life of a farmer and country gentleman. His own and his father's families were first released from debt; then, in 1597, he bought New Place, the finest house in Stratford, and soon added a tract of farming land to complete his estate. His profession may have prevented his acquiring the title of 'gentleman', or he may have only followed a custom of the time[1] when he applied for and obtained a coat of arms for his father, and so indirectly secured the title by inheritance. His home visits grew more and more frequent till, about the year 1611, he left London and retired permanently to Stratford.

Though still in the prime of life, Shakespeare soon abandoned his dramatic work for the comfortable life of a country gentleman. Of his later plays, *Coriolanus, Cymbeline, Winter's Tale*, and *Pericles* show a decided falling off from his previous work, and indicate another period of experimentation; this time not to test his own powers but to catch the fickle humour of the public. As is usually the case with a theatre-going people, they soon turned from serious drama to sentimental or more questionable spectacles; and with Fletcher, who worked with Shakespeare and succeeded him as the first playwright of London, the decline of the drama had already begun. In 1609, however, occurred an event which gave Shakespeare his chance for a farewell to the public. An English ship disappeared, and all on board were given up for lost. A year later the sailors returned home, and their arrival created intense excitement. They had been wrecked on the unknown Bermudas, and had lived there for ten months, terrified by mysterious noises which they thought came from spirits and devils. Five different accounts of this fascinating shipwreck were published, and the Bermudas became known as the 'Ile of Divels'. Shakespeare took this story—which caused as much popular interest as that later shipwreck which gave us *Robinson Crusoe*—and wove it into *The Tempest.* In the same year (1611) he probably sold his interest in the Globe and Blackfriars theatres, and his dramatic work was ended. A few plays were probably left unfinished[2] and were turned over to Fletcher and other dramatists.

---

[1] See Lee's *Life of William Shakespeare,* pp. 188-196.

[2] Like Henry VIII, and possibly the lost *Cardenio.*

Trinity Church, Stratford-on-Avon

That Shakespeare thought little of his success and had no idea that his dramas were the greatest that the world ever produced seems evident from the fact that he made no attempt to collect or publish his works, or even to save his manuscripts, which were carelessly left to stage managers of the theatres, and so found their way ultimately to the ragman. After a few years of quiet life, of which we have less record than of hundreds of simple country gentlemen of the time, Shakespeare died on the probable anniversary of his birth, April 23, 1616. He was given a tomb in the chancel of the parish church, not because of his preeminence in literature, but because of his interest in the affairs of a country village. And in the sad irony of fate, the broad stone that covered his tomb—now an object of veneration to the thousands that yearly visit the little church—was inscribed as follows:

Good friend, for Jesus' sake forbeare
To dig the dust enclosed heare;

Bleste be the man that spares these stones,
And curst be he that moves my bones.

This wretched doggerel, over the world's greatest poet, was intended, no doubt, as a warning to some stupid sexton, lest he should empty the grave and give the honoured place to some amiable gentleman who had given more tithes to the parish.

Works of Shakespeare. At the time of Shakespeare's death twenty-one plays existed in manuscripts in the various theatres. A few others had already been printed in quarto form, and the latter are the only publications that could possibly have met with the poet's own approval. More probably they were taken down in shorthand by some listener at the play and then 'pirated' by some publisher for his own profit. The first printed collection of his plays, now called the First Folio (1623), was made by two actors, Heming and Condell, who asserted that they had access to the papers of the poet and had made a perfect edition, 'in order to keep the memory of so worthy a friend and fellow alive'. This contains thirty-six of the thirty-seven plays generally attributed to Shakespeare, *Pericles* being omitted. This celebrated First Folio was printed from playhouse manuscripts and from printed quartos containing many notes and changes by individual actors and stage managers. Moreover, it was full of typographical errors, though the editors alleged great care and accuracy; and so, though it is the only authoritative edition we have, it is of little value in determining the dates, or the classification of the plays as they existed in Shakespeare's mind.

Four Periods

Notwithstanding this uncertainty, a careful reading of the plays and poems leaves us with an impression of four different periods of work, probably corresponding with the growth and experience of the poet's life. These are: (1) a period of early experimentation. It is marked by youthfulness and exuberance of imagination, by extravagance of language, and by the frequent use of rhymed couplets with his blank verse. The period dates from his arrival in London to 1595. Typical works of this first period are his early poems, *Love's Labour's Lost, Two Gentlemen of Verona,* and *Richard III.* (2) A period of rapid growth and development, from 1595 to 1600. Such plays as *The Merchant of Venice, Midsummer Night's Dream, As You Like It,* and *Henry IV,* all written in this period, show more careful and artistic work, better plots, and a marked increase in knowledge of human nature. (3) A period of gloom and depression, from 1600 to 1607, which marks the full maturity of his powers. What caused this evident sadness is unknown; but it is generally attributed to some personal experience, coupled with the political misfortunes of his friends, Essex and Southampton. The *Sonnets* with their note of personal disappointment, *Twelfth Night*, which is Shakespeare's 'farewell to mirth', and his great tragedies, *Hamlet, Lear, Macbeth, Othello*, and *Julius Cæsar*, belong to this period. (4) A period of restored serenity, of calm after storm, which marked the last years of the poet's literary work. *The Winter's Tale* and *The Tempest* are the best of his later plays; but they all show a falling off from his previous work, and indicate a second period of experimentation with the taste of a fickle public.

To read in succession four plays, taking a typical work from each of the above periods, is one of the very best ways of getting quickly at the real life and mind of Shakespeare. Following is a complete list with the approximate dates of his works, classified according to the above four periods.

FIRST PERIOD, EARLY EXPERIMENT. *Venus and Adonis, Rape of Lucrece*, 1594; *Titus Andronicus*, Henry VI (three parts), 1590-1591; *Love's Labour's Lost*, 1590; *Comedy of Errors, Two Gentlemen of Verona,* 1591-1592; *Richard-III*, 1593; *Richard II, King John*, 1594-1595.

SECOND PERIOD, DEVELOPMENT. *Romeo and Juliet, Midsummer Night's Dream*, 1595; *Merchant of Venice*, Henry IV (first part), 1596; Henry IV (second part), *Merry Wives of Windsor*, 1597; *Much Ado About Nothing,* 1598; *As You Like It, Henry V*, 1599.

THIRD PERIOD, MATURITY AND GLOOM. *Sonnets* (1600-?), *Twelfth Night*, 1600; *Taming of the Shrew, Julius Cæsar, Hamlet, Troilus and Cressida*, 1601-1602; *All's Well That Ends Well, Measure for Measure*, 1603; *Othello*, 1604; *King Lear*, 1605; *Macbeth*, 1606; *Antony and Cleopatra, Timon of Athens,* 1607.

FOURTH PERIOD, LATE Experiment. *Coriolanus, Pericles*, 1608; *Cymbeline*, 1609; *Winter's Tale*, 1610-1611; *The Tempest*, 1611; *Henry VIII* (unfinished).

Classification according to Source. In history, legend, and story, Shakespeare found the material for nearly all his dramas; and so they are often divided into three classes, called historical plays, like *Richard III* and *Henry V*; legendary or partly historical plays, like *Macbeth, King Lear*, and *Julius Cæsar*; and fictional plays, like *Romeo and Juliet* and *The Merchant of Venice.* Shakespeare invented few, if any, of the plots or stories upon which his dramas are founded, but borrowed them freely, after the custom of his age, wherever he found them. For his legendary and historical material he depended largely on *Holinshed's Chronicles of England, Scotland, and Ireland*, and on North's translation of Plutarch's famous *Lives.*

A full half of his plays are fictional, and in these he used the most popular romances of the day, seeming to depend most on the Italian storytellers. Only two or three of his plots, as in *Love's Labour's Lost* and *Merry Wives of Windsor*, are said to be original, and even these are doubtful. Occasionally Shakespeare made over an older play, as in *Henry VI, Comedy of Errors,* and *Hamlet;* and in one instance at least he seized upon an incident of shipwreck in which London was greatly interested, and made out of it the original and fascinating play of *The Tempest,* in much the same spirit which leads our modern playwrights when they dramatize a popular novel or a war story to catch the public fancy.

Classification according to Dramatic Type. Shakespeare's dramas are usually divided into three classes, called tragedies, comedies, and historical plays. Strictly speaking the drama has but two divisions, tragedy and comedy, in which are included the many subordinate forms of tragi-comedy, melodrama, lyric drama (opera), farce, etc. A tragedy is a drama in which the principal characters are involved in desperate circumstances or led by overwhelming passions. It is invariably serious and dignified. The movement is always stately, but grows more and more rapid as it

Property of the Metropolitan Museum of Art

Portia

After the portrait by John Everett Millais

approaches the climax; and the end is always calamitous, resulting in death or dire misfortune to the principals. As Chaucer's monk says, before he begins to 'biwayle in maner of tragedie':

> Tragedie is to seyn a certeyn storie
> Of him that stood in great prosperitee,
> And is y-fallen out of heigh degree
> Into miserie, and endeth wrecchedly.

A comedy, on the other hand, is a drama in which the characters are placed in more or less humourous situations. The movement is light and often mirthful, and the play ends in general good will and happiness. The historical drama aims to present some historical age or character, and may be either a comedy or a tragedy. The following list includes the best of Shakespeare's plays in each of the three classes; but the order indicates merely the author's personal opinion of the relative merits of the plays in each class. Thus *Merchant of Venice* would be the first of the comedies for the beginner to read, and *Julius Cæsar* is an excellent introduction to the historical plays and the tragedies.

COMEDIES. *Merchant of Venice, Midsummer Night's Dream, As You Like It, Winter's Tale, The Tempest, Twelfth Night.*
TRAGEDIES. *Romeo and Juliet, Macbeth, Hamlet, King Lear, Othello.*
HISTORICAL PLAYS. *Julius Cæsar, Richard III, Henry IV, Henry V, Coriolanus, Antony and Cleopatra.*

Doubtful Plays. It is reasonably certain that some of the plays generally attributed to Shakespeare are partly the work of other dramatists. The first of these doubtful plays, often called the Pre-Shakespearian Group, are *Titus Andronicus* and the first part of *Henry VI*. Shakespeare probably worked with Marlowe in the two last parts of *Henry VI* and in *Richard III*. The three plays, *Taming of the Shrew, Timon*, and *Pericles* are only partly Shakespeare's work, but the other authors are unknown. *Henry VIII* is the work of Fletcher and Shakespeare, opinion being divided as to whether Shakespeare helped Fletcher, or whether it was an unfinished work of Shakespeare which was put into Fletcher's hands for completion. *Two Noble Kinsmen* is a play not ordinarily found in editions of Shakespeare, but it is often placed among his doubtful works. The greater part of the play is undoubtedly by Fletcher. *Edward III* is one of several crude plays published at first anonymously and later attributed to Shakespeare by publishers who desired to sell their wares. It contains a few passages that strongly suggest Shakespeare; but the external evidence is all against his authorship.

Shakespeare's Poems. It is generally asserted that, if Shakespeare had written no plays, his poems alone would have given him a commanding place in the Elizabethan Age.

Nevertheless, in the various histories of our literature there is apparent a desire to praise and pass over all but the *Sonnets* as rapidly as possible; and the reason may be stated frankly. His two long poems, *'Venus and Adonis'* and *'The Rape of Lucrece'*, contain much poetic fancy; but it must be said of both that the subjects are unpleasant, and that they are dragged out to unnecessary length in order to show the play of youthful imagination. They were extremely popular in Shakespeare's day, but in comparison with his great dramatic works these poems are now of minor importance.

Shakespeare's *Sonnets*, one hundred and fifty-four in number, are the only direct expression of the poet's own feelings that we possess; for his plays are the most impersonal in all literature. They were published together in 1609; but if they had any unity in Shakespeare's mind, their plan and purpose are hard to discover. By some critics they are regarded as mere literary exercises; by others as the expression of some personal grief during the third period of the poet's literary career. Still others, taking a hint from the sonnet beginning 'Two loves I have, of comfort and despair', divide them all into two classes, addressed to a man who was Shakespeare's friend, and to a woman who disdained his love. The reader may well avoid such classifications and read a few *Sonnets,* like the twenty-ninth, for instance, and let them speak their own message. A few are trivial and artificial enough, suggesting the elabourate exercises of a piano player; but the majority are remarkable for their subtle thought and exquisite expression. Here and there is one, like that beginning

> When to the sessions of sweet silent thought
> I summon up remembrance of things past,

which will haunt the reader long afterwards, like the remembrance of an old German melody.

Shakespeare's Place and Influence. Shakespeare holds, by general acclamation, the foremost place in the world's literature, and his overwhelming greatness renders it difficult to criticize or even to praise him. Two poets only, Homer and Dante, have been named with him; but each of these wrote within narrow limits, while Shakespeare's genius included all the world of nature and of men. In a word, he is the universal poet. To study nature in his works is like exploring a new and beautiful country; to study man in his works is like going into a great city, viewing the motley crowd as one views a great masquerade in which past and present mingle freely and familiarly, as if the dead were all living again. And the marvellous thing, in this masquerade of all sorts and conditions of men, is that Shakespeare lifts the mask from every face, lets us see the man as he is in his own soul, and shows us in each one some germ of good, some 'soul of goodness' even in things evil. For Shakespeare strikes no uncertain note, and raises no doubts to add to the burden of your own. Good always overcomes evil in the long run; and love, faith, work, and duty are the four elements that in all ages make the world right. To criticize or praise the genius that creates these men and women is to criticize or praise humanity itself.

Of his influence in literature it is equally difficult to speak. Goethe expresses the common literary judgment when he says, 'I do not remember that any book or person or event in my life ever made so great an impression upon me as the plays of Shakespeare.' His influence upon our own language and thought is beyond calculation. Shakespeare and the King James Bible are the two great conservators of the English speech; and one who habitually reads them finds himself possessed of a style and vocabulary that are beyond criticism. Even those who read no Shakespeare are still unconsciously guided by him, for his thought and expression have so pervaded our life and literature that it is impossible, so long as one speaks the English language, to escape his influence.

His life was gentle, and the elements
So mixed in him, that Nature might stand up
And say to all the world, 'This was a man!'

V. SHAKESPEARE'S CONTEMPORARIES AND SUCCESSORS IN THE DRAMA

Decline of the Drama. It was inevitable that the drama should decline after Shakespeare, for the simple reason that there was no other great enough to fill his place. Aside from this, other causes were at work, and the chief of these was at the very source of the Elizabethan dramas. It must be remembered that our first playwrights wrote to please their audiences; that the drama rose in England because of the desire of a patriotic people to see something of the stirring life of the times reflected on the stage. For there were no papers or magazines in those days, and people came to the theatres not only to be amused but to be informed. Like children, they wanted to see a story acted; and like men, they wanted to know what it meant. Shakespeare fulfilled their desire. He gave them their story, and his genius was great enough to show in every play not only their own life and passions but something of the meaning of all life, and of that eternal justice which uses the war of human passions for its own great ends. Thus good and evil mingle freely in his dramas; but the evil is never attractive, and the good triumphs as inevitably as fate. Though his language is sometimes coarse, we are to remember that it was the custom of his age to speak somewhat coarsely, and that in language, as in thought and feeling, Shakespeare is far above most of his contemporaries.

American Memorial Window in the Church of the Holy Trinity, Stratford-on-Avon

With his successors all this was changed. The audience itself had gradually changed, and in place of plain people eager for a story and for information, we see a larger and larger proportion of those who went to the play because they had nothing else to do. They wanted amusement only, and since they had blunted by idleness the desire for simple and wholesome amusement, they called for something more sensational. Shakespeare's successors catered to the depraved tastes of this new audience. They lacked not only Shakespeare's genius, but his broad charity, his moral insight into life. With the exception of Ben Jonson, they neglected the simple fact that man in his deepest nature is a moral being, and that only a play which satisfies the whole nature of man by showing the triumph of the moral law can ever wholly satisfy an audience or a people. Beaumont and Fletcher, forgetting the deep meaning of life, strove for effect by increasing the sensationalism of their plays; Webster revelled in tragedies of blood and thunder; Massinger and Ford made another step downward, producing evil and licentious scenes for their own sake, making characters and situations more immoral till, notwithstanding these dramatists' ability, the stage had become insincere, frivolous, and bad. Ben Jonson's ode, 'Come Leave the Loathed Stage', is the judgment of a large and honest nature grown weary of the plays and the players of the time. We read with a sense of relief that in 1642, only twenty-six years after Shakespeare's death, both houses of Parliament voted to close the theatres as breeders of lies and immorality.

BEN JONSON (1573?-1637)

Personally Jonson is the most commanding literary figure among the Elizabethans. For twenty-five years he was the literary dictator of London, the chief of all the wits that gathered nightly at the old Devil Tavern. With his great learning, his ability, and his commanding position as poet laureate, he set himself squarely against his contemporaries and the romantic tendency of the age. For two things he fought bravely—to restore the classic form of the drama, and to keep the stage from its downward course. Apparently he failed; the romantic school fixed its hold more strongly than ever; the stage went swiftly to an end as sad as that of the early dramatists. Nevertheless his influence lived and grew more powerful till, aided largely by French influence, it resulted in the so-called classicism of the eighteenth century.

Ben Jonson

Life. Jonson was born at Westminster about the year 1573. His father, an educated gentleman, had his property confiscated and was himself thrown into prison by Queen Mary; so we infer the family was of some prominence. From his mother he received certain strong characteristics, and by a single short reference in Jonson's works we are led to see the kind of woman she was. It is while Jonson is telling Drummond of the occasion when he was thrown into prison, because some passages in the comedy of *Eastward Ho!* gave offence to King James, and he was in danger of a horrible death, after having his ears and nose cut off. He tells us how, after his pardon, he was banqueting with his friends, when his 'old mother' came in and showed a paper full of 'lusty strong poison', which she intended to mix with his drink just before the execution. And to show that she 'was no churl', she intended first to drink of the poison herself. The incident is all the more suggestive from the fact that Chapman and Marston, one his friend and the other his enemy, were first cast into prison as the authors of *Eastward Ho!* and rough Ben Jonson at once declared that he too had had a small hand in the writing and went to join them in prison.

Jonson's father came out of prison, having given up his estate, and became a minister. He died just before the son's birth, and two years later the mother married a bricklayer of London. The boy was sent to a private school, and later made his own way to Westminster school, where the submaster, Camden, struck by the boy's ability, taught and largely supported him. For a short time he may have studied at the university in Cambridge; but his stepfather soon set him to learning the bricklayer's trade. He ran away from this, and went with the English army to fight Spaniards in the Low Countries. His best known exploit there was to fight a duel between the lines with one of the enemy's soldiers, while both armies looked on. Jonson killed his man, and took his arms, and made his way back to his own lines in a way to delight the old Norman troubadours. He soon returned to England, and married precipitately when only nineteen or twenty years old. Five years later we find him employed, like Shakespeare, as actor and reviser of old plays in the theatre. Thereafter his life is a varied and stormy one. He killed an actor in a duel, and only escaped hanging by pleading 'benefit of clergy';[1] but he lost all his poor goods and was branded for life on his left thumb. In his first great play, *Every Man in His Humour* (1598), Shakespeare acted one of the parts; and that may have been the beginning of their long friendship. Other plays followed rapidly. Upon the accession of James, Jonson's masques won him royal favour, and he was made poet laureate. He now became undoubted leader of the literary men of his time, though his rough honesty and his hatred of the literary tendencies of the age made him quarrel with nearly all of them. In 1616, soon after Shakespeare's retirement, he stopped writing for the stage and gave himself up to study and serious work. In 1618 he travelled on foot to Scotland, where he visited Drummond, from whom we have the scant records of his varied life. His impressions of this journey, called *Foot Pilgrimage,* were lost in a fire before publication. Thereafter he produced less, and his work declined in vigor; but spite of growing poverty and infirmity we notice in his later work, especially in the unfinished *Sad Shepherd,* a certain mellowness and tender human sympathy which were lacking in his earlier productions. He died poverty stricken in 1637. Unlike Shakespeare's, his death was mourned as a national calamity, and he was buried with all honor in Westminster Abbey. On his grave was laid a marble slab, on which the words 'O rare Ben Jonson' were his sufficient epitaph.

Works of Ben Jonson. Jonson's work is in strong contrast with that of Shakespeare and of the later Elizabethan dramatists. Alone he

[1] A name given to the privilege—claimed by the mediaeval Church for its clergy—of being exempt from trial by the regular law courts. After the Reformation the custom survived for a long time, and special privileges were allowed to ministers and their families. Jonson claimed the privilege as a minister's son.

fought against the romantic tendency of the age, and to restore the classic standards. Thus the whole action of his drama usually covers only a few hours, or a single day. He never takes liberties with historical facts, as Shakespeare does, but is accurate to the smallest detail. His dramas abound in classical learning, are carefully and logically constructed, and comedy and tragedy are kept apart, instead of crowding each other as they do in Shakespeare and in life. In one respect his comedies are worthy of careful reading—they are intensely realistic, presenting men and women of the time exactly as they were. From a few of Jonson's scenes we can understand—better than from all the plays of Shakespeare—how men talked and acted during the Age of Elizabeth.

Every Man in His Humour

Jonson's first comedy, *Every Man in His Humour,* is a key to all his dramas. The word 'humour' in his age stood for some characteristic whim or quality of society. Jonson gives to his leading character some prominent humor, exaggerates it, as the cartoonist enlarges the most characteristic feature of a face, and so holds it before our attention that all other qualities are lost sight of; which is the method that Dickens used later in many of his novels. *Every Man in His Humour* was the first of three satires. Its special aim was to ridicule the humours of the city. The second, *Cynthia's Revels,* satirizes the humours of the court; while the third, *The Poetaster,* the result of a quarrel with his contemporaries, was levelled at the false standards of the poets of the age.

The three best known of Jonson's comedies are *Volpone, or the Fox, The Alchemist,* and *Epicoene*, or *the Silent Woman*. *Volpone* is a keen and merciless analysis of a man governed by an overwhelming love of money for its own sake. The first words in the first scene are a key to the whole comedy:

(*Volpone*)

Good morning to the day; and next, my gold!
Open the shrine that I may see my saint.

(*Mosca withdraws a curtain and discovers piles of gold, plate, jewels, etc.*)

Hail the world's soul, and mine!

Volpone's method of increasing his wealth is to play upon the avarice of men. He pretends to be at the point of death, and his 'suitors', who know his love of gain and that he has no heirs, endeavour hypocritically to sweeten his last moments by giving him rich presents, so that he will leave them all his wealth. The intrigues of these suitors furnish the story of the play, and show to what infamous depths avarice will lead a man.

The Alchemist is a study of quackery on one side and of gullibility on the other, founded on the mediæval idea of the philosopher's stone,[1] and applies as well to the patent medicines and get-rich-quick schemes of our day as to the peculiar forms of quackery with which Jonson was more familiar. In plot and artistic construction *The Alchemist* is an almost perfect specimen of the best English drama. It has some remarkably good passages, and is the most readable of Jonson's plays.

Epicœne, or the Silent Woman, is a prose comedy exceedingly well constructed, full of life, abounding in fun and unexpected situations. Here is a brief outline from which the reader may see of what materials Jonson made up his comedies.

The Silent Woman

The chief character is Morose, a rich old codger whose humour is a horror of noise. He lives in a street so narrow that it will admit no carnages; he pads the doors; plugs the keyhole; puts mattresses on the stairs. He dismisses a servant who wears squeaky boots; makes all the rest go about in thick stockings; and they must answer him by signs, since he cannot bear to hear anybody but himself talk. He disinherits his poor nephew Eugenie, and, to make sure that the latter will not get any money out of him, resolves to marry. His confidant in this delicate matter is Cutbeard the barber, who, unlike his kind, never speaks unless spoken to, and does not even knick his scissors as he works. Cutbeard (who is secretly in league with the nephew) tells him of Epicœne, a rare, silent woman, and Morose is so delighted with her silence that he resolves to marry her on the spot. Cutbeard produces

[1] A similar story of quackery is found in Chaucer, 'The Canon's Yeoman's Tale.'

a parson with a bad cold, who can speak only in a whisper, to marry them; and when the parson coughs after the ceremony Morose demands back five shillings of the fee. To save it the parson coughs more, and is hurriedly bundled out of the house. The silent woman finds her voice immediately after the marriage, begins to talk loudly and to make reforms in the household, driving Morose to distraction. A noisy dinner party from a neighbouring house, with drums and trumpets and a quarrelling man and wife, is skillfully guided in at this moment to celebrate the wedding. Morose flees for his life, and is found perched like a monkey on a cross-beam in the attic, with all his nightcaps tied over his ears. He seeks a divorce, but is driven frantic by the loud arguments of a lawyer and a divine, who are no other than Cutbeard and a sea captain disguised. When Morose is past all hope the nephew offers to release him from his wife and her noisy friends if he will allow him five hundred pounds a year. Morose offers him anything, everything, to escape his torment, and signs a deed to that effect. Then comes the surprise of the play when Eugenie whips the wig from Epicene and shows a boy in disguise.

It will be seen that the *Silent Woman*, with its rapid action and its unexpected situations, offers an excellent opportunity for the actors; but the reading of the play, as of most of Jonson's comedies, is marred by low intrigues showing a sad state of morals among the upper classes.

Besides these, and many other less known comedies, Jonson wrote two great tragedies, *Sejanus* (1603) and *Catiline* (1611), upon severe classical lines. After ceasing his work for the stage, Jonson wrote many masques in honour of James I and of Queen Anne, to be played amid elabourate scenery by the gentlemen of the court. The best of these are 'The Satyr', 'The Penates', 'Masque of Blackness', 'Masque of Beauty', 'Hue and Cry after Cupid', and 'The Masque of Queens'. In all his plays Jonson showed a strong lyric gift, and some of his little poems and songs, like 'The Triumph of Charis', 'Drink to Me Only with Thine Eyes', and 'To the Memory of my Beloved Mother', are now better known than his great dramatic works. A single volume of prose, called *Timber, or*

Discoveries made upon Men and Matter, is an interesting collection of short essays which are more like Bacon's than any other work of the age.

Beaumont and Fletcher. The work of these two men is so closely interwoven that, though Fletcher outlived Beaumont by nine years and the latter had no hand in some forty of the plays that bear their joint names, we still class them together, and only scholars attempt to separate their works so as to give each writer his due share. Unlike most of the Elizabethan dramatists, they both came from noble and cultured families and were university trained. Their work, in strong contrast with Jonson's, is intensely romantic, and in it all, however coarse or brutal the scene, there is still, as Emerson pointed out, the subtle 'recognition of gentility'.

Beaumont (1584-1616) was the brother of Sir John Beaumont of Leicestershire. From Oxford he came to London to study law, but soon gave it up to write for the stage. Fletcher (1579-1625) was the son of the bishop of London, and shows in all his work the influence of his high social position and of his Cambridge education. The two dramatists met at the Mermaid tavern under Ben Jonson's leadership and soon became inseparable friends, living and working together. Tradition has it that Beaumont supplied the judgment and the solid work of the play, while Fletcher furnished the high-coloured sentiment and the lyric poetry, without which an Elizabethan play would have been incomplete. Of their joint plays, the two best known are *Philaster,* whose old theme, like that of *Cymbeline* and *Griselda*, is the jealousy of a lover and the faithfulness of a girl, and *The Maid's Tragedy*. Concerning Fletcher's work the most interesting literary question is how much did he write of Shakespeare's *Henry VIII*, and how much did Shakespeare help him in *The Two Noble Kinsmen.*

John Webster. Of Webster's personal history we know nothing except that he was well known as a dramatist under James I. His extraordinary powers of expression rank him with Shakespeare; but his talent seems to have been largely devoted to the blood-and-thunder play begun by Marlowe. His two best known plays are *The White Devil* (pub. 1612) and *The Duchess of Malfi* (pub. 1623). The latter, inspite of its horrors, ranks him as one of the greatest masters of English tragedy. It must be remembered that he sought in this play to reproduce the Italian life of the sixteenth century, and for this no imaginary horrors are needed. The history of any Italian court or city in this period furnishes more vice and violence and dishonour than even the gloomy imagination of Webster could conceive. All the so-called blood tragedies of the Elizabethan period, from Thomas Kyd's *Spanish Tragedy* down, however much they may condemn the brutal taste of the English audiences, are still only so many searchlights thrown upon a history of horrible darkness.

Thomas Middleton (1570?-1627). Middleton is best known by two great plays, *The Changeling*[1] and Women Beware Women. In poetry and diction they are almost worthy at times to rank with Shakespeare's plays; otherwise, in their sensationalism and unnaturalness they do violence to the moral sense and are repulsive to the modern reader. Two earlier plays, *A Trick to catch the Old One*, his best comedy, and *A Fair Quarrel*, his earliest tragedy, are less mature in thought and expression, but more readable, because they seem to express Middleton's own idea of the drama rather than that of the corrupt court and playwrights of his later age.

Thomas Heywood (1580?-1650?). Heywood's life, of which we know little in detail, covers the whole period of the Elizabethan drama. To the glory of that drama he contributed, according to his own statement, the greater part, at least, of nearly two hundred and twenty plays. It was an enormous amount of work; but he seems to have been animated by the modern literary spirit of following the best market and striking while the financial iron is hot. Naturally

[1] In this and in *A Fair Quarrel* Middleton collaborated with William Rowley, of whom little is known except that he was an actor from *circa* 1607-1627.

good work was impossible, even to genius, under such circumstances, and few of his plays are now known. The two best, if the reader would obtain his own idea of Heywood's undoubted ability, are *A Woman killed with Kindness*, a pathetic story of domestic life, and *The Fair Maid of the West*, a melodrama with plenty of fighting of the popular kind.

Thomas Dekker (1570-?). Dekker is in pleasing contrast with most of the dramatists of the time. All we know of him must be inferred from his works, which show a happy and sunny nature, pleasant and good to meet. The reader will find the best expression of Dekker's personality and erratic genius in *The Shoemakers' Holiday*, a humorous study of plain working people, and *Old Fortunatus*, a fairy drama of the wishing hat and no end of money. Whether intended for children or not, it had the effect of charming the elders far more than the young people, and the play became immensely popular.

Massinger, Ford, Shirley. These three men mark the end of the Elizabethan drama. Their work, done largely while the struggle was on between the actors and the corrupt court, on one side, and the Puritans on the other, shows a deliberate turning away not only from Puritan standards but from the high ideals of their own art to pander to the corrupt taste of the upper classes.

Philip Massinger (1584-1640) was a dramatic poet of great natural ability; but his plots and situations are usually so strained and artificial that the modern reader finds no interest in them. In his best comedy, *A New Way to Pay Old Debts,* he achieved great popularity and gave us one figure, Sir Giles Overreach, which is one of the typical characters of the English stage. His best plays are *The Great Duke of Florence, The Virgin Martyr,* and *The Maid of Honour.*

John Ford (1586-1642?) and James Shirley (1596-1666) have left us little of permanent literary value, and their works are read only by those who wish to understand the whole rise and fall of the drama. An occasional scene in Ford's plays is as strong as anything that the Elizabethan Age produced; but as a whole the plays are unnatural and tiresome. Probably his best play is *The Broken Heart* (1633). Shirley was given to imitation of his predecessors, and his very imitation is characteristic of an age which had lost its inspiration. A single play, *Hyde Park*, with its frivolous, realistic dialogue, is sometimes read for its reflection of the fashionable gossipy talk of the day. Long before Shirley's death the actors said, 'Farewell! Othello's occupation's gone'. Parliament voted to close the theatres, thereby saving the drama from a more inglorious death by dissipation.[1]

VI. THE PROSE WRITERS

Francis Bacon (1561-1626)

In Bacon we see one of those complex and contradictory natures which are the despair of the biographer. If the writer be an admirer of Bacon, he finds too much that he must excuse or pass over in silence; and if he takes his stand on the law to condemn the avarice and dishonesty of his subject, he finds enough moral courage and nobility to make him question the justice of his own judgment. On the one hand is rugged Ben Jonson's tribute to his power and ability, and on the other Hallam's summary that he was 'a man who, being intrusted with the highest gifts of Heaven, habitually abused them for the poorest purposes of earth—hired them out for guineas, places, and titles in the service of injustice, covetousness, and oppression'.

Laying aside the opinions of others, and relying only upon the facts of Bacon's life, we find on the one side the politician, cold, calculating, selfish, and on the other the literary and scientific man with an impressive devotion to truth for its own great sake; here a man using questionable means to advance his own interests, and there a man seeking with zeal and endless labour to penetrate the secret ways of Nature, with no other object than to advance the interests of his fellow-men. So, in our ignorance of the secret motives

[1] The rader will find wholesome criticism of these writers, and selections from their works, in Charles Lamb's *Specimens of English Dramatic Poets,* an excellent book, which helps us to a better knowledge and appreciation of the lesser Elizabethan dramatists.

and springs of the man's life, judgment is necessarily suspended. Bacon was apparently one of those double natures that only God is competent to judge, because of the strange mixture of intellectual strength and moral weakness that is in them.

Life. Bacon was the son of Sir Nicholas Bacon, Lord Keeper of the Seal, and of the learned Ann Cook, sister-in-law to Lord Burleigh, greatest of the queen's statesmen. From these connections, as well as from native gifts, he was attracted to the court, and as a child was called by Elizabeth her 'Little Lord Keeper'. At twelve he went to Cambridge, but left the university after two years, declaring the whole plan of education to be radically wrong, and the system of Aristotle, which was the basis of all philosophy in those days, to be a childish delusion, since in the course of centuries it had 'produced no fruit, but only a jungle of dry and useless branches'. Strange, even for a sophomore of fourteen, thus to condemn the whole system of the universities; but such was the boy, and the system! Next year, in order to continue his education, he accompanied the English ambassador to France, where he is said to have busied himself chiefly with the practical studies of statistics and diplomacy.

Two years later he was recalled to London by the death of his father. Without money, and naturally with expensive tastes, he applied to his Uncle Burleigh for a lucrative position. It was in this application that he used the expression, so characteristic of the Elizabethan Age, that he 'had taken all knowledge for his province'. Burleigh, who misjudged him as a dreamer and self-seeker, not only refused to help him at the court but successfully opposed his advancement by Elizabeth. Bacon then took up the study of law, and was admitted to the bar in 1582. That he had not lost his philosophy in the mazes of the law is shown by his tract, written about this time, 'On the Greatest Birth of Time', which was a plea for his inductive system of philosophy, reasoning from many facts to one law, rather than from an assumed law to particular facts, which was the deductive method that had been in use for centuries. In his famous plea for progress Bacon demanded three things: the free investigation of nature, the discovery of facts instead of theories, and the verification of results by experiment rather than by argument. In our day these are the A, B, C of science, but in Bacon's time they seemed revolutionary.

As a lawyer he became immediately successful; his knowledge and power of pleading became widely known, and it was almost at the beginning of his career that Jonson wrote, 'The fear of every one that heard him speak was that he should make an end.' The publication of his Essays added greatly to his fame; but Bacon was not content. His head was buzzing with huge schemes—the pacification of unhappy Ireland, the simplification of English law, the reform of the church, the study of nature, the establishment of a new philosophy. Meanwhile, sad to say, he played the game of politics for his personal advantage. He devoted himself to Essex, the young and dangerous favourite of the queen, won his friendship, and then used him skilfully to better his own position. When the earl was tried for treason it was partly, at least, through Bacon's efforts that he was convicted and beheaded; and though Bacon claims to have been actuated by a high sense of justice, we are not convinced that he understood either justice or friendship in appearing as queen's counsel against the man who had befriended him. His coldbloodedness and lack of moral sensitiveness appear even in his essays on 'Love' and 'Friendship'. Indeed, we can understand his life only upon the theory that his intellectuality left him cold and dead to the higher sentiments of our humanity.

During Elizabeth's reign Bacon had sought repeatedly for high office, but had been blocked by Burleigh and perhaps also by the queen's own shrewdness in judging men. With the advent of James I (1603) Bacon devoted himself to the new ruler and rose rapidly in favour. He was knighted, and soon afterwards attained another object of his ambition in marrying a rich wife. The appearance of his great work, the *Advancement of Learning*, in 1605, was largely the result of the mental stimulus produced by his change in fortune. In 1613 he was made attorney-general, and speedily made enemies by using the office to increase his personal ends. He justified himself in his course by his devotion to the king's cause, and by the belief that the higher his position and the more ample his means the more he could do for science. It was in this year that Bacon wrote his series of *State Papers,* which show a marvellous grasp of the political tendencies of his age. Had his advice been followed, it would have certainly averted the struggle between king and Parliament that followed speedily. In 1617 he was appointed to his father's office, Lord Keeper of the Seal, and the next year to the high office of Lord Chancellor. With this office he received the title of Baron Verulam, and later of Viscount

St. Alban, which he affixed with some vanity to his literary work. Two years later appeared his greatest work, the *Novum Organum*, called after Aristotle's famous *Organon.*

Bacon did not long enjoy his political honors. The storm which had been long gathering against James's government broke suddenly upon Bacon's head. When Parliament assembled in 1621 it vented its distrust of James and his favourite Villiers by striking unexpectedly at their chief adviser. Bacon was sternly accused of accepting bribes, and the evidence was so great that he confessed that there was much political corruption abroad in the land, that he was personally guilty of some of it, and he threw himself upon the mercy of his judges. Parliament at that time was in no mood for mercy. Bacon was deprived of his office and was sentenced to pay the enormous fine of 40,000 pounds, to be imprisoned during the king's pleasure, and thereafter to be banished forever from Parliament and court. Though the imprisonment lasted only a few days and the fine was largely remitted, Bacon's hopes and schemes for political honours were ended; and it is at this point of appalling adversity that the nobility in the man's nature asserts itself strongly. If the reader be interested to apply a great man's philosophy to his own life, he will find the essay, 'Of Great Place', most interesting in this connection.

Bacon now withdrew permanently from public life, and devoted his splendid ability to literary and scientific work. He completed the *Essays,* experimented largely, wrote history, scientific articles, and one scientific novel, and made additions to his *Instauratio Magna,* the great philosophical work which was never finished. In the spring of 1626, while driving in a snowstorm, it occurred to him that snow might be used as a preservative instead of salt. True to his own method of arriving at truth, he stopped at the first house, bought a fowl, and proceeded to test his theory. The experiment chilled him, and he died soon after from the effects of his exposure. As Macaulay wrote, 'the great apostle of experimental philosophy was destined to be its martyr.'

Works of Bacon. Bacon's philosophic works, *The Advancement of Learning* and the *Novum Organum*, will be best understood in connection with the *Instauratio Magna*, or *The Great Institution of True Philosophy,* of which they were parts. The *Instauratio* was never completed, but the very idea of the work was magnificent—to sweep away the involved philosophy of the schoolmen and the educational systems of the universities, and to substitute a single great work which should be a complete education, 'a rich storehouse for the glory of the Creator and for the relief of man's estate'. The object of this education was to bring practical results to all the people, instead of a little selfish culture and much useless speculation, which, he conceived, were the only products of the universities.

The Instauratio Magna. This was the most ambitious, though it is not the best known, of Bacon's works. For the insight it gives us into the author's mind, we note here a brief outline of his subject. It was divided into six parts, as follows:

1. *Partitiones Scientiarum.* This was to be a classification and summary of all human knowledge. Philosophy and all speculation must be cast out and the natural sciences established as the basis of all education. The only part completed was *The Advancement of Learning,* which served as an introduction.

2. *Novum Organum,* or the 'new instrument', that is, the use of reason and experiment instead of the old Aristotelian logic. To find truth one must do two things: (a) get rid of all prejudices or idols, as Bacon called them. These 'idols' are four: 'idols of the tribe', that is, prejudices due to common methods of thought among all races; 'idols of the cave or den', that is, personal peculiarities and prejudices; 'idols of the marketplace', due to errors of language; and 'idols of the theatre', which are the unreliable traditions of men. (b) After discarding the above 'idols' we must interrogate nature; must collect facts by means of numerous experiments, arrange them in order, and then determine the law that underlies them.

It will be seen at a glance that the above is the most important of Bacon's works. The Organum was to be in several books, only two of which he completed, and these he wrote and rewrote twelve times until they satisfied him.

3. *Historia Naturalis et Experimentalis,* the study of all the phenomena of nature. Of four parts of this work which he completed, one of them at least, the *Sylva Sylvarum,* is decidedly at variance with his own idea of fact and experiment. It abounds in fanciful explanations, more worthy of the poetic than of the scientific mind. Nature is seen to be full of desires and instincts; the air 'thirsts' for light and fragrance; bodies rise or sink because they have an 'appetite' for height or depth; the qualities of bodies are the result of an 'essence', so that when we discover the essences

of gold and silver and diamonds it will be a simple matter to create as much of them as we may need.

4. *Scala Intellectus,* or 'Ladder of the Mind', is the rational application of the Organum to all problems. By it the mind should ascend step by step from particular facts and instances to general laws and abstract principles.

5. *Prodromi,* 'Prophecies or Anticipations', is a list of discoveries that men shall make when they have applied Bacon's methods of study and experimentation.

6. *Philosophia Secunda,* which was to be a record of practical results of the new philosophy when the succeeding ages should have applied it faithfully.

It is impossible to regard even the outline of such a vast work without an involuntary thrill of admiration for the bold and original mind which conceived it. 'We may', said Bacon, 'make no despicable beginnings. The destinies of the human race must complete the work ... for upon this will depend not only a speculative good but all the fortunes of mankind and all their power.' There is the unconscious expression of one of the great minds of the world. Bacon was like one of the architects of the Middle Ages, who drew his plans for a mighty cathedral, perfect in every detail from the deep foundation stone to the cross on the highest spire, and who gave over his plans to the builders, knowing that, in his own lifetime, only one tiny chapel would be completed; but knowing also that the very beauty of his plans would appeal to others, and that succeeding ages would finish the work which he dared to begin.

The Essays. Bacon's famous *Essays* is the one work which will interest all students of our literature. His *Instauratio* was in Latin, written mostly by paid helpers from short English abstracts. He regarded Latin as the only language worthy of a great work; but the world neglected his Latin to seize upon his English—marvellous English, terse, pithy, packed with thought, in an age that used endless circumlocutions. The first ten essays, published in 1597, were brief notebook jottings of Bacon's observations. Their success astonished the author, but not till fifteen years later were they republished and enlarged. Their charm grew upon Bacon himself, and during his retirement he gave more thought to the wonderful language which he had at first despised as much as Aristotle's philosophy. In 1612 appeared a second edition containing thirty-eight essays, and in 1625, the year before his death, he republished the *Essays* in their present form, polishing and enlarging the original ten to fifty-eight, covering a wide variety of subjects suggested by the life of men around him.

Concerning the best of these essays there are as many opinions as there are readers, and what one gets out of them depends largely upon his own thought and intelligence. In this respect they are like that Nature to which Bacon directed men's thoughts. The whole volume may be read through in an evening; but after one has read them a dozen times he still finds as many places to pause and reflect as at the first reading. If one must choose out of such a storehouse, we would suggest 'Studies', 'Goodness', 'Riches', 'Atheism', 'Unity in Religion', 'Adversity', 'Friendship', and 'Great Place' as an introduction to Bacon's worldly-wise philosophy.

Miscellaneous Works. Other works of Bacon are interesting as a revelation of the Elizabethan mind, rather than because of any literary value. *The New Atlantis* is a kind of scientific novel describing another Utopia as seen by Bacon. The inhabitants of Atlantis have banished Philosophy and applied Bacon's method of investigating Nature, using the results to better their own condition. They have a wonderful civilization, in which many of our later discoveries—academies of the sciences, observatories, balloons, submarines, the modification of species, and several others—were foreshadowed with a strange mixture of cold reason and poetic intuition. *De Sapientia Veterum* is a fanciful attempt to show the deep meaning underlying ancient myths—a meaning which would have astonished the myth makers themselves. *The History of Henry VII* is a calm, dispassionate, and remarkably accurate history, which makes us regret that Bacon did not do more historical work. Besides these are metrical versions of certain Psalms—which are valuable, in view of the controversy anent Shakespeare's plays, for showing Bacon's utter inability to write poetry—and a large number of letters and state papers showing the range and power of his intellect.

Bacon's Place and Work. Although Bacon was for the greater part of his life a busy man of affairs, one cannot read his work without becoming conscious of two things—a perennial freshness, which the world insists upon in all literature that is to endure, and an intellectual power which marks him as one of the great minds of the world.

Of late the general tendency is to give less and less prominence to his work in science and philosophy; but criticism of his *Instauratio,* in view of his lofty aim, is of small consequence. It is true that his 'science' today seems woefully inadequate; true also that, though he sought to discover truth, he thought perhaps to monopolize it, and so looked with the same suspicion upon Copernicus as upon the philosophers. The practical man who despises philosophy has simply misunderstood the thing he despises. In being practical and experimental in a romantic age he was not unique, as is often alleged, but only expressed the tendency of the English mind in all ages. Three centuries earlier the monk Roger Bacon did more practical experimenting than the Elizabethan sage; and the latter's famous 'idols' are strongly suggestive of the former's 'Four Sources of Human Ignorance.' Although Bacon did not make any of the scientific discoveries at which he aimed, yet the whole spirit of his work, especially of the *Organum,* has strongly influenced science in the direction of accurate observation and of carefully testing every theory by practical experiment. 'He that regardeth the clouds shall not sow', said a wise writer of old; and Bacon turned men's thoughts from the heavens above, with which they had been too busy, to the earth beneath, which they had too much neglected. In an age when men were busy with romance and philosophy, he insisted that the first object of education is to make a man familiar with his natural environment; from books he turned to men, from theory to fact, from philosophy to nature—and that is perhaps his greatest contribution to life and literature. Like Moses upon Pisgah, he stood high enough above his fellows to look out over a promised land, which his people would inherit, but into which he himself might never enter.

Richard Hooker (1554?-1600). In strong contrast with Bacon is Richard Hooker, one of the greatest prose writers of the Elizabethan Age. One must read the story of his life, an obscure and lowly life animated by a great spirit, as told by Izaak Walton, to appreciate the full force of this contrast. Bacon took all knowledge for his province, but mastered no single part of it. Hooker, taking a single theme, the law and practice of the English Church, so handled it that no scholar even of the present day would dream of superseding it or of building upon any other foundation than that which Hooker laid down. His one great work is *The Laws of Ecclesiastical Polity,*[1] a theological and argumentative book; but, entirely apart from its subject, it will be read wherever men desire to hear the power and stateliness of the English language. Here is a single sentence, remarkable not only for its perfect form but also for its expression of the reverence for law which lies at the heart of Anglo-Saxon civilization:

> Of law there can be no less acknowledged than that her seat is the bosom of God, her voice the harmony of the world; all things in heaven and earth do her homage; the very least as feeling her care, and the greatest as not exempted from her power; both angels and men, and creatures of what condition soever, though each in different sort and manner, yet all with uniform consent admiring her as the mother of their peace and joy.

Sidney and Raleigh. Among the prose writers of this wonderful literary age there are many others that deserve passing notice, though they fall far below the standard of Bacon and Hooker. Sir Philip Sidney (1554-1586), who has already been considered as a poet, is quite as well known by his prose works, *Arcadia*, a pastoral romance,

---

[1]The first five books were published 1594-1597, and are as Hooker wrote them. The last three books, published after his death, are of doubtful authorship, but they are thought to have been completed from Hooker's notes.

and the *Defense of Poesie*, one of our earliest literary essays. Sidney, whom the poet Shelley has eulogized, represents the whole romantic tendency of his age; while Sir Walter Raleigh (1552?-1618) represents its adventurous spirit and activity. The life of Raleigh is an almost incomprehensible mixture of the poet, scholar, and adventurer; now helping the Huguenots or the struggling Dutch in Europe, and now leading an expedition into the unmapped wilds of the New World; busy here with court intrigues, and there with piratical attempts to capture the gold-laden Spanish galleons; one moment sailing the high seas in utter freedom, and the next writing history and poetry to solace his imprisonment. Such a life in itself is a volume far more interesting than anything that he wrote. He is the restless spirit of the Elizabethan Age personified.

Raleigh's chief prose works are the *Discoverie of Guiana*, a work which would certainly have been interesting enough had he told simply what he saw, but which was filled with colonization schemes and visions of an *El Dorado* to fill the eyes and ears of the credulous; and the *History of the World*, written to occupy his prison hours. The history is a wholly untrustworthy account of events from creation to the downfall of the Macedonian Empire. It is interesting chiefly for its style, which is simple and dignified, and for the flashes of wit and poetry that break into the fantastic combination of miracles, traditions, hearsay, and state records which he called history. In the conclusion is the famous apostrophe to Death, which suggests what Raleigh might have done had he lived less strenuously and written more carefully.

> O eloquent, just, and mighty Death! whom none could advise thou hast persuaded; what none hath dared thou hast done; and whom all the world hath flattered thou only hast cast out of the world and despised; thou hast drawn together all the star-stretched greatness, all the pride, cruelty, and ambition of man, and covered it all over with these two narrow words, Hic jacet!

John Foxe (1516-1587). Foxe will be remembered always for his famous *Book of Martyrs*, a book that our elders gave to us on Sundays when we were young, thinking it good discipline for us to afflict our souls when we wanted to be roaming the sunlit fields, or when in our enforced idleness we would, if our own taste in the matter had been consulted, have made good shift to be quiet and happy with *Robinson Crusoe.* So we have a gloomy memory of Foxe, and something of a grievance, which prevent a just appreciation of his worth.

Foxe had been driven out of England by the Marian persecutions, and in a wandering but diligent life on the Continent he conceived the idea of writing a history of the persecutions of the church from the earliest days to his own. The part relating to England and Scotland was published, in Latin, in 1559 under a title as sonorous and impressive as the Roman office for the dead—*Rerum in Ecclesia Gestarum Maximarumque per Europam Persecutionum Commentarii.* On his return to England Foxe translated this work, calling it the *Acts and Monuments*; but it soon became known as the *Book of Martyrs*, and so it will always be called. Foxe's own bitter experience causes him to write with more heat and indignation than his saintly theme would warrant, and the 'holy tone' sometimes spoils a narrative that would be impressive in its bare simplicity. Nevertheless the book has made for itself a secure place in our literature. It is strongest in its record of humble men, like Rowland Taylor and Thomas Hawkes, whose sublime heroism, but for this narrative, would have been lost amid the great names and the great events that fill the Elizabethan Age.

Camden and Knox. Two historians, William Camden and John Knox, stand out prominently among the numerous historical writers of the age. *Camden's Britannia* (1586) is a monumental work, which marks the beginning of true antiquarian research in the field of history; and his *Annals of Queen Elizabeth* is worthy of a far higher place than has thus far been given it. John Knox, the reformer, in his *History of the Reformation in Scotland*, has some very vivid portraits of his helpers and enemies. The personal and aggressive elements enter too strongly for a work of history; but the autobiographical parts show rare literary power. His account of his famous interview with Mary Queen of Scots is clear-cut as a cameo, and shows the man's extraordinary power better than a whole volume of biography. Such scenes make one wish that more of his time had been given to literary work, rather than to the disputes and troubles of his own Scotch kirk.

Hakluyt and Purchas. Two editors of this age have made for themselves an enviable place in our literature. They are Richard Hakluyt (1552?-1616) and Samuel Purchas (1575?-1626). Hakluyt was a clergyman who in the midst of his little parish set himself to achieve two great patriotic ends—to promote the wealth and commerce of his country, and to preserve the memory of all his countrymen who added to the glory of the realm by their travels and explorations. To further the first object he concerned himself deeply with the commercial interests of the East India Company, with Raleigh's colonizing plans in Virginia, and with a translation of De Soto's travels in America. To further the second he made himself familiar with books of voyages in all foreign languages and with the brief reports of explorations of his own countrymen. His *Principal Navigations, Voyages, and Discoveries of the English Nation*, in three volumes, appeared first in 1589, and a second edition followed in 1598-1600. The first volume tells of voyages to the north; the second to India and the East; the third, which is as large as the other two, to the New World. With the exception of the very first voyage, that of King Arthur to Iceland in 517, which is founded on a myth, all the voyages are authentic accounts of the explorers themselves, and are immensely interesting reading even at the present day. No other book of travels has so well expressed the spirit and energy of the English race, or better deserves a place in our literature.

Samuel Purchas, who was also a clergyman, continued the work of Hakluyt, using many of the latter's unpublished manuscripts and condensing the records of numerous other voyages. His first famous book, *Purchas,* His *Pilgrimage*, appeared in 1613, and was followed by *Hakluytus Posthumus,* or *Purchas His Pilgrimes,* in 1625. The very name inclines one to open the book with pleasure, and when one follows his inclination—which is, after all, one of the best guides in literature—he is rarely disappointed. Though it falls far below the standard of Hakluyt, both in accuracy and literary finish, there is still plenty to make one glad that the book was written and that he can now comfortably follow Purchas on his pilgrimage.

Thomas North. Among the translators of the Elizabethan Age Sir Thomas North (1535?-1601?) is most deserving of notice because of his version of *Plutarch's Lives* (1579) from which Shakespeare took the characters and many of the incidents for three great Roman plays. Thus in North we read:

> Cæsar also had Cassius in great jealousy and suspected him much: whereupon he said on a time to his friends: 'What will Cassius do, think ye? I like not his pale looks'. Another time when Cæsar's friends warned him of Antonius and Dolabella, he answered them again, 'I never reckon of them; but these pale-visaged and carrion lean people, I fear them most', meaning Brutus and Cassius.

Shakespeare merely touches such a scene with the magic of his genius, and his Cæsar speaks:

> Let me have men about me that are fat:
> Sleek-headed men, and such as sleep o' nights.
> Yond Cassius has a lean and hungry look:
> He thinks too much: such men are dangerous.

A careful reading of North's *Plutarch* and then of the famous Roman plays shows to how great an extent Shakespeare was dependent upon his obscure contemporary.

North's translation, to which we owe so many heroic models in our literature, was probably made not from Plutarch but from Amyot's excellent French translation. Nevertheless he reproduces the spirit of the original, and notwithstanding our modern and more accurate translations, he remains the most inspiring interpreter of the great biographer whom Emerson calls 'the historian of heroism.'

Summary of the Age of Elizabeth. This period is generally regarded as the greatest in the history of our literature. Historically, we note in this age the tremendous impetus received from the Renaissance, from the Reformation, and from the exploration of the New World. It was marked by a strong national spirit, by patriotism, by religious tolerance, by social content, by intellectual progress, and by unbounded enthusiasm.

Such an age, of thought, feeling, and vigorous action, finds its best expression in the drama; and the wonderful development of the drama, culminating in Shakespeare, is the most significant characteristic of the Elizabethan period. Though the age produced some excellent prose works, it is essentially an age of poetry; and the poetry is remarkable for its variety, its freshness, its youthful and romantic feeling. Both the poetry and the drama were permeated by Italian influence, which was dominant in English literature from Chaucer to the Restoration. The literature of this age is often called the literature of the Renaissance, though, as we have seen, the Renaissance itself began much earlier, and for a century and a half added very little to our literary possessions.

In our study of this great age we have noted (1) the Non-dramatic Poets, that is, poets who did not write for the stage. The centre of this group is Edmund Spenser, whose *Shepherd's Calendar* (1579) marked the appearance of the first national poet since Chaucer's death in 1400. His most famous work is *The Faery Queen.* Associated with Spenser are the minor poets, Thomas Sackville, Michael Drayton, George Chapman, and Philip Sidney. Chapman is noted for his completion of Marlowe's poem, *Hero and Leander,* and for his translation of Homer's *Iliad* and *Odyssey.* Sidney, besides his poetry, wrote his prose romance *Arcadia,* and *The Defense of Poesie,* one of our earliest critical essays.

(2) The Rise of the Drama in England; the Miracle plays, Moralities, and Interludes; our first play, 'Ralph Royster Doyster'; the first true English comedy, 'Gammer Gurton's Needle', and the first tragedy, 'Gorboduc'; the conflict between classic and native ideals in the English drama.

(3) Shakespeare's Predecessors, Lyly, Kyd, Nash, Peele, Greene, Marlowe; the types of drama with which they experimented—the Marlowesque, one-man type, or tragedy of passion, the popular Chronicle plays, the Domestic drama, the Court or Lylian comedy, Romantic comedy and tragedy, Classical plays, and the Melodrama. Marlowe is the greatest of Shakespeare's predecessors. His four plays are 'Tamburlaine', 'Faustus', 'The Jew of Malta', and 'Edward II.'

(4) Shakespeare, his life, work, and influence.

(5) Shakespeare's Successors, Ben Jonson, Beaumont and Fletcher, Webster, Middleton, Heywood, Dekker; and the rapid decline of the drama. Ben Jonson is the greatest of this group. His chief comedies are 'Every Man in His Humour', 'The Silent Woman', and 'The Alchemist'; his tragedies are 'Sejanus' and 'Catiline.'

(6) The Prose Writers, of whom Bacon is the most notable. His chief philosophical work is the *Instauratio Magna* (incomplete), which includes 'The Advancement of Learning' and the 'Novum Organum'; but he is known to literary readers by his famous *Essays.* Minor prose writers are Richard Hooker, John Foxe, the historians Camden and Knox, the editors Hakluyt and Purchas, who gave us the stirring records of exploration, and Thomas North, the translator of Plutarch's *Lives.*

Selections for Reading. Spenser. Faery Queen, selections in Standard English Classics; Bk. I, in Riverside Literature Series, etc.; Shepherd's Calendar, in Cassell's National Library; Selected Poems, in Canterbury Poets Series; Minor Poems, in Temple Classics; Selections in Manly's English Poetry, or Ward's English Poets.

Minor Poets. Drayton, Sackville, Sidney, Chapman, Selections in Manly or Ward; Elizabethan songs, in Schelling's Elizabethan Lyrics, and in Palgrave's Golden Treasury; Chapman's Homer, in Temple Classics.

The Early Drama. Play of Noah's Flood, in Manly's Specimens of the Pre-Shakspearean Drama, or in Pollard's English Miracle Plays, Moralities and Interludes, or in Belles Lettres Series, sec. 2; L.T. Smith's The York Miracle Plays.

Lyly. Endymion, in Holt's English Readings.

Marlowe. Faustus, in Temple Dramatists, or Mermaid Series, or Morley's Universal Library, or Lamb's Specimens of English Dramatic Poets; Selections in Manly's English Poetry, or Ward's English Poets; Edward II, in Temple Dramatists, and in Holt's English Readings.

Shakespeare. Merchant of Venice, Julius Cæsar, Macbeth, etc., in Standard English Classics (edited, with notes, with special reference to college-entrance requirements). Good editions of single plays are numerous and cheap. Hudson's and Rolfe's and the Arden Shakespeare are suggested as satisfactory. The Sonnets, edited by Beeching, in Athenæum Press Series.

Ben Jonson. The Alchemist, in Canterbury Poets Series, or Morley's Universal Library; Selections in Manly's English Poetry, or Ward's English Poets, or Canterbury Poets Series; Selections from Jonson's Masques, in

Evans's English Masques; Timber, edited by Schelling, in Athenæum Press Series.

Bacon. Essays, school edition (Ginn and Company); Northup's edition, in Riverside Literature Series (various other inexpensive editions, in the Pitt Press, Golden Treasury Series, etc.); Advancement of Learning, Bk. I, edited by Cook (Ginn and Company). Compare selections from Bacon, Hooker, Lyly, and Sidney, in Manly's English Prose.

Bibliography.[1] History. *Textbook*, Montgomery, pp. 208-238; Cheyney, pp. 330-410; Green, ch. 7; Traill, Macaulay, Froude.

Special works. Creighton's The Age of Elizabeth; Hall's Society in the Elizabethan Age; Winter's Shakespeare's England; Goadby's The England of Shakespeare; Lee's Stratford on Avon; Harrison's Elizabethan England.

Literature. Saintsbury's History of Elizabethan Literature; Whipple's Literature of the Age of Elizabeth; S. Lee's Great Englishmen of the Sixteenth Century; Schilling's Elizabethan Lyrics, in Athenæum Press Series; Vernon Lee's Euphorion.

Spenser. Texts, Cambridge, Globe, and Aldine editions; Noel's Selected Poems of Spenser, in Canterbury Poets; Minor Poems, in Temple Classics; Arber's Spenser Anthology; Church's Life of Spenser, in English Men of Letters Series; Lowell's Essay, in Among My Books, or in Literary Essays, vol. 4; Hazlitt's Chaucer and Spenser, in Lectures on the English Poets; Dowden's Essay, in Transcripts and Studies.

The Drama. Texts, Manly's Specimens of the Pre-Shakesperean Drama, 2 vols., in Athenæum Press Series; Pollard's English Miracle Plays, Moralities and Interludes; the Temple Dramatists; Morley's Universal Library; Arber's English Reprints; Mermaid Series, etc.; Thayer's The Best Elizabethan Plays.

Gayley's Plays of Our Forefathers (Miracles, Moralities, etc.); Bates's The English Religious Drama; Schelling's The English Chronicle Play; Lowell's Old English Dramatists; Boas's Shakespeare and his Predecessors; Symonds's Shakespeare's Predecessors in the English Drama; Schelling's Elizabethan Drama; Lamb's Specimens of English Dramatic Poets; Introduction to Hudson's Shakespeare: His Life, Art, and Characters; Ward's History of English Dramatic Literature; Dekker's The Gull's Hornbook, in King's Classics.

---

[1] For titles and publishers of reference works see General Bibliography at the end of this book.

Marlowe. Works, edited by Bullen; chief plays in Temple Dramatists, Mermaid Series of English Dramatists, Morley's Universal Library, etc.; Lowell's Old English Dramatists; Symonds's introduction, in Mermaid Series; Dowden's Essay, in Transcripts and Studies.

Shakespeare. Good texts are numerous. Furness's Variorum edition is at present most useful for advanced work. Hudson's revised edition, each play in a single volume, with notes and introductions, will, when complete, be one of the very best for students' use.

Raleigh's Shakespeare, in English Men of Letters Series; Lee's Life of Shakespeare; Hudson's Shakespeare: his Life, Art, and Characters; Halliwell-Phillipps's Outlines of the Life of Shakespeare; Fleay's Chronicle History of the Life and Work of Shakespeare; Dowden's Shakespeare, a Critical Study of his Mind and Art; Shakespeare Primer (same author); Baker's The Development of Shakespeare as a Dramatist; Lounsbury's Shakespeare as a Dramatic Artist; The Text of Shakespeare (same author); Wendell's William Shakespeare; Bradley's Shakesperian Tragedy; Hazlitt's Shakespeare and Milton, in Lectures on the English Poets; Emerson's Essay, Shakespeare or the Poet; Lowell's Essay, in Among My Books; Lamb's Tales from Shakespeare; Mrs. Jameson's Shakespeare's Female Characters (called also Characteristics of Women); Rolfe's Shakespeare the Boy; Brandes's William Shakespeare; Moulton's Shakespeare as a Dramatic Artist; Mabie's William Shakespeare, Poet, Dramatist, and Man; The Shakespeare Apocrypha, edited by C. F. T. Brooke; Shakespeare's Holinshed, edited by Stone; Shakespeare Lexicon, by Schmidt; Concordance, by Bartlett; Grammar, by Abbott, or by Franz.

Ben Jonson. Texts in Mermaid Series, Temple Dramatists, Morley's Universal Library, etc.; Masques and Entertainments of Ben Jonson, edited by Morley, in Carisbrooke Library; Timber, edited by Schelling, in Athenæum Press Series.

Beaumont, Fletcher, etc. Plays in Mermaid Series, Temple Dramatists, etc.; Schelling's Elizabethan Drama; Lowell's Old English Dramatists; Lamb's Specimens of English Dramatic Poets; Fleay's Biographical Chronicle of the English Drama; Swinburne's Essays, in Essays in Prose and Poetry, and in Essays and Studies.

Bacon. Texts, Essays in Everyman's Library, etc.; Advancement of Learning in Clarendon Press Series, Library of English Classics, etc.; Church's Life of Bacon, in English Men of Letters Series; Nichol's Bacon's

Life and Philosophy; Francis Bacon, translated from the German of K. Fischer (excellent, but rare); Macaulay's Essay on Bacon.

Minor Prose Writers. Sidney's Arcadia, edited by Somers; Defense of Poesy, edited by Cook, in Athenæum Press Series; Arber's Reprints, etc.; Selections from Sidney's prose and poetry in the Elizabethan Library; Symonds's Life of Sidney, in English Men of Letters; Bourne's Life of Sidney, in Heroes of the Nations; Lamb's Essay on Sidney's *Sonnets,* in Essays of Elia.

Raleigh's works, published by the Oxford Press; Selections by Grosart, in Elizabethan Library; Raleigh's Last Fight of the Revenge, in Arber's Reprints; Life of Raleigh, by Edwards and by Gosse. Richard Hooker's works, edited by Keble, Oxford Press; Laws of Ecclesiastical Polity, in Everyman's Library, and in Morley's Universal Library; Life, in Walton's Lives, in Morley's Universal Library; Dowden's Essay, in Puritan and Anglican.

Lyly's Euphues, in Arber's Reprints; Endymion, edited by Baker; Campaspe, in Manly's Pre-Shaksperean Drama.

North's Plutarch's Lives, edited by Wyndham, in Tudor Library; school edition, by Ginn and Company. Hakluyt's Voyages, in Everyman's Library; Jones's introduction to Hakluyt's Diverse Voyages; Payne's Voyages of Elizabethan Seamen; Froude's Essay, in Short Studies on Great Subjects.

Suggestive Questions. 1. What historical conditions help to account for the great literature of the Elizabethan age? What are the general characteristics of Elizabethan literature? What type of literature prevailed, and why? What work seems to you to express most perfectly the Elizabethan spirit?

2. Tell briefly the story of Spenser's life. What is the story or argument of the *Faery Queen*? What is meant by the Spenserian stanza? Read and comment upon Spenser's 'Epithalamion.' Why does the 'Shepherd's Calendar' mark a literary epoch? What are the main qualities of Spenser's poetry? Can you quote or refer to any passage which illustrate these qualities? Why is he called the poets' poet?

3. For what is Sackville noted? What is the most significant thing about his 'Gorboduc'? Name other minor poets and tell what they wrote.

4. Give an outline of the origin and rise of the drama in England. What is meant by Miracle and Mystery plays? What purposes did they serve among the common people? How did they help the drama? What is meant by cycles of Miracle plays? How did the Moralities differ from

the Miracles? What was the chief purpose of the Interludes? What type of drama did they develop? Read a typical play, like 'Noah's Flood' or 'Everyman', and write a brief analysis of it.

5. What were our first plays in the modern sense? What influence did the classics exert on the English drama? What is meant by the dramatic unities? In what important respect did the English differ from the classic drama?

6. Name some of Shakespeare's predecessors in the drama? What types of drama did they develop? Name some plays of each type. Are any of these plays still presented on the stage?

7. What are Marlowe's chief plays? What is the central motive in each? Why are they called one-man plays? What is meant by Marlowe's 'mighty line'? What is the story of 'Faustus'? Compare 'Faustus' and Goethe's 'Faust', having in mind the story, the dramatic interest, and the literary value of each play.

8. Tell briefly the story of Shakespeare's life. What fact in his life most impressed you? How does Shakespeare sum up the work of all his predecessors? What are the four periods of his work, and the chief plays of each? Where did he find his plots? What are his romantic plays? his chronicle or historical plays? What is the difference between a tragedy and a comedy? Name some of Shakespeare's best tragedies, comedies, and historical plays. Which play of Shakespeare's seems to you to give the best picture of human life? Why is he called the myriad-minded Shakespeare? For what reasons is he considered the greatest of writers? Can you explain why Shakespeare's plays are still acted, while other plays of his age are rarely seen? If you have seen any of Shakespeare's plays on the stage, how do they compare in interest with a modern play?

9. What are Ben Jonson's chief plays? In what important respects did they differ from those of Shakespeare? Tell the story of *'The Alchemist'* or *'The Silent Woman'*. Name other contemporaries and successors of Shakespeare. Give some reasons for the preëminence of the Elizabethan drama. What causes led to its decline?

10. Tell briefly the story of Bacon's life. What is his chief literary work? His chief educational work? Why is he called a pioneer of modern science? Can you explain what is meant by the inductive method of learning? What subjects are considered in Bacon's *Essays*? What is the central idea of the essay you like best? What are the literary qualities of these essays? Do they appeal to the intellect or the emotions? What is

meant by the word 'essay', and how does Bacon illustrate the definition? Make a comparison between Bacon's essays and those of some more recent writer, such as Addison, Lamb, Carlyle, Emerson, or Stevenson, having in mind the subjects, style, and interest of both essayists.

11. Who are the minor prose writers of the Elizabethan Age? What did they write? Comment upon any work of theirs which you have read. What is the literary value of North's Plutarch? What is the chief defect in Elizabethan prose as a whole? What is meant by euphuism? Explain why Elizabethan poetry is superior to the prose.

CHRONOLOGY

Last Half of the Sixteenth and First Half of the Seventeenth Centuries

History	Literature
1558. Elizabeth (*d.* 1603)	1559. John Knox in Edinburgh
	1562(?). Gammer Gurton's Needle. Gorboduc
	1564. Birth of Shakespeare
1571. Rise of English Puritans	1576. First Theatre
1577. Drake's Voyage around the World	1579. Spenser's Shepherd's Calendar. Lyly's Euphues. North's Plutarch.
	1587. Shakespeare in London. Marlowe's Tamburlaine
1588. Defeat of the Armada	
	1590. Spenser's Faery Queen. Sidney's Arcadia
	1590-1595. Shakespeare's Early Plays
	1597-1625. Bacon's Essays
	1598-1614. Chapman's Homer
	1598. Ben Jonson's Every Man in His Humour
	1600-1607. Shakespeare's Tragedies
1603. James I (*d.* 1625)	
1604. Divine Right of Kings proclaimed	1605. Bacon's Advancement of Learning

HISTORY	LITERATURE
1607. Settlement at Jamestown, Virginia	1608. Birth of Milton
	1611. Translation (King James Version) of Bible
	1614. Raleigh's History
	1616. Death of Shakespeare
1620. Pilgrim Fathers at Plymouth	1620-1642. Shakespeare's successors. End of drama
	1620. Bacon's Novum Organum
	1622. First regular newspaper, The Weekly News
1625. Charles I	1626. Death of Bacon

CHAPTER 7

THE PURITAN AGE (1620-1660)

I. HISTORICAL SUMMARY

The Puritan Movement. In its broadest sense the Puritan movement may be regarded as a second and greater Renaissance, a rebirth of the moral nature of man following the intellectual awakening of Europe in the fifteenth and sixteenth centuries. In Italy, whose influence had been uppermost in Elizabethan literature, the Renaissance had been essentially pagan and sensuous. It had hardly touched the moral nature of man, and it brought little relief from the despotism of rulers. One can hardly read the horrible records of the Medici or the Borgias, or the political observations of Machiavelli, without marvelling at the moral and political degradation of a cultured nation. In the North, especially among the German and English peoples, the Renaissance was accompanied by a moral awakening, and it is precisely that awakening in England, "that greatest moral and political reform which ever swept over a nation in the short space of half a century," which is meant by the Puritan movement. We shall understand it better if we remember that it had two chief objects: the first was personal righteousness; the second was civil and religious liberty. In other words, it aimed to make men honest and to make them free.

Such a movement should be cleared of all the misconceptions which have clung to it since the Restoration, when the very name of Puritan was made ridiculous by the jeers of the gay courtiers of Charles II. Though the spirit of the movement was profoundly religious, the Puritans were not a religious sect; neither was the Puritan a narrow-minded and gloomy dogmatist, as he is still pictured even in the histories. Pym and Hampden and Eliot and Milton were Puritans; and in the long struggle for human liberty there are few names more honoured by freemen everywhere. Cromwell and Thomas Hooker were Puritans; yet Cromwell stood like a rock for religious tolerance; and Thomas Hooker, in Connecticut, gave to the world the first written constitution, in which freemen, before electing their officers, laid down the strict limits of the offices to which they were elected. That is a Puritan document, and it marks one of the greatest achievements in the history of government.

Wrong Ideas of the Puritans

From a religious view point Puritanism included all shades of belief. The name was first given to those who advocated certain changes in the form of worship of the reformed English Church under Elizabeth; but as the ideal of liberty rose in men's minds, and opposed to it were the king and his evil counsellors and the band of intolerant churchmen of whom Laud is the great example, then Puritanism became a great national movement. It included English churchmen as well as extreme Separatists, Calvinists, Covenanters, Catholic noblemen—all bound together in resistance to despotism in Church and State, and with a passion for liberty and righteousness such as the world has never since seen. Naturally such a movement had its extremes and excesses, and it is from a few zealots and fanatics that most of our misconceptions about the Puritans arise. Life was stern in those days, too stern perhaps, and the intensity of the struggle against despotism made men narrow and hard. In the triumph of Puritanism under Cromwell severe laws were passed, many simple pleasures were forbidden, and an austere standard of living was forced upon an unwilling people. So the criticism is made that the wild outbreak of immorality which followed the restoration of Charles was partly due to the unnatural restrictions of the Puritan era. The criticism is just; but we must not forget the whole spirit of the movement. That the Puritan prohibited Maypole dancing and horse racing is of small consequence beside the fact that he fought for liberty and justice, that he overthrew despotism and made a man's life and property safe from the tyranny of rulers. A great river is not judged by the foam on its surface, and certain austere laws and doctrines which we have ridiculed are but froth on the surface of the mighty Puritan current that has flowed steadily, like a river of life, through English and American history since the Age of Elizabeth.

Changing Ideals. The political upheaval of the period is summed up in the terrible struggle between the king and Parliament, which resulted in the death of Charles at the block and the establishment of the Commonwealth under Cromwell. For centuries the English people had been wonderfully loyal to their sovereigns; but deeper than their loyalty to kings was the old Saxon love for personal liberty. At times, as in the days of Alfred and Elizabeth, the two ideals went hand in hand; but more often they were in open strife, and a final struggle for supremacy was inevitable. The crisis came when James I, who had received the right of royalty from an act of Parliament, began, by the assumption of 'divine right', to ignore the Parliament which had created him. Of the civil war which followed in the reign of Charles I, and of the triumph of English freedom, it is unnecessary to write here. The blasphemy of a man's divine right to rule his fellow-men was ended. Modern England began with the charge of Cromwell's brigade of Puritans at Naseby.

Religious Ideals

Religiously the age was one of even greater ferment than that which marked the beginning of the Reformation. A great ideal, the ideal of a national church, was pounding to pieces, like a ship in the breakers, and in the confusion of such an hour the action of the various sects was like that of frantic passengers, each striving to save his possessions from the wreck. The Catholic church, as its name implies, has always held true to the ideal of a united church, a church which, like the great Roman government of the early centuries, can bring the splendour and authority of Rome to bear upon the humblest village church to the farthest ends of the earth. For a time that mighty ideal dazzled the German and English reformers; but the possibility of a united Protestant church perished with Elizabeth. Then, instead of the world-wide church which was the ideal of Catholicism, came the ideal of a purely national Protestantism. This was the ideal of Laud and the reactionary bishops, no less than of the scholarly Richard Hooker, of the rugged Scotch Covenanters, and of the Puritans of Massachusetts Bay. It is intensely interesting to note that Charles called Irish rebels and Scotch Highlanders to his aid by promising to restore their national religions; and that the English Puritans, turning to Scotland for help, entered into the solemn Covenant of 1643, establishing a national Presbyterianism, whose object was:

> To bring the churches of God in the three kingdoms to uniformity in religion and government, to preserve the rights of Parliament and the liberties of the Kingdom; ... that we and our posterity may as brethren live in faith and love, and the Lord may delight to live in the midst of us.

In this famous Covenant we see the national, the ecclesiastical, and the personal dream of Puritanism, side by side, in all their grandeur and simplicity.

Years passed, years of bitter struggle and heartache, before the impossibility of uniting the various Protestant sects was generally recognized. The ideal of a national church died hard, and to its death is due all the religious unrest of the period. Only as we remember the national ideal, and the struggle which it caused, can we understand the amazing life and work of Bunyan, or appreciate the heroic spirit of the American colonists who left home for a wilderness in order to give the new ideal of a free church in a free state its practical demonstration.

Literary Characteristics. In literature also the Puritan Age was one of confusion, due to the breaking up of old ideals. Mediæval standards of chivalry, the impossible loves and romances of which Spenser furnished the types, perished no less surely than the ideal of a national church; and in the absence of any fixed standard of literary criticism there was nothing to prevent the exaggeration of the 'metaphysical' poets, who are the literary parallels to religious sects like the Anabaptists. Poetry took new and startling forms in Donne and Herbert, and prose became as somber as Burton's *Anatomy of Melancholy*. The spiritual gloom which sooner or later fastens upon all the writers of this age, and which is unjustly attributed to Puritan influence, is due to the breaking up of accepted standards in government and religion. No people, from the Greeks to those of our own day, have suffered the loss of old ideals without causing its writers to cry, 'Ichabod! the glory has departed.' That is the unconscious tendency of literary men in all times, who look backward for their golden age; and it need not concern the student of literature, who, even in the break-up of cherished institutions, looks for some fore-gleams of a better light which is to break upon the world. This so-called gloomy age produced some minor poems of exquisite workmanship, and one great master of verse whose work would glorify any age or people—John Milton, in whom the indomitable Puritan spirit finds its noblest expression.

Puritan and Elizabethan Literature

There are three main characteristics in which Puritan literature differs from that of the preceding age: (1) Elizabethan literature, with all its diversity, had a marked unity in spirit, resulting from the patriotism of all classes and their devotion to a queen who, with all her faults, sought first the nation's welfare. Under the Stuarts all this was changed. The kings were the open enemies of the people; the country was divided by the struggle for political and religious liberty; and the literature was as divided in spirit as were the struggling parties. (2) Elizabethan literature is generally inspiring; it throbs with youth and hope and vitality. That which follows speaks of age and sadness; even its brightest hours are followed by gloom, and by the pessimism inseparable from the passing of old standards. (3) Elizabethan literature is intensely romantic; the romance springs from the heart of youth, and believes all things, even the impossible. The great schoolman's credo, 'I believe because it is impossible,' is a better expression of Elizabethan literature than of mediæval theology. In the literature of the Puritan period one looks in vain for romantic ardor. Even in the lyrics and love poems a critical, intellectual spirit takes its place, and whatever romance asserts itself is in form rather than in feeling, a fantastic and artificial adornment of speech rather than the natural utterance of a heart in which sentiment is so strong and true that poetry is its only expression.

II. LITERATURE OF THE PURITAN PERIOD

The Transition Poets. When one attempts to classify the literature of the first half of the seventeenth century, from the death of Elizabeth (1603) to the Restoration (1660), he realizes the impossibility of grouping poets by any accurate standard. The classifications attempted here have small dependence upon dates or sovereigns, and are suggestive rather than accurate. Thus Shakespeare and Bacon wrote largely in the reign of James I, but their work is Elizabethan in spirit; and Bunyan is no less a Puritan because he happened to write after the Restoration. The name Metaphysical poets, given by Dr. Johnson, is somewhat suggestive but not descriptive of the followers of Donne; the name Caroline or Cavalier poets brings to mind the careless temper of the Royalists who followed King Charles with a devotion of which he was unworthy; and the name Spenserian poets recalls the little band of dreamers who clung to Spenser's ideal, even while his romantic mediæval castle was battered down by Science at the one gate and Puritanism at the other. At the beginning of this bewildering confusion of ideals expressed in literature, we note a few writers who are generally known as Jacobean poets, but whom we have called the Transition poets because, with the later dramatists, they show clearly the changing standards of the age.

Samuel Daniel (1562-1619). Daniel, who is often classed with the first Metaphysical poets, is interesting to us for two reasons—for his use of the artificial sonnet, and for his literary desertion of Spenser as a model for poets. His *Delia,* a cycle of sonnets modelled, perhaps, after Sidney's *Astrophel and Stella,* helped to fix the custom of celebrating love or friendship by a series of Sonnets, to which some pastoral pseudonym was affixed. In his *Sonnets,* many of which rank with Shakespeare's, and in his later poetry, especially the beautiful 'Complaint of Rosamond' and his 'Civil Wars', he aimed solely at grace of expression, and became influential in giving to English poetry a greater individuality and independence than it had ever known. In matter he set himself squarely against the mediæval tendency:

> Let others sing of kings and paladines
> In aged accents and untimely words,
> Paint shadows in imaginary lines.

This fling at Spenser and his followers marks the beginning of the modern and realistic school, which sees in life as it is enough poetic material, without the invention of allegories and impossible heroines. Daniel's poetry, which was forgotten soon after his death, has received probably more homage than it deserves in the praises of Wordsworth, Southey, Lamb, and Coleridge. The latter says: 'Read Daniel, the admirable Daniel. The style and language are just such as any pure and manly writer of the present day would use. It seems quite modern in comparison with the style of Shakespeare.'

The Song Writers. In strong contrast with the above are two distinct groups, the Song Writers and the Spenserian poets. The close of the reign of Elizabeth was marked by an outburst of English songs, as remarkable in its sudden development as the rise of the drama. Two causes contributed to this result—the increasing influence of French instead of Italian verse, and the rapid development of music as an art at the close of the sixteenth century. The two song writers best worth studying are Thomas Campion (1567?-1619) and Nicholas Breton (1545?-1626?). Like all the lyric poets of the age, they are a curious mixture of the Elizabethan and the Puritan standards. They sing of sacred and profane love with the same zest, and a careless love song is often found on the same page with a plea for divine grace.

The Spenserian Poets. Of the Spenserian poets Giles Fletcher and Wither are best worth studying. Giles Fletcher (1588?-1623) has at times a strong suggestion of Milton (who was also a follower of Spenser in his early years) in the noble simplicity and majesty of his lines. His best known work, 'Christ's Victory and Triumph' (1610), was the greatest religious poem that had appeared in England since 'Piers Plowman', and is not an unworthy predecessor of *Paradise Lost.*

The life of George Wither (1588-1667) covers the whole period of English history from Elizabeth to the Restoration, and the enormous volume of his work covers every phase of the literature of two great ages. His life was a varied one; now as a Royalist leader against the Covenanters, and again announcing his Puritan convictions, and suffering in prison for his faith. At his best Wither is a lyric poet of great originality, rising at times to positive genius; but the bulk of his poetry is intolerably dull. Students of this period find him interesting as an epitome of the whole age in which he lived; but the average reader is more inclined to note with interest that he published in 1623 *Hymns and Songs of the Church,* the first hymn book that ever appeared in the English language.

The Metaphysical Poets. This name—which was given by Dr. Johnson in derision, because of the fantastic form of Donne's poetry—is often applied to all minor poets of the Puritan Age. We use the term here in a narrower sense, excluding the followers of Daniel and that later group known as the Cavalier poets. It includes Donne, Herbert, Waller, Denham, Cowley, Vaughan, Davenant, Marvell, and Crashaw. The advanced student finds them all worthy of study, not only for their occasional excellent poetry, but because of their influence on later literature. Thus Richard Crashaw (1613?-1649), the Catholic mystic, is interesting because his troubled life is singularly like Donne's, and his poetry is at times like Herbert's set on fire.[1] Abraham Cowley (1618-1667), who blossomed young and who, at twenty-five, was proclaimed the greatest poet in England, is now scarcely known even

[1] See, for instance, the 'Hymn to St. Theresa' and 'The Flaming Heart'.

by name, but his 'Pindaric Odes'[1] set an example which influenced English poetry throughout the eighteenth century. *Henry Vaughan* (1622-1695) is worthy of study because he is in some respects the forerunner of Wordsworth;[2] and Andrew Marvell (1621-1678), because of his loyal friendship with Milton, and because his poetry shows the conflict between the two schools of Spenser and Donne. Edmund Waller (1606-1687) stands between the Puritan Age and the Restoration. He was the first to use consistently the 'closed' couplet which dominated our poetry for the next century. By this, and especially by his influence over Dryden, the greatest figure of the Restoration, he occupies a larger place in our literature than a reading of his rather tiresome poetry would seem to warrant.

Of all these poets, each of whom has his special claim, we can consider here only Donne and Herbert, who in different ways are the types of revolt against earlier forms and standards of poetry. In feeling and imagery both are poets of a high order, but in style and expression they are the leaders of the fantastic school whose influence largely dominated poetry during the half century of the Puritan period.

JOHN DONNE (1573-1631)

Life. The briefest outline of Donne's life shows its intense human interest. He was born in London, the son of a rich iron merchant, at the time when the merchants of England were creating a new and higher kind of princes. On his father's side he came from an old Welsh family, and on his mother's side from the Heywoods and Sir Thomas More's family. Both families were Catholic, and in his early life persecution was brought near; for his brother died in prison for harbouring a proscribed priest, and his own education could not be continued in Oxford and Cambridge because of his religion. Such an experience generally sets a man's religious standards for life; but presently Donne, as he studied law at Lincoln's Inn, was investigating the philosophic grounds of all faith. Gradually, he left the

---

[1] So called from Pindar, the greatest lyric poet of Greece.

[2] See, for instance, 'Childhood', 'The Retreat' , 'Corruption', 'The Bird' , 'The Hidden Flower', for Vaughan's mystic interpretation of childhood and nature.

church in which he was born, renounced all denominations, and called himself simply Christian. Meanwhile he wrote poetry and shared his wealth with needy Catholic relatives. He joined the expedition of Essex for Cadiz in 1596, and for the Azores in 1597, and on sea and in camp found time to write poetry. Two of his best poems, 'The Storm' and 'The Calm', belong to this period. Next he travelled in Europe for three years, but occupied himself with study and poetry. Returning home, he became secretary to Lord Egerton, fell in love with the latter's young niece, Anne More, and married her; for which cause Donne was cast into prison. Strangely enough his poetical work at this time is not a song of youthful romance, but 'The Progress of the Soul', a study of transmigration. Years of wandering and poverty followed, until Sir George More forgave the young lovers and made an allowance to his daughter. Instead of enjoying his new comforts, Donne grew more ascetic and intellectual in his tastes. He refused also the flattering offer of entering the Church of England and of receiving a comfortable 'living.' By his 'Pseudo Martyr' he attracted the favour of James I, who persuaded him to be ordained, yet left him without any place or employment. When his wife died her allowance ceased, and Donne was left with seven children in extreme poverty. Then he became a preacher, rose rapidly by sheer intellectual force and genius, and in four years was the greatest of English preachers and Dean of St. Paul's Cathedral in London. There he 'carried some to heaven in holy raptures and led others to amend their lives', and as he leans over the pulpit with intense earnestness is likened by Izaak Walton to 'an angel leaning from a cloud.'

Here is variety enough to epitomize his age, and yet in all his life, stronger than any impression of outward weal or woe, is the sense of mystery that surrounds Donne. In all his work one finds a mystery, a hiding of some deep thing which the world would gladly know and share, and which is suggested in his haunting little poem, 'The Undertaking':

> I have done one braver thing
> Than all the worthies did;
> And yet a braver thence doth spring,
> Which is, to keep that hid.

Donne's Poetry. Donne's poetry is so uneven, at times so startling and fantastic, that few critics would care to recommend it to others.

Only a few will read his works, and they must be left to their own browsing, to find what pleases them, like deer which, in the midst of plenty, take a bite here and there and wander on, tasting twenty varieties of food in an hour's feeding. One who reads much will probably bewail Donne's lack of any consistent style or literary standard. For instance, Chaucer and Milton are as different as two poets could well be; yet the work of each is marked by a distinct and consistent style, and it is the style as much as the matter which makes the *Tales* or the *Paradise Lost* a work for all time.

Donne threw style and all literary standards to the winds; and precisely for this reason he is forgotten, though his great intellect and his genius had marked him as one of those who should do things 'worthy to be remembered.' While the tendency of literature is to exalt style at the expense of thought, the world has many men and women who exalt feeling and thought above expression; and to these Donne is good reading. Browning is of the same school, and compels attention. While Donne played havoc with Elizabethan style, he nevertheless influenced our literature in the way of boldness and originality; and the present tendency is to give him a larger place, nearer to the few great poets, than he has occupied since Ben Jonson declared that he was 'the first poet of the world in some things', but likely to perish 'for not being understood.' For to much of his poetry we must apply his own satiric verses on another's crudities:

> Infinite work! which doth so far extend
> That none can study it to any end.

GEORGE HERBERT (1593-1633)

'O day most calm, most bright', sang George Herbert, and we may safely take that single line as expressive of the whole spirit of his writings. Professor Palmer, whose scholarly edition of this poet's works is a model for critics and editors, calls Herbert the first in English poetry who spoke face to face with God. That may be true; but it is interesting to note that not a poet of the first half of the seventeenth century, not even the gayest of the Cavaliers, but has written some noble verse of prayer or aspiration, which expresses the underlying Puritan spirit of his age. Herbert is the greatest, the most consistent of them all. In all the others the Puritan struggles against the Cavalier, or the Cavalier breaks loose from the restraining Puritan; but in Herbert the struggle is past and peace has come. That his life was not all calm, that the Puritan in him had struggled desperately before it subdued the pride and idleness of the Cavalier, is evident to one who reads between his lines:

> I struck the board and cry'd, No more!
>   I will abroad.
> What? Shall I ever sigh and pine?
> My lines and life are free, free as the road,
> Loose as the wind.

There speaks the Cavalier of the university and the court; and as one reads to the end of the little poem, which he calls by the suggestive name of 'The Collar', he may know that he is reading condensed biography.

Those who seek for faults, for strained imagery and fantastic verse forms in Herbert's poetry, will find them in abundance; but it will better repay the reader to look for the deep thought and fine feeling that are hidden in these wonderful religious lyrics, even in those that appear most artificial. The fact that Herbert's reputation was greater, at times, than Milton's, and that his poems when published after his death had a large sale and influence, shows certainly that he appealed to the men of his age; and his poems will probably be read and appreciated, if only by the few, just so long as men are strong enough to understand the Puritan's spiritual convictions.

Life. Herbert's life is so quiet and uneventful that to relate a few biographical facts can be of little advantage. Only as one reads the whole story by Izaak Walton can he share the gentle spirit of Herbert's poetry. He was born at Montgomery Castle,[1] Wales, 1593, of a noble Welsh family. His

[1] There is some doubt as to whether he was born at the Castle, or at Black Hall Recent opinion inclines to the latter view.

university course was brilliant, and after graduation he waited long years in the vain hope of preferment at court. All his life he had to battle against disease, and this is undoubtedly the cause of the long delay before each new step in his course. Not till he was thirty-seven was he ordained and placed over the little church of Bemerton. How he lived here among plain people, in 'this happy corner of the Lord's field, hoping all things and blessing all people, asking his own way to Sion and showing others the way', should be read in Walton. It is a brief life, less than three years of work before being cut off by consumption, but remarkable for the single great purpose and the glorious spiritual strength that shine through physical weakness. Just before his death he gave some manuscripts to a friend, and his message is worthy of John Bunyan:

Deliver this little book to my dear brother Ferrar, and tell him he shall find in it a picture of the many spiritual conflicts that have passed betwixt God and my soul before I could subject mine to the will of Jesus my master, in whose service I have now found perfect freedom. Desire him to read it; and then, if he can think it may turn to the advantage of any dejected poor soul, let it be made public; if not, let him burn it, for I and it are less than the least of God's mercies.

Herbert's Poems. Herbert's chief work, The Temple, consists of over one hundred and fifty short poems suggested by the Church, her holidays and ceremonials, and the experiences of the Christian life. The first poem, 'The Church Porch', is the longest and, though polished with a care that foreshadows the classic school, the least poetical. It is a wonderful collection of condensed sermons, wise precepts, and moral lessons, suggesting Chaucer's 'Good Counsel', Pope's 'Essay on Man', and Polonius's advice to Laertes, in *Hamlet;* only it is more packed with thought than any of these. Of truthspeaking he says:

Dare to be true. Nothing can need a lie;
A fault which needs it most grows two thereby.

and of calmness in argument:

Calmness is great advantage: he that lets
Another chafe may warm him at his fire.

Among the remaining poems of The Temple one of the most suggestive is 'The Pilgrimage.' Here in six short stanzas, every line close-packed with thought, we have the whole of Bunyan's *Pilgrim's Progress.* The poem was written probably before Bunyan was born, but remembering the wide influence of Herbert's poetry, it is an interesting question whether Bunyan received the idea of his immortal work from this 'Pilgrimage.' Probably the best known of all his poems is the one called 'The Pulley', which generally appears, however under the name 'Rest', or 'The Gifts of God.'

When God at first made man,
Having a glass of blessings standing by,
Let us, said he, pour on him all we can:
Let the world's riches, which dispersed lie,
Contract into a span.

So strength first made a way;
Then beauty flowed; then wisdom, honor, pleasure.
When almost all was out, God made a stay,
Perceiving that, alone of all his treasure,
Rest in the bottom lay.

For, if I should, said he,
Bestow this jewel also on my creature,
He would adore my gifts instead of me,
And rest in Nature, not the God of Nature:
So both should losers be.

Yet let him keep the rest,
But keep them with repining restlessness:
Let him be rich and weary, that at least,
If goodness lead him not, yet weariness
May toss him to my breast.

Among the poems which may be read as curiosities of versification, and which arouse the wrath of the critics against the whole metaphysical school, are those like 'Easter Wings' and 'The

Altar', which suggest in the printed form of the poem the thing of which the poet sings. More ingenious is the poem in which rhyme is made by cutting off the first letter of a preceding word, as in the five stanzas of 'Paradise':

> I bless thee, Lord, because I grow
> Among thy trees, which in a row
> To thee both fruit and order owe.

And more ingenious still are odd conceits like the poem 'Heaven', in which Echo, by repeating the last syllable of each line, gives an answer to the poet's questions.

The Cavalier Poets. In the literature of any age there are generally found two distinct tendencies. The first expresses the dominant spirit of the times; the second, a secret or an open rebellion. So in this age, side by side with the serious and rational Puritan, lives the gallant and trivial Cavalier. The Puritan finds expression in the best poetry of the period, from Donne to Milton, and in the prose of Baxter and Bunyan; the Cavalier in a small group of poets—Herrick, Lovelace, Suckling, and Carew—who write songs generally in lighter vein, gay, trivial, often licentious, but who cannot altogether escape the tremendous seriousness of Puritanism.

Thomas Carew (1598?-1639?). Carew may be called the inventor of Cavalier love poetry, and to him, more than to any other, is due the peculiar combination of the sensual and the religious which marked most of the minor poets of the seventeenth century. His poetry is the Spenserian pastoral stripped of its refinement of feeling and made direct, coarse, vigorous. His poems, published in 1640, are generally, like his life, trivial or sensual; but here and there is found one, like the following, which indicates that with the Metaphysical and Cavalier poets a new and stimulating force had entered English literature:

> Ask me no more where Jove bestows,
> When June is past, the fading rose,
> For in your beauty's orient deep
> These flowers, as in their causes, sleep.

Ask me no more where those stars light
That downwards fall in dead of night,
For in your eyes they sit, and there
Fixed become as in their sphere.

Ask me no more if east or west
The phoenix builds her spicy nest,
For unto you at last she flies,
And in your fragrant bosom dies.

Robert Herrick (1591-1674).

Herrick is the true Cavalier, gay, devil-may-care in disposition, but by some freak of fate a clergyman of Dean Prior, in South Devon, a county made famous by him and Blackmore. Here, in a country parish, he lived discontentedly, longing for the joys of London and the Mermaid Tavern, his bachelor establishment consisting of an old housekeeper, a cat, a dog, a goose, a tame lamb, one hen—for which he thanked God in poetry because she laid an egg every day—and a pet pig that drank beer with Herrick out of a tankard. With admirable good nature, Herrick made the best of these uncongenial surroundings. He watched with sympathy the country life about him and caught its spirit in many lyrics, a few of which, like 'Corinna's Maying', 'Gather ye rosebuds while ye may', and 'To Daffodils', are among the best known in our language. His poems cover a wide range, from trivial love songs, pagan in spirit, to hymns of deep religious feeling. Only the best of his poems should be read; and these are remarkable for their exquisite sentiment and their graceful, melodious expression. The rest, since they reflect something of the coarseness of his audience, may be passed over in silence.

Late in life Herrick published his one book, *Hesperides* and *Noble Numbers* (1648). The latter half contains his religious poems, and one has only to read there the remarkable 'Litany' to see how the religious terror that finds expression in Bunyan's *Grace Abounding* could master even the most careless of Cavalier singers.

Suckling and Lovelace. Sir John Suckling (1609-1642) was one of the most brilliant wits of the court of Charles I, who wrote poetry as he exercised a horse or fought a duel, because it was considered a gentleman's accomplishment in those days. His poems, 'struck from his wild life like sparks from his rapier', are utterly trivial, and, even in his best known 'Ballad Upon a Wedding', rarely rise above mere doggerel. It is only the romance of his life—his rich, brilliant, careless youth, and his poverty and suicide in Paris, whither he fled because of his devotion to the Stuarts—that keeps his name alive in our literature.

In his life and poetry Sir Richard Lovelace (1618-1658) offers a remarkable parallel to Suckling, and the two are often classed together as perfect representatives of the followers of King Charles. Lovelace's *Lucasta*, a volume of love lyrics, is generally on a higher plane than Suckling's work; and a few of the poems like 'To Lucasta', and 'To Althea, from Prison', deserve the secure place they have won. In the latter occur the oft-quoted lines:

Stone walls do not a prison make,
Nor iron bars a cage;
Minds innocent and quiet take
That for an hermitage.
If I have freedom in my love,
And in my soul am free,
Angels alone that soar above
Enjoy such liberty.

JOHN MILTON (1608-1674)

Thy soul was like a star and dwelt apart;
Thou hadst a voice whose sound was like the sea—
Pure as the naked heavens, majestic, free;
So didst thou travel on life's common way
In cheerful godliness: and yet thy heart
The lowliest duties on herself did lay.

(From Wordsworth's 'Sonnet on Milton')

Shakespeare and Milton are the two figures that tower conspicuously above the goodly fellowship of men who have made our literature famous. Each is representative of the age that produced him, and together they form a suggestive commentary upon the two forces that rule our humanity—the force of impulse and the force of a fixed purpose. Shakespeare is the poet of impulse, of the loves, hates, fears, jealousies, and ambitions that swayed the men of his age. Milton is the poet of steadfast will and purpose, who moves like a god amid the fears and hopes and changing impulses of the world, regarding them as trivial and momentary things that can never swerve a great soul from its course.

It is well to have some such comparison in mind while studying the literature of the Elizabethan and the Puritan Age. While Shakespeare and Ben Jonson and their unequalled company of wits make merry at the Mermaid Tavern, there is already growing up on the same London street a poet who shall bring a new force into literature, who shall add to the Renaissance culture and love of beauty the tremendous moral earnestness of the Puritan. Such a poet must begin, as the Puritan always began, with his own soul, to discipline and enlighten it, before expressing its beauty in literature. 'He that would hope to write well hereafter in laudable things', says Milton, 'ought himself to be a true poem; that is, a composition and pattern of the best and most honourable things.' Here is a new proposition in art which suggests the lofty ideal of Fra Angelico, that before one can write literature, which is the expression of the ideal, he must first develop in himself the ideal man. Because Milton is human he must know the best in humanity; therefore he studies, giving his days to music, art, and literature, his nights to profound research and meditation. But because he knows that man is more than mortal he also prays, depending, as he tells us, on 'devout prayer to that Eternal Spirit who can enrich with all utterance and knowledge.' Such a poet is already in spirit far beyond the Renaissance, though he lives in the autumn of its glory and associates with its literary masters. 'There is a spirit in man', says the old Hebrew poet, 'and the inspiration of the

Almighty giveth him understanding.' Here, in a word, is the secret of Milton's life and writing. Hence his long silences, years passing without a word; and when he speaks it is like the voice of a prophet who begins with the sublime announcement, 'The Spirit of the Lord is upon me.' Hence his style, producing an impression of sublimity, which has been marked for wonder by every historian of our literature. His style was unconsciously sublime because he lived and thought consciously in a sublime atmosphere.

John Milton

Life of Milton. Milton is like an ideal in the soul, like a lofty mountain on the horizon. We never attain the ideal; we never climb the mountain; but life would be inexpressibly poorer were either to be taken away.

From childhood Milton's parents set him apart for the attainment of noble ends, and so left nothing to chance in the matter of training. His father, John Milton, is said to have turned Puritan while a student at Oxford and to have been disinherited by his family; whereupon he settled in London and prospered greatly as a scrivener, that is, a kind of notary. In character the elder Milton was a rare combination of scholar and businessman, a radical Puritan in politics and religion, yet a musician, whose hymn tunes are still sung, and a lover of art and literature. The poet's mother was a woman of refinement and social grace, with a deep interest in religion and in local charities. So the boy grew up in a home which combined the culture of the Renaissance with the piety and moral strength of early Puritanism. He begins, therefore, as the heir of one great age and the prophet of another.

Apparently the elder Milton shared Bacon's dislike for the educational methods of the time and so took charge of his son's training, encouraging his natural tastes, teaching him music, and seeking out a tutor who helped the boy to what he sought most eagerly, not the grammar and mechanism of Greek and Latin but rather the stories, the ideals, the poetry that hide in their incomparable literatures. At twelve years we find the boy already a scholar in spirit, unable to rest till after midnight because of the joy with which his study was rewarded. From boyhood two great principles seem to govern Milton's career: one, the love of beauty, of music, art, literature, and indeed of every form of human culture; the other, a steadfast devotion to duty as the highest object in human life.

A brief course at the famous St. Paul's school in London was the prelude to Milton's entrance to Christ's College, Cambridge. Here again he followed his natural bent and, like Bacon, found himself often in opposition to the authorities. Aside from some Latin poems, the most noteworthy song of this period of Milton's life is his splendid ode, 'On the Morning of Christ's Nativity', which was begun on Christmas day, 1629. Milton, while deep in the classics, had yet a greater love for his native literature. Spenser was for years his master; in his verse we find every evidence of his 'loving study' of Shakespeare, and his last great poems show clearly how he had been influenced by Fletcher's Christ's Victory and Triumph. But it is significant that this first ode rises higher than anything of the kind produced in the famous Age of Elizabeth.

While at Cambridge it was the desire of his parents that Milton should take orders in the Church of England; but the intense love of mental liberty which stamped the Puritan was too strong within him, and he refused to consider the 'oath of servitude', as he called it, which would mark his ordination. Throughout his life Milton, though profoundly religious, held aloof from the strife of sects. In belief, he belonged to the extreme Puritans, called Separatists, Independents, Congregationalists, of which our Pilgrim Fathers are the great examples; but he refused to be bound by any creed or church discipline:

> As ever in my great Task-Master's eye.

In this last line of one of his sonnets[1] is found Milton's rejection of every form of outward religious authority in face of the supreme Puritan principle, the liberty of the individual soul before God.

A long period of retirement followed Milton's withdrawal from the university in 1632. At his father's country home in Horton he gave himself up for six years to solitary reading and study, roaming over the wide fields of Greek, Latin, Hebrew, Spanish, French, Italian, and English

[1] 'On his being arrived to the Age of 'Twenty-three.'

literatures, and studying hard at mathematics, science, theology, and music—a curious combination. To his love of music we owe the melody of all his poetry, and we note it in the rhythm and balance which make even his mighty prose arguments harmonious. In 'Lycidas', 'L'Allegro', 'Il Penseroso', 'Arcades', 'Comus', and a few *'Sonnets'*, we have the poetic results of this retirement at Horton—few, indeed, but the most perfect of their kind that our literature has recorded.

Out of solitude, where his talent was perfected, Milton entered the busy world where his character was to be proved to the utmost. From Horton he travelled abroad, through France, Switzerland, and Italy, everywhere received with admiration for his learning and courtesy, winning the friendship of the exiled Dutch scholar Grotius, in Paris, and of Galileo in his sad imprisonment in Florence.[1] He was on his way to Greece when news reached him of the break between King and Parliament. With the practical insight which never deserted him Milton saw clearly the meaning of the news. His cordial reception in Italy, so chary of praise to anything not Italian, had reawakened in Milton the old desire to write an epic which England would 'not willingly let die'; but at thought of the conflict for human freedom all his dreams were flung to the winds. He gave up his travels and literary ambitions and hurried to England. 'For I thought it base', he says, 'to be travelling at my ease for intellectual culture while my fellow-countrymen at home were fighting for liberty.'

Then for nearly twenty years the poet of great achievement and still greater promise disappears. We hear no more songs, but only the prose denunciations and arguments which are as remarkable as his poetry. In all our literature there is nothing more worthy of the Puritan spirit than this laying aside of personal ambitions in order to join in the struggle for human liberty. In his best known sonnet, 'On His Blindness', which reflects his grief, not at darkness, but at his abandoned dreams, we catch the sublime spirit of this renunciation.

Milton's opportunity to serve came in the crisis of 1649. The king had been sent to the scaffold, paying the penalty of his own treachery, and England sat shivering at its own deed, like a child or a Russian peasant

[1] 'It is remarkable', says Lamartine, 'how often in the libraries of Italian princes and in the correspondence of great Italian writers of this period you find mentioned the name and fame of this young Englishman.'

who in sudden passion resists unbearable brutality and then is afraid of the consequences. Two weeks of anxiety, of terror and silence followed; then appeared Milton's *Tenure of Kings and Magistrates*. To England it was like the coming of a strong man, not only to protect the child, but to justify his blow for liberty. Kings no less than people are subject to the eternal principle of law; the divine right of a people to defend and protect themselves—that was the mighty argument which calmed a people's dread and proclaimed that a new man and a new principle had arisen in England. Milton was called to be Secretary for Foreign Tongues in the new government; and for the next few years, until the end of the Commonwealth, there were two leaders in England, Cromwell the man of action, Milton the man of thought. It is doubtful to which of the two humanity owes most for its emancipation from the tyranny of kings and prelates.

Two things of personal interest deserve mention in this period of Milton's life, his marriage and his blindness. In 1643 he married Mary Powell, a shallow, pleasure-loving girl, the daughter of a Royalist; and that was the beginning of sorrows. After a month, tiring of the austere life of a Puritan household, she abandoned her husband, who, with the same radical reasoning with which he dealt with affairs of state, promptly repudiated the marriage. His *Doctrine and Discipline of Divorce* and his *Tetrachordon* are the arguments to justify his position; but they aroused a storm of protest in England, and they suggest to a modern reader that Milton was perhaps as much to blame as his wife, and that he had scant understanding of a woman's nature. When his wife, fearing for her position, appeared before him in tears, all his ponderous arguments were swept aside by a generous impulse; and though the marriage was never a happy one, Milton never again mentioned his wife's desertion. The scene in *Paradise Lost,* where Eve comes weeping to Adam, seeking peace and pardon, is probably a reflection of a scene in Milton's own household. His wife died in 1653, and a few years later he married another, whom we remember for the sonnet, 'Methought I saw my late espouséd saint', in which she is celebrated. She died after fifteen months, and in 1663 he married a third wife, who helped the blind old man to manage his poor household.

From boyhood the strain on the poet's eyes had grown more and more severe; but even when his sight was threatened he held steadily to his purpose of using his pen in the service of his country. During the king's imprisonment a book appeared called *Eikon Basilike* (Royal Image), giving a rosy picture of the king's piety, and condemning the Puritans. The book speedily became famous and was the source of all Royalist arguments against the Commonwealth. In 1649 appeared Milton's *Eikonoklastes* (Image Breaker), which demolished the flimsy arguments of the *Eikon Basilike* as a charge of Cromwell's Ironsides had overwhelmed the king's followers. After the execution of the king appeared another famous attack upon the Puritans, *Defensio Regia pro Carlo I,* instigated by Charles II, who was then living in exile. It was written in Latin by Salmasius, a Dutch professor at Leyden, and was hailed by the Royalists as an invincible argument. By order of the Council of State, Milton prepared a reply. His eyesight had sadly failed, and he was warned that any further strain would be disastrous. His reply was characteristic of the man and the Puritan. As he had once sacrificed his poetry, so he was now ready, he said, to sacrifice his eyes also on the altar of English liberty. His magnificent *Defensio pro Populo Anglicano* is one of the most masterly controversial works in literature. The power of the press was already strongly felt in England, and the new Commonwealth owed its standing partly to Milton's prose, and partly to Cromwell's policy. The *Defensio* was the last work that Milton saw. Blindness fell upon him ere it was finished, and from 1652 until his death he laboured in total darkness.

The last part of Milton's life is a picture of solitary grandeur unequalled in literary history. With the Restoration all his labours and sacrifices for humanity were apparently wasted. From his retirement he could hear the bells and the shouts that welcomed back a vicious monarch, whose first act was to set his foot upon his people's neck. Milton was immediately marked for persecution; he remained for months in hiding; he was reduced to poverty, and his books were burned by the public hangman. His daughters, upon whom he depended in his blindness, rebelled at the task of reading to him and recording his thoughts. In the midst of all these sorrows we understand, in *Samson,* the cry of the blind champion of Israel:

> Now blind, disheartened, shamed, dishonored, quelled,
> To what can I be useful? wherein serve
> My nation, and the work from Heaven imposed?
> But to sit idle on the household hearth,
> A burdenous drone; to visitants a gaze,
> Or pitied object.

Milton's answer is worthy of his own great life. Without envy or bitterness he goes back to the early dream of an immortal poem and begins with superb consciousness of power to dictate his great epic.

Paradise Lost was finished in 1665, after seven years' labour in darkness. With great difficulty he found a publisher, and for the great work, now the most honored poem in our literature, he received less than certain verse makers of our day receive for a little song in one of our popular magazines. Its success was immediate, though, like all his work, it met with venomous criticism. Dryden summed up the impression made on thoughtful minds of his time when he said, 'This man cuts us all out, and the ancients too.' Thereafter a bit of sunshine came into his darkened home, for the work stamped him as one of the world's great writers, and from England and the Continent pilgrims came in increasing numbers to speak their gratitude.

The next year Milton began his *Paradise Regained.* In 1671 appeared his last important work, *Samson Agonistes,* the most powerful dramatic poem on the Greek model which our language possesses. The picture of Israel's mighty champion, blind, alone, afflicted by thoughtless enemies but preserving a noble ideal to the end, is a fitting close to the life work of the poet himself. For years he was silent, dreaming who shall say what dreams in his darkness, and saying cheerfully to his friends, 'Still guides the heavenly vision.' He died peacefully in 1674, the most sublime and the most lonely figure in our literature.

Milton's Early Poetry.[1] In his early work Milton appears as the inheritor of all that was best in Elizabethan literature, and his first work, the ode 'On the Morning of Christ's Nativity', approaches the high-water mark of lyric poetry in England. In the next six years, from 1631 to 1637, he wrote but little, scarcely more than two thousand lines, but these are among the most exquisite and the most perfectly finished in our language.

---

[1] In Milton's work we see plainly the progressive influence of the Puritan Age. Thus his Horton poems are joyous, almost Elizabethan in character; his prose is stern, militant, unyielding, like the Puritan in his struggle for liberty; his later poetry, following the apparent failure of Puritanism in the Restoration, has a note of sadness, yet proclaims the eternal principles of liberty and justice for which he had lived.

'L'Allegro' and 'Il Penseroso' are twin poems, containing many lines and short descriptive passages which linger in the mind like strains of music, and which are known and loved wherever English is spoken. 'L'Allegro' (the joyous or happy man) is like an excursion into the English fields at sunrise. The air is sweet; birds are singing; a multitude of sights, sounds, fragrances, fill all the senses; and to this appeal of nature the soul of man responds by being happy, seeing in every flower and hearing in every harmony some exquisite symbol of human life. 'Il Penseroso' takes us over the same ground at twilight and at moonrise. The air is still fresh and fragrant; the symbolism is, if possible, more tenderly beautiful than before; but the gay mood is gone, though its memory lingers in the afterglow of the sunset. A quiet thoughtfulness takes the place of the pure, joyous sensation of the morning, a thoughtfulness which is not sad, though like all quiet moods it is akin to sadness, and which sounds the deeps of human emotion in the presence of nature. To quote scattered lines of either poem is to do injustice to both. They should be read in their entirety the same day, one at morning, the other at eventide, if one is to appreciate their beauty and suggestiveness.

L'Allegro

The 'Masque of Comus' is in many respects the most perfect of Milton's poems. It was written in 1634 to be performed at Ludlow Castle before the earl of Bridgewater and his friends. There is a tradition that the earl's three children had been lost in the woods, and, whether true or not, Milton takes the simple theme of a person lost, calls in an Attendant Spirit to protect the wanderer, and out of this, with its natural action and melodious songs, makes the most exquisite pastoral drama that we possess. In form it is a masque, like those gorgeous products of the Elizabethan age of which Ben Jonson was the master. England had borrowed the idea of the masque from Italy and had used it as the chief entertainment at all festivals, until it had become to the nobles of England what the miracle play had been to the common people of a previous generation. Milton, with his

Comus

strong Puritan spirit, could not be content with the mere entertainment of an idle hour. 'Comus' has the gorgeous scenic effects, the music and dancing of other masques; but its moral purpose and its ideal teachings are unmistakable.

'The Triumph of Virtue' would be a better name for this perfect little masque, for its theme is that virtue and innocence can walk through any peril of this world without permanent harm. This eternal triumph of good over evil is proclaimed by the Attendant Spirit who has protected the innocent in this life and who now disappears from mortal sight to resume its life of joy:

> Mortals, that would follow me,
> Love Virtue; she alone is free.
> She can teach ye how to climb
> Higher than the sphery chime;
> Or if Virtue feeble were,
> Heaven itself would stoop to her.

While there are undoubted traces of Jonson and John Fletcher in Milton's 'Comus', the poem far surpasses its predecessors in the airy beauty and melody of its verses.

Lycidas

In the next poem, 'Lycidas', a pastoral elegy written in 1637, and the last of his Horton poems, Milton is no longer the inheritor of the old age, but the prophet of a new. A college friend, Edward King, had been drowned in the Irish Sea, and Milton follows the poetic custom of his age by representing both his friend and himself in the guise of shepherds leading the pastoral life. Milton also uses all the symbolism of his predecessors, introducing fauns, satyrs, and sea nymphs; but again the Puritan is not content with heathen symbolism, and so introduces a new symbol of the Christian shepherd responsible for the souls of men, whom he likens to hungry sheep that look up and are not fed. The Puritans and Royalists at this time were drifting rapidly apart, and Milton uses his new symbolism to denounce the abuses that had crept into the Church. In any other poet this moral teaching would hinder the free use of the imagination; but Milton seems equal to the task of combining high moral purpose with the noblest poetry. In its exquisite finish and exhaustless imagery 'Lycidas' surpasses most of the poetry of what is often called the pagan Renaissance.

Sonnets

Besides these well-known poems, Milton wrote in this early period a fragmentary masque called 'Arcades'; several Latin poems which, like his English, are exquisitely finished; and his famous 'Sonnets', which brought this Italian form of verse nearly to the point of perfection. In them he seldom wrote of love, the usual subject with his predecessors, but of patriotism, duty, music, and subjects of political interest suggested by the struggle into which England was drifting. Among these *Sonnets* each reader must find his own favourites. Those best known and most frequently quoted are 'On His Deceased Wife', 'To the Nightingale', 'On Reaching the Age of Twenty-three', 'The Massacre in Piedmont', and the two 'On His Blindness.'

Milton's Prose. Of Milton's prose works there are many divergent opinions, ranging from Macaulay's unbounded praise to the condemnation of some of our modern critics. From a literary view point Milton's prose would be stronger if less violent, and a modern writer would hardly be excused for using his language or his methods; but we must remember the times and the methods of his opponents. In his fiery zeal against injustice the poet is suddenly dominated by the soldier's spirit. He first musters his facts in battalions, and charges upon the enemy to crush and overpower without mercy. For Milton hates injustice and, because it is an enemy of his people, he cannot and will not spare it. When the victory is won, he exults in a pæan of victory as soul-stirring as the Song of Deborah. He is the poet again, spite of himself, and his mind fills with magnificent images. Even with a subject so dull, so barren of the bare possibilities of poetry, as his 'Animadversions upon the Remonstrants' Defense', he breaks out into an invocation, 'Oh, Thou that sittest in light and glory unapproachable, parent of angels and men', which is like a chapter from the Apocalypse. In such passages Milton's prose is, as Taine suggests, 'an outpouring of splendors', which suggests the noblest poetry.

Areopagitica

On account of their controversial character these prose works are seldom read, and it is probable that Milton never thought of them as worthy of a place in literature. Of them all Areopagitica has perhaps the most permanent interest and is best worth reading. In Milton's time there was a law forbidding the publication of books until they were endorsed by the official censor. Needless to say, the censor, holding his office and salary by favour, was naturally more concerned with the divine right of kings and bishops than with the delights of literature, and many books were suppressed for no better reason than that they were displeasing to the authorities. Milton protested against this, as against every other form of tyranny, and his *Areopagitica*—so called from the Areopagus or Forum of Athens, the place of public appeal, and the Mars Hill of St. Paul's address—is the most famous plea in English for the freedom of the press.

Milton's Later Poetry. Undoubtedly the noblest of Milton's works, written when he was blind and suffering, are *Paradise Lost, Paradise Regained*, and *Samson Agonistes.* The first is the greatest, indeed the only generally acknowledged epic in our literature since *Beowulf;* the last is the most perfect specimen of a drama after the Greek method in our language.

Paradise Lost

Of the history of the great epic we have some interesting glimpses. In Cambridge there is preserved a notebook of Milton's containing a list of nearly one hundred subjects[1] for a great poem, selected while he was a boy at the university. King Arthur attracted him at first; but his choice finally settled upon the Fall of Man, and we have four separate outlines showing Milton's proposed

---

[1] Of these sixty were taken from the Bible, thirty-three from English and five from Scotch history.

treatment of the subject. These outlines indicate that he contemplated a mighty drama or miracle play; but whether because of Puritan antipathy to plays and players, or because of the wretched dramatic treatment of religious subjects which Milton had witnessed in Italy, he abandoned the idea of a play and settled on the form of an epic poem; most fortunately, it must be conceded, for Milton had not the knowledge of men necessary for a drama. As a study of character *Paradise Lost* would be a grievous failure. Adam, the central character, is something of a prig; while Satan looms up a magnificent figure, entirely different from the devil of the miracle plays and completely overshadowing the hero both in interest and in manliness. The other characters, the Almighty, the Son, Raphael, Michael, the angels and fallen spirits, are merely mouthpieces for Milton's declamations, without any personal or human interest. Regarded as a drama, therefore, *Paradise Lost* could never have been a success; but as poetry, with its sublime imagery, its harmonious verse, its titanic background of heaven, hell, and the illimitable void that lies between, it is unsurpassed in any literature.

In 1658 Milton in his darkness sat down to dictate the work which he had planned thirty years before. In order to understand the mighty sweep of the poem it is necessary to sum up the argument of the twelve books, as follows:

Argument of Paradise Lost

Book I opens with a statement of the subject, the Fall of Man, and a noble invocation for light and divine guidance. Then begins the account of Satan and the rebel angels, their banishment from heaven, and their plot to oppose the design of the Almighty by dragging down his children, our first parents, from their state of innocence. The book closes with a description of the land of fire and endless pain where the fallen spirits abide, and the erection of Pandemonium, the palace of Satan. Book II is a description of the council of evil spirits, of Satan's consent to undertake the temptation of Adam and Eve, and his journey to the gates of hell, which are guarded by Sin and Death. Book III transports us to heaven again. God, foreseeing the fall, sends Raphael to warn Adam and Eve, so that their disobedience shall be upon their own heads. Then the Son offers himself a sacrifice, to take away the sin of the coming disobedience of man. At the end of this book Satan appears in a different scene, meets Uriel, the Angel of the Sun, inquires from him the way to earth, and takes his journey thither disguised as an angel of light. Book IV shows us Paradise and the innocent state of man. An angel guard is set over Eden, and Satan is arrested while tempting Eve in a dream, but is curiously allowed to go free again. Book V shows us Eve relating her dream to Adam, and then the morning prayer and the daily employment of our first parents. Raphael visits them, is entertained by a banquet (which Eve proposes in order to show him that all God's gifts are not kept in heaven), and tells them of the revolt of the fallen spirits. His story is continued in Book VI. In Book VII we read the story of the creation of the world as Raphael tells it to Adam and Eve. In Book VIII Adam tells Raphael the story of his own life and of his meeting with Eve. Book IX is the story of the temptation by Satan, following the account in Genesis. Book X records the divine judgment upon Adam and Eve; shows the construction by Sin and Death of a highway through chaos to the earth, and Satan's return to Pandemonium. Adam and Eve repent of their disobedience and Satan and his angels are turned into serpents. In Book XI, the Almighty accepts Adam's repentance, but condemns him to be banished from Paradise, and the archangel Michael is sent to execute the sentence. At the end of the book, after Eve's feminine grief at the loss of Paradise, Michael begins a prophetic vision of the destiny of man. Book XII continues Michael's vision. Adam and Eve are comforted by hearing of the future redemption of their race. The poem ends as they wander forth out of Paradise and the door closes behind them.

It will be seen that this is a colossal epic, not of a man or a hero, but of the whole race of men; and that Milton's characters are such as no human hand could adequately portray. But the scenes, the splendours of heaven, the horrors of hell, the serene beauty of Paradise, the sun and planets suspended between celestial light and gross darkness, are pictured with an imagination that is almost superhuman. The abiding interest of the poem is in these colossal pictures, and in the lofty thought and the marvellous melody with which they are impressed on our minds. The poem is in blank verse, and not until Milton used it did we learn the infinite variety and harmony of which it is capable. He played with it, changing its melody and movement on every page, 'as an organist out of a single theme develops an unending variety of harmony.'

Lamartine has described Paradise Lost as the dream of a Puritan fallen asleep over his Bible, and this suggestive description leads us to the curious fact that it is the dream, not the theology or the descriptions of Bible scenes, that chiefly interests us. Thus Milton describes the separation of earth and water, and there is little or nothing added to the simplicity and strength of Genesis; but the sunset which follows is Milton's own dream, and instantly we are transported to a land of beauty and poetry:

> Now came still Evening on, and Twilight grey
> Had in her sober livery all things clad;
> Silence accompanied; for beast and bird,
> They to their grassy couch, these to their nests
> Were slunk, all but the wakeful nightingale.
> She all night long her amorous descant sung:
> Silence was pleased. Now glowed the firmament
> With living sapphires; Hesperus, that led
> The starry host, rode brightest, till the Moon,
> Rising in clouded majesty, at length
> Apparent queen, unveiled her peerless light,
> And o'er the dark her silver mantle threw.

So also Milton's Almighty, considered purely as a literary character, is unfortunately tinged with the narrow and literal theology of the time. He is a being enormously egotistic, the despot rather than the servant of the universe, seated upon a throne with a chorus of angels about him eternally singing his praises and ministering to a kind of divine vanity. It is not necessary to search heaven for such a character; the type is too common upon earth. But in Satan Milton breaks away from crude mediæval conceptions; he follows the dream again, and gives us a character to admire and understand:

> 'Is this the region, this the soil, the clime',
> Said then the lost Archangel, 'this the seat
> That we must change for Heaven?—this mournful gloom

For that celestial light? Be it so, since He
Who now is sovran can dispose and bid
What shall be right: farthest from Him is best,
Whom reason hath equalled, force hath made supreme
Above his equals. Farewell, happy fields,
Where joy forever dwells! Hail, horrors! hail,
Infernal World! and thou, profoundest Hell,

Receive thy new possessor—one who brings
A mind not to be changed by place or time.
The mind is its own place, and in itself
Can make a Heaven of Hell, a Hell of Heaven.
What matter where, if I be still the same,
And what I should be, all but less than he
Whom thunder hath made greater? Here at least
We shall be free; the Almighty hath not built
Here for his envy, will not drive us hence:
Here we may reign secure; and, in my choice,
To reign is worth ambition, though in Hell:
Better to reign in Hell than serve in Heaven.'

In this magnificent heroism Milton has unconsciously immortalized the Puritan spirit, the same unconquerable spirit that set men to writing poems and allegories when in prison for the faith, and that sent them over the stormy sea in a cockle-shell to found a free commonwealth in the wilds of America.

For a modern reader the understanding of Paradise Lost presupposes two things—a knowledge of the first chapters of the Scriptures, and of the general principles of Calvinistic theology; but it is a pity to use the poem, as has so often been done, to teach a literal acceptance of one or the other. Of the theology of *Paradise Lost* the least said the better; but to the splendour of the Puritan dream and the glorious melody of its expression no words can do justice. Even a slight acquaintance will make the reader understand why it ranks with the *Divina Commedia* of Dante, and why it is generally accepted by critics as the greatest single poem in our literature.

Soon after the completion of *Paradise Lost,* Thomas Ellwood, a friend of Milton, asked one day after reading the manuscript, 'But what hast thou to say of Paradise Found?' It was in response to this suggestion that Milton wrote the second part of the great epic, known to us as *Paradise Regained.* The first tells how mankind, in the person of Adam, fell at the first temptation by Satan and became an outcast from Paradise and from divine grace; the second shows how mankind, in the person of Christ, withstands the tempter and is established once more in the divine favour. Christ's temptation in the wilderness is the theme, and Milton follows the account in the fourth chapter of Matthew's gospel. Though *Paradise Regained* was Milton's favourite, and though it has many passages of noble thought and splendid imagery equal to the best of *Paradise Lost,* the poem as a whole falls below the level of the first, and is less interesting to read.

Paradise Regained

In *Samson Agonistes* Milton turns to a more vital and personal theme, and his genius transfigures the story of Samson, the mighty champion of Israel, now blind and scorned, working as a slave among the Philistines. The poet's aim was to present in English a pure tragedy, with all the passion and restraint which marked the old Greek dramas. That he succeeded where others failed is due to two causes: first, Milton himself suggests the hero of one of the Greek tragedies—his sorrow and affliction give to his noble nature that touch of melancholy and calm dignity which is in perfect keeping with his subject. Second, Milton is telling his own story. Like Samson he had struggled mightily against the enemies of his race; he had taken a wife from the Philistines and had paid the penalty; he was blind, alone, scorned by his vain and thoughtless masters. To the essential action of the tragedy Milton could add, therefore, that touch of intense yet restrained personal feeling which carries more conviction than any argument. *Samson* is in many respects the most convincing of his works. Entirely apart from the interest of its subject and treatment, one may obtain from it a better idea of what great tragedy was among the Greeks than from any other work in our language.

Samson

Nothing is here for tears, nothing to wail
Or knock the breast, no weakness, no contempt,
Dispraise or blame—nothing but well and fair,
And what may quiet us in a death so noble.

III. PROSE WRITERS OF THE PURITAN PERIOD

John Bunyan (1628-1688)

As there is but one poet great enough to express the Puritan spirit, so there is but one commanding prose writer, John Bunyan. Milton was the child of the Renaissance, inheritor of all its culture, and the most profoundly educated man of his age. Bunyan was a poor, uneducated tinker. From the Renaissance he inherited nothing; but from the Reformation he received an excess of that spiritual independence which had caused the Puritan struggle for liberty. These two men, representing the extremes of English life in the seventeenth century, wrote the two works that stand today for the mighty Puritan spirit. One gave us the only epic since *Beowulf;* the other gave us our only great allegory, which has been read more than any other book in our language save the Bible.

John Bunyan

Life of Bunyan. Bunyan is an extraordinary figure; we must study him, as well as his books. Fortunately we have his life story in his own words, written with the same lovable modesty and sincerity that marked all his work. Reading that story now, in *Grace Abounding*, we see two great influences at work in his life. One, from within, was his own vivid imagination, which saw visions, allegories, parables, revelations, in every common event. The other, from without, was the spiritual ferment of the age, the multiplication of strange sects—Quakers, Free-Willers, Ranters, Anabaptists, Millenarians,--and the untempered zeal of all classes, like an engine without a balance wheel, when men were breaking away from authority and setting up their own religious standards. Bunyan's life is an epitome of that astonishing religious individualism which marked the close of the English Reformation.

He was born in the little village of Elstow, near Bedford, in 1628, the son of a poor tinker. For a little while the boy was sent to school, where he learned to read and write after a fashion; but he was soon busy in his father's shop, where, amid the glowing pots and the fire and smoke of his little forge, he saw vivid pictures of hell and the devils which haunted him all his life. When he was sixteen years old his father married the second time, whereupon Bunyan ran away and became a soldier in the Parliamentary army.

The religious ferment of the age made a tremendous impression on Bunyan's sensitive imagination. He went to church occasionally, only to find himself wrapped in terrors and torments by some fiery itinerant preacher; and he would rush violently away from church to forget his fears by joining in Sunday sports on the village green. As night came on the sports were forgotten, but the terrors returned, multiplied like the evil spirits of the parable. Visions of hell and the demons swarmed in his brain. He would groan aloud in his remorse, and even years afterwards he bemoans the sins of his early life. When we look for them fearfully, expecting some shocking crimes and misdemeanours, we find that they consisted of playing ball on Sunday and swearing. The latter sin, sad to say, was begun by listening to his father cursing some obstinate kettle which refused to be tinkered, and it was perfected in the Parliamentary army. One day his terrible swearing scared a woman, 'a very loose and ungodly wretch', as he tells us, who reprimanded him for his profanity. The reproach of the poor woman went straight home, like the voice of a prophet. All his profanity left him; he hung down his head with shame. 'I wished with all my heart', he says, 'that I might be a little child again, that my father might learn me to speak without this wicked way of swearing.' With characteristic vehemence Bunyan hurls himself upon a promise of Scripture, and instantly the reformation begins to work in his soul. He casts out the habit, root and branch, and finds to his astonishment that he can speak more freely and vigorously than before. Nothing is more characteristic of the man than this sudden seizing upon a text, which he had doubtless heard many times before, and being suddenly raised up or cast down by its influence.

With Bunyan's marriage to a good woman the real reformation in his life began. While still in his teens he married a girl as poor as himself. 'We came together', he says, 'as poor as might be, having not so much household stuff as a dish or spoon between us both.' The only dowry which the girl brought to her new home was two old, threadbare books, *The Plain Man's Pathway to Heaven,* and *The Practice of Piety*[1]. Bunyan read these books, which instantly gave fire to his imagination. He saw new visions and dreamed terrible new dreams of lost souls; his attendance at church grew exemplary; he began slowly and painfully to read the Bible for himself, but because of his own ignorance and the contradictory interpretations of Scripture which he heard on every side, he was tossed about like a feather by all the winds of doctrine.

The record of the next few years is like a nightmare, so terrible is Bunyan's spiritual struggle. One day he feels himself an outcast; the next the companion of angels; the third he tries experiments with the Almighty in order to put his salvation to the proof. As he goes along the road to Bedford he thinks he will work a miracle, like Gideon with his fleece. He will say to the little puddles of water in the horses' tracks, 'Be ye dry'; and to all the dry tracks he will say, 'Be ye puddles.' As he is about to perform the miracle a thought occurs to him: 'But go first under yonder hedge and pray that the Lord will make you able to perform a miracle.' He goes promptly and prays. Then he is afraid of the test, and goes on his way more troubled than before.

After years of such struggle, chased about between heaven and hell, Bunyan at last emerges into a saner atmosphere, even as Pilgrim came out of the horrible Valley of the Shadow. Soon, led by his intense feelings, he becomes an open-air preacher, and crowds of labourers gather about him on the village green. They listen in silence to his words; they end in groans and tears; scores of them amend their sinful lives. For the Anglo-Saxon people are remarkable for this, that however deeply they are engaged in business or pleasure, they are still sensitive as barometers to any true spiritual influence, whether of priest or peasant; they recognize what Emerson calls the 'accent of the Holy Ghost', and in this recognition of spiritual leadership lies the secret of their democracy. So this village tinker, with his

[1] The latter was by Lewis Bayly, bishop of Bangor. It is interesting to note that this book, whose very title is unfamiliar to us, was speedily translated into five different languages. It had an enormous sale, and ran through fifty editions soon after publication.

strength and sincerity, is presently the acknowledged leader of an immense congregation, and his influence is felt throughout England. It is a tribute to his power that, after the return of Charles II, Bunyan was the first to be prohibited from holding public meetings.

Concerning Bunyan's imprisonment in Bedford jail, which followed his refusal to obey the law prohibiting religious meetings without the authority of the Established Church, there is a difference of opinion. That the law was unjust goes without saying; but there was no religious persecution, as we understand the term. Bunyan was allowed to worship when and how he pleased; he was simply forbidden to hold public meetings, which frequently became fierce denunciations of the Established Church and government. His judges pleaded with Bunyan to conform with the law. He refused, saying that when the Spirit was upon him he must go up and down the land, calling on men everywhere to repent. In his refusal we see much heroism, a little obstinacy, and perhaps something of that desire for martyrdom which tempts every spiritual leader. That his final sentence to indefinite imprisonment was a hard blow to Bunyan is beyond question. He groaned aloud at the thought of his poor family, and especially at the thought of leaving his little blind daughter:

> I found myself a man encompassed with infirmities; the parting was like pulling the flesh from my bones.... Oh, the thoughts of the hardship I thought my poor blind one might go under would break my heart to pieces. Poor child, thought I, what sorrow thou art like to have for thy portion in this world; thou must be beaten, must beg, suffer hunger, cold, nakedness, and a thousand calamities, though I cannot now endure that the wind should blow upon thee.[1]

And then, because he thinks always in parables and seeks out most curious texts of Scripture, he speaks of 'the two milch kine that were to carry the ark of God into another country and leave their calves behind them.' Poor cows, poor Bunyan! Such is the mind of this extraordinary man.

With characteristic diligence Bunyan set to work in prison making shoe laces, and so earned a living for his family. His imprisonment lasted for nearly twelve years; but he saw his family frequently, and was for some time a regular preacher in the Baptist church in Bedford. Occasionally he even went about late at night, holding the proscribed meetings and

---

[1] Abridged from *Grace Abounding,* Part 3; Works (ed. 1873), p. 71.

increasing his hold upon the common people. The best result of this imprisonment was that it gave Bunyan long hours for the working of his peculiar mind and for study of his two only books, the King James Bible and Foxe's *Book of Martyrs*. The result of his study and meditation was *The Pilgrim's Progress,* which was probably written in prison, but which for some reason he did not publish till long after his release.

The years which followed are the most interesting part of Bunyan's strange career. The publication of *Pilgrim's Progress* in 1678 made him the most popular writer, as he was already the most popular preacher, in England. Books, tracts, sermons, nearly sixty works in all, came from his pen; and when one remembers his ignorance, his painfully slow writing, and his activity as an itinerant preacher, one can only marvel. His evangelistic journeys carried him often as far as London, and wherever he went crowds thronged to hear him. Scholars, bishops, statesmen went in secret to listen among the labourers, and came away wondering and silent. At Southwark the largest building could not contain the multitude of his hearers; and when he preached in London, thousands would gather in the cold dusk of the winter morning, before work began, and listen until he had made an end of speaking. 'Bishop Bunyan' he was soon called on account of his missionary journeys and his enormous influence.

What we most admire in the midst of all this activity is his perfect mental balance, his charity and humour in the strife of many sects. He was badgered for years by petty enemies, and he arouses our enthusiasm by his tolerance, his self-control, and especially by his sincerity. To the very end he retained that simple modesty which no success could spoil. Once when he had preached with unusual power some of his friends waited after the service to congratulate him, telling him what a 'sweet sermon' he had delivered. 'Aye', said Bunyan, 'you need not remind me; the devil told me that before I was out of the pulpit.'

For sixteen years this wonderful activity continued without interruption. Then, one day when riding through a cold storm on a labour of love, to reconcile a stubborn man with his own stubborn son, he caught a severe cold and appeared, ill and suffering but rejoicing in his success, at the house of a friend in Reading. He died there a few days later, and was laid away in Bunhill Fields burial ground, London, which has been ever since a *campo santo* to the faithful.

Works of Bunyan. The world's literature has three great allegories—Spenser's *Faery Queen,* Dante's *Divina Commedia,* and Bunyan's *Pilgrim's Progress.* The first appeals to poets, the second to scholars, the third to people of every age and condition. Here is a brief outline of the famous work:

Argument of Pilgrim's Progress

'As I walked through the wilderness of this world I lighted on a certain place where was a den [Bedford jail] and laid me down in that place to sleep; and, as I slept, I dreamed a dream.' So the story begins. He sees a man called Christian setting out with a book in his hand and a great load on his back from the city of Destruction. Christian has two objects—to get rid of his burden, which holds the sins and fears of his life, and to make his way to the Holy City. At the outset Evangelist finds him weeping because he knows not where to go, and points him to a wicket gate on a hill far away. As Christian goes forward his neighbours, friends, wife and children call to him to come back; but he puts his fingers in his ears, crying out, 'Life, life, eternal life', and so rushes across the plain.

Then begins a journey in ten stages, which is a vivid picture of the difficulties and triumphs of the Christian life. Every trial, every difficulty, every experience of joy or sorrow, of peace or temptation, is put into the form and discourse of a living character. Other allegorists write in poetry and their characters are shadowy and unreal; but Bunyan speaks in terse, idiomatic prose, and his characters are living men and women. There are Mr. Worldly Wiseman, a self-satisfied and dogmatic kind of man, youthful Ignorance, sweet Piety, courteous Demas, garrulous Talkative, honest Faithful, and a score of others, who are not at all the bloodless creatures of the *Romance of the Rose*, but men real enough to stop you on the road and to hold your attention. Scene after scene follows, in which are pictured many of our own spiritual experiences. There is the Slough of Despond, into which we all have fallen, out of which Pliable scrambles on the hither side and goes back grumbling, but through which Christian struggles mightily till Helpful stretches him a hand and drags him out on solid ground and bids him go on his way. Then come Interpreter's house, the Palace Beautiful, the Lions in the way, the Valley of Humiliation, the hard fight with the demon Apollyon, the more terrible Valley of the Shadow, Vanity Fair, and the trial of Faithful. The latter is condemned to death by a jury made up of Mr. Blindman, Mr. Nogood, Mr. Heady, Mr. Liveloose, Mr. Hatelight, and others of their kind to whom questions of justice are committed by the jury system. Most famous is Doubting Castle, where Christian and Hopeful are thrown into a dungeon by Giant Despair.

And then at last the Delectable Mountains of Youth, the deep river that Christian must cross, and the city of All Delight and the glorious company of angels that come singing down the streets. At the very end, when in sight of the city and while he can hear the welcome with which Christian is greeted, Ignorance is snatched away to go to his own place; and Bunyan quaintly observes, 'Then I saw that there was a way to hell even from the gates of heaven as well as from the city of Destruction. So I awoke, and behold it was a dream!'

Such, in brief, is the story, the great epic of a Puritan's individual experience in a rough world, just as Paradise Lost was the epic of mankind as dreamed by the great Puritan who had 'fallen asleep over his Bible.'

Success of Pilgrim's Progress

The chief fact which confronts the student of literature as he pauses before this great allegory is that it has been translated into seventy-five languages and dialects, and has been read more than any other book save one in the English language.

As for the secret of its popularity, Taine says, 'Next to the Bible, the book most widely read in England is the *Pilgrim's Progress*.... Protestantism is the doctrine of salvation by grace, and no writer has equalled Bunyan in making this doctrine understood.' And this opinion is echoed by the majority of our literary historians. It is perhaps sufficient answer to quote the simple fact that *Pilgrim's Progress* is not exclusively a Protestant study; it appeals to Christians of every name, and to Mohammedans and Buddhists in precisely the same way that it appeals to Christians. When it was translated into the languages of Catholic countries, like France and Portugal, only one or two incidents were omitted, and the story was almost as popular there as with English readers. The secret of its success is probably simple. It is, first of all, not a procession of shadows repeating the author's declamations, but a real story, the first extended story in our language. Our Puritan fathers may have read the story for religious instruction; but all classes of men have read it because they found in it a true personal experience told with strength, interest, humour—in a word, with all the qualities that such a story should possess. Young people have read it, first, for its intrinsic worth, because the dramatic interest of the story lured them on to the very end; and second, because it was their introduction to true allegory. The child with his imaginative mind—the man also, who has preserved his simplicity—naturally personifies objects, and takes pleasure in giving them powers of thinking and speaking like himself. Bunyan was the first writer to appeal to this pleasant and natural inclination in a way that all could understand. Add to this the fact that Pilgrim's Progress was the only book having any story interest in the great majority of English and American homes for a full century, and we have found the real reason for its wide reading.

Other Works of Bunyan

The Holy War, published in 1665, is the first important work of Bunyan. It is a prose *Paradise Lost,* and would undoubtedly be known as a remarkable allegory were it not overshadowed by its great rival. *Grace Abounding to the Chief of Sinners,* published in 1666, twelve years before *Pilgrim's Progress,* is the work from which we obtain the clearest insight into Bunyan's remarkable life, and to a man with historical or antiquarian tastes it is still excellent reading. In 1682 appeared *The Life and Death of Mr. Badman,* a realistic character study which is a precursor of the modern novel; and in 1684 the second part of *Pilgrim's Progress,* showing the journey of Christiana and her children to the city of All Delight. Besides these Bunyan published a multitude of treatises and sermons, all in the same style—direct, simple, convincing, expressing every thought and emotion perfectly in words that even a child can understand. Many of these are masterpieces, admired by working men and scholars alike for their thought and expression. Take, for instance, 'The Heavenly Footman', put it side by side with the best work of Latimer, and the resemblance in style is startling. It is difficult to realize that one work came from an ignorant tinker and the other from a great scholar, both engaged in the same general work. As Bunyan's one book was the Bible, we have here a suggestion of its influence in all our prose literature.

MINOR PROSE WRITERS

The Puritan Period is generally regarded as one destitute of literary interest; but that was certainly not the result of any lack of books or writers. Says Burton in his *Anatomy of Melancholy:*

> I have ... new books every day, pamphlets, currantoes, stories, whole catalogues of volumes of all sorts, new paradoxes, opinions, schisms, heresies, controversies in philosophy and religion. Now come tidings of weddings, maskings, entertainments, jubilees, embassies, sports, plays; then again, as in a new-shipped scene, treasons, cheatings, tricks, robberies, enormous villainies in all kinds, funerals, deaths, new discoveries, expeditions; now comical, then tragical matters.....

So the record continues, till one rubs his eyes and thinks he must have picked up by mistake the last literary magazine. And for all these kaleidoscopic events there were waiting a multitude of writers, ready to seize the abundant material and turn it to literary account for a tract, an article, a volume, or an encyclopedia.

Three Good Books

If one were to recommend certain of these books as expressive of this age of outward storm and inward calm, there are three that deserve more than a passing notice, namely, the *Religio Medici, Holy Living,* and *The Compleat Angler.* The first was written by a busy physician, a supposedly scientific man at that time; the second by the most learned of English churchmen; and the third by a simple merchant and fisherman. Strangely enough, these three great books—the reflections of nature, science, and revelation—all interpret human life alike and tell the same story of gentleness, charity, and noble living. If the age had produced only these three books, we could still be profoundly grateful to it for its inspiring message.

Robert Burton (1577-1640). Burton is famous chiefly as the author of the *Anatomy of Melancholy,* one of the most astonishing books in all literature, which appeared in 1621. Burton was a clergyman of the Established Church, an incomprehensible genius, given to broodings and melancholy and to reading of every conceivable kind of literature. Thanks to his wonderful memory, everything he read was stored up for use or ornament, till his mind resembled a huge curiosity shop. All his life he suffered from hypochondria, but curiously traced his malady to the stars rather than to his own liver. It is related of him that he used to suffer so from despondency that no help was to be found in medicine or theology; his only relief was to go down to the river and hear the bargemen swear at one another.

Burton's *Anatomy* was begun as a medical treatise on morbidness, arranged and divided with all the exactness of the schoolmen's demonstration of doctrines; but it turned out to be an enormous hodgepodge of quotations and references to authors, known and unknown, living and dead, which seemed to prove chiefly that 'much study is a weariness to the flesh.' By some freak of taste it became instantly popular, and was proclaimed one of the greatest books in literature. A few scholars still explore it with delight, as a mine of classic wealth; but the style is hopelessly involved, and to the ordinary reader most of his numerous references are now as unmeaning as a hyper-Jacobian surface.

Sir Thomas Browne (1605-1682). Browne was a physician who, after much study and travel, settled down to his profession in Norwich; but even then he gave far more time to the investigation of natural phenomena than to the barbarous practices which largely constituted the 'art' of medicine in his day. He was known far and wide as a learned doctor and an honest man, whose scientific studies had placed him in advance of his age, and whose religious views were liberal to the point of heresy. With this in mind, it is interesting to note, as a sign of the times, that this most scientific doctor was once called to give 'expert' testimony in the case of two old women who were being tried for the capital crime of witchcraft. He testified under oath that 'the fits were natural, but heightened by the devil's coöperating with the witches, at whose instance he [the alleged devil] did the villainies.'

Browne's great work is the *Religio Medici,* that is The Religion of a Physician (1642), which met with most unusual success.

Religio Medici

'Hardly ever was a book published in Britain', says Oldys, a chronicler who wrote nearly a century later, 'that made more noise than the *Religio Medici.*' Its success may be due largely to the fact that, among thousands of religious works, it was one of the few which saw in nature a profound revelation, and which treated purely religious subjects in a reverent, kindly, tolerant way, without ecclesiastical bias. It is still, therefore, excellent reading; but it is not so much the matter as the manner—the charm, the gentleness, the remarkable prose style—which has established the book as one of the classics of our literature.

Two other works of Browne are *Vulgar Errors* (1646), a curious combination of scientific and credulous research in the matter of popular superstition, and *Urn Burial,* a treatise suggested by the discovery of Roman burial urns at Walsingham. It began as an inquiry into the various methods of burial, but ended in a dissertation on the vanity of earthly hope and ambitions. From a literary point of view it is Browne's best work, but is less read than the *Religio Medici.*

Thomas Fuller (1608-1661). Fuller was a clergyman and royalist whose lively style and witty observations would naturally place him with the gay Caroline poets. His best known works are *The Holy War, The Holy State and the Profane State, Church History of Britain, and the History of the Worthies of England. The Holy and Profane State is chiefly a* biographical record, the first part consisting of numerous historical examples to be imitated, the second of examples to be avoided. *The Church History* is not a scholarly work, notwithstanding its author's undoubted learning, but is a lively and gossipy account which has at least one virtue, that it entertains the reader. The *Worthies,* the most widely read of his works, is a racy account of the important men of England. Fuller travelled constantly for years, collecting information from out-of-the-way sources and gaining a minute knowledge of his own country. This, with his overflowing humor and numerous anecdotes and illustrations, makes lively and interesting reading. Indeed, we hardly find a dull page in any of his numerous books.

Jeremy Taylor (1613-1667). Taylor was the greatest of the clergymen who made this period famous, a man who, like Milton, upheld a noble ideal in storm and calm, and himself lived it nobly. He has been called 'the Shakespeare of divines', and 'a kind of Spenser in a cassock', and both descriptions apply to him very well. His writings, with their exuberant fancy and their noble diction, belong rather to the Elizabethan than to the Puritan age.

From the large number of his works two stand out as representative of the man himself: *The Liberty of Prophesying* (1646), which Hallam calls the first plea for tolerance in religion, on a comprehensive basis and on deep-seated foundations; and The Rides and *Exercises of Holy Living* (1650). To the latter might be added its companion volume, Holy Dying, published in the following year. *The Holy Living and Dying,* as a single volume, was for many years read in almost every English cottage. With Baxter's *Saints' Rest, Pilgrim's Progress,* and the *King James Bible,* it often constituted the entire library of multitudes of Puritan homes; and as we read its noble words and breathe its gentle spirit, we cannot help wishing that our modern libraries were gathered together on the same thoughtful foundations.

Richard Baxter (1615-1691). This 'busiest man of his age' strongly suggests Bunyan in his life and writings. Like Bunyan, he was poor and uneducated, a nonconformist minister, exposed continually to insult and persecution; and, like Bunyan, he threw himself heart and soul into the conflicts of his age, and became by his public speech a mighty power among the common people. Unlike Jeremy Taylor, who wrote for the learned, and whose involved sentences and classical allusions are sometimes hard to follow, Baxter went straight to his mark, appealing directly to the judgment and feeling of his readers.

The number of his works is almost incredible when one thinks of his busy life as a preacher and the slowness of manual writing. In all, he left nearly one hundred and seventy different works, which if collected would make fifty or sixty volumes. As he wrote chiefly to influence men on the immediate questions of the day, most of this work has fallen into oblivion. His two most famous books are *The Saints' Everlasting Rest* and *A Call to the Unconverted,* both of which were exceedingly popular, running through scores of successive editions, and have been widely read in our own generation.

Izaak Walton (1593-1683). Walton was a small tradesman of London, who preferred trout brooks and good reading to the profits of business and the doubtful joys of a city life; so at fifty years, when he had saved a little money, he left the city and followed his heart out into the country. He began his literary work, or rather his recreation, by writing his famous Lives—kindly and readable appreciations of Donne, Wotton, Hooker, Herbert, and Sanderson, which stand at the beginning of modern biographical writing.

The Compleat Angler

In 1653 appeared *The Compleat Angler,* which has grown steadily in appreciation, and which is probably more widelyread than any other book on the subject of fishing. It begins with a conversation between a falconer, a hunter, and an angler; but the angler soon does most of the talking, as fishermen sometimes do; the hunter becomes a disciple, and learns by the easy method of hearing the fisherman discourse about his art. The conversations, it must be confessed, are often diffuse and pedantic; but they only make us feel most comfortably sleepy, as one invariably feels after a good day's fishing. So kindly is the spirit of the angler, so exquisite his appreciation of the beauty of the earth and sky, that one returns to the book, as to a favourite trout stream, with the undying expectation of catching something. Among a thousand books on angling it stands almost alone in possessing a charming style, and so it will probably be read as long as men go fishing. Best of all, it leads to a better appreciation of nature, and it drops little moral lessons into the reader's mind as gently as one casts a fly to a wary trout; so that one never suspects his better nature is being angled for. Though we have sometimes seen anglers catch more than they need, or sneak ahead of brother fishermen to the best pools, we are glad, for Walton's sake, to overlook such unaccountable exceptions, and agree with the milkmaid that 'we love all anglers, they be such honest, civil, quiet men'.

Summary of the Puritan Period. The half century between 1625 and 1675 is called the Puritan period for two reasons: first, because Puritan standards prevailed for a time in England; and second, because the greatest literary figure during all these years was the Puritan, John Milton. Historically the age was one of tremendous conflict. The Puritan struggled for righteousness and liberty, and because he prevailed, the age is one of moral and political revolution. In his struggle for liberty the Puritan overthrew the corrupt monarchy, beheaded Charles I, and established the Commonwealth under Cromwell. The Commonwealth lasted but a few years, and the restoration of Charles II in 1660 is often put as the end of the Puritan period. The age has no distinct limits, but overlaps the Elizabethan period on one side, and the Restoration period on the other.

The age produced many writers, a few immortal books, and one of the world's great literary leaders. The literature of the age is extremely diverse in character, and the diversity is due to the breaking up of the ideals of political and religious unity. This literature differs from that of the preceding age in three marked ways: (1) It has no unity of spirit, as in the days of Elizabeth, resulting from the patriotic enthusiasm of all classes. (2) In contrast with the hopefulness and vigour of Elizabethan writings, much of the literature of this period is sombre in character; it saddens rather than inspires us. (3) It has lost the romantic impulse of youth, and become critical and intellectual; it makes us think, rather than feel deeply.

In our study we have noted (1) the Transition Poets, of whom Daniel is chief; (2) the Song Writers, Campion and Breton; (3) the Spenserian Poets, Wither and Giles Fletcher; (4) the Metaphysical Poets, Donne and Herbert; (5) the Cavalier Poets, Herrick, Carew, Lovelace, and Suckling; (6) John Milton, his life, his early or Horton poems, his militant prose, and his last great poetical works; (7) John Bunyan, his extraordinary life, and his chief work, *The Pilgrim's Progress;* (8) the Minor Prose Writers, Burton, Browne, Fuller, Taylor, Baxter, and Walton. Three books selected from this group are Browne's *Religio Medici,* Taylor's *Holy Living and Dying,* and Walton's *Compleat Angler.*

Selections for Reading. *Milton.* Paradise Lost, books 1-2, L'Allegro, Il Penseroso, Comus, Lycidas, and selected Sonnets—all in Standard English

Classics; same poems, more or less complete, in various other series; Areopagitica and Treatise on Education, selections, in Manly's English Prose, or Areopagitica in Arber's English Reprints, Clarendon Press Series, Morley's Universal Library, etc.

Minor Poets. Selections from Herrick, edited by Hale, in Athenæum Press Series; selections from Herrick, Lovelace, Donne, Herbert, etc., in Manly's English Poetry, Golden Treasury, Oxford Book of English Verse, etc.; Vaughan's Silex Scintillans, in Temple Classics, also in the Aldine Series; Herbert's The Temple, in Everyman's Library, Temple Classics, etc.

Bunyan. The Pilgrim's Progress, in Standard English Classics, Pocket Classics, etc.; Grace Abounding, in Cassell's National Library.

Minor Prose Writers. Wentworth's Selections from Jeremy Taylor; Browne's *Religio Medici,* Walton's Compleat Angler, both in Everyman's Library, Temple Classics, etc.; selections from Taylor, Browne, and Walton in Manly's English Prose, also in Garnett's English Prose.

Bibliography.[1] *History. Textbook*, Montgomery, pp. 238-257; Cheyney, pp. 431-464; Green, ch. 8; Traill; Gardiner.

Special Works. Wakeling's King and Parliament (Oxford Manuals); Gardiner's The First Two Stuarts and the Puritan Revolution; Tulloch's English Puritanism and its Leaders; Lives of Cromwell by Harrison, by Church, and by Morley; Carlyle's Oliver Cromwell's Letters and Speeches.

Literature. Saintsbury's Elizabethan Literature (extends to 1660); Masterman's The Age of Milton; Dowden's Puritan and Anglican.

Milton. Texts, Poetical Works, Globe edition, edited by Masson; Cambridge Poets edition, edited by Moody; English Prose Writings, edited by Morley, in Carisbrooke Library; also in Bohn's Standard Library.

Masson's Life of John Milton (8 vols.); Life, by Garnett, by Pattison (English Men of Letters). Raleigh's Milton; Trent's John Milton; Corson's Introduction to Milton; Brooke's Milton, in Student's Library; Macaulay's Milton; Lowell's Essays, in Among My Books, and in Latest Literary Essays; M. Arnold's Essay, in Essays in Criticism; Dowden's Essay, in Puritan and Anglican.

---

[1] For titles and publishers of reference works, see General Bibliography at the end of this book.

Cavalier Poets. Schelling's Seventeenth Century Lyrics, in Athenæum Press Series; Cavalier and Courtier Lyrists, in Canterbury Poets Series; Gosse's Jacobean Poets; Lovelace, etc., in Library of Old Authors.

Donne. Poems, in Muses' Library; Life, in Walton's Lives, in Temple Classics, and in Morley's Universal Library; Life, by Gosse; Jessup's John Donne; Dowden's Essay, in New Studies; Stephen's Studies of a Biographer, vol. 3.

Herbert. Palmer's George Herbert; Poems and Prose Selections, edited by Rhys, in Canterbury Poets; Dowden's Essay, in Puritan and Anglican.

Bunyan. Brown's John Bunyan, His Life, Times, and Works; Life, by Venables, and by Froude (English Men of Letters); Essays by Macaulay, by Dowden, supra, and by Woodberry, in Makers of Literature.

Jeremy Taylor. Holy Living, Holy Dying, in Temple Classics, and in Bohn's Standard Library; Selections, edited by Wentworth; Life, by Heber, and by Gosse (English Men of Letters); Dowden's Essay, *supra.*

Thomas Browne. Works, edited by Wilkin; the same, in Temple Classics, and in Bohn's Library; Religio Medici, in Everyman's Library; essay by Pater, in Appreciations; by Dowden, *supra;* and by L. Stephen, in Hours in a Library; Life, by Gosse (English Men of Letters).

Izaak Walton. Works, in Temple Classics, Cassell's Library, and Morley's Library; Introduction, in A. Lang's Walton's Compleat Angler; Lowell's Essay, in Latest Literary Essays.

Suggestive Questions. 1. What is meant by the Puritan period? What were the objects and the results of the Puritan movement in English history?

2. What are the main characteristics of the literature of this period? Compare it with Elizabethan literature. How did religion and politics affect Puritan literature? Can you quote any passages or name any works which justify your opinion?

3. What is meant by the terms Cavalier poets, Spenserian poets, Metaphysical poets? Name the chief writers of each group. To whom are we indebted for our first English hymn book? Would you call this a work of literature? Why?

4. What are the qualities of Herrick's poetry? What marked contrasts are found in Herrick and in nearly all the poets of this period?

5. Who was George Herbert? For what purpose did he write? What qualities are found in his poetry?

6. Tell briefly the story of Milton's life. What are the three periods of his literary work? What is meant by the Horton poems? Compare 'L'Allegro' and 'Il Penseroso'. Are there any Puritan ideals in 'Comus'? Why is 'Lycidas' often put at the summit of English lyrical poetry? Give the main idea or argument of *Paradise Lost.* What are the chief qualities of the poem? Describe in outline *Paradise Regained* and *Samson Agonistes.* What personal element entered into the latter? What quality strikes you most forcibly in Milton's poetry? What occasioned Milton's prose works? Do they properly belong to literature? Why? Compare Milton and Shakespeare with regard to (1) knowledge of men, (2) ideals of life, (3) purpose in writing.

7. Tell the story of Bunyan's life. What unusual elements are found in his life and writings? Give the main argument of *The Pilgrim's Progress.* If you read the story before studying literature, tell why you liked or disliked it. Why is it a work for all ages and for all races? What are the chief qualities of Bunyan's style?

8. Who are the minor prose writers of this age? Name the chief works of Jeremy Taylor, Thomas Browne, and Izaak Walton. Can you describe from your own reading any of these works? How does the prose of this age compare in interest with the poetry? (Milton is, of course, excepted in this comparison.)

CHRONOLOGY

Seventeeth Century

History	Literature
	1621. Burton's Anatomy of Melancholy
	1623. Wither's Hymn Book
1625. Charles I Parliament dissolved	
1628. Petition of Right	1629. Milton's Ode on the Nativity
1630-1640. King rules without Parliament. Puritan migration to New England	1630-1633. Herbert's poems
	1632-1637. Milton's Horton poems

History	Literature
1640. Long Parliament	
1642. Civil War begins	1642. Browne's Religio Medici
1643. Scotch Covenant	
1643. Press censorship	1644. Milton's Areopagitica
1645. Battle of Naseby; triumph of Puritans	
1649. Execution of Charles I. Cavalier migration to Virginia	1649. Milton's Tenure of Kings
1649-1660. Commonwealth	1650. Baxter's Saints' Rest. Jeremy Taylor's Holy Living
	1651. Hobbes's Leviathan
1653-1658. Cromwell, Protector	1653. Walton's Complete Angler
1658-1660. Richard Cromwell	
1660. Restoration of Charles II	1663-1694. Dryden's dramas (next chapter)
	1666. Bunyan's Grace Abounding
	1667. Paradise Lost
	1674. Death of Milton
	1678. Pilgrim's Progress published (written earlier)

CHAPTER 8

PERIOD OF THE RESTORATION (1660-1700)

THE AGE OF FRENCH INFLUENCE

History of the Period. It seems a curious contradiction, at first glance, to place the return of Charles II at the beginning of modern England, as our historians are wont to do; for there was never a time when the progress of liberty, which history records, was more plainly turned backwards. The Puritan régime had been too severe; it had repressed too many natural pleasures. Now, released from restraint, society abandoned the decencies of life and the reverence for law itself, and plunged into excesses more unnatural than had been the restraints of Puritanism. The inevitable effect of excess is disease, and for almost an entire generation following the Restoration, in 1660, England lay sick of a fever. Socially, politically, morally, London suggests an Italian city in the days of the Medici; and its literature, especially its drama, often seems more like the delirium of illness than the expression of a healthy mind. But even a fever has its advantages. Whatever impurity is in the blood 'is burnt and purged away', and a man rises from fever with a new strength and a new idea of the value of life, like King Hezekiah, who after his sickness and fear of death resolved to 'go softly' all his days. The Restoration was the great crisis in English history; and that England lived through it was due solely to the strength and excellence of that Puritanism which she thought she had flung to the winds when she welcomed back a vicious monarch at Dover. The chief lesson of the

Restoration was this—that it showed by awful contrast the necessity of truth and honesty, and of a strong government of free men, for which the Puritan had stood like a rock in every hour of his rugged history. Through fever, England came slowly back to health; through gross corruption in society and in the state England learned that her people were at heart sober, sincere, religious folk, and that their character was naturally too strong to follow after pleasure and be satisfied. So Puritanism suddenly gained all that it had struggled for, and gained it even in the hour when all seemed lost, when Milton in his sorrow unconsciously portrayed the government of Charles and his Cabal in that tremendous scene of the council of the infernal peers in Pandemonium, plotting the ruin of the world.

The King and his Followers

Of the king and his followers it is difficult to write temperately. Most of the dramatic literature of the time is atrocious, and we can understand it only as we remember the character of the court and society for which it was written. Unspeakably vile in his private life, the king had no redeeming patriotism, no sense of responsibility to his country for even his public acts. He gave high offices to blackguards, stole from the exchequer like a common thief, played off Catholics and Protestants against each other, disregarding his pledges to both alike, broke his solemn treaty with the Dutch and with his own ministers, and betrayed his country for French money to spend on his own pleasures. It is useless to paint the dishonour of a court which followed gayly after such a leader. The first Parliament, while it contained some noble and patriotic members, was dominated by young men who remembered the excess of Puritan zeal, but forgot the despotism and injustice which had compelled Puritanism to stand up and assert the manhood of England. These young politicians vied with the king in passing laws for the subjugation of Church and State, and in their thirst for revenge upon all who had been connected with Cromwell's iron government. Once more a wretched formalism—that perpetual danger to the English Church—came to the front and exercised authority over the free churches. The House of Lords was largely increased by the creation of hereditary titles and estates for ignoble men and shameless women who had flattered the king's vanity. Even the Bench, that last strong refuge of English justice, was corrupted by the appointment of judges, like the brutal Jeffreys, whose aim, like that of their royal master, was to get money and to exercise power without personal responsibility. Amid all this dishonour the foreign influence and authority of Cromwell's strong government vanished like smoke. The valiant little Dutch navy swept the English fleet from the sea, and only the thunder of Dutch guns in the Thames, under the very windows of London, awoke the nation to the realization of how low it had fallen.

Two considerations must modify our judgment of this disheartening spectacle. First, the king and his court are not England. Though our histories are largely filled with the records of kings and soldiers, of intrigues and fighting, these no more express the real life of a people than fever and delirium express a normal manhood. Though king and court and high society arouse our disgust or pity, records are not wanting to show that private life in England remained honest and pure even in the worst days of the Restoration. While London society might be entertained by the degenerate poetry of Rochester and the dramas of Dryden and Wycherley, English scholars hailed Milton with delight; and the common people followed Bunyan and Baxter with their tremendous appeal to righteousness and liberty. Second, the king, with all his pretensions to divine right, remained only a figurehead; and the Anglo-Saxon people, when they tire of one figurehead, have always the will and the power to throw it overboard and choose a better one. The country was divided into two political parties: the Whigs, who sought to limit the royal power in the interests of Parliament and the people; and the Tories, who strove to check the growing power of the people in the interests of their hereditary rulers. Both parties, however, were largely devoted to the Anglican Church; and when James II, after four years of misrule, attempted to establish a national Catholicism by intrigues which aroused the protest of the Pope[1] as well as of Parliament, then Whigs and Tories, Catholics and Protestants, united in England's last great revolution.

Revolution of 1688

The complete and bloodless Revolution of 1688, which called William of Orange to the throne, was simply the indication of England's restored health and sanity. It proclaimed that she had not long forgotten, and could never again forget, the lesson taught her by Puritanism in its hundred years of struggle and sacrifice. Modern England was firmly established by the Revolution, which was brought about by the excesses of the Restoration.

[1] Guizot's *History of the Revolution in England.*

Literary Characteristics. In the literature of the Restoration we note a sudden breaking away from old standards, just as society broke away from the restraints of Puritanism. Many of the literary men had been driven out of England with Charles and his court, or else had followed their patrons into exile in the days of the Commonwealth. On their return they renounced old ideals and demanded that English poetry and drama should follow the style to which they had become accustomed in the gaiety of Paris. We read with astonishment in Pepys's Diary (1660-1669) that he has been to see a play called *Midsummer Night's Dream,* but that he will never go again to hear Shakespeare, 'for it is the most insipid, ridiculous play that ever I saw in my life'. And again we read in the diary of Evelyn—another writer who reflects with wonderful accuracy the life and spirit of the Restoration—'I saw *Hamlet* played; but now the old plays begin to disgust this refined age, since his Majesty's being so long abroad'. Since Shakespeare and the Elizabethans were no longer interesting, literary men began to imitate the French writers, with whose works they had just grown familiar; and here begins the so-called period of French influence, which shows itself in English literature for the next century, instead of the Italian influence which had been dominant since Spenser and the Elizabethans.

French Influence

One has only to consider for a moment the French writers of this period, Pascal, Bossuet, Fénelon, Malherbe, Corneille, Racine, Molière—all that brilliant company which makes the reign of Louis XIV the Elizabethan Age of French literature—to see how far astray the early writers of the Restoration went in their wretched imitation. When a man takes another for his model, he should copy virtues not vices; but unfortunately many English writers reversed the rule, copying the vices of French comedy without any of its wit or delicacy or abundant ideas. The poems of Rochester, the plays of Dryden, Wycherley, Congreve, Vanbrugh, and Farquhar, all popular in their day, are mostly unreadable. Milton's 'sons of Belial, flown with insolence and wine', is a good expression of the vile character of the court writers and of the

London theatres for thirty years following the Restoration. Such work can never satisfy a people, and when Jeremy Collier,[1] in 1698, published a vigorous attack upon the evil plays and the play-wrights of the day, all London, tired of the coarseness and excesses of the Restoration, joined the literary revolution, and the corrupt drama was driven from the stage.

With the final rejection of the Restoration drama we reach a crisis in the history of our literature. The old Elizabethan spirit, with its patriotism, its creative vigour, its love of romance, and the Puritan spirit with its moral earnestness and individualism, were both things of the past; and at first there was nothing to take their places. Dryden, the greatest writer of the age, voiced a general complaint when he said that in his prose and poetry he was 'drawing the outlines' of a new art, but had no teacher to instruct him. But literature is a progressive art, and soon the writers of the age developed two marked tendencies of their own—the tendency to realism, and the tendency to that preciseness and elegance of expression which marks our literature for the next hundred years.

New Tendencies

In realism—that is, the representation of men exactly as they are, the expression of the plain, unvarnished truth without regard to ideals or romance—the tendency was at first thoroughly bad. The early Restoration writers sought to paint realistic pictures of a corrupt court and society, and, as we have suggested, they emphasized vices rather than virtues, and gave us coarse, low plays without interest or moral significance. Like Hobbes, they saw only the externals of man, his body and appetites, not his soul and its ideals; and so, like most realists, they resemble a man lost in the woods, who wanders aimlessly around in circles, seeing the confusing trees but never the whole forest, and who seldom thinks of climbing the nearest high hill to get his bearings. Later, however, this tendency to realism became more wholesome.

Realism

[1] Jeremy Collier (1650-1726), a clergyman and author, noted for his scholarly *Ecclesiastical History of Great Britain* (1708-1714) and his *Short View of the Immorality and Profaneness of the English Stage* (1698). The latter was largely instrumental in correcting the low tendency of the Restoration drama.

While it neglected romantic poetry, in which youth is eternally interested, it led to a keener study of the practical motives which govern human action.

Formalism

The second tendency of the age was toward directness and simplicity of expression, and to this excellent tendency our literature is greatly indebted. In both the Elizabethan and the Puritan ages the general tendency of writers was towards extravagance of thought and language. Sentences were often involved, and loaded with Latin quotations and classical allusions. The Restoration writers opposed this vigorously. From France they brought back the tendency to regard established rules for writing, to emphasize close reasoning rather than romantic fancy, and to use short, clean-cut sentences without an unnecessary word. We see this French influence in the Royal Society,[1] which had for one of its objects the reform of English prose by getting rid of its 'swellings of style', and which bound all its members to use 'a close, naked, natural way of speaking ... as near to mathematical plainness as they can'. Dryden accepted this excellent rule for his prose, and adopted the heroic couplet, as the next best thing, for the greater part of his poetry. As he tells us himself:

> And this unpolished rugged verse I chose
> As fittest for discourse, and nearest prose.

It is largely due to him that writers developed that formalism of style, that precise, almost mathematical elegance, miscalled classicism, which ruled English literature for the next century.[2]

---

[1] The Royal Society, for the investigation and discussion of scientific questions, was founded in 1662, and soon included practically of the literary and scientific men of the age. It encouraged the work of Isaac Newton, who was one of its members; and its influence for truth—at a time when men were still trying to compound the philosopher's stone, calculating men's actions from the stars, and hanging harmless old women for witches—can hardly be overestimated.

[2] If the reader would see this in concrete form, let him read a paragraph of Milton's prose, or a stanza of his poetry, and compare its exuberant, melodious diction with Dryden's concise method of writing.

Another thing which the reader will note with interest in Restoration literature is the adoption of the heroic couplet; that is, two iambic pentameter lines which rhyme together, as the most suitable form of poetry. Waller,[1] who began to use it in 1623, is generally regarded as the father of the couplet, for he is the first poet to use it consistently in the bulk of his poetry. Chaucer had used the rhymed couplet wonderfully well in his *Canterbury Tales,* but in Chaucer it is the poetical thought more than the expression which delights us. With the Restoration writers, form counts for everything. Waller and Dryden made the couplet the prevailing literary fashion, and in their hands the couplet becomes 'closed'; that is, each pair of lines must contain a complete thought, stated as precisely as possible. Thus Waller writes:

The Couplet

> The soul's dark cottage, battered and decayed,
> Lets in new light through chinks that time has made.[2]

That is a kind of aphorism such as Pope made in large quantities in the following age. It contains a thought, is catchy, quotable, easy to remember; and the Restoration writers delighted in it. Soon this mechanical closed couplet, in which the second line was often made first,[3] almost excluded all other forms of poetry. It was dominant in England for a full century, and we have grown familiar with it, and somewhat weary of its monotony, in such famous poems as Pope's 'Essay on Man' and Goldsmith's 'Deserted Village'. These, however, are essays rather than poems. That even the couplet is capable of melody and variety is shown in Chaucer's Tales and in Keats's exquisite *Endymion.*

These four things, the tendency to vulgar realism in the drama, a general formalism which came from following set rules, the

---

[1] Edmund Waller (1606-1687), the most noted poet of the Restoration period until his pupil Dryden appeared. His works are now seldom read.

[2] From *Divine Poems,* 'Old Age and Death'.

[3] Following the advice of Boileau (1676-1711), a noted French critic, whom Voltaire called 'the lawgiver of Parnassus'.

development of a simpler and more direct prose style, and the prevalence of the heroic couplet in poetry are the main characteristics of Restoration literature. They are all exemplified in the work of one man, John Dryden.

John Dryden (1631-1700)

Dryden is the greatest literary figure of the Restoration, and in his work we have an excellent reflection of both the good and the evil tendencies of the age in which he lived. If we can think for a moment of literature as a canal of water, we may appreciate the figure that Dryden is the 'lock by which the waters of English poetry were let down from the mountains of Shakespeare and Milton to the plain of Pope'; that is, he stands between two very different ages, and serves as a transition from one to the other.

Life. Dryden's life contains so many conflicting elements of greatness and littleness that the biographer is continually taken away from the facts, which are his chief concern, to judge motives, which are manifestly outside his knowledge and business. Judged by his own opinion of himself, as expressed in the numerous prefaces to his works, Dryden was the soul of candor, writing with no other master than literature, and with no other object than to advance the welfare of his age and nation. Judged by his acts, he was apparently a time-server, catering to a depraved audience in his dramas, and dedicating his work with much flattery to those who were easily cajoled by their vanity into sharing their purse and patronage. In this, however, he only followed the general custom of the time, and is above many of his contemporaries.

Dryden was born in the village of Aldwinkle, Northamptonshire, in 1631. His family were prosperous people, who brought him up in the strict Puritan faith, and sent him first to the famous Westminster school and then to Cambridge. He made excellent use of his opportunities and studied eagerly, becoming one of the best educated men of his age, especially in the classics. Though of remarkable literary taste, he showed little evidence of literary ability up to the age of thirty. By his training and family connections he was allied to the Puritan party, and his only well-known work of this period, the 'Heroic Stanzas,' was written on the death of Cromwell:

His grandeur he derived from Heaven alone,
For he was great ere Fortune made him so;
And wars, like mists that rise against the sun,
Made him but greater seem, not greater grow.

In these four lines, taken almost at random from the 'Heroic Stanzas', we have an epitome of the thought, the preciseness, and the polish that mark all his literary work.

This poem made Dryden well known, and he was in a fair way to become the new poet of Puritanism when the Restoration made a complete change in his methods. He had come to London for a literary

Library at Trinity College, Cambridge

life, and when the Royalists were again in power he placed himself promptly on the winning side. His 'Astraea Redux', a poem of welcome to Charles II, and his 'Panegyric to his Sacred Majesty', breathe more devotion to 'the old goat', as the king was known to his courtiers, than had his earlier poems to Puritanism.

In 1667 he became more widely known and popular by his 'Annus Mirabilis', a narrative poem describing the terrors of the great fire in

London and some events of the disgraceful war with Holland; but with the theatres reopened and nightly filled, the drama offered the most attractive field to one who made his living by literature; so Dryden turned to the stage and agreed to furnish three plays yearly for the actors of the King's Theatre. For nearly twenty years, the best of his life, Dryden gave himself up to this unfortunate work. Both by nature and habit he seems to have been clean in his personal life; but the stage demanded unclean plays, and Dryden followed his audience. That he deplored this is evident from some of his later work, and we have his statement that he wrote only one play, his best, to please himself. This was *All for Love,* which was written in blank verse, most of the others being in rimed couplets.

During this time Dryden had become the best known literary man of London, and was almost as much a dictator to the literary set which gathered in the taverns and coffee-houses as Ben Jonson had been before him. His work, meanwhile, was rewarded by large financial returns, and by his being appointed poet laureate and collector of the port of London. The latter office, it may be remembered, had once been held by Chaucer.

At fifty years of age, and before Jeremy Collier had driven his dramas from the stage, Dryden turned from dramatic work to throw himself into the strife of religion and politics, writing at this period his numerous prose and poetical treatises. In 1682 appeared his Religio Laici (Religion of a Layman), defending the Anglican Church against all other sects, especially the Catholics and Presbyterians; but three years later, when James II came to the throne with schemes to establish the Roman faith, Dryden turned Catholic and wrote his most famous religious poem, 'The Hind and the Panther', beginning:

> A milk-white Hind, immortal and unchanged,
> Fed on the lawns and in the forest ranged;
> Without unspotted, innocent within,
> She feared no danger, for she knew no sin.

This hind is a symbol for the Roman Church; and the Anglicans, as a panther, are represented as persecuting the faithful. Numerous other sects—Calvinists, Anabaptists, Quakers—were represented by the wolf, boar, hare, and other animals, which gave the poet an excellent chance for exercising his satire. Dryden's enemies made the accusation, often since repeated, of hypocrisy in thus changing his church; but that he was sincere in the matter can now hardly be questioned, for he knew how to 'suffer for the faith' and to be true to his religion, even when it meant misjudgment and loss of fortune. At the Revolution of 1688 he refused allegiance to William of Orange; he was deprived of all his offices and pensions, and as an old man was again thrown back on literature as his only means of livelihood. He went to work with extraordinary courage and energy, writing plays, poems, prefaces for other men, eulogies for funeral occasions—every kind of literary work that men would pay for. His most successful work at this time was his translations, which resulted in the complete Æneid and many selections from Homer, Ovid, and Juvenal, appearing in English rhymed couplets. His most enduring poem, the splendid ode called 'Alexander's Feast', was written in 1697. Three years later he published his last work, *Fables,* containing poetical paraphrases of the tales of Boccaccio and Chaucer, and the miscellaneous poems of his last years. Long prefaces were the fashion in Dryden's day, and his best critical work is found in his introductions. The preface to the *Fables* is generally admired as an example of the new prose style developed by Dryden and his followers.

From the literary view point these last troubled years were the best of Dryden's life, though they were made bitter by obscurity and by the criticism of his numerous enemies. He died in 1700 and was buried near Chaucer in Westminster Abbey.

Works of Dryden. The numerous dramatic works of Dryden are best left in that obscurity into which they have fallen. Now and then they contain a bit of excellent lyric poetry, and in *All for Love,* another version of *Antony and Cleopatra*, where he leaves his cherished heroic couplet for the blank verse of Marlowe and Shakespeare, he shows what he might have done had he not sold his talents to a depraved audience. On the whole, reading his plays is like nibbling at a rotting apple; even the good spots are affected by the decay, and one ends by throwing the whole thing into the garbage can, where most of the dramatic works of this period belong.

Poems

The controversial and satirical poems are on a higher plane; though, it must be confessed, Dryden's satire often strikes us as cutting and revengeful, rather than witty. The best known of these, and a masterpiece of its kind, is 'Absalom and

Achitophel', which is undoubtedly the most powerful political satire in our language. Taking the Bible story of David and Absalom, he uses it to ridicule the Whig party and also to revenge himself upon his enemies. Charles II appeared as King David; his natural son, the Duke of Monmouth, who was mixed up in the Rye House Plot, paraded as Absalom; Shaftesbury was Achitophel, the evil counsellor; and the Duke of Buckingham was satirized as Zimri. The poem had enormous political influence, and raised Dryden, in the opinion of his contemporaries, to the front rank of English poets. Two extracts from the powerful characterizations of Achitophel and Zimri are given here to show the style and spirit of the whole work.

(SHAFTESBURY)

Of these the false Achitophel was first;
A name to all succeeding ages cursed:
For close designs and crooked counsels fit;
Sagacious, bold, and turbulent of wit;
Restless, unfixed in principles and place;
In power unpleased, impatient of disgrace:
A fiery soul, which, working out its way,
Fretted the pygmy body to decay....
A daring pilot in extremity,
Pleased with the danger, when the waves went high
He sought the storms: but for a calm unfit,
Would steer too nigh the sands to boast his wit.
Great wits are sure to madness near allied,
And thin partitions do their bounds divide;
Else why should he, with wealth and honour blest,
Refuse his age the needful hours of rest?
Punish a body which he could not please;
Bankrupt of life, yet prodigal of ease?
And all to leave what with his toil he won,
To that unfeathered two-legged thing, a son....
In friendship false, implacable in hate;
Resolved to ruin or to rule the state;...

Then seized with fear, yet still affecting fame,
Usurped a patriot's all-atoning name.
So easy still it proves in factious times
With public zeal to cancel private crimes.

(THE DUKE OF BUCKINGHAM)

Some of their chiefs were princes of the land;
In the first rank of these did Zimri stand,
A man so various, that he seemed to be
Not one, but all mankind's epitome:
Stiff in opinions, always in the wrong,
Was everything by starts and nothing long;
But, in the course of one revolving moon,
Was chymist, fiddler, statesman, and buffoon;
Then all for women, painting, rhyming, drinking,
Besides ten thousand freaks that died in thinking.
Blest madman, who could every hour employ
With something new to wish or to enjoy!
Railing and praising were his usual themes,
And both, to show his judgment, in extremes:
So over-violent, or over-civil,
That every man with him was God or devil.

Of the many miscellaneous poems of Dryden, the curious reader will get an idea of his sustained narrative power from the *Annus Mirabilis.* The best expression of Dryden's literary genius, however, is found in 'Alexander's Feast', which is his most enduring ode, and one of the best in our language.

Prose and Criticism

As a prose writer Dryden had a very marked influence on our literature in shortening his sentences, and especially in writing naturally, without depending on literary ornamentation to give effect to what he is saying. If we compare his prose with that of Milton, or Browne, or Jeremy Taylor, we note that Dryden cares less for style than any of the others, but takes more pains to state his thought clearly and concisely, as men speak when they wish to be understood. The classical school, which followed the Restoration, looked to Dryden as a leader, and to him we owe largely that tendency to exactness of expression which marks our subsequent prose writing. With his prose, Dryden rapidly developed his critical ability, and became the foremost critic[1] of his age. His criticisms, instead of being published as independent works, were generally used as prefaces or introductions to his poetry. The best known of these criticisms are the preface to the *Fables,* 'Of Heroic Plays', 'Discourse on Satire', and especially the 'Essay of Dramatic Poesy' (1668), which attempts to lay a foundation for all literary criticism.

Dryden's Influence on Literature. Dryden's place among authors is due partly to his great influence on the succeeding age of

Westminster

classicism. Briefly, this influence may be summed up by noting the three new elements which he brought into our literature. These

[1] By a critic we mean simply one who examines the literary works of various ages, separates the good from the bad, and gives the reasons for his classification. It is noticeable that critical writings increase in an age, like that of the Restoration, when great creative works are wanting.

are: (1) the establishment of the heroic couplet as the fashion for satiric, didactic, and descriptive poetry; (2) his development of a direct, serviceable prose style such as we still cultivate; and (3) his development of the art of literary criticism in his essays and in the numerous prefaces to his poems. This is certainly a large work for one man to accomplish, and Dryden is worthy of honour, though comparatively little of what he wrote is now found on our bookshelves.

Samuel Butler (1612-1680). In marked contrast with Dryden, who devoted his life to literature and won his success by hard work, is Samuel Butler, who jumped into fame by a single, careless work, which represents not any serious intent or effort, but the pastime of an idle hour. We are to remember that, though the Royalists had triumphed in the Restoration, the Puritan spirit was not dead, nor even sleeping, and that the Puritan held steadfastly to his own principles. Against these principles of justice, truth, and liberty there was no argument, since they expressed the manhood of England; but many of the Puritan practices were open to ridicule, and the Royalists, in revenge for their defeat, began to use ridicule without mercy. During the early years of the Restoration doggerel verses ridiculing Puritanism, and burlesque—that is, a ridiculous representation of serious subjects, or a serious representation of ridiculous subjects—were the most popular form of literature with London society. Of all this burlesque and doggerel the most famous is Butler's *Hudibras,* a work to which we can trace many of the prejudices that still prevail against Puritanism.

Of Butler himself we know little; he is one of the most obscure figures in our literature. During the days of Cromwell's Protectorate he was in the employ of Sir Samuel Luke, a crabbed and extreme type of Puritan nobleman, and here he collected his material and probably wrote the first part of his burlesque, which, of course, he did not dare to publish until after the Restoration.

Hudibras is plainly modeled upon the Don Quixote of Cervantes. It describes the adventures of a fanatical justice of the peace, Sir Hudibras, and of his squire, Ralpho, in their endeavour to put down all innocent pleasures. In Hudibras and Ralpho the two extreme types of the Puritan party, Presbyterians and Independents, are mercilessly ridiculed. When the poem first appeared in public, in 1663, after circulating secretly for years in manuscript, it became at once enormously popular. The king carried a copy in his pocket, and courtiers vied with each other in quoting its most scurrilous passages. A second and a third part, continuing the adventures of Hudibras, were published in 1664 and 1668. At best the work is a wretched doggerel, but it was clever enough and strikingly original; and since it expressed the Royalist spirit towards the Puritans, it speedily found its place in a literature which reflects every phase of human life. A few odd lines are given here to show the character of the work, and to introduce the reader to the best known burlesque in our language:

Hudibras

He was in logic a great critic,
Profoundly skilled in analytic;
He could distinguish, and divide
A hair 'twixt south and southwest side;
On either which he would dispute,
Confute, change hands, and still confute;
He'd undertake to prove, by force
Of argument, a man's no horse;
He'd run in debt by disputation,
And pay with ratiocination.

For he was of that stubborn crew
Of errant saints, whom all men grant
To be the true Church Militant;
Such as do build their faith upon
The holy text of pike and gun;
Decide all controversies by
Infallible artillery;

And prove their doctrine orthodox
By apostolic blows and knocks;
Compound for sins they are inclined to,
By damning those they have no mind to.

Hobbes and Locke. Thomas Hobbes (1588-1679) is one of the writers that puzzle the historian with a doubt as to whether or not he should be included in the story of literature. The one book for which he is famous is called *Leviathan, or the Matter, Form, and Power of a Commonwealth* (1651). It is partly political, partly a philosophical book, combining two central ideas which challenge and startle the attention, namely, that self-interest is the only guiding power of humanity, and that blind submission to rulers is the only true basis of government.[1] In a word, Hobbes reduced human nature to its purely animal aspects, and then asserted confidently that there was nothing more to study. Certainly, therefore, as a reflection of the underlying spirit of Charles and his followers it has no equal in any purely literary work of the time.

John Locke (1632-1704) is famous as the author of a single great philosophical work, the *Essay concerning Human Understanding* (1690). This is a study of the nature of the human mind and of the origin of ideas, which, far more than the work of Bacon and Hobbes, is the basis upon which English philosophy has since been built. Aside from their subjects, both works are models of the new prose, direct, simple, convincing, for which Dryden and the Royal Society

---

[1] Two other principles of this book should be noted: (1) that all power originates in the people; and (2) that the object of all government is the common good. Here evidently is a democratic doctrine, which abolishes the divine right of kings; but Hobbes immediately destroys democracy by another doctrine—that the power given by the people to the ruler could not be taken away. Hence the Royalists could use the book to justify the despotism of the Stuarts on the ground that the people had chosen them. This part of the book is in direct opposition to Milton's *Defense of the English People.*

laboured. They are known to every student of philosophy, but are seldom included in a work of literature.[1]

Evelyn and Pepys. These two men, John Evelyn (1620-1706) and Samuel Pepys (1633-1703), are famous as the writers of diaries, in which they jotted down the daily occurrences of their own lives, without any thought that the world would ever see or be interested in what they had written.

Evelyn was the author of *Sylva*, the first book on trees and forestry in English, and *Terra,* which is the first attempt at a scientific study of agriculture; but the world has lost sight of these two good books, while it cherishes his diary, which extends over the greater part of his life and gives us vivid pictures of society in his time, and especially of the frightful corruption of the royal court.

Pepys's Diary

Pepys began life in a small way as a clerk in a government office, but soon rose by his diligence and industry to be Secretary of the Admiralty. Here he was brought into contact with every grade of society, from the king's ministers to the poor sailors of the fleet. Being inquisitive as a blue jay, he investigated the rumours and gossip of the court, as well as the small affairs of his neighbours, and wrote them all down in his diary with evident interest. But because he chattered most freely, and told his little book a great many secrets which it were not well for the world to know, he concealed everything in shorthand—and here again he was like the blue jay, which carries off and hides every bright trinket it discovers. The *Diary* covers the years from 1660 to 1669, and gossips about everything, from

[1] Locke's *Treatises on Government* should also be mentioned, for they are of profound interest to American students of history and political science. It was from Locke that the framers of the Declaration of Independence and of the Constitution drew many of their ideas, and even some of their most striking phrases. 'All men are endowed with certain inalienable rights'; 'life, liberty, and the pursuit of happiness'; 'the origin and basis of government is in the consent of the governed'—these and many more familiar and striking expressions are from Locke. It is interesting to note that he was appointed to draft a constitution for the new province of Carolina; but his work was rejected—probably bacause it was too democratic for the age in which he lived.

his own position and duties at the office, his dress and kitchen and cook and children, to the great political intrigues of office and the scandals of high society. No other such minute picture of the daily life of an age has been written. Yet for a century and a half it remained entirely unknown, and not until 1825 was Pepys's shorthand deciphered and published. Since then it has been widely read, and is still one of the most interesting examples of diary writing that we possess. Following are a few extracts,[1] covering only a few days in April, 1663, from which one may infer the minute and interesting character of the work that this clerk, politician, president of the Royal Society, and general busybody wrote to please himself:

April 1st. I went to the Temple to my Cozen Roger Pepys, to see and talk with him a little: who tells me that, with much ado, the Parliament do agree to throw down Popery; but he says it is with so much spite and passion, and an endeavour of bringing all Nonconformists into the same condition, that he is afeard matters will not go so well as he could wish.... To my office all the afternoon; Lord! how Sir J. Minnes, like a mad coxcomb, did swear and stamp, swearing that Commissioner Pett hath still the old heart against the King that ever he had, ... and all the damnable reproaches in the world, at which I was ashamed, but said little; but, upon the whole, I find him still a foole, led by the nose with stories told by Sir W. Batten, whether with or without reason. So, vexed in my mind to see things ordered so unlike gentlemen, or men of reason, I went home and to bed.

3d. To White Hall and to Chappell, which being most monstrous full, I could not go into my pew, but sat among the quire. Dr. Creeton, the Scotchman, preached a most admirable, good, learned, honest, and most severe sermon, yet comicall.... He railed bitterly ever and anon against John Calvin and his brood, the Presbyterians, and against the present terme, now in use, of 'tender consciences'. He ripped up Hugh Peters (calling him the execrable skellum), his preaching and stirring up the mayds of the city to bring in their bodkins and thimbles. Thence going out of White Hall, I met Captain Grove, who did give me a letter directed to myself from himself. I discerned money to be in it, and took it, knowing, as I found it

[1] A few slight changes and omissions from the original text, as given in Wheatley's edition of Pepys (London, 1892,9 vols.), are not indicated in these brief quotations.

to be, the proceed of the place I have got him, the taking up of vessels for Tangier. But I did not open it till I came home to my office, and there I broke it open, not looking into it till all the money was out, that I might say I saw no money in the paper, if ever I should be questioned about it. There was a piece of gold and 4£ in silver.

4th. To my office. Home to dinner, whither by and by comes Roger Pepys, etc. Very merry at, before, and after dinner, and the more for that my dinner was great, and most neatly dressed by our owne only mayde. We had a fricasee of rabbits and chickens, a leg of mutton boiled, three carps in a dish, a great dish of a side of lambe, a dish of roasted pigeons, a dish of four lobsters, three tarts, a lamprey pie (a most rare pie), a dish of anchovies, good wine of several sorts, and all things mighty noble and to my great content.

5th (Lord's day). Up and spent the morning, till the Barber came, in reading in my chamber part of Osborne's Advice to his Son, which I shall not never enough admire for sense and language, and being by and by trimmed, to Church, myself, wife, Ashwell, etc. Home and, while dinner was prepared, to my office to read over my vows with great affection and to very good purpose. Then to church again, where a simple bawling young Scot preached.

19th (Easter day). Up and this day put on my close-kneed coloured suit, which, with new stockings of the colour, with belt and new gilt-handled sword, is very handsome. To church alone, and after dinner to church again, where the young Scotchman preaching, I slept all the while. After supper, fell in discourse of dancing, and I find that Ashwell hath a very fine carriage, which makes my wife almost ashamed of herself to see herself so outdone; but tomorrow she begins to learn to dance for a month or two. So to prayers and to bed. Will being gone, with my leave, to his father's this day for a day or two, to take physique these holydays.

23d. St. George's day and Coronacion, the King and Court being at Windsor, at the installing of the King of Denmarke by proxy and the Duke of Monmouth.... Spent the evening with my father. At cards till late, and being at supper, my boy being sent for some mustard to a neat's tongue, the rogue staid half an houre in the streets, it seems at a bonfire, at which I was very angry, and resolve to beat him tomorrow.

24th. Up betimes, and with my salt eele went down into the parler and there got my boy and did beat him till I was fain to take breath two or three times, yet for all I am afeard it will make the boy never the better, he is grown so hardened in his tricks, which I am sorry for, he being capable of making a brave man, and is a boy that I and my wife love very well.

Summary of the Restoration Period. The chief thing to note in England during the Restoration is the tremendous social reaction from the restraints of Puritanism, which suggests the wide swing of a pendulum from one extreme to the other. For a generation many natural pleasures had been suppressed; now the theatres were reopened, bull and bear baiting revived, and sports, music, dancing—a wild delight in the pleasures and vanities of this world replaced that absorption in 'other-worldliness' which characterized the extreme of Puritanism.

In literature the change is no less marked. From the Elizabethan drama playwrights turned to coarse, evil scenes, which presently disgusted the people and were driven from the stage. From romance, writers turned to realism; from Italian influence with its exuberance of imagination they turned to France, and learned to repress the emotions, to follow the head rather than the heart, and to write in a clear, concise, formal style, according to set rules. Poets turned from the noble blank verse of Shakespeare and Milton, from the variety and melody which had characterized English poetry since Chaucer's day, to the monotonous heroic couplet with its mechanical perfection.

The greatest writer of the age is John Dryden, who established the heroic couplet as the prevailing verse form in English poetry, and who developed a new and serviceable prose style suited to the practical needs of the age. The popular ridicule of Puritanism in burlesque and doggerel is best exemplified in Butler's Hudibras. The realistic tendency, the study of facts and of men as they are, is shown in the work of the Royal Society, in the philosophy of Hobbes and Locke, and in the diaries of Evelyn and Pepys, with their minute pictures of social life. The age was one of transition from the exuberance and vigour of Renaissance literature to the formality and polish of the Augustan Age. In strong contrast with the preceding ages, comparatively little of Restoration literature is familiar to modern readers.

Selections for Reading. *Dryden.* Alexander's Feast, Song for St. Cecilia's Day, selections from Absalom and Achitophel, Religio Laici, Hind and Panther, Annus Mirabilis—in Manly's English Poetry, or Ward's English Poets, or Cassell's National Library; Palamon and Arcite (Dryden's version of Chaucer's tale), in Standard English Classics, Riverside Literature, etc.; Dryden's An Essay of Dramatic Poesy, in Manly's, or Garnett's, English Prose.

Butler. Selections from Hudibras, in Manly's English Poetry, Ward's English Poets, or Morley's Universal Library.

Pepys. Selections in Manly's English Prose; the Diary in Everyman's Library.

Bibliography. History. *Textbook,* Montgomery, pp. 257-280; Cheyney, pp. 466-514; Green, ch. 9; Traill; Gardiner; Macaulay.

Special Works. Sydney's Social Life in England from the Restoration to the Revolution; Airy's The English Restoration and Louis XIV; Hale's The Fall of the Stuarts.

Literature. Garnett's The Age of Dryden; Dowden's Puritan and Anglican.

Dryden. Poetical Works, with Life, edited by Christie; the same, edited by Noyes, in Cambridge Poets Series; Life and Works (18 vols.), by Walter Scott, revised (1893) by Saintsbury; Essays, edited by Ker; Life, by Saintsbury (English Men of Letters); Macaulay's Essay; Lowell's Essay, in Among My Books (or in Literary Essays, vol. 3); Dowden's Essay, supra.

Butler. Hudibras, in Morley's Universal Library; Poetical Works, edited by Johnson; Dowden's Essay, supra.

Pepys. Diary in Everyman's Library; the same, edited by Wheatley (8 vols.); Wheatley's Samuel Pepys and the World He Lived In; Stevenson's Essay, in Familiar Studies of Men and Books.

The Restoration Drama. Plays in the Mermaid Series; Hazlitt's Lectures on the English Comic Writers; Meredith's Essay on Comedy and the Comic Spirit; Lamb's Essay on the Artificial Comedy; Thackeray's Essay on Congreve, in English Humorists.

Suggestive Questions. 1. What marked change in social conditions followed the Restoration? How are these changes reflected in literature?

2. What are the chief characteristics of Restoration literature? Why is this period called the Age of French influence? What new tendencies were introduced? What effect did the Royal Society and the study of science have upon English prose? What is meant by realism? by formalism?

3. What is meant by the heroic couplet? Explain why it became the prevailing form of English poetry. What are its good qualities and its defects?

Name some well-known poems which are written in couplets. How do Dryden's couplets compare with Chaucer's? Can you explain the difference?

4. Give a brief account of Dryden's life. What are his chief poetical works? For what new object did he use poetry? Is satire a poetical subject? Why is a poetical satire more effective than a satire in prose? What was Dryden's contribution to English prose? What influence did he exert on our literature?

5. What is Butler's *Hudibras?* Explain its popularity. Read a passage and comment upon it, first, as satire; second, as a description of the Puritans. Is *Hudibras* poetry? Why?

6. Name the philosophers and political economists of this period. Can you explain why Hobbes should call his work *Leviathan?* What important American documents show the influence of Locke?

7. Tell briefly the story of Pepys and his *Diary.* What light does the latter throw on the life of the age? Is the Diary a work of literature? Why?

CHRONOLOGY

Last Half of the Seventeenth Century

History	Literature
1649. Execution of Charles I	
1649-1660. Commonwealth	1651. Hobbes's Leviathan
1660. Restoration of Charles II	1660-1669. Pepys's Diary
	1662. Royal Society founded
	1663. Butler's Hudibras
1665-1666. Plague and Fire of London War with Holland	
1667. Dutch fleet in the Thames	1667. Milton's Paradise Lost. Dryden's Annus Mirabilis
	1663-1694. Dryden's dramas
	1671. Paradise Regained
	1678. Pilgrim's Progress published
1680. Rise of Whigs and Tories	
	1681. Dryden's Absalom and Achitophel

History	Literature
1685. James II Monmouth's Rebellion	
	1687. Newton's Principia proves the law of gravitation
1688. English Revolution, William of Orange called to throne	
1689. Bill of Rights. Toleration Act	
	1690. Locke's Human Understanding
	1698. Jeremy Collier attacks stage
	1700. Death of Dryden

CHAPTER 9

EIGHTEENTH-CENTURY LITERATURE (1700-1800)

I. AUGUSTAN OR CLASSIC AGE

History of the Period. The Revolution of 1688, which banished the last of the Stuart kings and called William of Orange to the throne, marks the end of the long struggle for political freedom in England. Thereafter the Englishman spent his tremendous energy, which his forbears had largely spent in fighting for freedom, in endless political discussions and in efforts to improve his government. In order to bring about reforms, votes were now necessary; and to get votes the people of England must be approached with ideas, facts, arguments, information. So the newspaper was born,[1] and literature in its widest sense, including the book, the newspaper, and the magazine, became the chief instrument of a nation's progress.

The first half of the eighteenth century is remarkable for the rapid social development in England. Hitherto men had been more or less governed by the narrow, isolated standards of the Middle Ages, and when they differed they fell speedily to blows. Now for the first time they set themselves to the task of learning the art of living together, while still holding different opinions. In a single generation nearly two thousand public coffee-houses, each a centre of sociability, sprang up in London alone, and the number of private clubs

Social Development

[1] The first daily newspaper, *The Daily Courant*, appeared in London in 1702.

is quite as astonishing.[1] This new social life had a marked effect in polishing men's words and manners. The typical Londoner of Queen Anne's day was still rude, and a little vulgar in his tastes; the city was still very filthy, the streets unlighted and infested at night by bands of rowdies and 'Mohawks'; but outwardly men sought to refine their manners according to prevailing standards; and to be elegant, to have 'good form', was a man's first duty, whether he entered society or wrote literature. One can hardly read a book or poem of the age without feeling this superficial elegance. Government still had its opposing Tory and Whig parties, and the Church was divided into Catholics, Anglicans, and Dissenters; but the growing social life offset many antagonisms, producing at least the outward impression of peace and unity. Nearly every writer of the age busied himself with religion as well as with party politics, the scientist Newton as sincerely as the churchman Barrow, the philosophical Locke no less earnestly than the evangelical Wesley; but nearly all tempered their zeal with moderation, and argued from reason and Scripture, or used delicate satire upon their opponents, instead of denouncing them as followers of Satan. There were exceptions, of course; but the general tendency of the age was toward toleration. Man had found himself in the long struggle for personal liberty; now he turned to the task of discovering his neighbour, of finding in Whig and Tory, in Catholic and Protestant, in Anglican and Dissenter, the same general human characteristics that he found in himself. This good work was helped, moreover, by the spread of education and by the growth of the national spirit, following the victories of Marlborough on the Continent. In the midst of heated argument it needed only a word—Gibraltar, Blenheim, Ramillies, Malplaquet—or a poem of victory written in a garret[2] to tell the patriotic people that under their many differences they were all alike Englishmen.

In the latter half of the century the political and social progress is almost bewildering. The modern form of cabinet government responsible to Parliament and the people had been established under George I; and in 1757 the cynical and corrupt practices of Walpole, premier of the first Tory cabinet, were replaced by the more enlightened policies of Pitt. Schools were established; clubs and coffee houses increased; books and

---

[1] See Lecky, *England in the Eighteenth Century.*

[2] Addison's 'Campaign' (1704), written to celebrate the battle of Blenheim.

magazines multiplied until the press was the greatest visible power in England; the modern great dailies, the *Chronicle, Post,* and *Times,* began their career of public education. Religiously, all the churches of England felt the quickening power of that tremendous spiritual revival known as Methodism, under the preaching of Wesley and Whitefield. Outside her own borders three great men—Clive in India, Wolfe on the Plains of Abraham, Cook in Australia and the islands of the Pacific—were unfurling the banner of St. George over the untold wealth of new lands, and spreading the worldwide empire of the Anglo-Saxons.

Literary Characteristics. In every preceding age we have noted especially the poetical works, which constitute, according to Matthew Arnold, the glory of English literature. Now for the first time we must chronicle the triumph of English prose. A multitude of practical interests arising from the new social and political conditions demanded expression, not simply in books, but more especially in pamphlets, magazines, and newspapers. Poetry was inadequate for such a task; hence the development of prose, of the 'unfettered word', as Dante calls it—a development which astonishes us by its rapidity and excellence. The graceful elegance of Addison's essays, the terse vigour of Swift's satires, the artistic finish of Fielding's novels, the sonorous eloquence of Gibbon's history and of Burke's orations—these have no parallel in the poetry of the age. Indeed, poetry itself became prosaic in this respect, that it was used not for creative works of imagination, but for essays, for satire, for criticism—for exactly the same practical ends as was prose. The poetry of the first half of the century, as typified in the work of Pope, is polished and witty enough, but artificial; it lacks fire, fine feeling, enthusiasm, the glow of the Elizabethan Age and the moral earnestness of Puritanism. In a word, it interests us as a study of life, rather than delights or inspires us by its appeal to the imagination. The variety and excellence of prose works, and the development of a serviceable prose style, which had been begun by Dryden, until it served to express clearly every human interest and emotion—these are the chief literary glories of the eighteenth century.

An Age of Prose

In the literature of the preceding age we noted two marked tendencies—the tendency to realism in subject-matter, and the tendency to polish and refinement of expression. Both these tendencies were continued in the Augustan Age, and are seen clearly in the poetry of Pope, who brought the couplet to perfection, and in the prose of Addison. A third tendency is shown in the prevalence of satire, resulting from the unfortunate union of politics with literature. We have already noted the power of the press in this age, and the perpetual strife of political parties. Nearly every writer of the first half of the century was used and rewarded by Whigs or Tories for satirizing their enemies and for advancing their special political interests. Pope was a marked exception, but he nevertheless followed the prose writers in using satire too largely in his poetry. Now satire—that is, a literary work which searches out the faults of men or institutions in order to hold them up to ridicule—is at best a destructive kind of criticism. A satirist is like a labourer who clears away the ruins and rubbish of an old house before the architect and builders begin on a new and beautiful structure. The work may sometimes be necessary, but it rarely arouses our enthusiasm. While the satires of Pope, Swift, and Addison are doubtless the best in our language, we hardly place them with our great literature, which is always constructive in spirit; and we have the feeling that all these men were capable of better things than they ever wrote.

Satire

The Classic Age. The period we are studying is known to us by various names. It is often called the Age of Queen Anne; but, unlike Elizabeth, this 'meekly stupid' queen had practically no influence upon our literature. The name Classic Age is more often heard; but in using it we should remember clearly these three different ways in which the word 'classic' is applied to literature: (1) the term 'classic' refers, in general, to writers of the highest rank in any nation. As used in our literature, it was first applied to the works of the great Greek and Roman writers, like Homer and Virgil; and any English book which followed the simple and noble method of these writers was said to have a classic style. Later the term was enlarged to cover the great literary works of other ancient nations; so that the Bible and the Avestas, as well as the Iliad and the Æneid, are called classics. (2) Every national literature has at least one period in which an unusual number of great writers are producing books, and this is called the classic period of a nation's literature. Thus the reign of Augustus is the classic or golden age of Rome; the generation of Dante is the classic age of Italian literature; the age of Louis XIV is the French classic age; and the age of Queen Anne is often called the classic age of England. (3) The word 'classic' acquired an entirely different meaning in the period we are studying; and we shall better understand this by reference to the preceding ages. The Elizabethan writers were led by patriotism, by enthusiasm, and, in general, by romantic emotions. They wrote in a natural style, without regard to rules; and though they exaggerated and used too many words, their works are delightful because of their vigour and freshness and fine feeling. In the following age patriotism had largely disappeared from politics and enthusiasm from literature. Poets no longer wrote naturally, but artificially, with strange and fantastic verse forms to give effect, since fine feeling was wanting. And this is the general character of the poetry of the Puritan Age.[1] Gradually our writers rebelled against the exaggerations of both the natural and the fantastic style. They demanded that poetry should follow exact rules; and in this they were influenced by French writers, especially by Boileau and Rapin, who insisted on precise methods of writing poetry, and who professed to have discovered their rules in the classics of Horace and Aristotle. In our study of the Elizabethan drama we noted the good influence of the classic movement in insisting upon that beauty of form and definiteness of expression which characterize the dramas of Greece and Rome; and in the work of Dryden and his followers we see a revival of classicism in the

---

[1] Great writers in every age, men like Shakespeare and Milton, make their own style. They are therefore not included in this summary. Among the minor writers also there are exceptions to the rule; and fine feeling is often manifest in the poetry of Donne, Herbert, Vaughan, and Herrick.

effort to make English literature conform to rules established by the great writers of other nations. At first the results were excellent, especially in prose; but as the creative vigour of the Elizabethans was lacking in this age, writing by rule soon developed a kind of elegant formalism, which suggests the elabourate social code of the time. Just as a gentleman might not act naturally, but must follow exact rules in doffing his hat, or addressing a lady, or entering a room, or wearing a wig, or offering his snuffbox to a friend, so our writers lost individuality and became formal and artificial. The general tendency of literature was to look at life critically, to emphasize intellect rather than imagination, the form rather than the content of a sentence. Writers strove to repress all emotion and enthusiasm, and to use only precise and elegant methods of expression. This is what is often meant by the 'classicism' of the ages of Pope and Johnson. It refers to the critical, intellectual spirit of many writers, to the fine polish of their heroic couplets or the elegance of their prose, and not to any resemblance which their work bears to true classic literature. In a word, the classic movement had become pseudo-classic, that is a false or sham classicism; and the latter term is now often used to designate a considerable part of eighteenth-century literature.[1] To avoid this critical difficulty we have adopted the term Augustan Age, a name chosen by the writers themselves, who saw in Pope, Addison, Swift, Johnson, and Burke the modern parallels to Horace, Virgil, Cicero, and all that brilliant company who made Roman literature famous in the days of Augustus.

---

[1] We have endeavoured here simply to show the meaning of terms in general use in our literature; but it must be remembered that it is impossible to classify or to give a descriptive name to the writers of any period or century. While 'classic' or 'pseudoclassic' may apply to a part of eighteenth-century literature, every age has both its romantic and its classic movements. In this period the revolt against classicism is shown in the revival of romantic poetry under Gray, Collins, Burns, and Thomson, and in the beginning of the English novel under Defoe, Richardson, and Fielding. These poets and novelists, who have little or no connection with classicism, belong chronologically to the period we are studying. They are reserved for special treatment in the sections following.

ALEXANDER POPE (1688-1744)

Pope is in many respects a unique figure. In the first place, he was for a generation 'the poet' of a great nation. To be sure, poetry was limited in the early eighteenth century; there were few lyrics, little or no love poetry, no epics, no dramas or songs of nature worth considering; but in the narrow field of satiric and didactic verse Pope was the undisputed master. His influence completely dominated the poetry of his age, and many foreign writers, as well as the majority of English poets, looked to him as their model. Second, he was a remarkably clear and adequate reflection of the spirit of the age in which he lived. There is hardly an ideal, a belief, a doubt, a fashion, a whim of Queen Anne's time, that is not neatly expressed in his poetry. Third, he was the only important writer of that age who gave his whole life to letters. Swift was a clergyman and politician; Addison was secretary of state; other writers depended on patrons or politics or pensions for fame and a livelihood; but Pope was independent, and had no profession but literature. And fourth, by the sheer force of his ambition he won his place, and held it, in spite of religious prejudice, and in the face of physical and temperamental obstacles that would have discouraged a stronger man. For Pope was deformed and sickly, dwarfish in soul and body. He knew little of the world of nature or of the world of the human heart. He was lacking, apparently, in noble feeling, and instinctively chose a lie when the truth had manifestly more advantages. Yet this jealous, peevish, waspish little man became the most famous poet of his age and the acknowledged leader of English literature. We record the fact with wonder and admiration; but we do not attempt to explain it.

Life. Pope was born in London in 1688, the year of the Revolution. His parents were both Catholics, who presently removed from London and settled in Binfield, near Windsor, where the poet's childhood was passed. Partly because of an unfortunate prejudice against Catholics in the public schools, partly because of his own weakness and deformity, Pope received very little school education, but browsed for himself among English books and picked up a smattering of the classics. Very early he began to write poetry, and records the fact with his usual vanity:

> As yet a child, nor yet a fool to fame,
> I lisped in numbers, for the numbers came.

Being debarred by his religion from many desirable employments, he resolved to make literature his life work; and in this he resembled Dryden, who, he tells us, was his only master, though much of his work seems to depend on Boileau, the French poet and critic.[1] When only sixteen years old he had written his 'Pastorals'; a few years later appeared his 'Essay on Criticism', which made him famous. With the publication of the *Rape of the Lock,* in 1712, Pope's name was known and honoured all over England, and this dwarf of twenty-four years, by the sheer force of his own ambition, had jumped to the foremost place in English letters. It was soon after this that Voltaire called him 'the best poet of England and, at present, of all the world',—which is about as near the truth as Voltaire generally gets in his numerous universal judgments. For the next twelve years Pope was busy with poetry, especially with his translations of Homer; and his work was so successful financially that he bought a villa at Twickenham, on the Thames, and remained happily independent of wealthy patrons for a livelihood.

Led by his success, Pope returned to London and for a time endeavoured to live the gay and dissolute life which was supposed to be suitable for a literary genius; but he was utterly unfitted for it, mentally and physically, and soon retired to Twickenham. There he gave himself up to poetry, manufactured a little garden more artificial than his verses, and cultivated his friendship with Martha Blount, with whom for many years he spent a good part of each day, and who remained faithful to him to the end of his life. At Twickenham he wrote his *Moral Epistles* (poetical satires modelled after Horace) and revenged himself upon all his critics in the bitter abuse of the *Dunciad.* He died in 1744 and was buried at Twickenham, his religion preventing him from the honour, which was certainly his due, of a resting place in Westminster Abbey.

---

[1] Pope's satires, for instance, are strongly suggested in Boileau; his *Rape of the Lock* is much like the mock-heroic *Le Lutrin;* and the 'Essay on Criticism', which made him famous, is an English edition and improvement of *L' Art Poetique.* The last was, in turn, a combination of the Ars Poetica of Horace and of many well-known rules of the classicists.

Works of Pope. For convenience we may separate Pope's work into three groups, corresponding to the early, middle, and later period of his life. In the first he wrote his 'Pastorals', 'Windsor Forest', 'Messiah', 'Essay on Criticism', 'Eloise to Abelard', and the *Rape of the Lock;* in the second, his translations of Homer; in the third the *Dunciad* and the *Epistles,* the latter containing the famous 'Essay on Man' and the 'Epistle to Dr. Arbuthnot', which is in truth his 'Apologia', and in which alone we see Pope's life from his own viewpoint.

Essay on Criticism

The 'Essay on Criticism' sums up the art of poetry as taught first by Horace, then by Boileau and the eighteenth-century classicists. Though written in heroic couplets, we hardly consider this as a poem but rather as a storehouse of critical maxims. 'For fools rush in where angels fear to tread'; 'To err is human, to forgive divine', 'A little learning is a dangerous thing',—these lines, and many more like them from the same source, have found their way into our common speech, and are used, without thinking of the author, whenever we need an apt quotation.

Rape of the Lock

The Rape of the Lock is a masterpiece of its kind, and comes nearer to being a 'creation' than anything else that Pope has written. The occasion of the famous poem was trivial enough. A fop at the court of Queen Anne, one Lord Petre, snipped a lock of hair from the abundant curls of a pretty maid of honour named Arabella Fermor. The young lady resented it, and the two families were plunged into a quarrel which was the talk of London. Pope, being appealed to, seized the occasion to construct, not a ballad, as the Cavaliers would have done, nor an epigram, as French poets love to do, but a long poem in which all the mannerisms of society are pictured in minutest detail and satirized with the most delicate wit. The first edition, consisting of two cantos, was published in 1712; and it is amazing now to read of the trivial character of London court life at the time when English soldiers were battling for a great continent in the French and Indian wars. Its instant success caused Pope to lengthen the poem by three more cantos; and in order to make a more perfect burlesque of an epic poem, he introduces gnomes, sprites, sylphs, and salamanders,[1] instead of the gods of the great epics, with which his readers were familiar. The poem is modelled after two foreign satires: *Boileau's Le Lutrin* (reading desk), a satire on the French clergy, who raised a huge quarrel over the location of a lectern; and *La Secchia Rapita* (stolen bucket), a famous Italian satire on the petty causes of the endless Italian wars. Pope, however, went far ahead of his masters in style and in delicacy of handling a mock-heroic theme, and during his lifetime the *Rape of the Lock* was considered as the greatest poem of its kind in all literature. The poem is still well worth reading; for as an expression of the artificial life of the age—of its cards, parties, toilettes, lapdogs, tea-drinking, snuff-taking, and idle vanities—it is as perfect in its way as *Tamburlaine,* which reflects the boundless ambition of the Elizabethans.

Pope's Translations

The fame of Pope's *Iliad,* which was financially the most successful of his books, was due to the fact that he interpreted Homer in the elegant, artificial language of his own age. Not only do his words follow literary fashions, but even the Homeric characters lose their strength and become fashionable men of the court. So the criticism of the scholar Bentley was most appropriate when he said, 'It is a pretty poem, Mr. Pope, but you must not call it Homer'. Pope translated the entire *Iliad* and half of the *Odyssey;* and the latter work was finished by two Cambridge scholars, Elijah Fenton and William Broome, who imitated the mechanical couplets so perfectly that it is difficult to distinguish their work from that of the greatest poet of the age. A single selection is given to show how, in the nobler passages, even Pope may faintly suggest the elemental grandeur of Homer:

> The troops exulting sat in order round,
> And beaming fires illumined all the ground.

[1] These are the four kinds of spirits inhabiting the four elemetns, according to the Rosicrucians—a fantastic sect of spiritualists of the age. In the dedication of the poem Pope says he took the idea from a French book called *Le Comte de Gabalis.*

As when the moon, refulgent lamp of night,
O'er Heaven's clear azure spreads her sacred light,
When not a breath disturbs the deep serene,
And not a cloud o'ercasts the solemn scene;
Around her throne the vivid planets roll,
And stars unnumbered gild the glowing pole,
O'er the dark trees a yellower verdure shed,
And tip with silver every mountain's head.

Essay on Man

The 'Essay' is the best known and the most quoted of all Pope's works. Except in form it is not poetry, and when one considers it as an essay and reduces it to plain prose, it is found to consist of numerous literary ornaments without any very solid structure of thought to rest upon. The purpose of the essay is, in Pope's words, to 'vindicate the ways of God to Man'; and as there are no unanswered problems in Pope's philosophy, the vindication is perfectly accomplished in four poetical epistles, concerning man's relations to the universe, to himself, to society, and to happiness. The final result is summed up in a few well-known lines:

All nature is but art, unknown to thee;
All chance, direction which thou canst not see;
All discord, harmony not understood;
All partial evil, universal good:
And, spite of pride, in erring reason's spite,
One truth is clear, whatever is, is right.

Like the 'Essay on Criticism', the poem abounds in quotable lines, such as the following, which make the entire work well worth reading:

Hope springs eternal in the human breast:
Man never is, but always to be blest.

Know then thyself, presume not God to scan;
The proper study of Mankind is Man.

The same ambition can destroy or save,
And makes a patriot as it makes a knave.

Honour and shame from no condition rise;
Act well your part, there all the honour lies.

Vice is a monster of so frightful mien,
As, to be hated, needs but to be seen;
Yet seen too oft, familiar with her face,
We first endure, then pity, then embrace.

Behold the child, by Nature's kindly law,
Pleased with a rattle, tickled with a straw:
Some livelier plaything gives his youth delight,
A little louder, but as empty quite:
Scarfs, garters, gold, amuse his riper stage,
And beads and prayer books are the toys of age:
Pleased with this bauble still, as that before;
Till tired he sleeps, and Life's poor play is o'er.[1]

Miscellaneous Works

The Dunciad (that is the 'Iliad of the Dunces') began originally as a controversy concerning Shakespeare, but turned out to be a coarse and revengeful satire upon all the literary men of the age who had aroused Pope's anger by their criticism or lack of appreciation of his genius. Though brilliantly written and immensely popular at one time, its present effect on the reader is to arouse a sense of pity that a man of such acknowledged power and position should abuse both by devoting his talents to personal spite and petty quarrels. Among the rest of his numerous works the reader will find Pope's estimate of himself best set forth in his 'Epistle to Dr. Arbuthnot', and it will be well to close our study of this strange mixture of vanity and greatness with 'The Universal Prayer', which shows at least that Pope had considered, and judged himself, and that all further judgment is consequently superfluous.

---

[1] Compare this with Shakespeare's 'All the world's a stage', in *As You Like It,* II, 7.

Jonathan Swift (1667-1745)

In each of Marlowe's tragedies we have the picture of a man dominated by a single passion, the lust of power for its own sake. In each we see that a powerful man without self-control is like a dangerous instrument in the hands of a child; and the tragedy ends in the destruction of the man by the ungoverned power which he possesses. The life of Swift is just such a living tragedy. He had the power of gaining wealth, like the hero of the *Jew of Malta;* yet he used it scornfully, and in sad irony left what remained to him of a large property to found a hospital for lunatics. By hard work he won enormous literary power, and used it to satirize our common humanity. He wrested political power from the hands of the Tories, and used it to insult the very men who had helped him, and who held his fate in their hands. By his dominant personality he exercised a curious power over women, and used it brutally to make them feel their inferiority. Being loved supremely by two good women, he brought sorrow and death to both, and endless misery to himself. So his power brought always tragedy in its wake. It is only when we remember his life of struggle and disappointment and bitterness that we can appreciate the personal quality in his satire, and perhaps find some sympathy for this greatest genius of all the Augustan writers.

Jonathan Swift

Life. Swift was born in Dublin, of English parents, in 1667. His father died before he was born; his mother was poor, and Swift, though proud as Lucifer, was compelled to accept aid from relatives, who gave it grudgingly. At the Kilkenny school, and especially at Dublin University, he detested the curriculum, reading only what appealed to his own nature;

but, since a degree was necessary to his success, he was compelled to accept it as a favour from the examiners, whom he despised in his heart. After graduation the only position open to him was with a distant relative, Sir William Temple, who gave him the position of private secretary largely on account of the unwelcome relationship.

Temple was a statesman and an excellent diplomatist; but he thought himself to be a great writer as well, and he entered into a literary controversy concerning the relative merits of the classics and modern literature. Swift's first notable work, *The Battle of the Books,* written at this time but not published, is a keen satire upon both parties in the controversy. The first touch of bitterness shows itself here; for Swift was in a galling position for a man of his pride, knowing his intellectual superiority to the man who employed him, and yet being looked upon as a servant and eating at the servants' table. Thus he spent ten of the best years of his life in the pretty Moor Park, Surrey, growing more bitter each year and steadily cursing his fate. Nevertheless he read and studied widely, and, after his position with Temple grew unbearable, quarrelled with his patron, took orders, and entered the Church of England. Some years later we find him settled in the little church of Laracor, Ireland—a country which he disliked intensely, but whither he went because no other 'living' was open to him.

In Ireland, faithful to his church duties, Swift laboured to better the condition of the unhappy people around him. Never before had the poor of his parishes been so well cared for; but Swift chafed under his yoke, growing more and more irritated as he saw small men advanced to large positions, while he remained unnoticed in a little country church—largely because he was too proud and too blunt with those who might have advanced him. While at Laracor he finished his *Tale of a Tub,* a satire on the various churches of the day, which was published in London with the *Battle of the Books* in 1704. The work brought him into notice as the most powerful satirist of the age, and he soon gave up his church to enter the strife of party politics. The cheap pamphlet was then the most powerful political weapon known; and as Swift had no equal at pamphlet writing, he soon became a veritable dictator. For several years, especially from 1710 to 1713, Swift was one of the most important figures in London. The Whigs feared the lash of his satire; the Tories feared to lose his support. He was courted, flattered, cajoled on every side; but the use

Trinity College, Dublin

he made of his new power is sad to contemplate. An unbearable arrogance took possession of him. Lords, statesmen, even ladies were compelled to sue for his favour and to apologize for every fancied slight to his egoism. It is at this time that he writes in his *Journal to Stella:*

Mr. Secretary told me the Duke of Buckingham had been talking much about me and desired my acquaintance. I answered it could not be, for he had not yet made sufficient advances; then Shrewsbury said he thought the Duke was not used to make advances. I said I could not help that, for I always expected advances in proportion to men's quality, and more from a Duke than any other man.

Writing to the Duchess of Queensberry he says:

I am glad you know your duty; for it has been a known and established rule above twenty years in England that the first advances have been constantly made me by all ladies who aspire to my acquaintance, and the greater their quality the greater were their advances.

When the Tories went out of power Swift's position became uncertain. He expected and had probably been promised a bishopric in England, with a seat among the peers of the realm; but the Tories offered him instead the place of dean of St. Patrick's Cathedral in Dublin. It was galling to a man of his proud spirit; but after his merciless satire on religion, in *The Tale of a Tub,* any ecclesiastical position in England was rendered impossible. Dublin was the best he could get, and he accepted it bitterly, once more cursing the fate which he had brought upon himself.

With his return to Ireland begins the last act in the tragedy of his life. His best known literary work, *Gulliver's Travels,* was done here; but the bitterness of life grew slowly to insanity, and a frightful personal sorrow, of which he never spoke, reached its climax in the death of Esther Johnson, a beautiful young woman, who had loved Swift ever since the two had met in Temple's household, and to whom he had written his *Journal to Stella.* During the last years of his life a brain disease, of which he had shown frequent symptoms, fastened its terrible hold upon Swift, and he became by turns an idiot and a madman. He died in 1745, and when his will was opened it was found that he had left all his property to found St. Patrick's Asylum for lunatics and incurables. It stands today as the most suggestive monument of his peculiar genius.

The Works of Swift. From Swift's life one can readily foresee the kind of literature he will produce. Taken together his works are a monstrous satire on humanity; and the spirit of that satire is shown clearly in a little incident of his first days in London. There was in the city at that time a certain astrologer named Partridge, who duped the public by calculating nativities from the stars, and by selling a yearly almanac predicting future events. Swift, who hated all shams, wrote, with a great show of learning, his famous *Bickerstaff Almanac,* containing 'Predictions for the Year 1708, as Determined by the Unerring Stars'. As Swift rarely signed his name to any literary work, letting it stand or fall on its own merits, his burlesque appeared over the pseudonym of Isaac Bickerstaff, a name afterwards made famous by Steele in *The Tatler.* Among the predictions was the following:

> My first prediction is but a trifle; yet I will mention it to show how ignorant those sottish pretenders to astrology are in their own concerns: it relates to Partridge the almanack maker; I have consulted the star of his nativity by my own rules, and find he will infallibly die upon the 29th of March next, about eleven at night, of a raging fever; therefore I advise him to consider of it, and settle his affairs in time.

On March 30, the day after the prediction was to be fulfilled, there appeared in the newspapers a letter from a revenue officer giving the details of Partridge's death, with the doings of the bailiff and the coffin maker; and on the following morning appeared an elabourate 'Elegy of Mr. Partridge'. When poor Partridge, who suddenly found himself without customers, published a denial of the burial, Swift answered with an elabourate 'Vindication of Isaac Bickerstaff', in which he proved by astrological rules that Partridge was dead, and that the man now in his place was an impostor trying to cheat the heirs out of their inheritance.

Character of Swift's Satire

This ferocious joke is suggestive of all Swift's satires. Against any case of hypocrisy or injustice he sets up a remedy of precisely the same kind, only more atrocious, and defends his plan with such seriousness that the satire overwhelms the reader with a sense of monstrous falsity. Thus his solemn 'Argument to prove that the Abolishing of Christianity may be attended with Some Inconveniences' is such a frightful satire upon the abuses of Christianity by its professed followers that it is impossible for us to say whether Swift intended to point out needed reforms, or to satisfy his conscience,[1] or to perpetrate a joke on the Church, as he had done on poor Partridge. So also with his 'Modest Proposal', concerning the children of Ireland, which sets up the proposition that poor Irish farmers ought to raise children as dainties, to be eaten, like roast pigs, on the tables of prosperous Englishmen. In this most characteristic work it is impossible to find Swift or his motive. The injustice under which Ireland suffered, her perversity in raising large families to certain poverty, and the indifference of English politicians to her suffering and protests are all mercilessly portrayed; but why? That is still the unanswered problem of Swift's life and writings.

---

[1] It is only fair to point out that Swift wrote this and two other pamphlets on religion at a time when he knew that they would damage, if not destroy, his own prospects of political advancement.

Swift's two greatest satires are his *Tale of a Tub* and *Gulliver's Travels*. The *Tale* began as a grim exposure of the alleged weaknesses of three principal forms of religious belief, Catholic, Lutheran, and Calvinist, as opposed to the Anglican; but it ended in a satire upon all science and philosophy.

Tale of a Tub

Swift explains his whimsical title by the custom of mariners in throwing out a tub to a whale, in order to occupy the monster's attention and divert it from an attack upon the ship—which only proves how little Swift knew of whales or sailors. But let that pass. His book is a tub thrown out to the enemies of Church and State to keep them occupied from further attacks or criticism; and the substance of the argument is that all churches, and indeed all religion and science and statesmanship, are arrant hypocrisy. The best known part of the book is the allegory of the old man who died and left a coat (which is Christian Truth) to each of his three sons, Peter, Martin, and Jack, with minute directions for its care and use. These three names stand for Catholics, Lutherans, and Calvinists; and the way in which the sons evade their father's will and change the fashion of their garment is part of the bitter satire upon all religious sects. Though it professes to defend the Anglican Church, that institution fares perhaps worse than the others; for nothing is left to her but a thin cloak of custom under which to hide her alleged hypocrisy.

In *Gulliver's Travels* the satire grows more unbearable. Strangely enough, this book, upon which Swift's literary fame generally rests, was not written from any literary motive, but rather as an outlet for the author's own bitterness against fate and human society. It is still read with pleasure, as *Robinson Crusoe* is read, for the interesting adventures of the hero; and fortunately those who read it generally overlook its degrading influence and motive.

Gulliver's Travels

Gulliver's Travels records the pretended four voyages of one Lemuel Gulliver, and his adventures in four astounding countries. The first book tells of his voyage and shipwreck in Lilliput, where the inhabitants are about as tall as one's thumb, and all their acts and motives are on the same dwarfish scale. In the petty quarrels of these dwarfs we are supposed to see the littleness of humanity. The statesmen who obtain place and favour by cutting monkey capers on the tight rope before their sovereign, and the two great parties, the Littleendians and Bigendians, who plunge the country into civil war over the momentous question of whether an egg should be broken on its big or on its little end, are satires on the politics of Swift's own day and generation. The style is simple and convincing; the surprising situations and adventures are as absorbing as those of Defoe's masterpiece; and altogether it is the most interesting of Swift's satires.

On the second voyage Gulliver is abandoned in Brobdingnag, where the inhabitants are giants, and everything is done upon an enormous scale. The meanness of humanity seems all the more detestable in view of the greatness of these superior beings. When Gulliver tells about his own people, their ambitions and wars and conquests, the giants can only wonder that such great venom could exist in such little insects.

In the third voyage Gulliver continues his adventures in Laputa, and this is a satire upon all the scientists and philosophers. Laputa is a flying island, held up in the air by a loadstone; and all the professors of the famous academy at Lagado are of the same airy constitution. The philosopher who worked eight years to extract sunshine from cucumbers is typical of Swift's satiric treatment of all scientific problems. It is in this voyage that we hear of the Struldbrugs, a ghastly race of men who are doomed to live upon earth after losing hope and the desire for life. The picture is all the more terrible in view of the last years of Swift's own life, in which he was compelled to live on, a burden to himself and his friends.

In these three voyages the evident purpose is to strip off the veil of habit and custom, with which men deceive themselves, and show the crude vices of humanity as Swift fancies he sees them. In the fourth voyage the merciless satire is carried out to its logical conclusion. This brings us to the land of the Houyhnhnms, in which horses, superior and intelligent creatures, are the ruling animals. All our interest, however, is centred on the Yahoos, a frightful race, having the form and appearance of men, but living in unspeakable degradation.

The *Journal to Stella,* written chiefly in the years 1710-1713 for the benefit of Esther Johnson, is interesting to us for two reasons. It is, first, an excellent commentary on contemporary characters and political events, by one of the most powerful and original minds of the age; and second, in its love passages and purely personal descriptions it gives us the best picture we possess of Swift himself at the summit of his power and influence. As we read now its words of tenderness for the woman who loved him, and who brought almost the only ray of sunlight into his life, we can only wonder and be silent. Entirely different are his *Drapier's Letters,* a model of political harangue and of popular argument, which roused an unthinking English public and did much benefit to Ireland by preventing the politicians' plan of debasing the Irish coinage. Swift's poems, though vigorous and original (like Defoe's, of the same period), are generally satirical, often coarse, and seldom rise above doggerel. Unlike his friend Addison, Swift saw, in the growing polish and decency of society, only a mask for hypocrisy; and he often used his verse to shock the new-born modesty by pointing out some native ugliness which his diseased mind discovered under every beautiful exterior.

Miscellaneous Works

That Swift is the most original writer of his time, and one of the greatest masters of English prose, is undeniable. Directness, vigour, simplicity, mark every page. Among writers of that age he stands almost alone in his disdain of literary effects. Keeping his object steadily before him, he drives straight on to the end, with a convincing power that has never been surpassed in our language. Even in his most grotesque creations, the reader never loses the sense of reality, of being present as an eyewitness of the most impossible events, so powerful and convincing is Swift's prose. Defoe had the same power; but in writing *Robinson Crusoe,* for instance, his task was comparatively easy, since his hero and his adventures were both natural; while Swift gives reality to pygmies, giants, and the most impossible situations, as easily as if he were writing of facts. Notwithstanding these excellent qualities, the ordinary reader will do well to confine himself to Gulliver's Travels and a book of well-chosen selections. For, it must be confessed, the bulk of Swift's work is not wholesome reading. It is too terribly satiric and destructive; it emphasizes the faults and failings of humanity; and so runs counter to the general course of our literature, which from Cynewulf to Tennyson follows the Ideal, as Merlin followed

Character of Swift's Prose

the Gleam,[1] and is not satisfied till the hidden beauty of man's soul and the divine purpose of his struggle are manifest.

JOSEPH ADDISON (1672-1719)

In the pleasant art of living with one's fellows, Addison is easily a master. It is due to his perfect expression of that art, of that new social life which, as we have noted, was characteristic of the Age of Anne, that Addison occupies such a large place in the history of literature. Of less power and originality than Swift, he nevertheless wields, and deserves to wield, a more lasting influence. Swift is the storm, roaring against the ice and frost of the late spring of English life. Addison is the sunshine, which melts the ice and dries the mud and makes the earth thrill with light and hope. Like Swift, he despised shams, but unlike him, he never lost faith in humanity; and in all his satires there is a gentle kindliness which makes one think better of his fellow-men, even while he laughs at their little vanities.

Joseph Addison

Addison's Influence

Two things Addison did for our literature which are of inestimable value. First, he overcame a certain corrupt tendency bequeathed by Restoration literature. It was the apparent aim of the low drama, and even of much of the poetry of that age, to make virtue ridiculous and vice attractive. Addison set himself squarely against this unworthy tendency. To strip off the mask of vice, to show its ugliness and deformity, but to reveal virtue in its own native loveliness—that was Addison's purpose; and he succeeded so well that never, since his day, has

---

[1] See Tennyson's 'Merlin and the Gleam'.

our English literature seriously followed after false gods. As Macaulay says, 'So effectually did he retort on vice the mockery which had recently been directed against virtue, that since his time the open violation of decency has always been considered amongst us a sure mark of a fool.' And second, prompted and aided by the more original genius of his friend Steele, Addison seized upon the new social life of the clubs and made it the subject of endless pleasant essays upon types of men and manners. *The Tatler* and *The Spectator* are the beginning of the modern essay; and their studies of human character, as exemplified in Sir Roger de Coverley, are a preparation for the modern novel.

Life. Addison's life, like his writings, is in marked contrast to that of Swift. He was born in Milston, Wiltshire, in 1672. His father was a scholarly English clergyman, and all his life Addison followed naturally the quiet and cultured ways to which he was early accustomed. At the famous Charterhouse School, in London, and in his university life at Oxford, he excelled in character and scholarship and became known as a writer of graceful verses. He had some intention, at one time, of entering the Church, but was easily persuaded by his friends to take up the government service instead. Unlike Swift, who abused his political superiors, Addison took the more tactful way of winning the friendship of men in large places. His lines to Dryden won that literary leader's instant favour, and one of his Latin poems, 'The Peace of Ryswick' (1697), with its kindly appreciation of King William's statesmen, brought him into favourable political notice. It brought him also a pension of three hundred pounds a year, with a suggestion that he travel abroad and cultivate the art of diplomacy; which he promptly did to his own great advantage.

From a literary viewpoint the most interesting work of Addison's early life is his *Account of the Greatest English Poets* (1693), written while he was a fellow of Oxford University. One rubs his eyes to find Dryden lavishly praised, Spenser excused or patronized, while Shakespeare is not even mentioned. But Addison was writing under Boileau's 'classic' rules; and the poet, like the age, was perhaps too artificial to appreciate natural genius.

While he was travelling abroad, the death of William and the loss of power by the Whigs suddenly stopped Addison's pension; necessity brought him home, and for a time he lived in poverty and obscurity.

Then occurred the battle of Blenheim, and in the effort to find a poet to celebrate the event, Addison was brought to the Tories' attention. His poem, 'The Campaign', celebrating the victory, took the country by storm. Instead of making the hero slay his thousands and ten thousands, like the old epic heroes, Addison had some sense of what is required in a modern general, and so made Marlborough direct the battle from the outside, comparing him to an angel riding on the whirlwind:

> 'Twas then great Marlbro's mighty soul was proved,
> That, in the shock of charging hosts unmoved,
> Amidst confusion, horror, and despair,
> Examined all the dreadful scenes of war;
> In peaceful thought the field of death surveyed,
> To fainting squadrons sent the timely aid,
> Inspired repulsed battalions to engage,
> And taught the doubtful battle where to rage.
> So when an angel by divine command
> With rising tempests shakes a guilty land,
> (Such as of late o'er pale Britannia past,)
> Calm and serene he drives the furious blast;
> And, pleased th' Almighty's orders to perform,
> Rides in the whirlwind, and directs the storm.

That one doubtful simile made Addison's fortune. Never before or since was a poet's mechanical work so well rewarded. It was called the finest thing ever written, and from that day Addison rose steadily in political favour and office. He became in turn Undersecretary, member of Parliament, Secretary for Ireland, and finally Secretary of State. Probably no other literary man, aided by his pen alone, ever rose so rapidly and so high in office.

The rest of Addison's life was divided between political duties and literature. His essays for the *Tatler* and *Spectator,* which we still cherish, were written between 1709 and 1714; but he won more literary fame by his classic tragedy *Cato,* which we have almost forgotten. In 1716 he married a widow, the Countess of Warwick, and went to live at her home, the famous Holland House. His married life lasted only three years, and was probably not a happy one. Certainly he never wrote of women except with gentle satire, and he became more and more a clubman, spending most of his time in the clubs and coffee houses of London.

Up to this time his life had been singularly peaceful; but his last years were shadowed by quarrels, first with Pope, then with Swift, and finally with his lifelong friend Steele. The first quarrel was on literary grounds, and was largely the result of Pope's jealousy. The latter's venomous caricature of Addison as Atticus shows how he took his petty revenge on a great and good man who had been his friend. The other quarrels with Swift, and especially with his old friend Steele, were the unfortunate result of political differences, and show how impossible it is to mingle literary ideals with party politics. He died serenely in 1719. A brief description from Thackeray's *English Humorists* is his best epitaph:

> A life prosperous and beautiful, a calm death; an immense fame and affection afterwards for his happy and spotless name.

Works of Addison. The most enduring of Addison's works are his famous *Essays,* collected from the *Tatler* and *Spectator.* We have

The Essays

spoken of him as a master of the art of gentle living, and these essays are a perpetual inducement to others to know and to practice the same fine art. To an age of fundamental coarseness and artificiality he came with a wholesome message of refinement and simplicity, much as Ruskin and Arnold spoke to a later age of materialism; only Addison's success was greater than theirs because of his greater knowledge of life and his greater faith in men. He attacks all the little vanities and all the big vices of his time, not in Swift's terrible way, which makes us feel hopeless of humanity, but with a kindly ridicule and gentle humour which takes speedy improvement for granted. To read Swift's brutal 'Letters to a Young Lady', and then to read Addison's 'Dissection of a Beau's Head' and his 'Dissection of a Coquette's Heart', is to know at once the secret of the latter's more enduring influence.

Three other results of these delightful essays are worthy of attention: first, they are the best picture we possess of the new social life of England, with its many new interests; second, they advanced the art of literary criticism to a much higher stage than it had ever before reached, and however much we differ from their judgment and their interpretation of such a man as Milton, they certainly led Englishmen to a better knowledge and appreciation of their own literature; and finally, in Ned Softly the literary dabbler, Will Wimble the poor relation, Sir Andrew Freeport the merchant, Will Honeycomb the fop, and Sir Roger the country gentleman, they give us characters that live forever as part of that goodly company which extends from Chaucer's country parson to Kipling's Mulvaney. Addison and Steele not only introduced the modern essay, but in such characters as these they herald the dawn of the modern novel. Of all his essays the best known and loved are those which introduce us to Sir Roger de Coverley, the genial dictator of life and manners in the quiet English country.

Addison's Style

In style these essays are remarkable as showing the growing perfection of the English language. Johnson says, 'Whoever wishes to attain an English style, familiar but not coarse, and elegant but not ostentatious, must give his days and nights to the volumes of Addison.' And again he says, 'Give nights and days, sir, to the study of Addison if you mean to be a good writer, or, what is more worth, an honest man.' That was good criticism for its day, and even at the present time critics are agreed that Addison's Essays are well worth reading once for their own sake, and many times for their influence in shaping a clear and graceful style of writing.

Poems

Addison's poems, which were enormously popular in his day, are now seldom read. His *Cato,* with its classic unities and lack of dramatic power, must be regarded as a failure, if we study it as tragedy; but it offers an excellent example of the rhetoric and fine sentiment which were then considered the essentials of good writing. The best scene from this tragedy is in the fifth act, where Cato soliloquizes, with Plato's *Immortality of the Soul* open in his hand, and a drawn sword on the table before him:

> It must be so—Plato, thou reason'st well!—
> Else whence this pleasing hope, this fond desire,
> This longing after immortality?
> Or whence this secret dread, and inward horror,

Of falling into nought? why shrinks the soul
Back on herself, and startles at destruction?
'Tis the divinity that stirs within us;
'Tis heaven itself, that points out an hereafter,
And intimates eternity to man.

Many readers make frequent use of one portion of Addison's poetry without knowing to whom they are indebted. His devout nature found expression in many hymns, a few of which are still used and loved in our churches. Many a congregation thrills, as Thackeray did, to the splendid sweep of his 'God in Nature', beginning, 'The spacious firmament on high.' Almost as well known and loved are his 'Traveller's Hymn', and his 'Continued Help', beginning, 'When all thy mercies, O my God.' The latter hymn—written in a storm at sea off the Italian coast, when the captain and crew were demoralized by terror–shows that poetry, especially a good hymn that one can sing in the same spirit as one would say his prayers, is sometimes the most practical and helpful thing in the world.

Richard Steele (1672-1729). Steele was in almost every respect the antithesis of his friend and fellow-worker—a rollicking, good-hearted, emotional, lovable Irishman. At the Charterhouse School and at Oxford he shared everything with Addison, asking nothing but love in return. Unlike Addison, he studied but little, and left the university to enter the Horse Guards. He was in turn soldier, captain, poet, playwright, essayist, member of Parliament, manager of a theatre, publisher of a newspaper, and twenty other things—all of which he began joyously and then abandoned, sometimes against his will, as when he was expelled from Parliament, and again because some other interest of the moment had more attraction. His poems and plays are now little known; but the reader who searches them out will find one or two suggestive things about Steele himself. For instance, he loves children; and he is one of the few writers of his time who show a sincere and unswerving respect for womanhood. Even more than Addison he ridicules vice and makes virtue lovely. He is the originator of the *Tatler*, and joins with Addison in creating the *Spectator*—the two periodicals which, in the short space of less than four years, did more to influence subsequent literature than all other magazines of the century combined. Moreover, he is the original genius of Sir Roger, and of many other characters and essays for which Addison usually receives the whole credit. It is often impossible in the *Tatler* essays to separate the work of the two men; but the majority of critics hold that the more original parts, the characters, the thought, the overflowing kindliness, are largely Steele's creation; while to Addison fell the work of polishing and perfecting the essays, and of adding that touch of humour which made them the most welcome literary visitors that England had ever received.

The Tatler and The Spectator. On account of his talent in writing political pamphlets, Steele was awarded the position of official gazetteer. While in this position, and writing for several small newspapers, the idea occurred to Steele to publish a paper which should contain not only the political news, but also the gossip of the clubs and coffee-houses, with some light essays on the life and manners of the age. The immediate result—for Steele never let an idea remain idle—was the famous Tatler, the first number of which appeared April 12, 1709. It was a small folio sheet, appearing on post days, three times a week, and it sold for a penny a copy. That it had a serious purpose is evident from this dedication to the first volume of collected *Tatler* essays:

> The general purpose of this paper is to expose the false arts of life, to pull off the disguises of cunning, vanity, and affectation, and to recommend a general simplicity in our dress, our discourse, and our behaviour.

The success of this unheard-of combination of news, gossip, and essay was instantaneous. Not a club or a coffee-house in London could afford to be without it, and over its pages began the first general interest in contemporary English life as expressed in literature. Steele at first wrote the entire paper and signed his essays with the name of Isaac Bickerstaff, which had been made famous by Swift a few years before. Addison is said to have soon recognized one of his own remarks to Steele, and the secret of the authorship was out. From that time Addison was a regular contributor, and occasionally other writers added essays on the new social life of England.[1]

Steele lost his position as gazetteer, and the *Tatler* was discontinued after less than two years' life, but not till it won an astonishing popularity and made ready the way for its successor. Two months later, on March 1, 1711, appeared the first number of the *Spectator*. In the new magazine politics and news, as such, were ignored; it was a literary magazine, pure and simple, and its entire contents consisted of a single light essay. It was considered a crazy venture at the time, but its instant success proved that men were eager for some literary expression of the new social ideals. The following whimsical letter to the editor may serve to indicate the part played by the Spectator in the daily life of London:

> Mr. Spectator—Your paper is a part of my tea equipage; and my servant knows my humour so well, that in calling for my breakfast this morning (it being past my usual hour) she answered, the Spectator was not yet come in, but the tea kettle boiled, and she expected it every moment.

It is in the incomparable Spectator papers that Addison shows himself most 'worthy to be remembered.' He contributed the majority of its essays, and in its first number appears this description of the Spectator, by which name Addison is now generally known:

> There is no place of general resort wherein I do not often make my appearance; sometimes I am seen thrusting my head into a round of politicians at Will's [Coffee-house] and listening with great attention to the narratives that are made in those little circular audiences. Sometimes I smoke a pipe at Child's, and, whilst I seem attentive to nothing but *The Postman,* overhear the conversation of every table in the room. I appear on Sunday nights at St. James's, and sometimes join the little committee of politics in the inner room, as one who comes to hear and improve. My face is likewise very well known at the Grecian, the Cocoa Tree, and

[1] Of the *Tatler* essays Addison contributed forty-two; thirty-six others were written in collabouration with Steele; while at least a hunderd and eighty are the work of Steele alone.

in the theatres both of Drury Lane and the Haymarket. I have been taken for a merchant upon the Exchange for above these ten years; and sometimes pass for a Jew in the assembly of stock jobbers at Jonathan's.... Thus I live in the world rather as a spectator of mankind than as one of the species,... which is the character I intend to preserve in this paper.

The large place which these two little magazines hold in our literature seems most disproportionate to their short span of days. In the short space of four years in which Addison and Steele worked together the light essay was established as one of the most important forms of modern literature, and the literary magazine won its place as the expression of the social life of a nation.

Samuel Johnson (1709-1784)

The reader of Boswell's *Johnson,* after listening to endless grumblings and watching the clumsy actions of the hero, often finds himself wondering why he should end his reading with a profound respect for this 'old bear' who is the object of Boswell's grovelling attention. Here is a man who was certainly not the greatest writer of his age, perhaps not even a great writer at all, but who was nevertheless the dictator of English letters, and who

Samuel Johnson

still looms across the centuries of a magnificent literature as its most striking and original figure. Here, moreover, is a huge, fat, awkward man, of vulgar manners and appearance, who monopolizes conversation, argues violently, abuses everybody, clubs down opposition—'Madam' (speaking to his cultivated hostess at table), 'talk no more nonsense'; 'Sir' (turning to a distinguished guest), 'I perceive you are a vile Whig.' While talking he makes curious animal sounds, 'sometimes giving a half whistle, sometimes clucking like a hen'; and when he has concluded a violent dispute and laid his opponents low by dogmatism or ridicule, he leans back to 'blow out his breath like a whale' and gulp down numberless cups of hot tea. Yet this curious dictator of an elegant age was a veritable lion, much sought after by society; and around him in his own poor house gathered the foremost artists, scholars, actors, and literary men of London—all honouring the man, loving him, and listening to his dogmatism as the Greeks listened to the voice of their oracle.

What is the secret of this astounding spectacle? If the reader turns naturally to Johnson's works for an explanation, he will be disappointed. Reading his verses, we find nothing to delight or inspire us, but rather gloom and pessimism, with a few moral observations in rhymed couplets:

> But, scarce observed, the knowing and the bold
> Fall in the general massacre of gold;
> Wide-wasting pest! that rages unconfined,
> And crowds with crimes the records of mankind;
> For gold his sword the hireling ruffian draws,
> For gold the hireling judge distorts the laws;
> Wealth heaped on wealth nor truth nor safety buys;
> The dangers gather as the treasures rise.[1]

That is excellent common sense, but it is not poetry; and it is not necessary to hunt through Johnson's bulky volumes for the information, since any moralist can give us offhand the same doctrine. As for his *Rambler* essays, once so successful, though we marvel at the big words, the carefully balanced sentences, the classical allusions, one might as well try to get interested in an old-fashioned, three-hour sermon. We read a few pages listlessly, yawn, and go to bed.

---

[1] From 'The Vanity of Human Wishes'.

Since the man's work fails to account for his leadership and influence, we examine his personality; and here everything is interesting. Because of a few oft-quoted passages from Boswell's biography, Johnson appears to us as an eccentric bear, who amuses us by his growlings and clumsy antics. But there is another Johnson, a brave, patient, kindly, religious soul, who, as Goldsmith said, had 'nothing of the bear but his skin'; a man who battled like a hero against poverty and pain and melancholy and the awful fear of death, and who overcame them manfully. 'That trouble passed away; so will this', sang the sorrowing Deor in the first old Anglo-Saxon lyric; and that expresses the great and suffering spirit of Johnson, who in the face of enormous obstacles never lost faith in God or in himself. Though he was a reactionary in politics, upholding the arbitrary power of kings and opposing the growing liberty of the people, yet his political theories, like his manners, were no deeper than his skin; for in all London there was none more kind to the wretched, and none more ready to extend an open hand to every struggling man and woman who crossed his path. When he passed poor homeless Arabs sleeping in the streets he would slip a coin into their hands, in order that they might have a happy awakening; for he himself knew well what it meant to be hungry. Such was Johnson—a 'mass of genuine manhood', as Carlyle called him, and as such, men loved and honoured him.[1]

Life of Johnson. Johnson was born in Lichfield, Staffordshire, in 1709. He was the son of a small bookseller, a poor man, but intelligent and fond of literature, as booksellers invariably were in the good days when every town had its bookshop. From his childhood Johnson had to struggle against physical deformity and disease and the consequent disinclination to hard work. He prepared for the university, partly in the schools, but largely by omnivorous reading in his father's shop, and when he entered

[1] A very lovable side of Johnson's nature is shown by his doing penance in the public marketplace for his unfilial conduct as a boy. (See, in Hawthorne's *Our Old Home,* the article on 'Lichfield and Johnson'.) His sterling manhood is recalled in his famous letter to Lord Chesterfield, refusing the latter's patronage for the *Dictionary.* The student should read this incident entire, in Boswell's *Life of Johnson.*

Oxford he had read more classical authors than had most of the graduates. Before finishing his course he had to leave the university on account of his poverty, and at once he began his long struggle as a hack writer to earn his living.

At twenty-five years he married a woman old enough to be his mother—a genuine love match, he called it—and with her dowry of £800 they started a private school together, which was a dismal failure. Then, without money or influencial friends, he left his home and wife in Lichfield and tramped to London, accompanied only by David Garrick, afterwards the famous actor, who had been one of his pupils. Here, led by old associations, Johnson made himself known to the booksellers, and now and then earned a penny by writing prefaces, reviews, and translations.

It was a dog's life, indeed, that he led there with his literary brethren. Many of the writers of the day, who are ridiculed in Pope's heartless *Dunciad,* having no wealthy patrons to support them, lived largely in the streets and taverns, sleeping on an ash heap or under a wharf, like rats; glad of a crust, and happy over a single meal which enabled them to work for a while without the reminder of hunger. A few favoured ones lived in wretched lodgings in Grub Street, which has since become a synonym for the fortunes of struggling writers.[1] Often, Johnson tells us, he walked the streets all night long, in dreary weather, when it was too cold to sleep, without food or shelter. But he wrote steadily for the booksellers and for the *Gentleman's Magazine,* and presently he became known in London and received enough work to earn a bare living.

The works which occasioned this small success were his poem, 'London', and his *Life of the Poet Savage,* a wretched life, at best, which were perhaps better left without a biographer. But his success was genuine, though small, and presently the booksellers of London are coming to him to ask him to write a dictionary of the English language. It was an enormous work, taking nearly eight years of his time, and long before he had finished it he had eaten up the money which he received for his labour. In the leisure intervals of this work he wrote 'The Vanity of

---

[1] In Johnson's Dictionary we find this definition: 'Grub-street, the name of a street in London much inhabited by writers of small histories, dictionaries, and temporary poems; whence any mean production is called Grub-street'.

Human Wishes' and other poems, and finished his classic tragedy of *Irene.*

Led by the great success of the *Spectator,* Johnson started two magazines, *The Rambler* (1750—1752) and *The Idler* (1758—1760). Later *The Rambler* essays were published in book form and ran rapidly through ten editions; but the financial returns were small, and Johnson spent a large part of his earnings in charity. When his mother died, in 1759, Johnson, although one of the best known men in London, had no money, and hurriedly finished *Rasselas,* his only romance, in order, it is said, to pay for his mother's burial.

It was not till 1762, when Johnson was fifty-three years old, that his literary labours were rewarded in the usual way by royalty, and he received from George III a yearly pension of three hundred pounds. Then began a little sunshine in his life. With Joshua Reynolds, the artist, he founded the famous Literary Club, of which Burke, Pitt, Fox, Gibbon, Goldsmith, and indeed all the great literary men and politicians of the time, were members. This is the period of Johnson's famous conversations, which were caught in minutest detail by Boswell and given to the world. His idea of conversation, as shown in a hundred places in Boswell, is to overcome your adversary at any cost; to knock him down by arguments, or, when these fail, by personal ridicule; to dogmatize on every possible question, pronounce a few oracles, and then desist with the air of victory. Concerning the philosopher Hume's view of death he says: 'Sir, if he really thinks so, his perceptions are disturbed, he is mad. If he does not think so, he lies.' Exit opposition. There is nothing more to be said. Curiously enough, it is often the palpable blunders of these monologues that now attract us, as if we were enjoying a good joke at the dictator's expense. Once a lady asked him, 'Dr. Johnson, why did you define *pastern* as the knee of a horse?' 'Ignorance, madame, pure ignorance', thundered the great authority.

When seventy years of age, Johnson was visited by several book-sellers of the city, who were about to bring out a new edition of the English poets, and who wanted Johnson, as the leading literary man of London, to write the prefaces to the several volumes. The result was his *Lives of the Poets,* as it is now known, and this is his last literary work. He died in his poor Fleet Street house, in 1784, and was buried among England's honoured poets in Westminster Abbey.

Johnson's Works. 'A book', says Dr. Johnson, 'should help us either to enjoy life or to endure it.' Judged by this standard, one is puzzled what to recommend among Johnson's numerous books. The two things which belong among the things 'worthy to be remembered' are his *Dictionary* and his *Lives of the Poets,* though both these are valuable, not as literature, but rather as a study of literature. The *Dictionary,* as the first ambitious attempt at an English lexicon, is extremely valuable, notwithstanding the fact that his derivations are often faulty, and that he frequently exercises his humour or prejudice in his curious definitions. In defining 'oats', for example, as a grain given in England to horses and in Scotland to the people, he indulges his prejudice against the Scotch, whom he never understood, just as, in his definition of 'pension', he takes occasion to rap the writers who had flattered their patrons since the days of Elizabeth; though he afterwards accepted a comfortable pension for himself. With characteristic honesty he refused to alter his definition in subsequent editions of the *Dictionary.*

The English Dictionary

The *Lives of the Poets* are the simplest and most readable of his literary works. For ten years before beginning these biographies he had given himself up to conversation, and the ponderous style of his *Rambler* essays here gives way to a lighter and more natural expression. As criticisms they are often misleading, giving praise to artificial poets, like Cowley and Pope, and doing scant justice or abundant injustice to nobler poets like Gray and Milton; and they are not to be compared with those found in Thomas Warton's *History of English Poetry,* which was published in the same generation. As biographies, however, they are excellent reading, and we owe to them some of our best known pictures of the early English poets.

Lives of the Poets

Of Johnson's poems the reader will have enough if he glance over 'The Vanity of Human Wishes.' His only story, *Rasselas, Prince of Abyssinia,* is a matter of rhetoric rather than of romance, but is interesting still to the reader who wants to hear Johnson's personal views of society, philosophy, and religion. Any

Poems and Essays

one of his *Essays,* like that on 'Reading,' or *'The Pernicious Effects of Revery,'* will be enough to acquaint the reader with the Johnsonese style, which was once much admired and copied by orators, but which happily has been replaced by a more natural way of speaking. Most of his works, it must be confessed, are rather tiresome. It is not to his books, but rather to the picture of the man himself, as given by Boswell, that Johnson owes his great place in our literature.

BOSWELL'S 'LIFE OF JOHNSON'

In James Boswell (1740-1795) we have another extraordinary figure—a shallow little Scotch barrister, who trots about like a dog at the heels of his big master, frantic at a caress and grovelling at a cuff, and abundantly contented if only he can be near him and record his oracles. All his life long Boswell's one ambition seems to have been to shine in the reflected glory of great men, and his chief task to record their sayings and doings. When he came to London, at twenty-two years of age, Johnson, then at the beginning of his great fame, was to this insatiable little glory-seeker like a Silver Doctor to a hungry trout. He sought an introduction as a man seeks gold, haunted every place where Johnson declaimed, until in Davies's bookstore the supreme opportunity came. This is his record of the great event:

> I was much agitated [says Boswell] and recollecting his prejudice against the Scotch, of which I had heard much, I said to Davies, 'Don't tell him where I come from.' 'From Scotland', cried Davies roguishly. 'Mr. Johnson', said I, 'I do indeed come from Scotland, but I cannot help it.'... 'That, sir' [cried Johnson], 'I find is what a very great many of your countrymen cannot help.' This stroke stunned me a good deal; and when we had sat down I felt myself not a little embarrassed, and apprehensive of what might come next.

Then for several years, with a persistency that no rebuffs could abate, and with a thick skin that no amount of ridicule could render sensitive, he follows Johnson; forces his way into the Literary Club, where he is not welcome, in order to be near his idol; carries him off on a visit to the Hebrides; talks with him on every possible occasion; and, when he is not invited to a feast, waits outside the house or tavern in order to walk home with his master in the thick fog of the early morning. And the moment the oracle is out of sight and in bed, Boswell patters home to record in detail all that he has seen and heard. It is to his minute record that we owe our only perfect picture of a great man; all his vanity as well as his greatness, his prejudices, superstitions, and even the details of his personal appearance:

> There is the gigantic body, the huge face seamed with the scars of disease, the brown coat, the black worsted stockings, the gray wig with the scorched foretop, the dirty hands, the nails bitten and pared to the quick. We see the eyes and mouth moving with convulsive twitches; we see the heavy form rolling; we hear it puffing; and then comes the 'Why, sir!' and the 'What then, sir?' and the 'No, sir!' and the 'You don't see your way through the question, sir!'[1]

To Boswell's record we are indebted also for our knowledge of those famous conversations, those wordy, knockdown battles, which made Johnson famous in his time and which still move us to wonder. Here is a specimen conversation, taken almost at random from a hundred such in Boswell's incomparable biography. After listening to Johnson's prejudice against Scotland, and his dogmatic utterances on Voltaire, Robertson, and twenty others, an unfortunate theorist brings up a recent essay on the possible future life of brutes, quoting some possible authority from the sacred scriptures:

> Johnson, who did not like to hear anything concerning a future state which was not authorized by the regular canons of orthodoxy, discouraged this talk; and being offended at its continuation, he watched an opportunity to give the gentleman a blow of reprehension. So when the poor speculatist, with a serious, metaphysical, pensive face, addressed him, 'But really, sir, when we see a very sensible dog, we don't know what to think of him'; Johnson, rolling with joy at the thought which beamed in his eye, turned quickly round and replied, 'True, sir; and when we see a very

[1] From Macaulay's review of Boswell's *Life of Johnson*.

foolish fellow, we don't know what to think of him.' He then rose up, strided to the fire, and stood for some time laughing and exulting.

Then the oracle proceeds to talk of scorpions and natural history, denying facts, and demanding proofs which nobody could possibly furnish:

He seemed pleased to talk of natural philosophy. 'That woodcocks', said he, 'fly over the northern countries is proved, because they have been observed at sea. Swallows certainly sleep all the winter. A number of them conglobulate together by flying round and round, and then all in a heap throw themselves under water and lie in the bed of a river.' He told us one of his first essays was a Latin poem upon the glowworm: I am sorry I did not ask where it was to be found.

Then follows an astonishing array of subjects and opinions. He catalogues libraries, settles affairs in China, pronounces judgment on men who marry women superior to themselves, flouts popular liberty, hammers Swift unmercifully, and adds a few miscellaneous oracles, most of which are about as reliable as his knowledge of the hibernation of swallows.

When I called upon Dr. Johnson next morning I found him highly satisfied with his colloquial prowess the preceding evening. 'Well', said he, 'we had good talk.' 'Yes, sir' [says I], 'you tossed and gored several persons.'

Far from resenting this curious mental dictatorship, his auditors never seem to weary. They hang upon his words, praise him, flatter him, repeat his judgments all over London the next day, and return in the evening hungry for more. Whenever the conversation begins to flag, Boswell is like a woman with a parrot, or like a man with a dancing bear. He must excite the creature, make him talk or dance for the edification of the company. He sidles obsequiously towards his hero and, with utter irrelevancy, propounds a question of theology, a social theory, a fashion of dress or marriage, a philosophical conundrum: 'Do you think, sir, that natural affections are born with us?' or, 'Sir, if you were shut up in a castle and a newborn babe with you, what would you do?' Then follow more Johnsonian laws, judgments, oracles; the insatiable audience clusters around him and applauds; while Boswell listens, with shining face, and presently goes home to write the wonder down. It is an astonishing spectacle; one does not know whether to laugh or grieve over it. But we know the man, and the audience, almost as well as if we had been there; and that, unconsciously, is the superb art of this matchless biographer.

When Johnson died the opportunity came for which Boswell had been watching and waiting some twenty years. He would shine in the world now, not by reflection, but by his own luminosity. He gathered together his endless notes and records, and began to write his biography; but he did not hurry. Several biographies of Johnson appeared, in the four years after his death, without disturbing Boswell's perfect complacency. After seven years' labour he gave the world his *Life of Johnson.* It is an immortal work; praise is superfluous; it must be read to be appreciated. Like the Greek sculptors, the little slave produced a more enduring work than the great master. The man who reads it will know Johnson as he knows no other man who dwells across the border; and he will lack sensitiveness, indeed, if he lay down the work without a greater love and appreciation of all good literature.

Later Augustan Writers. With Johnson, who succeeded Dryden and Pope in the chief place of English letters, the classic movement had largely spent its force; and the latter half of the eighteenth century gives us an imposing array of writers who differ so widely that it is almost impossible to classify them. In general, three schools of writers are noticeable: first, the classicists, who, under Johnson's lead, insisted upon elegance and regularity of style; second, the romantic poets, like Collins, Gray, Thomson, and Burns, who revolted from Pope's artificial couplets and wrote of nature and the human heart[1]; third, the early novelists, like Defoe and Fielding,

[1] Many of the writers show a mingling of the classic and the romantic tendencies. Thus Goldsmith followed Johnson and opposed the romanticists; but his *Deserted Village is* romantic in spirit, though its classic couplets are almost as mechanical as Pope's. So Burke's orations are 'elegantly classic' in style, but are illumined by bursts of emotion and romantic feeling.

who introduced a new type of literature. The romantic poets and the novelists are reserved for special chapters; and of the other writers—Berkeley and Hume in philosophy; Robertson, Hume, and Gibbon in history; Chesterfield and Lady Montagu in letter writing; Adam Smith in economics; Pitt, Burke, Fox, and a score of lesser writers in politics—we select only two, Burke and Gibbon, whose works are most typical of the Augustan, that is the elegant, classic style of prose writing.

EDMUND BURKE (1729–1797)

To read all of Burke's collected works, and so to understand him thoroughly, is something of a task. Few are equal to it. On the other hand, to read selections here and there, as most of us do, is to get a wrong idea of the man and to join either in fulsome praise of his brilliant oratory, or in honest confession that his periods are ponderous and his ideas often buried under Johnsonian verbiage. Such are the contrasts to be found on successive pages of Burke's twelve volumes, which cover the enormous range of the political and economic thought of the age, and which mingle fact and fancy, philosophy, statistics, and brilliant flights of the imagination, to a degree never before seen in English literature. For Burke belongs in spirit to the new romantic school, while in style he is a model for the formal classicists. We can only glance at the life of this marvellous Irishman, and then consider his place in our literature.

Life. Burke was born in Dublin, the son of an Irish barrister, in 1729. After his university course in Trinity College he came to London to study law, but soon gave up the idea to follow literature, which in turn led him to politics. He had the soul, the imagination of a poet, and the law was only a clog to his progress. His two first works, *A Vindication of Natural Society and The Origin of Our Ideas of the Sublime and the Beautiful,* brought him political as well as literary recognition, and several small offices were in turn given to him. When thirty-six years old he was elected to Parliament as member from Wendover; and for the next thirty years he was the foremost figure in the House of Commons and the most eloquent orator which that body has ever known. Pure and incorruptible in his politics as in his personal life, no more learned or devoted servant of the Commonwealth ever pleaded for justice and human liberty. He was at the summit of his influence at the time when the colonies were struggling for independence; and the fact that he championed their cause in one of his greatest speeches, 'On Conciliation with America', gives him an added interest in the eyes of American readers. His championship of America is all the more remarkable from the fact that, in other matters, Burke was far from liberal. He set himself squarely against the teachings of the romantic writers, who were enthusiastic over the French Revolution; he denounced the principles of the Revolutionists, broke with the liberal Whig party to join the Tories, and was largely instrumental in bringing on the terrible war with France, which resulted in the downfall of Napoleon.

It is good to remember that, in all the strife and bitterness of party politics, Burke held steadily to the noblest personal ideals of truth and honesty; and that in all his work, whether opposing the slave trade, or pleading for justice for America, or protecting the poor natives of India from the greed of corporations, or setting himself against the popular sympathy for France in her desperate struggle, he aimed solely at the welfare of humanity. When he retired on a pension in 1794, he had won, and he deserved, the gratitude and affection of the whole nation.

Works. There are three distinctly marked periods in Burke's career, and these correspond closely to the years in which he was busied with the affairs of America, India, and France successively. The first period was one of prophecy. He had studied the history and temper of the American colonies, and he warned England of the disaster which must follow her persistence in ignoring the American demands, and especially the American spirit. His great speeches, 'On American Taxation' and 'On Conciliation with America', were delivered in 1774 and 1775, preceding the Declaration of Independence. In this period Burke's labour seemed all in vain; he lost his cause, and England her greatest colony.

The second period is one of denunciation rather than of prophecy. England had won India; but when Burke studied the methods of her victory and understood the soulless way in which millions of poor natives were made to serve the interests of an

English monopoly, his soul rose in revolt, and again he was the champion of an oppressed people. His two greatest speeches of this period are 'The Nabob of Arcot's Debts' and his tremendous 'Impeachment of Warren Hastings.' Again he apparently lost his cause, though he was still fighting on the side of right. Hastings was acquitted, and the spoliation of India went on; but the seeds of reform were sown, and grew and bore fruit long after Burke's labours were ended.

The third period is, curiously enough, one of reaction. Whether because the horrors of the French Revolution had frightened him with the danger of popular liberty, or because his own advance in office and power had made him side unconsciously with the upper classes, is unknown. That he was as sincere and noble now as in all his previous life is not questioned. He broke with the liberal Whigs and joined forces with the reactionary Tories. He opposed the romantic writers, who were on fire with enthusiasm over the French Revolution, and thundered against the dangers which the revolutionary spirit must breed, forgetting that it was a revolution which had made modern England possible. Here, where we must judge him to have been mistaken in his cause, he succeeded for the first time. It was due largely to Burke's influence that the growing sympathy for the French people was checked in England, and war was declared, which ended in the frightful victories of Trafalgar and Waterloo.

Burke's best known work of this period is his *Reflections on the French Revolution,* which he polished and revised again on and again before it was finally printed. This ambitious literary essay, though it met with remarkable success, is a disappointment to the reader. Though of Celtic blood, Burke did not understand the French, or the principles for which the common people were fighting in their own way[1]; and his denunciations and apostrophes to France suggest a preacher without humour, hammering away at sinners who are not present in his congregation.

Eassy on Revolution

[1] A much more interesting work is Thomas Paine's *Right of Man,* which was written in answer to Burke's essay, and which had enormous influence in England and America.

The essay has few illuminating ideas, but a great deal of Johnsonian rhetoric, which make its periods tiresome, notwithstanding our admiration for the brilliancy of its author. More significant is one of Burke's first essays, *A Philosophical Inquiry Into the Origin of Our Ideas of the Sublime and Beautiful,* which is sometimes read in order to show the contrast in style with Addison's Spectator essays on the 'Pleasures of the Imagination.'

Burke's Orations

Burke's best known speeches, 'On Conciliation with America', 'American Taxation', and the 'Impeachment of Warren Hastings', are still much studied in our schools as models of English prose; and this fact tends to give them an exaggerated literary importance. Viewed purely as literature, they have faults enough; and the first of these, so characteristic of the Classic Age, is that they abound in fine rhetoric but lack simplicity.[1] In a strict sense, these eloquent speeches are not literature, to delight the reader and to suggest ideas, but studies in rhetoric and in mental concentration. All this, however, is on the surface. A careful study of any of these three famous speeches reveals certain admirable qualities which account for the important place they are given in the study of English. First, as showing the stateliness and the rhetorical power of our language, these speeches are almost unrivalled. Second, though Burke speaks in prose, he is essentially a poet, whose imagery, like that of Milton's prose works, is more remarkable than that of many of our writers of verse. He speaks in figures, images, symbols; and the musical cadence of his sentences reflects the influence of his wide reading of poetry. Not only in

---

[1] In the same year, 1775, in which Burke's magnificent 'Conciliation' oration was delivered, Patrick Henry amde a remarkable little speech before a gathering of delegates in Virginia. Both men were pleading the same cause of justice, and were actuated by the same high ideals. A very interesting contrast, however, may be drawn between the methods and the effects of Henry's speech and of Burke's more brilliant oration. Burke makes us wonder at his learning, his brilliancy, his eloquence; but he does not move us to action. Patrick Henry calls us, and we spring to follow him. That suggests the essential difference between the two orators.

Edmund Burke
From an old print

figurative expression, but much more in spirit, he belongs with the poets of the revival. At times his language is pseudo-classic, reflecting the influence of Johnson and his school; but his thought is always romantic; he is governed by ideal rather than by practical interests, and a profound sympathy for humanity is perhaps his most marked characteristic.

Third, the supreme object of these orations, so different from the majority of political speeches, is not to win approval or to gain votes, but to establish the truth. Like our own Lincoln, Burke had a superb faith in the compelling power of the truth, a faith in men also, who, if the history of our race means anything, will not willingly follow a lie. The methods of these two great leaders are strikingly similar in this respect, that each repeats his idea in many ways, presenting the truth from different viewpoints, so that it will appeal to men of widely different experiences. Otherwise the two men are in marked contrast. The uneducated Lincoln speaks in simple, homely words, draws his illustrations from the farm, and often adds a humorous story, so apt and 'telling' that his hearers can never forget the point of his argument. The scholarly Burke speaks in ornate, majestic periods, and searches all history and all literature for his illustrations. His wealth of imagery and allusions, together with his rare combination of poetic and logical reasoning, make these orations remarkable, entirely apart from their subject and purpose.

Fourth (and perhaps most significant of the man and his work), Burke takes his stand squarely upon the principle of justice. He has studied history, and he finds that to establish justice, between man and man and between nation and nation, has been the supreme object of every reformer since the world began. No small or merely temporary success attracts him; only the truth will suffice for an argument; and nothing less than justice will ever settle a question permanently. Such is his platform, simple as the Golden Rule, unshakeable as the moral law. Hence, though he apparently fails of his immediate desire in each of these three orations, the principle for which he contends cannot fail. As a modern writer says of Lincoln, 'The full, rich flood of his life through the nation's pulse is yet beating'; and his words are still potent in shaping the course of English politics in the way of justice.

EDWARD GIBBON (1737-1794)

To understand Burke or Johnson, one must read a multitude of books and be wary in his judgment; but with Gibbon the task is comparatively easy, for one has only to consider two books, his *Memoirs* and the first volume of his *History,* to understand the author. In his *Memoirs* we have an interesting reflection of Gibbon's own personality—a man who looks with satisfaction on the material side of things, who seeks always the easiest path for himself, and avoids life's difficulties and responsibilities. 'I sighed as a lover; but I obeyed as a son', he says, when, to save his inheritance, he gave up the woman he loved and came home to enjoy the paternal loaves and fishes. That is suggestive of the man's whole life. His *History,* on the other hand, is a remarkable work. It was the first in our language to be written on scientific principles, and with a solid basis of fact; and the style is the very climax of that classicism which had ruled England for an entire century. Its combination of historical fact and literary style makes *The Decline and Fall of the Roman Empire* the one thing of Gibbon's life that is 'worthy to be remembered.'

Gibbon's History. For many years Gibbon had meditated, like Milton, upon an immortal work, and had tried several historical subjects, only to give them up idly. In his *Journal* he tells us how his vague resolutions were brought to a focus:

> It was at Rome, on the fifteenth of October, 1764, as I sat musing amidst the ruins of the Capitol, while the barefooted friars were singing vespers in the Temple of Jupiter, that the idea of writing the decline and fall of the city first started to my mind.

Twelve years later, in 1776, Gibbon published the first volume of *The Decline and Fall of the Roman Empire*; and the enormous success of the work encouraged him to go on with the other five volumes, which were published at intervals during the next twelve years. The History begins with the reign of *Trajan*, in A.D. 98, and 'builds a straight Roman road' through the confused histories of thirteen centuries, ending with the fall of the Byzantine Empire in 1453. The scope of the History is enormous. It includes not only the decline of the Roman Empire, but such movements as the descent of the northern barbarians, the spread of Christianity, the reorganization of the European nations, the establishment of the great Eastern Empire, the rise of Mohammedanism, and the splendour of the Crusades. On the one hand it lacks philosophical insight, being satisfied with facts without comprehending the causes; and, as Gibbon seems lacking in ability to understand spiritual and religious movements, it is utterly inadequate in its treatment of the tremendous influence of Christianity. On the other hand, Gibbon's scholarship leaves little to criticize; he read enormously, sifted his facts out of multitudes of books and records, and then marshalled them in the imposing array with which we have grown familiar. Moreover, he is singularly just and discriminating in the use of all documents and authorities at his command. Hence he has given us the first history in English that has borne successfully the test of modern research and scholarship.

The style of the work is as imposing as his great subject. Indeed, with almost any other subject the sonorous roll of his majestic sentences would be out of place. While it deserves all the adjectives that have been applied to it by enthusiastic admirers—finished, elegant, splendid, rounded, massive, sonorous, copious, elabourate, ornate, exhaustive—it must be confessed, though one whispers the confession, that the style sometimes obscures our interest in the narrative. As he sifted his facts from a multitude of sources, so he often hides them again in endless periods, and one must often sift them out again in order to be quite sure of even the simple facts. Another drawback is that Gibbon is hopelessly worldly in his point of view; he loves pageants and crowds rather than individuals, and he is lacking in enthusiasm and in spiritual insight. The result is so frankly material at times that one wonders if he is not reading of forces or machines, rather than of human beings. A little reading of his History here and there is an excellent thing, leaving one impressed with the elegant classical style and the scholarship; but a continued reading is very apt to leave us longing for simplicity, for naturalness, and, above all, for the glow of enthusiasm which makes the dead heroes live once more in the written pages.

This judgment, however, must not obscure the fact that the book had a remarkably large sale; and that this, of itself, is an evidence that multitudes of readers found it not only erudite, but readable and interesting.

II. THE REVIVAL OF ROMANTIC POETRY

> The old order changeth, yielding place to new;
> And God fulfils Himself in many ways,
> Lest one good custom should corrupt the world.
>
> Tennyson's 'The Passing of Arthur'.

The Meaning of Romanticism. While Dryden, Pope, and Johnson were successively the dictators of English letters, and while, under their leadership, the heroic couplet became the fashion of poetry, and literature in general became satiric or critical in spirit, and formal in expression, a new romantic movement quietly made its appearance. Thomson's *The Seasons* (1730) was the first noteworthy poem of the romantic revival; and the poems and the poets increased steadily in number and importance till, in the age of Wordsworth and Scott, the spirit of Romanticism dominated our literature more completely than Classicism had ever done. This romantic movement—which Victor Hugo calls 'liberalism in literature'—is simply the expression of life as seen by imagination, rather than by prosaic 'common sense', which was the central doctrine of English philosophy in the eighteenth century. It has six prominent characteristics which distinguish it from the so-called classic literature which we have just studied:

1. The romantic movement was marked, and is always marked, by a strong reaction and protest against the bondage of rule and

custom, which, in science and theology, as well as in literature, generally tend to fetter the free human spirit.

2. Romanticism returned to nature and to plain humanity for its material, and so is in marked contrast to Classicism, which had confined itself largely to the clubs and drawing-rooms, and to the social and political life of London. Thomson's *Seasons,* whatever its defects, was a revelation of the natural wealth and beauty which, for nearly a century, had been hardly noticed by the great writers of England.

3. It brought again the dream of a golden age[1] in which the stern realities of life were forgotten and the ideals of youth were established as the only permanent realities. 'For the dreamer lives forever, but the toiler dies in a day', expresses, perhaps, only the wild fancy of a modern poet; but, when we think of it seriously, the dreams and ideals of a people are cherished possessions long after their stone monuments have crumbled away and their battles are forgotten. The romantic movement emphasized these eternal ideals of youth, and appealed to the human heart as the classic elegance of Dryden and Pope could never do.

4. Romanticism was marked by intense human sympathy, and by a consequent understanding of the human heart. Not to intellect or to science does the heart unlock its treasures, but rather to the touch of a sympathetic nature; and things that are hidden from the wise and prudent are revealed unto children. Pope had no appreciable humanity; Swift's work is a frightful satire; Addison delighted polite society, but had no message for plain people; while even Johnson, with all his kindness, had no feeling for men in the mass, but supported Sir Robert Walpole in his policy of letting evils alone until forced by a revolution to take notice of humanity's appeal. With the romantic revival all this was changed. While Howard was working heroically for prison reform, and Wilberforce for the liberation of the slaves, Gray wrote his 'short and simple

[1] The romantic revival is marked by renewed interest in mediæval ideals and literatre; and to this interest is due the succes of Walpole's romance. *The Castle of Otranto,* and of Chatterton's forgeries known as the *Rowley Papers.*

annals of the poor', and Goldsmith his *Deserted Village*, and Cowper sang,

> My ear is pained,
> My soul is sick with every day's report
> Of wrong and outrage with which earth is filled.
> There is no flesh in man's obdurate heart,
> It does not feel for man.[1]

This sympathy for the poor, and this cry against oppression, grew stronger and stronger till it culminated in 'Bobby' Burns, who, more than any other writer in any language, is the poet of the unlettered human heart.

5. The romantic movement was the expression of individual genius rather than of established rules. In consequence, the literature of the revival is as varied as the characters and moods of the different writers. When we read Pope, for instance, we have a general impression of sameness, as if all his polished poems were made in the same machine; but in the work of the best romanticists there is endless variety. To read them is like passing through a new village, meeting a score of different human types, and finding in each one something to love or to remember. Nature and the heart of man are as new as if we had never studied them. Hence, in reading the romanticists, who went to these sources for their material, we are seldom wearied but often surprised; and the surprise is like that of the sunrise, or the sea, which always offers some new beauty and stirs us deeply, as if we had never seen it before.

6. The romantic movement, while it followed its own genius, was not altogether unguided. Strictly speaking, there is no new movement either in history or in literature; each grows out of some good thing which has preceded it, and looks back with reverence to past masters. Spenser, Shakespeare, and Milton were the inspiration of the romantic revival; and we can hardly read a poem

[1] From *The Task*, Book II.

of the early romanticists without finding a suggestion of the influence of one of these great leaders.[1]

There are various other characteristics of Romanticism, but these six–the protest against the bondage of rules, the return to nature and the human heart, the interest in old sagas and mediæval romances as suggestive of a heroic age, the sympathy for the toilers of the world, the emphasis upon individual genius, and the return to Milton and the Elizabethans, instead of to Pope and Dryden, for literary models—are the most noticeable and the most interesting. Remembering them, we shall better appreciate the work of the following writers who, in varying degree, illustrate the revival of romantic poetry in the eighteenth century.

THOMAS GRAY (1716-1771)

> The curfew tolls the knell of parting day;
> The lowing herd wind slowly o'er the lea;
> The plowman homeward plods his weary way,
> And leaves the world to darkness and to me.
>
> Now fades the glimmering landscape on the sight,
> And all the air a solemn stillness holds,
> Save where the beetle wheels his droning flight,
> And drowsy tinklings lull the distant folds.

So begins 'the best known poem in the English language', a poem full of the gentle melancholy which marks all early romantic poetry. It should be read entire, as a perfect model of its kind. Not even Milton's 'Il Penseroso', which it strongly suggests, excels it in beauty and suggestiveness.

Life of Gray. The author of the famous 'Elegy' is the most scholarly and well-balanced of all the early romantic poets. In his youth he was a

---

[1] See, for instance, Phelps, *Beginnings of the Romantic Movement,* for a list of Spenserian imitators from 1700 to 1775.

weakling, the only one of twelve children who survived infancy; and his unhappy childhood, the tyranny of his father, and the separation from his loved mother, gave to his whole life the stamp of melancholy which is noticeable in all his poems. At the famous Eton school and again at Cambridge, he seems to have followed his own scholarly tastes rather than the curriculum, and was shocked, like Gibbon, at the general idleness and aimlessness of university life. One happy result of his school life was his friendship for Horace Walpole, who took him abroad for a three years' tour of the Continent.

Thomas Gray

No better index of the essential difference between the classical and the new romantic school can be imagined than that which is revealed in the letters of Gray and Addison, as they record their impressions of foreign travel. Thus, when Addison crossed the Alps, some twenty-five years before, in good weather, he wrote: 'A very troublesome journey.... You cannot imagine how I am pleased with the sight of a plain.' Gray crossed the Alps in the beginning of winter, 'wrapped in muffs, hoods and masks of beaver, fur boots, and bearskins', but wrote ecstatically, 'Not a precipice, not a torrent, not a cliff but is pregnant with religion and poetry'.

On his return to England, Gray lived for a short time at Stoke Poges, where he wrote his 'Ode on Eton', and probably sketched his 'Elegy', which, however, was not finished till 1750, eight years later. During the latter years of his shy and scholarly life he was Professor of Modern History and Languages at Cambridge, without any troublesome work of lecturing to students. Here he gave himself up to study and to poetry, varying his work by 'prowlings' among the manuscripts of the new British Museum, and by his 'Lilliputian' travels in England and Scotland. He died in his rooms at Pembroke College in 1771, and was buried in the little churchyard of Stoke Poges.

Works of Gray. Gray's Letters, published in 1775, are excellent reading, and his *Journal* is still a model of natural description; but it is to a single small volume of poems that he owes his fame and his place in literature. These poems divide themselves naturally

Church at Stoke Poges

into three periods, in which we may trace the progress of Gray's emancipation from the classic rules which had so long governed English literature. In the first period he wrote several minor poems, of which the best are his 'Hymn to Adversity' and the odes 'To Spring' and 'On a Distant Prospect of Eton College'. These early poems reveal two suggestive things: first, the appearance of that melancholy which characterizes all the poetry of the period; and second, the study of nature, not for its own beauty or truth, but rather as a suitable background for the play of human emotions.

The second period shows the same tendencies more strongly developed. The 'Elegy Written in a Country Churchyard' (1750), the most perfect poem of the age, belongs to this period. To read Milton's 'Il Penseroso' and Gray's 'Elegy' is to see the beginning and the perfection of that 'literature of melancholy' which largely occupied English poets for more than a century. Two other well-known poems of this second period are the Pindaric odes, 'The Progress of Poesy' and 'The Bard'. The first is strongly suggestive of Dryden's 'Alexander's Feast', but shows Milton's influence in a greater melody and variety of expression. 'The Bard' is, in every way, more romantic and original. An old minstrel, the last of the Welsh singers, halts King Edward and his army in a wild mountain pass, and with fine poetic frenzy prophecies the terror and desolation which must ever follow the tyrant. From its first line, 'Ruin seize thee, ruthless King!' to the end, when the old bard plunges from his lofty crag and disappears in the river's flood, the poem thrills with the fire of an ancient and noble race of men. It breaks absolutely with the classical school and proclaims a literary declaration of independence.

In the third period Gray turns momentarily from his Welsh material and reveals a new field of romantic interest in two Norse poems, 'The Fatal Sisters' and 'The Descent of Odin' (1761). Gray translated his material from the Latin, and though these two poems lack much of the elemental strength and grandeur of the Norse sagas, they are remarkable for calling attention to the unused wealth of literary material that was hidden in Northern mythology. To Gray and to Percy (who published his *Northern Antiquities* in 1770) is due in large measure the profound interest in the old Norse sagas which has continued to our own day.

Taken together, Gray's works form a most interesting commentary on the varied life of the eighteenth century. He was a scholar, familiar with all the intellectual interests of his age, and his work has much of the precision and polish of the classical school; but he shares also the reawakened interest in nature, in common man, and in mediæval culture, and his work is generally romantic both in style and in spirit. The same conflict between the classic and romantic schools, and the triumph of Romanticism, is shown clearly in the most versatile of Gray's contemporaries, Oliver Goldsmith.

OLIVER GOLDSMITH (1728-1774)

Because *The Deserted Village* is one of the most familiar poems in our language, Goldsmith is generally given a high place among the poets of the romantic dawn. But the Village, when we read it carefully, turns out to be a rhymed essay in the style of Pope's famous *Essay on Man;* it owes its popularity to the sympathetic memories which it awakens, rather than to its poetic excellence. It is as a prose writer that Goldsmith excels. He is an essayist, with Addison's fine polish but with more sympathy for human life; he is a dramatist, one of the very few who have ever written a comedy that can keep its popularity unchanged while a century rolls over its head; but greater, perhaps, than the poet and essayist and dramatist is Goldsmith the novelist, who set himself to the important work of purifying the early novel of its brutal and indecent tendencies, and who has given us, in *The Vicar of Wakefield,* one of the most enduring characters in English fiction. In his manner, especially in his poetry, Goldsmith was too much influenced by his friend Johnson and the classicists; but in his matter, in his sympathy for nature and human life, he belongs unmistakably to the new romantic school. Altogether he is the most versatile, the most charming, the most inconsistent, and the most lovable genius of all the literary men who made famous the age of Johnson.

Oliver Goldsmith

Life. Goldsmith's career is that of an irresponsible, unbalanced genius, which would make one despair if the man himself did not remain so lovable in all his inconsistencies. He was born in the village of Pallas, Ireland, the son of a poor Irish curate whose noble character is portrayed in Dr. Primrose, of *The Vicar of Wakefield,* and in the country parson of

The Deserted Village. After an unsatisfactory course in various schools, where he was regarded as hopelessly stupid, Goldsmith entered Trinity College, Dublin, as a sizar, that is a student who pays with labour for his tuition. By his escapades he was brought into disfavour with the authorities, but that troubled him little. He was also wretchedly poor, which troubled him less; for when he earned a few shillings by writing ballads for street singers, his money went oftener to idle beggars than to the paying of his honest debts. After three years of university life he ran away, in dime-novel fashion, and nearly starved to death before he was found and brought back in disgrace. Then he worked a little, and obtained his degree in 1749.

Strange that such an idle and irresponsible youth should have been urged by his family to take holy orders; but such was the fact. For two years more Goldsmith laboured with theology, only to be rejected when he presented himself as a candidate for the ministry. He tried teaching, and failed. Then his fancy turned to America, and, provided with money and a good horse, he started off for Cork, where he was to embark for the New World. He loafed along the pleasant Irish ways, missed his ship, and presently turned up cheerfully amongst his relatives, minus all his money, and riding a sorry nag called Fiddleback, for which he had traded his own on the way.[1]

He borrowed fifty pounds more, and started for London to study law, but speedily lost his money at cards, and again appeared, amiable and irresponsible as ever, among his despairing relatives. The next year they sent him to Edinburgh to study medicine. Here for a couple of years he became popular as a singer of songs and a teller of tales, to whom medicine was only a troublesome affliction. Suddenly the Wanderlust seized him and he started abroad, ostensibly to complete his medical education, but in reality to wander like a cheerful beggar over Europe, singing and playing his flute for food and lodging. He may have studied a little at Leyden and at Padua, but that was only incidental. After a year or more of vagabondage he returned to London with an alleged medical degree, said to have been obtained at Louvain or Padua.

The next few years are a pitiful struggle to make a living as tutor, apothecary's assistant, comedian, usher in a country school, and finally as

[1] Such is Goldsmith's version of a somewhat suspicious adventure, whose details are unknown.

a physician in Southwark. Gradually he drifted into literature, and lived from hand to mouth by doing hack work for the London booksellers. Some of his essays and his *Citizen of the World* (1760-1761) brought him to the attention of Johnson, who looked him up, was attracted first by his poverty and then by his genius, and presently declared him to be 'one of the first men we now have as an author'. Johnson's friendship proved invaluable, and presently Goldsmith found himself a member of the exclusive Literary Club. He promptly justified Johnson's confidence by publishing The *Traveller* (1764), which was hailed as one of the finest poems of the century. Money now came to him liberally, with orders from the booksellers; he took new quarters in Fleet Street and furnished them gorgeously; but he had an inordinate vanity for bright-coloured clothes, and faster than he earned money he spent it on velvet cloaks and in indiscriminate charity. For a time he resumed his practice as a physician, but his fine clothes did not bring patients, as he expected; and presently he turned to writing again, to pay his debts to the booksellers. He produced several superficial and grossly inaccurate schoolbooks—like his *Animated Nature* and his histories of England, Greece, and Rome—which brought him bread and more fine clothes, and his *Vicar of Wakefield, The Deserted Village,* and *She Stoops to Conquer,* which brought him undying fame.

After meeting with Johnson, Goldsmith became the object of Boswell's magpie curiosity; and to Boswell's *Life of Johnson* we are indebted for many of the details of Goldsmith's life—his homeliness, his awkward ways, his drolleries and absurdities, which made him alternately the butt and the wit of the famous Literary Club. Boswell disliked Goldsmith, and so draws an unflattering portrait, but even this does not disguise the contagious good humor which made men love him. When in his forty-seventh year, he fell sick of a fever, and with childish confidence turned to a quack medicine to cure himself. He died in 1774, and Johnson placed a tablet, with a sonorous Latin epitaph, in Westminster Abbey, though Goldsmith was buried elsewhere. 'Let not his frailties be remembered; he was a very great man', said Johnson; and the literary world—which, like that old dictator, is kind enough at heart, though often rough in its methods—is glad to accept and record the verdict.

Works of Goldsmith. Of Goldsmith's early essays and his later school histories little need be said. They have settled into their own place, far out of sight of the ordinary reader. Perhaps the most interesting of these is a series of letters for the *Public Ledger* (afterwards published as *The Citizen of the World*), written from the viewpoint of an alleged Chinese traveller, and giving the latter's comments on English civilization.[1] The following five works are those upon which Goldsmith's fame chiefly rests:

The Traveller (1764) made Goldsmith's reputation among his contemporaries, but is now seldom read, except by students who would understand how Goldsmith was, at one time, dominated by Johnson and his pseudo-classic ideals. It is a long poem, in rhymed couplets, giving a survey and criticism of the social life of various countries in Europe, and reflects many of Goldsmith's own wanderings and impressions.

The Deserted Village

The Deserted Village (1770), though written in the same mechanical style, is so permeated with honest human sympathy, and voices so perfectly the revolt of the individual man against institutions, that a multitude of common people heard it gladly, without consulting the critics as to whether they should call it good poetry. Notwithstanding its faults, to which Matthew Arnold has called sufficient attention, it has become one of our best known poems, though we cannot help wishing that the monotony of its couplets had been broken by some of the Irish folk songs and ballads that charmed street audiences in Dublin, and that brought Goldsmith a welcome from the French peasants wherever he stopped to sing. In the village parson and the schoolmaster, Goldsmith has increased Chaucer's list by two lovable characters that will endure as long as the English language. The criticism that the picture of prosperous 'Sweet Auburn' never applied to any village in Ireland is just, no doubt, but it is outside the question. Goldsmith was a hopeless dreamer, bound to see everything, as he saw his debts and his gay clothes, in a purely idealistic way.

The Good-Natured Man and *She Stoops to Conquer* are Goldsmith's two comedies. The former, a comedy of character, though it has

---

[1] Goldsmith's idea, which was borrowed from Walpole, reappears in the pseudo *Letters from a Chinese Official,* which recently attracted considerable attention.

some laughable scenes and one laughable character, Croaker, met with failure on the stage, and has never been revived with any success. The latter, a comedy of intrigue, is one of the few plays that has never lost its popularity. Its lively, bustling scenes, and its pleasantly absurd characters, Marlowe, the Hardcastles, and Tony Lumpkin, still hold the attention of modern theatre goers; and nearly every amateur dramatic club sooner or later places *She Stoops to Conquer* on its list of attractions.

The Vicar of Wakefield

The Vicar of Wakefield is Goldsmith's only novel, and the first in any language that gives to home life an enduring romantic interest. However much we admire the beginnings of the English novel, to which we shall presently refer, we are nevertheless shocked by its frequent brutalities and indecencies. Goldsmith, like Steele, had the Irish reverence for pure womanhood, and this reverence made him shun as a pest the vulgarity and coarseness in which contemporary novelists, like Smollett and Sterne, seemed to delight. So he did for the novel what Addison and Steele had done for the satire and the essay; he refined and elevated it, making it worthy of the old Anglo-Saxon ideals which are our best literary heritage.

Briefly, *The Vicar of Wakefield* is the story of a simple English clergyman, Dr. Primrose, and his family, who pass from happiness through great tribulation. Misfortunes, which are said never to come singly, appear in this case in flocks; but through poverty, sorrow, imprisonment, and the unspeakable loss of his daughters, the Vicar's faith in God and man emerges triumphant. To the very end he is like one of the old martyrs, who sings *Alleluia* while the lions roar about him and his children in the arena. Goldsmith's optimism, it must be confessed, is here stretched to the breaking point. The reader is sometimes offered fine Johnsonian phrases where he would naturally expect homely and vigorous language; and he is continually haunted by the suspicion that, even in this best of all possible worlds, the Vicar's clouds of affliction were somewhat too easily converted into showers of blessing; yet he is forced to read on, and at the end he confesses gladly that Goldsmith has succeeded in making a most interesting story out of material that, in other hands, would have developed either a burlesque or a brutal tragedy. Laying aside all romantic passion, intrigue, and adventure, upon which other novelists depended, Goldsmith, in this simple story of common life, has accomplished three noteworthy results: he has made human fatherhood almost a divine thing; he has glorified the moral sentiments which cluster about the family life as the center of civilization; and he has given us, in Dr. Primrose, a striking and enduring figure, which seems more like a personal acquaintance than a character in a book.

William Cowper (1731–1800)

In Cowper we have another interesting poet, who, like Gray and Goldsmith, shows the struggle between romantic and classic ideals. In his first volume of poems, Cowper is more hampered by literary fashions than was Goldsmith in his *Traveller* and his *Deserted Village.* In his second period, however, Cowper uses blank verse freely; and his delight in nature and in homely characters, like the teamster and the mail carrier of *The Task,* shows that his classicism is being rapidly thawed out by romantic feeling. In his later work, especially his immortal 'John Gilpin', Cowper flings fashions aside, gives Pegasus the reins, takes to the open road, and so proves himself a worthy predecessor of Burns, who is the most spontaneous and the most interesting of all the early romanticists.

Life. Cowper's life is a pathetic story of a shy and timid genius, who found the world of men too rough, and who withdrew to nature like a wounded animal. He was born at Great Berkhamstead, Hertfordshire, in 1731, the son of an English clergyman. He was a delicate, sensitive child, whose early life was saddened by the death of his mother and by his neglect at home. At six years he was sent away to a boys' school, where he was terrified by young barbarians who made his life miserable. There was one atrocious bully into whose face Cowper could never look; he recognized his enemy by his shoe buckles, and shivered at his approach. The fierce invectives of his 'Tirocinium, or a Review of Schools' (1784), shows how these school experiences had affected his mind and health.

For twelve years he studied law, but at the approach of a public examination for an office he was so terrified that he attempted suicide.

William Cowper

The experience unsettled his reason, and the next twelve months were spent in an asylum at St. Alban's. The death of his father, in 1756, had brought the poet a small patrimony, which placed him above the necessity of struggling, like Goldsmith, for his daily bread. Upon his recovery he boarded for years at the house of the Unwins, cultured people who recognized the genius hidden in this shy and melancholy yet quaintly humorous man. Mrs. Unwin, in particular, cared for him as a son; and whatever happiness he experienced in his poor life was the result of the devotion of this good woman, who is the 'Mary' of all his poems.

A second attack of insanity was brought on by Cowper's morbid interest in religion, influenced, perhaps, by the untempered zeal of one John Newton, a curate, with whom Cowper worked in the small parish of Olney, and with whom he compiled the famous Olney Hymns. The rest of his life, between intervals of melancholia or insanity, was spent in gardening, in the care of his numerous pets, and in writing his poems, his translation of Homer, and his charming letters. His two best known poems were suggested by a lively and cultivated widow, Lady Austen, who told him the story of John Gilpin and called for a ballad on the subject. She also urged him to write a long poem in blank verse; and when he demanded a subject, she whimsically suggested the sofa, which was a new article of furniture at that time. Cowper immediately wrote 'The Sofa', and, influenced by the poetic possibilities that lie in unexpected places, he added to this poem from time to time, and called his completed work *The Task.* This was published in 1785, and the author was instantly recognized as one of the chief poets of his age. The last years of his life were a long battle with insanity, until death mercifully ended the struggle in 1800. His last poem, 'The Castaway', is a cry of despair, in which, under guise of a man washed overboard in a storm, he describes himself perishing in the sight of friends who are powerless to help.

Cowper's Works. Cowper's first volume of poems, containing 'The Progress of Error', 'Truth', 'Table Talk', etc., is interesting chiefly as showing how the poet was bound by the classical rules of his age. These poems are dreary, on the whole, but a certain gentleness, and especially a vein of pure humor, occasionally rewards the reader. For Cowper was a humorist, and only the constant shadow of insanity kept him from becoming famous in that line alone.

The Task

The Task, written in blank verse, and published in 1785, is Cowper's longest poem. Used as we are to the natural poetry of Wordsworth and Tennyson, it is hard for us to appreciate the striking originality of this work. Much of it is conventional and 'wooden', to be sure, like much of Wordsworth's poetry; but when, after reading the rhymed essays and the artificial couplets of Johnson's age, we turn suddenly to Cowper's description of homely scenes, of woods and brooks, of ploughmen and teamsters and the letter carrier on his rounds, we realize that we are at the dawn of a better day in poetry:

He comes, the herald of a noisy world,
With spatter'd boots, strapp'd waist, and frozen locks:
News from all nations lumbering at his back.
True to his charge, the close-packed load behind,
Yet careless what he brings, his one concern
Is to conduct it to the destined inn,
And, having dropped the expected bag, pass on.
He whistles as he goes, light-hearted wretch,
Cold and yet cheerful: messenger of grief
Perhaps to thousands, and of joy to some;
To him indifferent whether grief or joy.
Houses in ashes, and the fall of stocks,
Births, deaths, and marriages, epistles wet
With tears that trickled down the writer's cheeks

Fast as the periods from his fluent quill,
Or charged with amorous sighs of absent swains,
Or nymphs responsive, equally affect
His horse and him, unconscious of them all.

Miscellaneous Works

Cowper's most labourious work, the translation of Homer in blank verse, was published in 1791. Its stately, Milton-like movement, and its better rendering of the Greek, make this translation far superior to Pope's artificial couplets. It is also better, in many respects, than Chapman's more famous and more fanciful rendering; but for some reason it was not successful, and has never received the recognition which it deserves. Entirely different in spirit are the poet's numerous hymns, which were published in the Olney Collection in 1779, and which are still used in our churches. It is only necessary to mention a few first lines—'God moves in a mysterious way', 'Oh, for a closer walk with God', 'Sometimes a light surprises'—to show how his gentle and devout spirit has left its impress upon thousands who now hardly know his name. With Cowper's charming *Letters,* published in 1803, we reach the end of his important works, and the student who enjoys reading letters will find that these rank among the best of their kind. It is not, however, for his ambitious works that Cowper is remembered, but rather for his minor poems, which have found their own way into so many homes. Among these, the one that brings quickest response from hearts that understand is his little poem, 'On the Receipt of My Mother's Picture', beginning with the striking line, 'Oh, that those lips had language'. Another, called 'Alexander Selkirk', beginning, 'I am monarch of all I survey', suggests how Selkirk's experiences as a castaway (which gave Defoe his inspiration for *Robinson Crusoe*) affected the poet's timid nature and imagination. Last and most famous of all is his immortal 'John Gilpin'. Cowper was in a terrible fit of melancholy when Lady Austen told him the story, which proved to be better than medicine, for all night long chuckles and suppressed laughter were heard in the poet's bedroom. Next morning at breakfast he recited the ballad that had afforded its author so much delight in the making. The student should read it, even if he reads nothing else by Cowper; and he will be lacking in humour or appreciation if he is not ready to echo heartily the last stanza:

Now let us sing, Long live the King,
And Gilpin, long live he!
And when he next doth ride abroad
May I be there to see.

ROBERT BURNS (1759-1796)

After a century and more of Classicism, we noted with interest the work of three men, Gray, Goldsmith, and Cowper, whose poetry, like the chorus of awakening birds, suggests the dawn of another day. Two other poets of the same age suggest the sunrise. The first is the ploughman Burns, who speaks straight from the heart to the primitive emotions of the race; the second is the mystic Blake, who only half understands his own thoughts, and whose words stir a sensitive nature as music does, or the moon in midheaven, rousing in the soul those vague desires and aspirations which ordinarily sleep, and which can never be expressed because they have no names. Blake lived his shy, mystic, spiritual life in the crowded city, and his message is to the few who can understand. Burns lived his sad, toilsome, erring life in the open air, with the sun and the rain, and his songs touch all the world. The latter's poetry, so far as it has a philosophy, rests upon two principles which the classic school never understood—that common people are at heart

Robert Burns

romantic and lovers of the ideal, and that simple human emotions furnish the elements of true poetry. Largely because he follows these two principles, Burns is probably the greatest song writer of the world. His poetic creed may be summed up in one of his own stanzas:

> Give me ae spark o' Nature's fire,
> That's a' the learning I desire;
> Then, though I trudge thro' dub an' mire
> At pleugh or cart,
> My Muse, though hamely in attire,
> May touch the heart.

Life.[1] Burns's life is 'a life of fragments', as Carlyle called it; and the different fragments are as unlike as the noble 'Cotter's Saturday Night' and the rant and riot of 'The Jolly Beggars'. The details of this sad and disjointed life were better, perhaps, forgotten. We call attention only to the facts which help us to understand the man and his poetry.

Burns was born in a clay cottage at Alloway, Scotland, in the bleak winter of 1759. His father was an excellent type of the Scotch peasant of those days—a poor, honest, God-fearing man, who toiled from dawn till dark to wrest a living for his family from the stubborn soil. His tall figure was bent with unceasing labour; his hair was thin and gray, and in his eyes was the careworn, hunted look of a peasant driven by poverty and unpaid rents from one poor farm to another. The family often fasted of necessity, and lived in solitude to avoid the temptation of spending their hard-earned money. The children went barefoot and bareheaded in all weathers, and shared the parents' toil and their anxiety over the rents. At thirteen Bobby, the eldest, was doing a peasant's full day's labour; at sixteen he was chief labourer on his father's farm; and he describes the life as 'the cheerless gloom of a hermit, and the unceasing moil of a galley slave'. In 1784 the father, after a lifetime of toil, was saved from a debtor's prison by consumption and death. To rescue something from the wreck of the home, and to win a poor chance of bread for the family, the two older boys set up a claim for arrears of wages that had

---

[1] Fitz-Greene Halleck's poem 'To a Rose from near Alloway Kirk' (1822) is a good appreciation of Burns and his poetry. It might be well to read this poem before the sad story of Burns's life.

never been paid. With the small sum allowed them, they buried their father, took another farm, Mossgiel, in Mauchline, and began again the long struggle with poverty.

Such, in outline, is Burns's own story of his early life, taken mostly from his letters. There is another and more pleasing side to the picture, of which we have glimpses in his poems and in his Commonplace Book. Here we see the boy at school; for like most Scotch peasants, the father gave his boys the best education he possibly could. We see him following the plough, not like a slave, but like a free man, crooning over an old Scotch song and making a better one to match the melody. We see him stop the plough to listen to what the wind is saying, or turn aside lest he disturb the birds at their singing and nest making. At supper we see the family about the table, happy notwithstanding their scant fare, each child with a spoon in one hand and a book in the other. We hear Betty Davidson reciting, from her great store, some heroic ballad that fired the young hearts to enthusiasm and made them forget the day's toil. And in 'The Cotter's Saturday Night' we have a glimpse of Scotch peasant life that makes us almost reverence these heroic men and women, who kept their faith and their self-respect in the face of poverty, and whose hearts, under their rough exteriors, were tender and true as steel.

A most unfortunate change in Burns's life began when he left the farm, at seventeen, and went to Kirkoswald to study surveying.

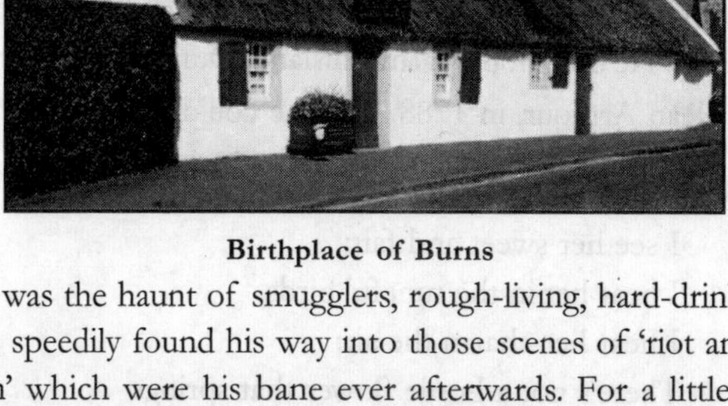

Birthplace of Burns

The town was the haunt of smugglers, rough-living, hard-drinking men; and Burns speedily found his way into those scenes of 'riot and roaring dissipation' which were his bane ever afterwards. For a little while he studied diligently, but one day, while taking the altitude of the sun, he saw a pretty girl in the neighbouring garden, and love put trigonometry to flight. Soon he gave up his work and wandered back to the farm and poverty again.

When twenty-seven years of age Burns first attracted literary attention, and in the same moment sprang to the first place in Scottish letters. In despair over his poverty and personal habits, he resolved to emigrate to Jamaica, and gathered together a few of his early poems, hoping to sell them for enough to pay the expenses of his journey. The result was the famous Kilmarnock edition of Burns, published in 1786, for which he was offered twenty pounds. It is said that he even bought his ticket, and on the night before the ship sailed wrote his 'Farewell to Scotland', beginning, 'The gloomy night is gathering fast', which he intended to be his last song on Scottish soil.

In the morning he changed his mind, led partly by some dim foreshadowing of the result of his literary adventure; for the little book took all Scotland by storm. Not only scholars and literary men, but 'even ploughboys and maid servants', says a contemporary, eagerly spent their hard-earned shillings for the new book. Instead of going to Jamaica, the young poet hurried to Edinburgh to arrange for another edition of his work. His journey was a constant ovation, and in the capital he was welcomed and feasted by the best of Scottish society. This inexpected triumph lasted only one winter. Burns's fondness for taverns and riotous living shocked his cultured entertainers, and when he returned to Edinburgh next winter, after a pleasure jaunt through the Highlands, he received scant attention. He left the city in anger and disappointment, and went back to the soil where he was more at home.

The last few years of Burns's life are a sad tragedy, and we pass over them hurriedly. He bought the farm Ellisland, Dumfriesshire, and married the faithful Jean Armour, in 1788. That he could write of her,

I see her in the dewy flowers,
I see her sweet and fair;
I hear her in the tunefu' birds,
I hear her charm the air:
There's not a bonie flower that springs
By fountain, shaw, or green;

There's not a bonie bird that sings,
But minds me o' my Jean,

is enough for us to remember. The next year he was appointed exciseman, that is collector of liquor revenues, and the small salary, with the return from his poems, would have been sufficient to keep his family in modest comfort, had he but kept away from taverns. For a few years his life of alternate toil and dissipation was occasionally illumined by his splendid lyric genius, and he produced many songs—'Bonnie Doon', 'My Love's like a Red, Red Rose', 'Auld Lang Syne', 'Highland Mary', and the soul-stirring 'Scots wha hae', composed while galloping over the moor in a storm—which have made the name of Burns known wherever the English language is spoken, and honoured wherever Scotchmen gather together. He died miserably in 1796, when only thirty-seven years old. His last letter was an appeal to a friend for money to stave off the bailiff, and one of his last poems a tribute to Jessie Lewars, a kind lassie who helped to care for him in his illness. This last exquisite lyric, 'O wert thou in the cauld blast', set to Mendelssohn's music, is one of our best known songs, though its history is seldom suspected by those who sing it.

The Poetry of Burns. The publication of the Kilmarnock Burns, with the title *Poems Chiefly in the Scottish Dialect* (1786), marks an epoch in the history of English Literature, like the publication of Spenser's *Shepherd's Calendar.* After a century of cold and formal poetry, relieved only by the romanticism of Gray and Cowper, these fresh inspired songs went straight to the heart, like the music of returning birds in springtime. It was a little volume, but a great book; and we think of Marlowe's line, 'Infinite riches in a little room', in connection with it. Such poems as 'The Cotter's Saturday Night', 'To a Mouse', 'To Mountain Daisy', 'Man was Made To Mourn', 'The Twa Dogs', 'Address to the Deil', and 'Halloween', suggest that the whole spirit of the romantic revival is embodied in this obscure ploughman. Love, humour, pathos, the response to nature—all the poetic qualities that touch the human heart are here; and the heart was touched as it had not been since the days of Elizabeth. If the reader will note again the six characteristics of the romantic movement, and then read six poems of Burns, he will see at once how perfectly this one man expresses the new idea. Or take a single suggestion—

Ae fond kiss, and then we sever!
Ae farewell, and then forever!
Deep in heart-wrung tears I'll pledge thee,
Warring sighs and groans I'll wage thee.
Who shall say that Fortune grieves him
While the star of hope she leaves him?
Me, nae cheerfu' twinkle lights me;
Dark despair around benights me.
I'll ne'er blame my partial fancy,
Naething could resist my Nancy;
But to see her was to love her;
Love but her, and love forever.
Had we never lov'd sae kindly,
Had we never lov'd sae blindly,
Never met—or never parted—
We had ne'er been broken-hearted.

The 'essence of a thousand love tales' is in that one little song. Because he embodies the new spirit of romanticism, critics give him a high place in the history of our literature; and because his songs go straight to the heart, he is the poet of common men.

Songs for Music

Of Burns's many songs for music little need be said. They have found their way into the hearts of a whole people, and there they speak for themselves. They range from the exquisite 'O wert thou in the cauld blast', to the tremendous appeal to Scottish patriotism in 'Scots wha hae wi' Wallace bled', which, Carlyle said, should be sung with the throat of the whirlwind. Many of these songs were composed in his best days, when following the plough or resting after his work, while the music of some old Scotch song was ringing in his head. It is largely because he thought of music while he composed that so many of his poems have the singing quality, suggesting a melody as we read them.

Among his poems of nature, 'To a Mouse' and 'To a Mountain Daisy' are unquestionably the best, suggesting the poetical possibilities that daily pass unnoticed under our feet. These two poems are as near as Burns ever comes to appreciating nature for its own sake. The majority of his poems, like 'Winter' and 'Ye banks and braes o' bonie Doon', regard nature in the same way that Gray regarded it, as a background for the play of human emotions.

Of his poems of emotion there is an immense number. It is a curious fact that the world is always laughing and crying at the same moment; and we can hardly read a page of Burns without finding this natural juxtaposition of smiles and tears. It is noteworthy also that all strong emotions, when expressed naturally, lend themselves to poetry; and Burns, more than any other writer, has an astonishing faculty of describing his own emotions with

The Auld Brig, Ayr (Ayr Bridge)

vividness and simplicity, so that they appeal instantly to our own. One cannot read, 'I love my Jean', for instance, without being in love with some idealized woman; or 'To Mary in Heaven', without sharing the personal grief of one who has loved and lost.

Besides the songs of nature and of human emotion, Burns has given us a large number of poems for which no general title can be given. Noteworthy among these are 'A man's a man for a' that', which voices the new romantic estimate of humanity; 'The Vision', from which we get a strong impression of Burns's early ideals; the 'Epistle to a Young Friend', from which, rather than from his satires, we learn Burns's personal views of religion and honour; the 'Address to the Unco Guid', which is the poet's plea for mercy in judgment; and 'A Bard's Epitaph', which, as a summary of his own life, might well be written at the end of his poems. 'Halloween', a picture of rustic merrymaking, and 'The Twa Dogs' a contrast between the rich and poor, are generally classed among the poet's best works; but one unfamiliar with the Scotch dialect will find them rather difficult.

Of Burns's longer poems the two best worth reading are 'The Cotter's Saturday Night' and 'Tam o' Shanter',—the one giving the most perfect picture we possess of a noble poverty; the other being the most lively and the least objectionable of his humorous works. It would be difficult to find elsewhere such a combination of the gruesome and the ridiculous as is packed up in 'Tam o' Shanter'. With the exception of these two, the longer poems add little to the author's fame or to our own enjoyment. It is better for the beginner to read Burns's exquisite songs and gladly to recognize his place in the hearts of the people, and forget the rest, since they only sadden us and obscure the poet's better nature.

William Blake (1757-1827)

Piping down the valleys wild,
    Piping songs of pleasant glee,
On a cloud I saw a child,
    And he laughing said to me:

'Pipe a song about a lamb;
    So I piped with merry cheer.
'Piper, pipe that song again;
    'So I piped: he wept to hear.

'Piper, sit thee down and write
    In a book, that all may read;

'So he vanished from my sight,
And I plucked a hollow reed,

And I made a rural pen,
And I stained the water clear,
And I wrote my happy songs
Every child may joy to hear.[1]

Of all the romantic poets of the eighteenth century, Blake is the most independent and the most original. In his earliest work, written when he was scarcely more than a child, he seems to go back to the Elizabethan songwriters for his models; but for the greater part of his life he was the poet of inspiration alone, following no man's lead, and obeying no voice but that which he heard in his own mystic soul. Though the most extraordinary literary genius of his age, he had practically no influence upon it. Indeed, we hardly yet understand this poet of pure fancy, this mystic, this transcendental madman, who remained to the end of his busy life an incomprehensible child.

Life. Blake, the son of a London tradesman, was a strange, imaginative child, whose soul was more at home with brooks and flowers and fairies than with the crowd of the city streets. Beyond learning to read and write, he received no education; but he began, at ten years, to copy prints and to write verses. He also began a long course of art study, which resulted in his publishing his own books, adorned with marginal engravings coloured by hand—an unusual setting, worthy of the strong artistic sense that shows itself in many of his early verses. As a child he had visions of God and the angels looking in at his window; and as a man he thought he received visits from the souls of the great dead, Moses, Virgil, Homer, Dante, Milton—'majestic shadows, gray but luminous', he calls them. He seems never to have asked himself the question how far these visions were pure illusions, but believed and trusted them implicitly. To him all nature was a vast spiritual symbolism, wherein he saw elves, fairies, devils, angels—all looking at him in friendship or enmity through the eyes of flowers and stars:

[1] Introduction, *Songs of Innocence.*

With the blue sky spread over with wings,
And the mild sun that mounts and sings;
With trees and fields full of fairy elves,
And little devils who fight for themselves;
With angels planted in hawthorne bowers,
And God himself in the passing hours.

And this curious, pantheistic conception of nature was not a matter of creed, but the very essence of Blake's life. Strangely enough, he made no attempt to found a new religious cult, but followed his own way, singing cheerfully, working patiently, in the face of discouragement and failure. That writers of far less genius were exalted to favour, while he remained poor and obscure, does not seem to have troubled him in the least. For over forty years he laboured diligently at book engraving, guided in his art by Michael Angelo. but inventing his own curious designs, at which we still wonder. The illustrations for Young's 'Night Thoughts', for Blair's 'Grave', and the 'Inventions to the Book of Job', show the peculiarity of Blake's mind quite as clearly as his poems. While he worked at his trade he flung off—for he never seemed to compose—disjointed visions and incomprehensible rhapsodies, with an occasional little gem that still sets our hearts to singing:

Ah, sunflower, weary of time,
Who countest the steps of the sun;
Seeking after that sweet golden clime
Where the traveller's journey is done;

Where the youth pined away with desire,
And the pale virgin shrouded in snow,
Rise from their graves, and aspire
Where my sunflower wishes to go!

That is a curious flower to find growing in the London street; but it suggests Blake's own life, which was outwardly busy and quiet, but inwardly full of adventure and excitement. His last huge prophetic works, like *Jerusalem* and *Milton* (1804), were dictated to him, he declares, by supernatural means, and even against his own will. They are only half intelligible, but here and there one sees flashes of the same poetic beauty that marks his little poems. Critics generally dismiss Blake with the word 'madman'; but that is only an evasion. At best, he is the writer of exquisite lyrics; at worst, he is mad only 'north-northwest', like *Hamlet;* and the puzzle is to find the method in his madness. The most amazing thing about him is the perfectly sane and cheerful way in which he moved through poverty and obscurity, flinging out exquisite poems or senseless rhapsodies, as a child might play with gems or straws or sunbeams indifferently. He was a gentle, kindly, most unworldly little man, with extraordinary eyes, which seem even in the lifeless portraits to reflect some unusual hypnotic power. He died obscurely, smiling at a vision of Paradise, in 1827. That was nearly a century ago, yet he still remains one of the most incomprehensible figures in our literature.

Works of Blake. The *Poetical Sketches,* published in 1783, is a collection of Blake's earliest poetry, much of it written in boyhood. It contains much crude and incoherent work, but also a few lyrics of striking originality. Two later and better known volumes are *Songs of Innocence* and *Songs of Experience*, reflecting two widely different views of the human soul. As in all his works, there is an abundance of apparently worthless stuff in these songs; but, in the language of miners, it is all 'pay dirt'; it shows gleams of golden grains that await our sifting, and now and then we find a nugget unexpectedly:

> My lord was like a flower upon the brows
> Of lusty May; ah life as frail as flower!
> My lord was like a star in highest heaven
> Drawn down to earth by spells and wickedness;
> My lord was like the opening eye of day;
> But he is darkened; like the summer moon
> Clouded; fall'n like the stately tree, cut down;
> The breath of heaven dwelt among his leaves.

On account of the chaotic character of most of Blake's work, it is well to begin our reading with a short book of selections, containing the best songs of these three little volumes. Swinburne calls Blake the only poet of 'supreme and simple poetic genius' of the eighteenth century, 'the one man of that age fit, on all accounts, to rank with the old great masters.'[1] The praise is doubtless extravagant, and the criticism somewhat intemperate; but when we have read 'The Evening Star', 'Memory', 'Night', 'Love', 'To the Muses', 'Spring', 'Summer', 'The Tiger', 'The Lamb', 'The Clod and the Pebble', we may possibly share Swinburne's enthusiasm. Certainly, in these three volumes we have some of the most perfect and the most original songs in our language.

Of Blake's longer poems, his titanic prophecies and apocalyptic splendours, it is impossible to write justly in such a brief work as this. Outwardly they suggest a huge chaff pile, and the scattered grains of wheat hardly warrant the labour of winnowing. The curious reader will get an idea of Blake's amazing mysticism by dipping into any of the works of his middle life—*Urizen, Gates of Paradise, Marriage of Heaven and Hell, America, The French Revolution,* or *The Vision of the Daughters of Albion.* His latest works, like *Jerusalem* and *Milton*, are too obscure to have any literary value. To read any of these works casually is to call the author a madman; to study them, remembering Blake's songs and his genius, is to quote softly his own answer to the child who asked about the land of dreams:

> 'O what land is the land of dreams,
> What are its mountains and what are its streams?
> —O father, I saw my mother there,
> Among the lilies by waters fair.'
>
> 'Dear child, I also by pleasant streams
> Have wandered all night in the land of dreams;
> But though calm and warm the waters wide,
> I could not get to the other side.'

Minor Poets of the Revival

We have chosen the five preceding poets, Gray, Goldsmith, Cowper, Burns, and Blake, as the most typical and the most interesting of the writers who proclaimed the dawn of

[1] Swinburne's *William Blake.*

Romanticism in the eighteenth century. With them we associate a group of minor writers, whose works were immensely popular in their own day. The ordinary reader will pass them by, but to the student they are all significant as expressions of very different phases of the romantic revival.

James Thomson (1700-1748). Thomson belongs among the pioneers of Romanticism. Like Gray and Goldsmith, he wavered between pseudo-classic and the new romantic ideals, and for this reason, if for no other, his early work is interesting, like the uncertainty of a child who hesitates whether to creep safely on all fours or risk a fall by walking. He is 'worthy to be remembered' for three poems—'Rule Britannia', which is still one of the national songs of England *The Castle of Indolence* and *The Seasons.* The dreamy and romantic Castle (1748), occupied by enchanter Indolence and his willing captives in the land of Drowsyhed, is purely Spenserian in its imagery, and is written in the Spenserian stanza. *The Seasons* (1726-1730), written in blank verse, describes the sights and sounds of the changing year and the poet's own feelings in the presence of nature. These two poems, though rather dull to a modern reader, were significant of the early romantic revival in three ways: they abandoned the prevailing heroic couplet; they went back to the Elizabethans, instead of to Pope, for their models; and they called attention to the long-neglected life of nature as a subject for poetry.

William Collins (1721-1759). Collins, the friend and disciple of Thomson, was of a delicate, nervous temperament, like Cowper; and over him also brooded the awful shadow of insanity. His first work, Oriental Eclogues (1742), is romantic in feeling, but is written in the prevailing mechanical couplets. All his later work is romantic in both thought and expression. His 'Ode on the Popular Superstitions of the Highlands' (1750) is an interesting event in the romantic revival, for it introduced a new world, of witches, pygmies, fairies, and mediæval kings, for the imagination to play in. Collins's best known poems are the odes 'To Simplicity', 'To Fear', 'To the Passions', the little unnamed lyric beginning 'How sleep the brave', and the exquisite 'Ode to Evening.' In reading the latter, one is scarcely aware that the lines are so delicately balanced that they have no need of rhyme to accentuate their melody.

George Crabbe (1754-1832). Crabbe is an interesting combination of realism and romanticism, his work of depicting common life being, at times, vaguely suggestive of Fielding's novels. *The Village* (1783), a poem without a rival as a picture of the workingmen of his age, is sometimes like Fielding in its coarse vigour, and again like Dryden in its precise versification. The poem was not successful at first, and Crabbe abandoned his literary dreams. For over twenty years he settled down as a clergyman in a country parish, observing keenly the common life about him. Then he published more poems, exactly like *The Village,* which immediately brought him fame and money. They brought him also the friendship of Walter Scott, who, like others, regarded Crabbe as one of the first poets of the age. These later poems, *The Parish Register* (1807), *The Borough* (1810), *Tales in Verse* (1812), and *Tales of the Hall* (1819), are in the same strain. They are written in couplets; they are reflections of nature and of country life; they contain much that is sordid and dull, but are nevertheless real pictures of real men and women, just as Crabbe saw them, and as such they are still interesting. Goldsmith and Burns had idealized the poor, and we admire them for their sympathy and insight. It remained for Crabbe to show that in wretched fishing villages, in the lives of hard-working men and women, children, labourers, smugglers, paupers—all sorts and conditions of common men—there is abundant romantic without exaggerating or idealizing their vices and virtues.

James Macpherson (1736-1796). In Macpherson we have an unusual figure, who catered to the new romantic interest in the old epic heroes, and won immense though momentary fame, by a series of literary forgeries. Macpherson was a Scotch schoolmaster, an educated man, but evidently not over-tender of conscience, whose imagination had been stirred by certain old poems which he may have heard in Gaelic among the Highlanders. In 1760 he published his *Fragments of Ancient Poetry collected in the Highlands,* and alleged that his work was but a translation of Gaelic manuscripts. Whether the work of itself would have attracted attention is doubtful; but the fact that an abundance of literary material might be awaiting discovery led to an interest such as now attends the opening of an Egyptian tomb, and a subscription was promptly raised in Edinburgh to send Macpherson through the Highlands to collect more 'manuscripts.' The result was the epic *Fingal* (1762), 'that lank and lamentable counterfeit of poetry', as Swinburne calls it, which the author professed to have translated from the Gaelic of the poet Ossian. Its success was astonishing, and Macpherson followed it up with *Temora* (1763), another epic in the same strain. In both these works Macpherson succeeds in giving an air of primal grandeur to his heroes; the characters are big and shadowy; the imagery is at times magnificent; the language is a kind of chanting, bombastic prose:

> Now Fingal arose in his might and thrice he reared his voice. Cromla answered around, and the sons of the desert stood still. They bent their red faces to earth, ashamed at the presence of Fingal. He came like a cloud of rain in the days of the sun, when slow it rolls on the hill, and fields expect the shower. Swaran beheld the terrible king of Morven, and stopped in the midst of his course. Dark he leaned on his spear rolling his red eyes around. Silent and tall he seemed as an oak on the banks of Lubar, which had its branches blasted of old by the lightning of heaven. His thousands pour around the hero, and the darkness of battle gathers on the hill.[1]

The publication of this gloomy, imaginative work produced a literary storm. A few critics, led by Dr. Johnson, demanded to see the original manuscripts, and when Macpherson refused to produce them,[2] the Ossianic poems were branded as a forgery; nevertheless

[1] There are several omissions from the text in this fragment from Fingal.

[2] Several fragments of Gaelic poetry, attributed to Ossian or Oisin, are now knwon to have existed at that time in the Highlands. Macpherson used these as a basis for his epic, but most of the details were furnished by his own imagination. The alleged text of 'Ossian' was published in 1807, some eleven years after Macpherson's death. It only added another mystery to the forgery; for, while it embodied a few old and probably genuine fragments, the bulk of it seems to be Macpherson's work translated back into Gaelic.

they had enormous success. Macpherson was honored as a literary explorer; he was given an official position, carrying a salary for life; and at his death, in 1796, he was buried in Westminster Abbey. Blake, Burns, and indeed most of the poets of the age were influenced by this sham poetry. Even the scholarly Gray was deceived and delighted with 'Ossian'; and men as far apart as Goethe and Napoleon praised it immoderately.

Thomas Chatterton (1752-1770). This 'marvellous boy', to whom Keats dedicated his 'Endymion', and who is celebrated in Shelley's 'Adonais', is one of the saddest and most interesting figures of the romantic revival. During his childhood he haunted the old church of St. Mary Redcliffe, in Bristol, where he was fascinated by the mediæval air of the place, and especially by one old chest, known as Canynge's coffer, containing musty documents which had been preserved for three hundred years. With strange, uncanny intentness the child pored over these relics of the past, copying them instead of his writing book, until he could imitate not only the spelling and language but even the handwriting of the original. Soon after the 'Ossian' forgeries appeared, Chatterton began to produce documents, apparently very old, containing mediæval poems, legends, and family histories, centering around two characters—Thomas Rowley, priest and poet, and William Canynge, merchant of Bristol in the days of Henry VI. It seems incredible that the whole design of these mediæval romances should have been worked out by a child of eleven, and that he could reproduce the style and the writing of Caxton's day so well that the printers were deceived; but such is the fact. More and more *Rowley Papers,* as they were called, were produced by Chatterton—apparently from the archives of the old church; in reality from his own imagination—delighting a large circle of readers, and deceiving all but Gray and a few scholars who recognized the occasional misuse of fifteenth-century English words. All this work was carefully finished, and bore the unmistakable stamp of literary genius. Reading now his 'Ælla', or the 'Ballad of Charite', or the long poem in ballad style called 'Bristowe Tragedie', it is hard to realize that it is a boy's work. At seventeen years of age Chatterton went for a literary career to London, where he soon afterwards took poison and killed himself in a fit of childish despondency, brought on by poverty and hunger.

Thomas Percy (1729-1811). To Percy, bishop of the Irish church, in Dromore, we are indebted for the first attempt at a systematic collection of the folk songs and ballads which are counted among the treasures of a nation's literature.[1] In 1765 he published, in three volumes, his famous *Reliques of Ancient English Poetry.* The most valuable part of this work is the remarkable collection of old English and Scottish ballads, such as 'Chevy Chase', the 'Nut Brown Mayde', 'Children of the Wood', 'Battle of Otterburn', and many more, which but for his labour might easily have perished. We have now much better and more reliable editions of these same ballads; for Percy garbled his materials, adding and subtracting freely, and even inventing a few ballads of his own. Two motives probably influenced him in this. First, the different versions of the same ballad varied greatly; and Percy, in changing them to suit himself, took the same liberty as had many other writers in dealing with the same material. Second, Percy was under the influence of Johnson and his school, and thought it necessary to add a few elegant ballads 'to atone for the rudeness of the more obsolete poems.' That sounds queer now, used as we are to exactness in dealing with historical and literary material; but it expresses the general spirit of the age in which he lived.

Notwithstanding these drawbacks, Percy's Reliques marks an epoch in the history of Romanticism, and it is difficult to measure its influence on the whole romantic movement. Scott says of it, 'The first time I could scrape a few shillings together, I bought myself a copy of these beloved volumes; nor do I believe I ever read a book half so frequently, or with half the enthusiasm.' Scott's own poetry is strongly modelled upon these early ballads,

---

[1] For various other collections of songs and ballads, antedating Percy's, see Phelps's *Beginnings of the English Romantic Movement,* ch. vii.

and his *Minstrelsy of the Scottish Border* is due chiefly to the influence of Percy's work.

Besides the *Reliques,* Percy has given us another good work in his *Northern Antiquities* (1770) translated from the French of Mallet's *History of Denmark.* This also was of immense influence, since it introduced to English readers a new and fascinating mythology, more rugged and primitive than that of the Greeks; and we are still, in music as in letters, under the spell of Thor and Odin, of Frea and the Valkyr maidens, and of that stupendous drama of passion and tragedy which ended in the 'Twilight of the Gods.' The literary world owes a debt of gratitude to Percy, who wrote nothing of importance himself, but who, by collecting and translating the works of other men, did much to hasten the triumph of Romanticism in the nineteenth century.

III. THE FIRST ENGLISH NOVELISTS

The chief literary phenomena of the complex eighteenth century are the reign of so-called Classicism, the revival of romantic poetry, and the discovery of the modern novel. Of these three, the last is probably the most important. Aside from the fact that the novel is the most modern, and at present the most widely read and influential type of literature, we have a certain pride in regarding it as England's original contribution to the world of letters. Other great types of literature, like the epic, the romance, and the drama, were first produced by other nations; but the idea of the modern novel seems to have been worked out largely on English soil;[1] and in the number and the fine quality of her novelists, England has hardly been rivalled by any other nation. Before we study the writers who developed this new type of literature, it is well to consider briefly its meaning and history.

[1] The first books to which the term 'novel', in the modern sense, may be applied, appeared almost simultaneously in England, France, and Germany. The rapid development of the English novel had an immense influence in all European nations.

Meaning of the Novel. Probably the most significant remark made by the ordinary reader concerning a work of fiction takes the form of a question: Is it a good story? For the reader of today is much like the child and the primitive man in this respect, that he must be attracted and held by the story element of a narrative before he learns to appreciate its style or moral significance. The story element is therefore essential to the novel; but where the story originates is impossible to say. As well might we seek for the origin of the race; for wherever primitive men are found, there we see them gathering eagerly about the story-teller. In the halls of our Saxon ancestors the scop and the tale-bringer were ever the most welcome guests; and in the bark wigwams of the American Indians the man who told the legends of Hiawatha had an audience quite as attentive as that which gathered at the Greek festivals to hear the story of Ulysses's wanderings. To man's instinct or innate love for a story we are indebted for all our literature; and the novel must in some degree satisfy this instinct, or fail of appreciation.

The Story Element

The second question which we ask concerning a work of fiction is, How far does the element of imagination enter into it? For upon the element of imagination depends, largely, our classification of works of fiction into novels, romances, and mere adventure stories. The divisions here are as indefinite as the border land between childhood and youth, between instinct and reason; but there are certain principles to guide us. We note, in the development of any normal child, that there comes a time when for his stories he desires knights, giants, elves, fairies, witches, magic, and marvellous adventures which have no basis in experience. He tells extraordinary tales about himself, which may be only the vague remembrances of a dream or the creations of a dawning imagination—both of which are as real to him as any other part of life. When we say that such a child 'romances', we give exactly the right name to it; for this sudden interest in extraordinary beings and events marks the development of the human imagination—running riot at first, because it is not guided

The Romance

by reason, which is a later development—and to satisfy this new interest the romance[1] was invented. The romance is, originally, a work of fiction in which the imagination is given full play without being limited by facts or probabilities. It deals with extraordinary events, with heroes whose powers are exaggerated, and often adds the element of superhuman or supernatural characters. It is impossible to draw the line where romance ends; but this element of excessive imagination and of impossible heroes and incidents is its distinguishing mark in every literature.

The Novel

Where the novel begins it is likewise impossible to say; but again we have a suggestion in the experience of every reader. There comes a time, naturally and inevitably, in the life of every youth when the romance no longer enthralls him. He lives in a world of facts; gets acquainted with men and women, some good, some bad, but all human; and he demands that literature shall express life as he knows it by experience. This is the stage of the awakened intellect, and in our stories the intellect as well as the imagination must now be satisfied. At the beginning of this stage we delight in *Robinson Crusoe;* we read eagerly a multitude of adventure narratives and a few so-called historical novels; but in each case we must be lured by a story, must find heroes and 'moving accidents by flood and field' to appeal to our imagination; and though the hero and the adventure may be exaggerated, they must both be natural and within the bounds of probability. Gradually the element of adventure or surprising incident grows less and less important, as we learn that true life is not adventurous, but a plain, heroic matter of work and duty, and the daily choice between good and evil. Life is the most real thing in the world now—not the life of kings, or heroes, or superhuman creatures, but the individual life with its struggles and temptations and triumphs or failures, like our own; and any work that faithfully represents life

[1] The name 'romance' was given at first to any story in one of the Romance languages, like the French metrical romances, which we have considered. Because these stories were brought to England at a time when the childish mind of the Middle Ages delighted in the most impossible stories, the name 'romance' was retained to cover any work of the unbridled imagination.

becomes interesting. So we drop the adventure story and turn to the novel. For the novel is a work of fiction in which the imagination and the intellect combine to express life in the form of a story and the imagination is always directed and controlled by the intellect. It is interested chiefly, not in romance or adventure, but in men and women as they are; it aims to show the motives and influences which govern human life, and the effects of personal choice upon character and destiny. Such is the true novel,[1] and as such it opens a wider and more interesting field than any other type of literature.

Precursors of the Novel. Before the novel could reach its modern stage, of a more or less sincere attempt to express human life and character, it had to pass through several centuries of almost imperceptible development. Among the early precursors of the novel we must place a collection of tales known as the Greek Romances, dating from the second to the sixth centuries. These are imaginative and delightful stories of ideal love and marvellous adventure,[2] which

---

[1]This division of works of fiction into romances and novels is a somewhat arbitrary one, but it seems, on the whole, the most natural and the most satisfactory. Many writers use the generic term 'novel' to include all prose fiction. They divide novels into two classes, stories and romances; the story being a form of the novel which relates certain incidents of life with as little complexity as possible; and the romance being a form of novel which describes life as led by strong emotions into complex and unusual circumstances. Novels are otherwise divided into novels of personality, like *The Vicar of Wakefield* and *Silas Marner,* historical novels, like *Ivanhoe;* novels of romance, like *Lorna Doone;* and novels of purpose, like *Oliver Twist* and *Uncle Tom's Cabin.* All such classifications are imperfect, and the best of them is open to objections.

[2]. One of these tales was called *The Wonderful Things beyond Thule.* It is the story of a youth, Dinias, who for love of a girl, Dercyllis, did heroic things and undertook many adventures, including a journey to the frozen north, and another to the moon. A second tale, *Ephesiaca,* is the story of a man and a maid, each of whom scoffs at love. They meet and fall desperately in love; but the course of true love does not run smooth, and they separate, and suffer, and go through many perils, before they 'live happily ever after'. This tale is the source of the mediæval story, *Apollonius of Tyre,* which is used in dower's *Confessio Amantis* and in Shakespeare's *Pericles.* A third tale is the pastoral love story, *Daphnis and Chloe,* which reappeared in many forms in subsequent literature.

profoundly affected romance writing for the next thousand years. A second group of predecessors is found in the Italian and Spanish pastoral romances, which were inspired by the Eclogues of Virgil. These were extremely popular in the fourteenth and fifteenth centuries, and their influence is seen later in Sidney's *Arcadia,* which is the best of this type in English.

The third and most influential group of predecessors of the novel is made up of the romances of chivalry, such as are found in Malory's *Morte d'Arthur*. It is noticeable, in reading these beautiful old romances in different languages, that each nation changes them somewhat, so as to make them more expressive of national traits and ideals. In a word, the old romance tends inevitably towards realism, especially in England, where the excessive imagination is curbed and the heroes become more human. In Malory, in the unknown author of *Sir Gawain and the Green Knight*, and especially in Chaucer, we see the effect of the practical English mind in giving these old romances a more natural setting, and in making the heroes suggest, though faintly, the men and women of their own day. *The Canterbury Tales*, with their story interest and their characters delightfully true to nature, have in them the suggestion, at least, of a connected story whose chief aim is to reflect life as it is.

In the Elizabethan Age the idea of the novel grows more definite. In Sidney's *Arcadia* (1580), a romance of chivalry, the pastoral setting at least is generally true to nature; our credulity is not taxed, as in the old romances, by the continual appearance of magic or miracles; and the characters, though idealized till they become tiresome, occasionally give the impression of being real men and women. In Bacon's *The New Atlantis* (1627) we have the story of the discovery by mariners of an unknown country, inhabited by a superior race of men, more civilized than ourselves—an idea which had been used by More in his *Utopia* in 1516. These two books are neither romances nor novels, in the strict sense, but studies of social institutions. They use the connected story as a means of teaching moral lessons, and of bringing about needed reforms; and this valuable suggestion has been adopted by many of our modern writers in the so-called problem novels and novels of purpose.

Nearer to the true novel is Lodge's romantic story of *Rosalynde*, which was used by Shakespeare in *As You Like It.* This was modelled upon the Italian novella, or short story, which became very popular in England during the Elizabethan Age. In the same age we have introduced into England the Spanish picaresque novel (from *picaro,* a knave or rascal), which at first was a kind of burlesque on the mediæval romance, and which took for its hero some low scoundrel or outcast, instead of a knight, and followed him through a long career of scandals and villainies. One of the earliest types of this picaresque novel in English is Nash's The *Unfortunate Traveller,* or *the Life of Jack Wilton* (1594), which is also a forerunner of the historical novel, since its action takes place during that gorgeous interview between Henry VIII and the king of France on the Field of the Cloth of Gold. In all these short stories and picaresque novels the emphasis was laid not so much on life and character as on the adventures of the hero; and the interest consisted largely in wondering what would happen next, and how the plot would end. The same method is employed in all trashy novels and it is especially the bane of many modern story-writers. This excessive interest in adventures or incidents for their own sake, and not for their effect on character, is what distinguishes the modern adventure story from the true novel.

In the Puritan Age we approach still nearer to the modern novel, especially in the work of Bunyan; and as the Puritan always laid emphasis on character, stories appeared having a definite moral purpose. Bunyan's *The Pilgrim's Progress* (1678) differs from the *Faery Queen,* and from all other mediæval allegories, in this important respect—that the characters, far from being bloodless abstractions, are but thinly disguised men and women. Indeed, many a modern man, reading the story of the Christian, has found in it the reflection of his own life and experience. In *The Life and Death of Mr. Badman* (1682) we have another and even more realistic study of a man as he was in Bunyan's day. These two striking figures, Christian and

Mr. Badman, belong among the great characters of English fiction. Bunyan's good work—his keen insight, his delineation of character, and his emphasis upon the moral effects of individual action—was carried on by Addison and Steele some thirty years later. The character of Sir Roger de Coverley is a real reflection of English country life in the eighteenth century; and with Steele's domestic sketches in *The Tatler, The Spectator,* and *The Guardian* (1709-1713), we definitely cross the borderland that lies outside of romance, and enter the region of character study where the novel has its beginning.

The Discovery of the Modern Novel. Notwithstanding this long history of fiction, to which we have called attention, it is safe to say that, until the publication of Richardson's *Pamela* in 1740, no true novel had appeared in any literature. By a true novel we mean simply a work of fiction which relates the story of a plain human life, under stress of emotion, which depends for its interest not on incident or adventure, but on its truth to nature. A number of English novelists—Goldsmith, Richardson, Fielding, Smollett, Sterne–all seem to have seized upon the idea of reflecting life as it is, in the form of a story, and to have developed it simultaneously. The result was an extraordinary awakening of interest, especially among people who had never before been greatly concerned with literature. We are to remember that, in previous periods, the number of readers was comparatively small; and that, with the exception of a few writers like Langland and Bunyan, authors wrote largely for the upper classes. In the eighteenth century the spread of education and the appearance of newspapers and magazines led to an immense increase in the number of readers; and at the same time the middle-class people assumed a foremost place in English life and history. These new readers and this new, powerful middle class had no classic tradition to hamper them. They cared little for the opinions of Dr. Johnson and the famous Literary Club; and, so far as they read fiction at all, they apparently took little interest in the exaggerated romances of impossible heroes and the picaresque stories of intrigue and villainy which had interested the upper classes. Some new type of literature was demanded, this new type must express the new ideal of the eighteenth century, namely, the value and the importance of the individual life. So the novel was born, expressing, though in a different way, exactly the same ideals of personality and of the dignity of common life which were later proclaimed in the American and in the French Revolution, and were welcomed with rejoicing by the poets of the romantic revival. To tell men, not about knights or kings or types of heroes, but about themselves in the guise of plain men and women, about their own thoughts and motives and struggles, and the results of actions upon their own characters—this was the purpose of our first novelists. The eagerness with which their chapters were read in England, and the rapidity with which their work was copied abroad, show how powerfully the new discovery appealed to readers everywhere.

Before we consider the work of these writers who first developed the modern novel, we must glance at the work of a pioneer, Daniel Defoe, whom we place among the early novelists for the simple reason that we do not know how else to classify him.

DANIEL DEFOE (1661(?)-1731)

To Defoe is often given the credit for the discovery of the modern novel; but whether or not he deserves that honor is an open question. Even a casual reading of *Robinson Crusoe* (1719), which generally heads the list of modern fiction, shows that this exciting tale is largely an adventure story, rather than the study of human character which Defoe probably intended it to be. Young people still read it as they might a dime novel, skipping its moralizing passages and hurrying on to more adventures; but they seldom appreciate the excellent mature reasons which banish the dime novel to a secret place in the haymow, while *Crusoe* hangs proudly on the Christmas tree or holds an honoured place on the family book shelf. Defoe's *Apparition of Mrs. Veal, Memoirs of a Cavalier,* and *Journal of the Plague Year* are such mixtures of fact, fiction, and credulity that they defy classification; while other so-called 'novels', like *Captain Singleton, Moll Flanders*, and *Roxana*, are but, little better

Daniel Defoe

than picaresque stories, with a deal of unnatural moralizing and repentance added for puritanical effect. In *Crusoe,* Defoe brought the realistic adventure story to a very high stage of its development; but his works hardly deserve to be classed as true novels, which must subordinate incident to the faithful portrayal of human life and character.

Life. Defoe was the son of a London butcher named Foe, and kept his family name until he was forty years of age, when he added the aristocratic prefix with which we have grown familiar. The events of his busy seventy years of life, in which he passed through all extremes, from poverty to wealth, from prosperous brickmaker to starveling journalist, from Newgate prison to immense popularity and royal favour, are obscure enough in details; but four facts stand out clearly, which help the reader to understand the character of his work. First, Defoe was a jack-at-all-trades, as well as a writer; his interest was largely with the working classes, and notwithstanding many questionable practices, he seems to have had some continued purpose of educating and uplifting the common people. This partially accounts for the enormous popularity of his works, and for the fact that they were criticised by literary men as being 'fit only for the kitchen.' Second, he was a radical Nonconformist in religion, and was intended by his father for the independent ministry. The Puritan zeal for reform possessed him, and he tried to do by his pen what Wesley was doing by his preaching, without, however, having any great measure of the latter's sincerity or singleness of purpose. This zeal for reform marks all his numerous works, and accounts for the moralizing to be found everywhere. Third, Defoe was a journalist and pamphleteer, with a reporter's eye for the picturesque and a newspaper man's instinct for making a 'good story.' He wrote an immense number of pamphlets, poems, and magazine articles; conducted several papers—one of the most popular, the *Review,* being issued from prison–and the fact that they often blew hot and cold upon the same question was hardly noticed. Indeed, so extraordinarily interesting and plausible were Defoe's articles that he generally managed to keep employed by the party in power, whether Whig or Tory. This long journalistic career, lasting half a century, accounts for his direct, simple, narrative style, which holds us even now by its intense reality. To Defoe's genius we are also indebted for two discoveries, the 'interview' and the leading editorial, both of which are still in daily use in our best newspapers.

The fourth fact to remember is that Defoe knew prison life; and thereby hangs a tale. In 1702 Defoe published a remarkable pamphlet called 'The Shortest Way with the Dissenters', supporting the claims of the free churches against the 'High Fliers', that is Tories and Anglicans. In a vein of grim humour which recalls Swift's 'Modest Proposal', Defoe advocated hanging all dissenting ministers, and sending all members of the free churches into exile; and so ferociously realistic was the satire that both Dissenters and Tories took the author literally. Defoe was tried, found guilty of seditious libel, and sentenced to be fined, to stand three days in the pillory, and to be imprisoned. Hardly had the sentence been pronounced when Defoe wrote his 'Hymn to the Pillory'—

> Hail hieroglyphic state machine,
> Contrived to punish fancy in—

a set of doggerel verses ridiculing his prosecutors, which Defoe, with a keen eye for advertising, scattered all over London. Crowds flocked to cheer him in the pillory; and seeing that Defoe was making popularity out of persecution, his enemies bundled him off to Newgate prison. He turned this experience also to account by publishing a popular newspaper, and by getting acquainted with rogues, pirates, smugglers, and miscellaneous outcasts, each one with a 'good story' to be used later. After his release from prison, in 1704, he turned his knowledge of criminals to further account, and entered the government employ as a kind of spy or secret-service agent. His prison experience, and the further knowledge of criminals gained in over twenty years as a spy, accounts for his numerous stories of thieves and pirates, *Jonathan Wild* and *Captain Avery,* and also for his later novels, which deal almost exclusively with villains and outcasts.

When Defoe was nearly sixty years of age he turned to fiction and wrote the great work by which he is remembered. Robinson Crusoe was an instant success, and the author became famous all over Europe. Other stories followed rapidly, and Defoe earned money enough to retire to

Newington and live in comfort; but not idly, for his activity in producing fiction is rivalled only by that of Walter Scott. Thus, in 1720 appeared *Captain Singleton, Duncan Campbell*, and *Memoirs of a Cavalier*; in 1722, *Colonel Jack, Moll Flanders*, and the amazingly realistic *Journal of the Plague Year*. So the list grows with astonishing rapidity, ending with the *History of the Devil* in 1726.

In the latter year Defoe's secret connection with the government became known, and a great howl of indignation rose against him in the public print, destroying in an hour the popularity which he had gained by a lifetime of intrigue and labour. He fled from his home to London, where he died obscurely, in 1731, while hiding from real or imaginary enemies.

Works of Defoe. At the head of the list stands Robinson Crusoe (1719-1720), one of the few books in any literature which has held its popularity undiminished for nearly two centuries. The story is based upon the experiences of Alexander Selkirk, or Selcraig, who had been marooned in the island of Juan Fernandez, off the coast of Chile, and who had lived there in solitude for five years. On his return to England in 1709, Selkirk's experiences became known, and Steele published an account of them in *The Englishman,* without, however, attracting any wide attention. That Defoe used Selkirk' s story is practically certain; but with his usual duplicity he claimed to have written *Crusoe* in 1708, a year before Selkirk's return. However that may be, the story itself is real enough to have come straight from a sailor's logbook. Defoe, as shown in his *Journal of the Plague Year* and his *Memoirs of a Cavalier,* had the art of describing things he had never seen with the accuracy of an eyewitness.

Robinson Crusoe

The charm of the story is its intense reality, in the succession of thoughts, feelings, incidents, which every reader recognizes to be absolutely true to life. At first glance it would seem that one man on a desert island could not possibly furnish the material for a long story; but as we read we realize with amazement that every slightest thought and action—the saving of the cargo of the shipwrecked vessel, the preparation for defence against imaginary foes, the intense agitation over the discovery of a footprint in the sand—is a record of what the reader himself would do and feel if he were alone in such a place. Defoe's long and varied experience now stood him in good stead; in fact, he 'was the only man of letters in his time who might have been thrown on a desert island without finding himself at a loss what to do';[1] and he puts himself so perfectly in his hero's place that he repeats his blunders as well as his triumphs. Thus, what reader ever followed Defoe's hero through weary, feverish months of building a huge boat, which was too big to be launched by one man, without recalling some boy who spent many stormy days in shed or cellar building a boat or doghouse, and who, when the thing was painted and finished, found it a foot wider than the door, and had to knock it to pieces? This absolute naturalness characterizes the whole story. It is a study of the human will also—of patience, fortitude, and the indomitable Saxon spirit overcoming all obstacles; and it was this element which made Rousseau recommend Robinson Crusoe as a better treatise on education than anything which Aristotle or the moderns had ever written. And this suggests the most significant thing about Defoe's masterpiece, namely, that the hero represents the whole of human society, doing with his own hands all the things which, by the division of labour and the demands of modern civilization, are now done by many different workers. He is therefore the type of the whole civilized race of men.

In the remaining works of Defoe, more than two hundred in number, there is an astonishing variety; but all are marked by the same simple, narrative style, and the same intense realism. The best known of these are the *Journal of the Plague Year,* in which the horrors of a frightful plague are minutely recorded; the *Memoirs of a Cavalier,* so realistic that Chatham quoted it as history in Parliament; and several picaresque novels, like *Captain Singleton, Colonel Jack, Moll Flanders,* and *Roxana.* The last work is by some critics given a very high place in realistic fiction, but like the other

[1] Minto's *Life of Defoe*, p. 139.

three, and like Defoe's minor narratives of Jack Sheppard and Cartouche, it is a disagreeable study of vice, ending with a forced and unnatural repentance.

SAMUEL RICHARDSON (1689-1761)

To Richardson belongs the credit of writing the first modern novel. He was the son of a London joiner, who, for economy's sake, resided in some unknown town in Derbyshire, where Samuel was born in 1689. The boy received very little education, but he had a natural talent for writing letters, and even as a boy we find him frequently employed by working-girls to write their love letters for them. This early experience, together with his fondness for the society of 'his dearest ladies' rather than of men, gave him that intimate knowledge of the hearts of sentimental and uneducated women which is manifest in all his work. Moreover, he was a keen observer of manners, and his surprisingly accurate descriptions often compel us to listen, even when he is most tedious. At seventeen years of age he went to London and learned the printer's trade, which he followed to the end of his life. When fifty years of age he had a small reputation as a writer of elegant epistles, and this reputation led certain publishers to approach him with a proposal that he write a series of *Familiar Letters,* which could be used as models by people unused to writing. Richardson gladly accepted the proposal, and had the happy inspiration to make these letters tell the connected story of a girl's life. Defoe had told an adventure story of human life on a desert island, but Richardson would tell the story of a girl's inner life in the midst of English neighbours. That sounds simple enough now, but it marked an epoch in the history of literature. Like every other great and simple discovery, it makes us wonder why some one had not thought of it before.

Richardson's Novels. The result of Richardson's inspiration was *Pamela,* or *Virtue Rewarded*, an endless series of letters[1] telling of

[1] These were not what the booksellers expected. They wanted a 'handy letter writer', something like a book of etiquette; and it was published in 1741, a few months after Pamela.

the trials, tribulations, and the final happy marriage of a too sweet young maiden, published in four volumes extending over the years 1740 and 1741. Its chief fame lies in the fact that it is our first novel in the modern sense. Aside from this important fact, and viewed solely as a novel, it is sentimental, grandiloquent, and wearisome. Its success at the time was enormous, and Richardson began another series of letters (he could tell a story in no other way) which occupied his leisure hours for the next six years. The result was *Clarissa* or *The History of a Young Lady*, published in eight volumes in 1747-1748. This was another, and somewhat better, sentimental novel; and it was received with immense enthusiasm. Of all Richardson's heroines Clarissa is the most human. In her doubts and scruples of conscience, and especially in her bitter grief and humiliation, she is a real woman, in marked contrast with the mechanical hero, Lovelace, who simply illustrates the author's inability to portray a man's character. The dramatic element in this novel is strong, and is increased by means of the letters, which enable the reader to keep close to the characters of the story and to see life from their different viewpoints. Macaulay, who was deeply impressed by *Clarissa,* is said to have made the remark that, were the novel lost, he could restore almost the whole of it from memory.

Richardson now turned from his middle-class heroines, and in five or six years completed another series of letters, in which he attempted to tell the story of a man and an aristocrat. The result was *Sir Charles Grandison* (1754), a novel in seven volumes, whose hero was intended to be a model of aristocratic manners and virtues for the middle-class people, who largely constituted the novelist's readers. For Richardson, who began in *Pamela* with the purpose of teaching his hearers how to write, ended with the deliberate purpose of teaching them how to live; and in most of his work his chief object was, in his own words, to inculcate virtue and good deportment. His novels, therefore, suffer as much from his purpose as from his own limitations. Notwithstanding his tedious moralizing and his other defects, Richardson in these three books gave something entirely new to the literary world, and the world appreciated the gift. This was the story of human life, told from within, and depending for its interest not on incident or adventure, but on its truth to human nature. Reading his work is, on the whole, like examining the antiquated model of a stern-wheel steamer; it is interesting for its undeveloped possibilities rather than for its achievement.

HENRY FIELDING (1707-1754)

Life. Judged by his ability alone, Fielding was the greatest of this new group of novel writers, and one of the most artistic that our literature has produced. He was born in East Stour, Dorsetshire, in 1707. In contrast with Richardson, he was well educated, having spent several years at the famous Eton school, and taken a degree in letters at the University of Leyden in 1728. Moreover, he had a deeper knowledge of life, gained from his own varied and sometimes riotous experience. For several years after returning from Leyden he gained a precarious living by writing plays, farces, and buffooneries for the stage. In 1735 he married an admirable woman, of whom we have glimpses in two of his characters, Amelia, and Sophia Western, and lived extravagantly on her little fortune at East Stour. Having used up all his money, he returned to London and studied law, gaining his living by occasional plays and by newspaper work. For ten years, or more, little is definitely known of him, save that he published his first novel, *Joseph Andrews,* in 1742, and that he was made justice of the peace for Westminster in 1748. The remaining years of his life, in which his best novels were written, were not given to literature, but rather to his duties as magistrate, and especially to breaking up the gangs of thieves and cut-throats which infested the streets of London after nightfall. He died in Lisbon, whither he had gone for his health, in 1754, and lies buried there in the English cemetery. The pathetic account of this last journey, together with an inkling of the generosity and kind-heartedness of the man, notwithstanding the scandals and irregularities of his life, are found in his last work, the *Journal of a Voyage to Lisbon.*

Fielding's Work. Fielding's first novel, *Joseph Andrews* (1742), was inspired by the success of *Pamela,* and began as a burlesque of the false sentimentality and the conventional virtues of Richardson's heroine. He took for his hero the alleged brother of Pamela, who was exposed to the same kind of temptations, but who, instead of being rewarded for his virtue, was unceremoniously turned out of doors by his mistress. There the burlesque ends; the hero takes to the open road, and Fielding forgets all about Pamela in telling the adventures of Joseph and his companion, Parson Adams. Unlike Richardson, who has no humour, who minces words, and moralizes, and dotes on the sentimental woes of his heroines, Fielding is direct, vigorous, hilarious, and coarse to the point of vulgarity. He is full of animal spirits, and he tells the story of a vagabond life, not for the sake of moralizing, like Richardson, or for emphasizing a forced repentance, like Defoe, but simply because it interests him, and his only concern is 'to laugh men out of their follies.' So his story, though it abounds in unpleasant incidents, generally leaves the reader with the strong impression of reality.

Fielding's later novels are *Jonathan Wild,* the story of a rogue, which suggests Defoe's narrative; *The History of Tom Jones, a Foundling* (1749), his best work; and *Amelia* (1751), the story of a good wife in contrast with an unworthy husband. His strength in all these works is in the vigorous but coarse figures, like those of Jan Steen's pictures, which fill most of his pages; his weakness is in lack of taste, and in barrenness of imagination or invention, which leads him to repeat his plots and incidents with slight variations. In all his work sincerity is perhaps the most marked characteristic. Fielding likes virile men, just as they are, good and bad, but detests shams of every sort. His satire has none of Swift's bitterness, but is subtle as that of Chaucer, and good-natured as that of Steele. He never moralizes, though some of his powerfully drawn scenes suggest a deeper moral lesson than anything in Defoe or Richardson; and he never judges even the worst of his characters without remembering his own frailty and tempering justice with mercy. On the whole, though much of his work is perhaps in bad taste and is too coarse for pleasant or profitable reading, Fielding must be regarded as an artist, a very great artist, in realistic fiction; and the advanced student who reads him will probably concur in the judgment of a modern critic that, by giving us genuine pictures of men and women of his own age, without moralizing over their vices and virtues, he became the real founder of the modern novel.

SMOLLETT AND STERNE

Tobias Smollett (1721-1771) apparently tried to carry on Fielding's work; but he lacked Fielding's genius, as well as his humour and inherent kindness, and so crowded his pages with the horrors and brutalities which are sometimes mistaken for realism. Smollett was a physician, of eccentric manners and ferocious instincts, who developed his unnatural peculiarities by going as a surgeon on a battleship, where he seems to have picked up all the evils of the navy and of the medical profession to use later in his novels.

Smollett's Novels

His three best known works are *Roderick Random* (1748), a series of adventures related by the hero; *Peregrine Pickle* (1751) in which he reflects with brutal directness the worst of his experiences at sea; and *Humphrey Clinker* (1771), his last work, recounting the mild adventures of a Welsh family in a journey through England and Scotland. This last alone can be generally read without arousing the reader's profound disgust. Without any particular ability, he models his novels on *Don Quixote,* and the result is simply a series of coarse adventures which are characteristic of the picaresque novel of his age. Were it not for the fact that he unconsciously imitates *Jonson's Every Man in His Humour*, he would hardly be named among our writers of fiction; but in seizing upon some grotesque habit or peculiarity and making a character out of it—such as Commodore Trunnion in *Peregrine Pickle,* Matthew Bramble *in Humphrey Clinker*, and Bowling in *Roderick Random*—he laid the foundation for that exaggeration in portraying human eccentricities which finds a climax in Dickens's caricatures.

Lawrence Sterne (1713-1768) has been compared to a 'little bronze satyr of antiquity in whose hollow body exquisite odours were stored.' That is true, so far as the satyr is concerned; for a more weazened, unlovely personality would be hard to find. The only question in the comparison is in regard to the character of the odours, and that is a matter of taste. In his work he is the reverse of Smollett, the latter being given over to coarse vulgarities, which are often mistaken for realism; the former to whims and vagaries and sentimental tears, which frequently only disguise a sneer at human grief and pity.

Sterne's Work

The two books by which Sterne is remembered are *Tristram Shandy* and *A Sentimental Journey through France and Italy.* These are termed novels for the simple reason that we know not what else to call them. The former was begun, in his own words, 'with no real idea of how it was to turn out'; its nine volumes, published at intervals from 1760 to 1767, proceeded in the most aimless way, recording the experiences of the eccentric Shandy family; and the book was never finished. Its strength lies chiefly in its brilliant style, the most remarkable of the age, and in its odd characters, like Uncle Toby and Corporal Trim, which, with all their eccentricities, are so humanized by the author's genius that they belong among the great 'creations' of our literature. The *Sentimental Journey* is a curious combination of fiction, sketches of travel, miscellaneous essays on odd subjects—all marked by the same brilliancy of style, and all stamped with Sterne's false attitude towards everything in life. Many of its best passages were either adapted or taken bodily from Burton, Rabelais, and a score of other writers; so that, in reading Sterne, one is never quite sure how much is his own work, though the mark of his grotesque genius is on every page.

The First Novelists and their Work. With the publication of Goldsmith's *Vicar of Wakefield* in 1766 the first series of English novels came to a suitable close. Of this work, with its abundance of homely sentiment clustering about the family life as the most sacred of Anglo-Saxon institutions, we have already spoken[1]. If we accept *Robinson Crusoe*, as an adventure story, the *Vicar of Wakefield* is the only novel of the period which can be freely

[1] see p. 315

recommended to all readers, as giving an excellent idea of the new literary type, which was perhaps more remarkable for its promise than for its achievement. In the short space of twenty-five years there suddenly appeared and flourished a new form of literature, which influenced all Europe for nearly a century, and which still furnishes the largest part of our literary enjoyment. Each successive novelist brought some new element to the work, as when Fielding supplied animal vigour and humour to Richardson's analysis of a human heart, and Sterne added brilliancy, and Goldsmith emphasized purity and the honest domestic sentiments which are still the greatest ruling force among men. So these early workers were like men engaged in carving a perfect cameo from the reverse side. One works the profile, another the eyes, a third the mouth and the fine lines of character; and not till the work is finished, and the cameo turned, do we see the complete human face and read its meaning. Such, in a parable, is the story of the English novel.

Summary of the Eighteenth Century. The period we are studying is included between the English Revolution of 1688 and the beginning of the French Revolution of 1789. Historically, the period begins in a remarkable way by the adoption of the Bill of Rights in 1689. This famous bill was the third and final step in the establishment of constitutional government, the first step being the Great Charter (1215), and the second the Petition of Right (1628). The modern form of cabinet government was established in the reign of George I (1714-1727). The foreign prestige of England was strengthened by the victories of Marlborough on the Continent, in the War of the Spanish Succession; and the bounds of empire were enormously increased by Clive in India, by Cook in Australia and the islands of the Pacific, and by English victories over the French in Canada and the Mississippi Valley, during the Seven Years', or French and Indian, Wars. Politically, the country was divided into Whigs and Tories: the former seeking greater liberty for the people; the latter upholding the king against popular government. The continued strife between these two political parties had a direct (and generally a harmful) influence on literature, as many of the great writers were used by the Whig or Tory party to advance its own interests and to satirize its enemies. Notwithstanding this perpetual strife of parties, the age is remarkable for the rapid social development, which soon expressed itself in literature.

Clubs and coffeehouses multiplied, and the social life of these clubs resulted in better manners, in a general feeling of toleration, and especially in a kind of superficial elegance which shows itself in most of the prose and poetry of the period. On the other hand, the moral standard of the nation was very low; bands of rowdies infested the city streets after nightfall; bribery and corruption were the rule in politics; and drunkenness was frightfully prevalent among all classes. Swift's degraded race of Yahoos is a reflection of the degradation to be seen in multitudes of London saloons. This low standard of morals emphasizes the importance of the great Methodist revival under Whitefield and Wesley, which began in the second quarter of the eighteenth century.

The literature of the century is remarkably complex, but we may classify it all under three general heads—the Reign of so-called Classicism, the Revival of Romantic Poetry, and the Beginning of the Modern Novel. The first half of the century, especially, is an age of prose, owing largely to the fact that the practical and social interests of the age demanded expression. Modern newspapers, like the *Chronicle*, *Post,* and *Times,* and literary magazines, like the *Tatler* and *Spectator*, which began in this age, greatly influenced the development of a serviceable prose style. The poetry of the first half of the century, as typified in Pope, was polished, unimaginative, formal; and the closed couplet was in general use, supplanting all other forms of verse. Both prose and poetry were too frequently satiric, and satire does not tend to produce a high type of literature. These tendencies in poetry were modified, in the latter part of the century, by the revival of romantic poetry.

In our study we have noted: (1) the Augustan or Classic Age; the meaning of Classicism; the life and work of Alexander Pope, the greatest poet of the age; of Jonathan Swift, the satirist; of Joseph Addison, the essayist; of Richard Steele, who was the original genius of the *Tatler* and the *Spectator*; of Samuel Johnson, who for nearly half a century was the dictator of English letters; of James Boswell, who gave us the immortal *Life of Johnson*; of Edmund Burke, the greatest of English orators; and of Edward Gibbon, the historian, famous for his *Decline and Fall of the Roman Empire.*

(2) The Revival of Romantic Poetry; the meaning of Romanticism; the life and work of Thomas Gray; of Oliver Goldsmith, famous as poet, dramatist, and novelist; of William Cowper; of Robert Burns, the greatest of Scottish poets; of William Blake, the mystic; and the minor

poets of the early romantic movement—James Thomson, William Collins, George Crabbe, James Macpherson, author of the Ossian poems, Thomas Chatterton, the boy who originated the Rowley Papers, and Thomas Percy, whose work for literature was to collect the old ballads, which he called the *Reliques of Ancient English Poetry,* and to translate the stories of Norse mythology in his *Northern Antiquities.*

(3) The First English Novelists; the meaning and history of the modern novel; the life and work of Daniel Defoe, author of *Robinson Crusoe,* who is hardly to be called a novelist, but whom we placed among the pioneers; and the novels of Richardson, Fielding, Smollett, Sterne, and Goldsmith.

Selections for Reading. Manly's English Poetry and Manly's English Prose (Ginn and Company) are two excellent volumes containing selections from all authors studied. Ward's English Poets (4 vols.), Craik's English Prose Selections (5 vols.), and Garnett's English Prose from Elizabeth to Victoria are useful for supplementary reading. All important works should be read entire, in one of the following inexpensive editions, published for school use. (For titles and publishers, see General Bibliography at end of this book.)

Pope. Rape of the Lock and Other Poems, edited by Parrott, in Standard English Classics. Various other school editions of the Essay on Man, and Rape of the Lock, in Riverside Literature Series, Pocket Classics, etc.; Pope's Iliad, I, VI, XXII, XXIV, in Standard English Classics, etc. Selections from Pope, edited by Reed, in Holt's English Readings.

Swift. Gulliver's Travels, school edition by Ginn and Company; also in Temple Classics, etc. Selections from Swift, edited by Winchester, in Athenæum Press (announced); the same, edited by Craik, in Clarendon Press; the same, edited by Prescott, in Holt's English Readings. Battle of the Books, in King's Classics, Bohn's Library, etc.

Addison and Steele. Sir Roger de Coverley Papers, in Standard English Classics, Riverside Literature, etc.; Selections from Addison, edited by Wendell and Greenough, and Selections from Steele, edited by Carpenter, both in Athenæum Press; various other selections, in Golden Treasury Series, Camelot Series, Holt's English Readings, etc.

Johnson. Lives of the Poets, in Cassell's National Library; Selected Essays, edited by G.B. Hill (Dent); Selections, in Little Masterpieces Series; Rasselas, in Holt's English Readings, and in Morley's Universal Library.

Boswell. Life of Johnson (2 vols.), in Everyman's Library; the same (3 vols.), in Library of English Classics; also in Temple Classics, and Bohn's Library.

Burke. American Taxation, Conciliation with America, Letter to a Noble Lord, in Standard English Classics; various speeches, in Pocket Classics, Riverside Literature Series, etc.; Selections, edited by B. Perry (Holt); Speeches on America (Heath, etc.).

Gibbon. The Student's Gibbon, abridged (Murray); Memoirs, edited by Emerson, in Athenæum Press.

Gray. Selections, edited by W.L. Phelps, in Athenæum Press; Selections from Gray and Cowper, in Canterbury Poets, Riverside Literature, etc.; Gray's Elegy, in Selections from Five English Poets (Ginn and Company).

Goldsmith. Deserted Village, in Standard English Classics, etc.; Vicar of Wakefield, in Standard English Classics, Everyman's Library, King's Classics, etc.; She Stoops to Conquer, in Pocket Classics, Belles Lettres Series, etc.

Cowper. Selections, edited by Murray, in Athenæum Press; Selections, in Cassell's National Library, Canterbury Poets, etc.; The Task, in Temple Classics.

Burns. Representative Poems, with Carlyle's Essay on Burns, edited by C.L. Hanson, in Standard English Classics; Selections, in Pocket Classics, Riverside Literature, etc.

Blake. Poems, edited by W.B. Yeats, in Muses' Library; Selections, in Canterbury Poets, etc.

Minor Poets. Thomson, Collins, Crabbe, etc. Selections, in Manly's English Poetry. Thomson's The Seasons, and Castle of Indolence, in Modern Classics; the same poems in Clarendon Press, and in Temple Classics; Selections from Thomson, in Cassell's National Library. Chatterton's poems, in Canterbury Poets. Macpherson's Ossian, in Canterbury Poets. Percy's Reliques, in Everyman's Library, Chandos Classics, Bohn's Library, etc. More recent and reliable collections of popular ballads, for school use, are Gummere's Old English Ballads, in Athenæum Press; The Ballad Book, edited by Allingham, in Goldern Treasury Series; Gayley and Flaherty's Poetry of the People (Ginn and Company), etc. See Bibliography on p. 64.

Defoe. Robinson Crusoe, school edition, by Ginn and Company; the same in Pocket Classics, etc.; Journal of the Plague Year, edited by Hurlbut (Ginn and Company); the same, in Everyman's Library, etc.; Essay on Projects, in Cassell's National Library.

The Novelists. Manly's English Prose; Craik's English Prose Selections, vol. 4; Goldsmith's Vicar of Wakefield (see above); Selected Essays of Fielding, edited by Gerould, in Athenæum Press.

Bibliography.[1] **History.** *Textbook,* Montgomery, pp. 280-322; Cheyney, pp. 516-574. *General Works,* Greene, ch. 9, sec. 7, to ch. 10, sec. 4; Traill, Gardiner, Macaulay, etc. Special Works, Lecky's History of England in the Eighteenth Century, vols. 1-3; Morris's The Age of Queen Anne and the Early Hanoverians (Epochs of Modern History); Seeley's The Expansion of England; Macaulay's Clive, and Chatham; Thackeray's The Four Georges, and the English Humorists; Ashton's Social Life in the Reign of Queen Anne; Susan Hale's Men and Manners of the Eighteenth Century; Sydney's England and the English in the Eighteenth Century.

Literature. *General Works.* The Cambridge Literature, Taine, Saintsbury, etc. *Special Works.* Perry's English Literature in the Eighteenth Century; L. Stephen's English Literature in the Eighteenth Century; Seccombe's The Age of Johnson; Dennis's The Age of Pope; Gosse's History of English Literature in the Eighteenth Century; Whitwell's Some Eighteenth Century Men of Letters (Cowper, Sterne, Fielding, Goldsmith, Gray, Johnson, and Boswell); Johnson's Eighteenth Century Letters and Letter Writers; Williams's English Letters and Letter Writers of the Eighteenth Century; Minto's Manual of English Prose Writers; Clark's Study of English Prose Writers; Bourne's English Newspapers; J.B. Williams's A History of English Journalism; L. Stephen's History of English Thought in the Eighteenth Century.

The Romantic Revival. W.L. Phelps's The Beginnings of the English Romantic Movement; Beers's English Romanticism in the Eighteenth Century.

The Novel. Raleigh's The English Novel; Simonds's An Introduction to the Study of English Fiction; Cross's The Development of the English Novel; Jusserand's The English Novel in the Time of Shakespeare; Stoddard's The Evolution of the English Novel; Warren's The History of the English Novel previous to the Seventeenth Century; Masson's British Novelists and their Styles; S. Lanier's The English Novel; Hamilton's the Materials and Methods of Fiction; Perry's A Study of Prose Fiction.

[1] For titles and publishers of general reference works, and of inexpensive texts, see General Bibliography at end of this book.

Pope. Texts: Works in Globe Edition, edited by A.W. Ward; in Cambridge Poets, edited by H.W. Boynton; Satires and Epistles, in Clarendon Press; Letters, in English Letters and Letter Writers of the Eighteenth Century, edited by H. Williams (Bell). Life: by Courthope; by L. Stephen (English Men of Letters Series); by Ward, in Globe Edition; by Johnson, in Lives of the Poets (Cassell's National Library, etc.). Criticism: Essays, by L. Stephen, in Hours in a Library; by Lowell, in My Study Windows; by De Quincey, in Biographical Essays, and in Essays on the Poets; by Thackeray, in English Humorists; by Sainte-Beuve, in English Portraits. Warton's Genius and Writings of Pope (interesting chiefly from the historical view point, as the first definite and extended attack on Pope's writings).

Swift. Texts: Works, 19 vols., ed. by Walter Scott (Edinburgh, 1814-1824); best edition of prose works is edited by T. Scott, with introduction by Lecky, 12 vols. (Bonn's Library); Selections, edited by Winchester (Ginn and Company); also in Camelot Series, Carisbrooke Library, etc., Journal to Stella, (Dutton, also Putnam); Letters, in Eighteenth Century Letters and Letter Writers, ed. by T.B. Johnson. Life: by L. Stephen (English Men of Letters); by Collins; by Craik; by J. Forster; by Macaulay; by Walter Scott; by Johnson, in Lives of the Poets. Criticism: Essays, by Thackeray, in English Humorists; by A. Dobson, in Eighteenth Century Vignettes; by Masson, in the Three Devils and Other Essays.

Addison. Texts: Works, in Bohn's British Classics; Selections, in Athenaeum Press, etc. Life: by Lucy Aiken; by Courthope (English Men of Letters); by Johnson, in Lives of the Poets. Criticism: Essays, by Macaulay; by Thackeray.

Steele. Texts: Selections, edited by Carpenter in Athenæum Press (Ginn and Company); various other Selections published by Putnam, Bangs, in Camelot Series, etc.; Plays, edited by Aitken, in Mermaid Series. Life: by Aitken; by A. Dobson (English Worthies Series). Criticism: Essays by Thackeray; by Dobson, in Eighteenth Century Vignettes.

Johnson. Texts: Works, edited by Walesby, 11 vols. (Oxford, 1825); the same, edited by G.B. Hill, in Clarendon Press. Essays, edited by G.B. Hill (Dent); the same, in Camelot series; Rasselas, various school editions, by Ginn and Company, Holt, etc.; Selections from Lives of the Poets, with Macaulay's Life of Johnson, edited by Matthew Arnold (Macmillan). Life: Boswell's Life of Johnson, in Everyman's Library, Temple Classics, Library of English Classics, etc.; by L. Stephen (English Men of Letters); by

Grant. Criticism: G.B. Hill's Dr. Johnson, his Friends and Critics; Essays, by L. Stephen, in Hours in a Library; by Macaulay, Birrell, etc.

Boswell. Texts: Life of Johnson, edited by G.B. Hill (London, 1874); various other editions (see above). Life: by Fitzgerald (London, 1891); Roger's Boswelliana (London, 1874). Whitfield's Some Eighteenth Century Men of Letters.

Burke. Texts: Works, 12 vols. (Boston, 1871); reprinted, 6 vols., in Bohn's Library; Selected Works, edited by Payne, in Clarendon Press; On the Sublime and Beautiful, in Temple Classics. For various speeches, see Selections for Reading, above. Life: by Prior; by Morley (English Men of Letters). Criticism: Essay, by Birrell, in Obiter Dicta. See also Dowden's French Revolution and English Literature, and Woodrow Wilson's Mere Literature.

Gibbon. Texts: Decline and Fall of the Roman Empire, edited by Bury, 7 vols. (London, 1896-1900); various other editions; The Student's Gibbon, abridged (Murray); Memoirs, edited by Emerson, in Athenæum Press (Ginn and Company). Life: by Morison (English Men of Letters). Criticism: Essays, by Birrell, in Collected Essays and Res Judicatæ; by Stephen, in Studies of a Biographer; by Robertson, in Pioneer Humanists; by Frederick Harrison, in Ruskin and Other Literary Estimates; by Bagehot, in Literary Studies; by Sainte-Beuve, in English Portraits. See also Anton's Masters in History.

Sheridan. Texts: Speeches, 5 vols. (London, 1816); Plays, edited by W.F. Rae (London, 1902); the same, edited by R. Dircks, in Camelot Series; Major Dramas, in Athenæum Press; Plays also in Morley's Universal Library, Macmillan's English Classics, etc. Life: by Rae; by M. Oliphant (English Men of Letters); by L. Sanders (Great Writers).

Gray. Texts: Works, edited by Gosse (Macmillan); Poems, in Routledge's Pocket Library, Chandos Classics, etc.; Selections, in Athenæum Press, etc.; Letters, edited by D.C. Tovey (Bohn). Life: by Gosse (English Men of Letters). Criticism: Essays, by Lowell, in Latest Literary Essays; by M. Arnold, in Essays in Criticism; by L. Stephen, in Hours in a Library; by A. Dobson, in Eighteenth Century Vignettes.

Goldsmith. Texts: edited by Masson, Globe edition; Works, edited by Aiken and Tuckerman (Crowell); the same, edited by A. Dobson (Dent); Morley's Universal Library; Arber's The Goldsmith Anthology (Frowde). See also Selections for Reading, above. Life: by Washington Irving; by A. Dobson (Great Writer's Series); by Black (English Men of Letters); by J.

Forster; by Prior. Criticism: Essays, by Macaulay; by Thackeray; by De Quincey; by A. Dobson, in Miscellanies.

Cowper. Texts: Works, Globe and Aldine editions; also in Chandos Classics; Selections, in Athenæum Press, Canterbury Poets, etc. The Correspondence of William Cowper, edited by T. Wright, 4 vols. (Dodd, Mead & Company). Life: by Goldwin Smith (English Men of Letters); by Wright; by Southey. Criticism: Essays, by L. Stephen; by Bagehot; by SainteBeuve; by Birrell; by Stopford Brooke; by A. Dobson (see above). See also Woodberry's Makers of Literature.

Burns. Texts: Works, Cambridge Poets Edition (containing Henley's Study of Burns), Globe and Aldine editions, Clarendon Press, Canterbury Poets, etc.; Selections, in Athenæum Press, etc.; Letters, in Camelot Series. Life: by Cunningham; by Henley; by Setoun; by Blackie (Great Writers); by Shairp (English Men of Letters). Criticism: Essays, by Carlyle; by R.L. Stevenson, in Familiar Studies; by Hazlitt, in Lectures on the English Poets; by Stopford Brooke, in Theology in the English Poets; by J. Forster, in Great Teachers.

Blake. Texts: Poems, Aldine edition; also in Canterbury Poets; Complete Works, edited by Ellis and Yeats (London, 1893); Selections, edited by W.B. Yeats, in the Muses' Library (Dutton); Letters, with Life by F. Tatham, edited by A.G.B. Russell (Scribner's, 1896). Life: by Gilchrist; by Story; by Symon. Criticism: Swinburne's William Blake, a Critical Study; Ellis's The Real Blake (McClure, 1907); Elizabeth Cary's The Art of William Blake (Moffat, Yard & Company, 1907). Essay, by A.C. Benson, in Essays.

Thomson. Texts: Works, Aldine edition; The Seasons, and Castle of Indolence, in Clarendon Press, etc. Life: by Bayne; by G.B. Macaulay (English Men of Letters). Essay, by Hazlitt, in Lectures on the English Poets.

Collins. Works, edited by Bronson, in Athenæum Press; also in Aldine edition. Life: by Johnson, in Lives of the Poets. Essay, by Swinburne, in Miscellanies. See also Beers's English Romanticism in the Eighteenth Century.

Crabbe. Works, with memoir by his son, G. Crabbe, 8 vols. (London, 1834-1835); Poems, edited by A.W. Ward, 3 vols., in Cambridge English Classics (Cambridge, 1905); Selections, in Temple Classics, Canterbury Poets, etc. Life: by Kebbel (Great Writers); by Ainger (English Men of Letters). Essays, by L. Stephen, in Hours in a Library; by Woodberry, in Makers of Literature; by Saintsbury, in Essays in English Literature; by

Courthope, in Ward's English Poets; by Edward Fitzgerald, in Miscellanies; by Hazlitt, in Spirit of the Age.

Macpherson. Texts: Ossian, in Canterbury Poets; Poems, translated by Macpherson, edited by Todd (London, 1888). Life and Letters, edited by Saunders (London, 1894). Criticism: J.S. Smart's James Macpherson (Nutt, 1905). See also Beers's English Romanticism. For relation of Macpherson's work to the original Ossian, see Dean of Lismore's Book, edited by MacLauchlan (Edinburgh, 1862); also Poems of Ossian, translated by Clerk (Edinburgh, 1870).

Chatterton. Works, edited by Skeat (London, 1875); Poems, in Canterbury Poets. Life: by Russell; by Wilson; Masson's Chatterton, a Biography. Criticism: C.E. Russell's Thomas Chatterton (Moffatt, Yard & Company); Essays, by Watts-Dunton, in Ward's English Poets; by Masson, in Essays Biographical and Critical. See also Beers's English Romanticism.

Percy. Reliques, edited by Wheatley (London, 1891); the same, in Everyman's Library, Chandos Classics, etc. Essay, by J.W. Hales, Revival of Ballad Poetry, in Folia Literaria. See also Beers's English Romanticism, etc. (Special works, above.)

Defoe. Texts: Romances and Narratives, edited by Aitken (Dent); Poems and Pamphlets, in Arber's English Garner, vol. 8; school editions of Robinson Crusoe, and Journal of the Plague Year (Ginn and Company, etc.); Captain Singleton, and Memoirs of a Cavalier, in Everyman's Library; Early Writings, in Carisbrooke Library (Routledge). Life: by W. Lee; by Minto (English Men of Letters); by Wright; also in Westminster Biographies (Small, Maynard). Essay, by L. Stephen, in Hours in a Library.

Richardson. Works: edited by L. Stephen (London, 1883); edited by Philips, with life (New York, 1901); Correspondence, edited by A. Barbauld, 6 vols. (London, 1804). Life: by Thomson; by A. Dobson. Essays, by L. Stephen, in Hours in a Library; by A. Dobson, in Eighteenth Century Vignettes.

Fielding. Works: Temple Edition, edited by Saintsbury (Dent); Selected Essays, in Athenæum Press; Journal of a Voyage to Lisbon, in Cassell's National Library. Life: by Dobson (English Men of Letters); Lawrence's Life and Times of Fielding. Essays, by Lowell; by Thackeray; by L. Stephen; by A. Dobson (see above); by G.B. Smith, in Poets and Novelists.

Smollett. Works, edited by Saintsbury (London, 1895); Works, edited by Henley (Scribner). Life: by Hannah (Great Writers); by Smeaton; by

Chambers. Essays, by Thackeray; by Henley; by Dobson, in Eighteenth Century Vignettes.

Sterne. Works: edited by Saintsbury (Dent); Tristram Shandy, and A Sentimental Journey, in Temple Classics, Morley's Universal Library, etc. Life: by Fitzgerald; by Traill (English Men of Letters); Life and Times, by W.L. Cross (Macmillan). Essays, by Thackeray; by Bagehot, in Literary Studies.

Horace Walpole. Texts: Castle of Otranto, in King's Classics, Cassell's National Library, etc. Letters, edited by C.D. Yonge. Morley's Walpole, in Twelve English Statesmen (Macmillan). Essay, by L. Stephen, in Hours in a Library. See also Beers's English Romanticism.

Frances Burney (Madame d'Arblay). Texts: Evelina, in Temple Classics, 2 vols. (Macmillan). Diary and Letters, edited by S.C. Woolsey. Seeley's Fanny Burney and her Friends. Essay, by Macaulay.

Suggestive Questions. 1. Describe briefly the social development of the eighteenth century. What effect did this have on literature? What accounts for the prevalence of prose? What influence did the first newspapers exert on life and literature? How do the readers of this age compare with those of the Age of Elizabeth?

2. How do you explain the fact that satire was largely used in both prose and poetry? Name the principal satires of the age. What is the chief object of satire? of literature? How do the two objects conflict?

3. What is the meaning of the term 'classicism', as applied to the literature of this age? Did the classicism of Johnson, for instance, have any relation to classic literature in its true sense? Why is this period called the Augustan Age? Why was Shakespeare not regarded by this age as a classical writer?

4. *Pope.* In what respect is Pope a unique writer? Tell briefly the story of his life. What are his principal works? How does he reflect the critical spirit of his age? What are the chief characteristics of his poetry? What do you find to copy in his style? What is lacking in his poetry? Compare his subjects with those of Burns or Tennyson or Milton, for instance. How would Chaucer or Burns tell the story of the Rape of the Lock? What similarity do you find between Pope's poetry and Addison's prose?

5. *Swift.* What is the general character of Swift's work? Name his chief satires. What is there to copy in his style? Does he ever strive for ornament or effect in writing? Compare Swift's *Gulliver's Travels* with

Defoe's *Robinson Crusoe,* in style, purpose of writing, and interest. What resemblances do you find in these two contemporary writers? Can you explain the continued popularity of *Gulliver's Travels*?

6. *Addison and Steele.* What great work did Addison and Steele do for literature? Make a brief comparison between these two men, having in mind their purpose, humour, knowledge of life, and human sympathy, as shown, for instance, in No. 112 and No. 2 of the Spectator Essays. Compare their humour with that of Swift. How is their work a preparation for the novel?

7. *Johnson.* For what is Dr. Johnson famous in literature? Can you explain his great influence? Compare his style with that of Swift or Defoe. What are the remarkable elements in Boswell's *Life of Johnson?* Write a description of an imaginary meeting of Johnson, Goldsmith, and Boswell in a coffee-house.

8. *Burke.* For what is Burke remarkable? What great objects influenced him in the three periods of his life? Why has he been called a romantic poet who speaks in prose? Compare his use of imagery with that of other writers of the period. What is there to copy and what is there to avoid in his style? Can you trace the influence of Burke's American speeches on later English politics? What similarities do you find between Burke and Milton, as revealed in their prose works?

9. *Gibbon.* For what is Gibbon 'worthy to be remembered'? Why does he mark an epoch in historical writing? What is meant by the scientific method of writing history? Compare Gibbon's style with that of Johnson. Contrast it with that of Swift, and also with that of some modern historian, Parkman, for example.

10. What is meant by the term 'romanticism?' What are its chief characteristics? How does it differ from classicism? Illustrate the meaning from the work of Gray, Cowper or Burns. Can you explain the prevalence of melancholy in romanticism?

11. *Gray.* What are the chief works of Gray? Can you explain the continued popularity of his 'Elegy'? What romantic elements are found in his poetry? What resemblances and what differences do you find in the works of Gray and of Goldsmith?

12. *Goldsmith.* Tell the story of Goldsmith's life. What are his chief works? Show from *The Deserted Village* the romantic and the so-called classic elements in his work. What great work did he do for the early novel, in *The Vicar of Wakefield?* Can you explain the popularity of *She*

Stoops to Conquer? Name some of Goldsmith's characters who have found a permanent place in our literature. What personal reminiscences have you noted in *The Traveller, The Deserted Village,* and *She Stoops to Conquer?*

13. *Cowper.* Describe Cowper's *The Task.* How does it show the romantic spirit? Give passages from 'John Gilpin' to illustrate Cowper's humour.

14. *Burns.* Tell the story of Burns's life. Some one has said, 'The measure of a man's sin is the difference between what he is and what he might be.' Comment upon this, with reference to Burns. What is the general character of his poetry? Why is he called the poet of common men? What subjects does he choose for his poetry? Compare him, in this respect, with Pope. What elements in the poet's character are revealed in such poems as 'To a Mouse' and 'To a Mountain Daisy'? How do Burns and Gray regard nature? What poems show his sympathy with the French Revolution, and with democracy? Read 'The Cotter's Saturday Night', and explain its enduring interest. Can you explain the secret of Burns's great popularity?

15. *Blake.* What are the characteristics of Blake's poetry? Can you explain why Blake, though the greatest poetic genius of the age, is so little appreciated?

16. *Percy.* In what respect did Percy's *Reliques* influence the romantic movement? What are the defects in his collection of ballads? Can you explain why such a crude poem as 'Chevy Chase' should be popular with an age that delighted in Pope's 'Essay on Man'?

17. *Macpherson.* What is meant by Macpherson's 'Ossian'? Can you account for the remarkable success of the Ossianic forgeries?

18. *Chatterton.* Tell the story of Chatterton and the Rowley Poems. Read Chatterton's 'Bristowe Tragedie', and compare it, in style and interest, with the old ballads, like 'The Battle of Otterburn' or 'The Hunting of the Cheviot' (all in Manly's *English Poetry*).

19. *The First Novelists.* What is meant by the modern novel? How does it differ from the early romance and from the adventure story? What are some of the precursors of the novel? What was the purpose of stories modelled after *Don Quixote?* What is the significance of *Pamela?* What elements did Fielding add to the novel? What good work did Goldsmith's *Vicar of Wakefield* accomplish? Compare Goldsmith, in this respect, with Steele and Addison.

CHRONOLOGY

End of Seventeenth and the Eighteenth Century

History	Literature
	1683-1719. Defoe's early writings
1689. William and Mary Bill of Rights. Toleration Act	
	1695. Press made free
1700(?). Beginning of London clubs	
1702. Anne (*d.* 1714) War of Spanish Succession	
	1702. First daily newspaper
1704. Battle of Blenheim	1704. Addison's The Campaign Swift's Tale of a Tub
1707. Union of England and Scotland	
	1709. The Tatler Johnson born (d. 1784)
	1710-1713. Swift in London. Journal to Stella
	1711. The Spectator
	1712. Pope's Rape of the Lock
1714. George I (*d.* 1727)	
	1719. Robinson Crusoe
1721. Cabinet government, Walpole first prime minister	
	1726. Gulliver's Travels
	1726-1730. Thomson's The Seasons
1727. George II (*d.* 1760)	
	1732-1734. Essay on Man
1738. Rise of Methodism	
	1740. Richardson's Pamela
1740. War of Austrian Succession	
	1742. Fielding's Joesph Andrews
1746. Jacobite Rebellion	
	1749. Fielding's Tom Jones
	1750-1752. Johnson's The Rambler
1750-1757. Conquest of India	1751. Gray's Elegy
	1755. Johnson's Dictionary
1756. War with France	

History	Literature
1759. Wolf at Quebec	
1760. George III (d. 1820)	1760-1767. Sterne's Tristram Shandy
	1764. Johnson's Literary Club
1765. Stamp Act	1765. Percy's Reliques
	1766. Goldsmith's Vicar of Wakefield
	1770. Goldsmith's Deserted Village
	1771. Beginning of great newspapers
1773. Boston Tea Party	
1774. Howard's prison reforms	1774-1775. Burke's American speeches
1775. American Revolution	1776-1788. Gibbon's Rome
1776. Declaration of Independence	1779. Cowper's Olney Hymns
	1779-81. Johnson's Lives of the Poets
1783. Treaty of Paris	1783. Blake's Poetical Sketches
	1785. Cowper's The Task The London Times
1786. Trial of Warren Hastings	1786. Burns's first poems (the Kilmarnock Burns) Burke's Warren Hastings
1789-1799. French Revolution	
	1790. Burke's French Revolution
	1791. Boswell's Life of Johnson
1793. War with France	

CHAPTER 10

THE AGE OF ROMANTICISM (1800-1850)

THE SECOND CREATIVE PERIOD OF ENGLISH LITERATURE

The first half of the nineteenth century records the triumph of Romanticism in literature and of democracy in government; and the two movements are so closely associated, in so many nations and in so many periods of history, that one must wonder if there be not some relation of cause and effect between them. Just as we understand the tremendous energizing influence of Puritanism in the matter of English liberty by remembering that the common people had begun to read, and that their book was the Bible, so we may understand this age of popular government by remembering that the chief subject of romantic literature was the essential nobleness of common men and the value of the individual. As we read now that brief portion of history which lies between the Declaration of Independence (1776) and the English Reform Bill of 1832, we are in the presence of such mighty political upheavals that 'the age of revolution' is the only name by which we can adequately characterize it. Its great historic movements become intelligible only when we read what was written in this period; for the French Revolution and the American commonwealth, as well as the establishment of a true democracy in England by the Reform Bill, were the inevitable results of ideas which literature had spread rapidly through the civilized world. Liberty is fundamentally an ideal; and that ideal—beautiful, inspiring, compelling, as a loved banner in the wind—was kept steadily before men's minds by a multitude of books and pamphlets as far apart as Burns's *Poems* and Thomas Paine's *Rights of Man*—all read eagerly by the common people, all proclaiming the dignity of common life, and all uttering the same passionate cry against every form of class or caste oppression.

First the dream, the ideal in some human soul; then the written word which proclaims it, and impresses other minds with its truth and beauty; then the united and determined effort of men to make the dream a reality—that seems to be a fair estimate of the part that literature plays, even in our political progress.

Historical Summary. The period we are considering begins in the latter half of the reign of George III and ends with the accession of Victoria in 1837. When on a foggy morning in November, 1783, King George entered the House of Lords and in a trembling voice recognized the independence of the United States of America, he unconsciously proclaimed the triumph of that free government by free men which had been the ideal of English literature for more than a thousand years; though it was not till 1832, when the Reform Bill became the law of the land, that England herself learned the lesson taught her by America, and became the democracy of which her writers had always dreamed.

The French Revolution

The half century between these two events is one of great turmoil, yet of steady advance in every department of English life. The storm centre of the political unrest was the French Revolution, that frightful uprising which proclaimed the natural rights of man and the abolition of class distinctions. Its effect on the whole civilized world is beyond computation. Patriotic clubs and societies multiplied in England, all asserting the doctrine of Liberty, Equality, Fraternity, the watchwords of the Revolution. Young England, led by Pitt the younger, hailed the new French republic and offered it friendship; old England, which pardons no revolutions but her own, looked with horror on the turmoil in France and, misled by Burke and the nobles of the realm, forced the two nations into war. Even Pitt saw a blessing in this at first; because the sudden zeal for fighting a foreign nation—which by some horrible perversion is generally called patriotism—might turn men's thoughts from their own to their neighbours' affairs, and so prevent a threatened revolution at home.

Economic Conditions

The causes of this threatened revolution were not political but economic. By her inventions in steel and machinery, and by her monopoly of the carrying trade, England had become 'the workshop of the world'. Her wealth had increased beyond her wildest dreams; but the unequal distribution of that wealth was a spectacle to make angels weep. The invention of machinery at first threw thousands of skilled hand workers out of employment; in order to protect a few agriculturists, heavy duties were imposed on corn and wheat, and bread rose to famine prices just when labouring men had the least money to pay for it. There followed a curious spectacle. While England increased in wealth, and spent vast sums to support her army and subsidize her allies in Europe, and while nobles, landowners, manufacturers, and merchants lived in increasing luxury, a multitude of skilled labourers were clamouring for work. Fathers sent their wives and little children into the mines and factories, where sixteen hours' labour would hardly pay for the daily bread; and in every large city were riotous mobs made up chiefly of hungry men and women. It was this unbearable economic condition, and not any political theory, as Burke supposed, which occasioned the danger of another English revolution.

It is only when we remember these conditions that we can understand two books, Adam Smith's *Wealth of Nations* and Thomas Paine's *Rights of Man,* which can hardly be considered as literature, but which exercised an enormous influence in England. Smith was a Scottish thinker, who wrote to uphold the doctrine that labour is the only source of a nation's wealth, and that any attempt to force labour into unnatural channels, or to prevent it by protective duties from freely obtaining the raw materials for its industry, is unjust and destructive. Paine was a curious combination of Jekyll and Hyde, shallow and untrustworthy personally, but with a passionate devotion to popular liberty. His *Rights of Man* published in London in 1791, was like one of Burns's lyric outcries against institutions which oppressed humanity. Coming so soon after the destruction of the Bastille, it added fuel to the flames kindled in England by the French Revolution. The author was driven out of the country, on the curious ground that he endangered the English constitution, but not until his book had gained a wide sale and influence.

All these dangers, real and imaginary, passed away when England turned from the affairs of France to remedy her own economic conditions.

Reforms

The long Continental war came to an end with Napoleon's overthrow at Waterloo, in 1815; and England, having gained enormously in prestige abroad, now turned to the work of reform at home. The destruction of the African slave trade; the mitigation of horribly unjust laws, which included poor debtors and petty criminals in the same class; the prevention of child labour; the freedom of the press; the extension of manhood suffrage; the abolition of restrictions against Catholics in Parliament; the establishment of hundreds of popular schools, under the leadership of Andrew Bell and Joseph Lancaster—these are but a few of the reforms which mark the progress of civilization in a single half century. When England, in 1833, proclaimed the emancipation of all slaves in all her colonies, she unconsciously proclaimed her final emancipation from barbarism.

Literary Characteristics of the Age. It is intensely interesting to note how literature at first reflected the political turmoil of the age; and then, when the turmoil was over and England began her mighty work of reform, how literature suddenly developed a new creative spirit, which shows itself in the poetry of Wordsworth, Coleridge, Byron, Shelley, Keats, and in the prose of Scott, Jane Austen, Lamb, and De Quincey—a wonderful group of writers, whose patriotic enthusiasm suggests the Elizabethan days, and whose genius has caused their age to be known as the second creative period of our literature. Thus in the early days, when old institutions seemed crumbling with the Bastille, Coleridge and Southey formed their youthful scheme of a 'Pantisocracy on the banks of the Susquehanna'—an ideal commonwealth, in which the principles of More's *Utopia* should be put in practice. Even Wordsworth, fired with political enthusiasm, could write,

Romantic Enthusiasm

> Bliss was it in that dawn to be alive,
> But to be young was very heaven.

The essence of Romanticism was, it must be remembered, that literature must reflect all that is spontaneous and unaffected in nature and in man and be free to follow its own fancy in its own way. We have already noted this characteristic in the work of the Elizabethan dramatists, who followed their own genius in opposition to all the laws of the critics. In Coleridge we see this independence expressed in 'Kubla Khan' and 'The Ancient Mariner', two dream pictures, one of the populous Orient, the other of the lonely sea. In Wordsworth this literary independence led him inward to the heart of common things. Following his own instinct, as Shakespeare does, he too

> Finds tongues in trees, books in the running brooks,
> Sermons in stones, and good in everything.

And so, more than any other writer of the age, he invests the common life of nature, and the souls of common men and women, with glorious significance. These two poets, Coleridge and Wordsworth, best represent the romantic genius of the age in which they lived, though Scott had a greater literary reputation, and Byron and Shelley had larger audiences.

An Age of Poetry

The second characteristic of this age is that it is emphatically an age of poetry. The previous century, with its practical outlook on life, was largely one of prose; but now, as in the Elizabethan Age, the young enthusiasts turned as naturally to poetry as a happy man to singing. The glory of the age is in the poetry of Scott, Wordsworth, Coleridge, Byron, Shelley, Keats, Moore, and Southey. Of its prose works, those of Scott alone have attained a very wide reading, though the essays of Charles Lamb and the novels of Jane Austen have slowly won for their authors a secure place in the history of our literature. Coleridge and Southey (who with Wordsworth form the trio of so-called Lake Poets) wrote far more prose than poetry; and Southey's prose is much better than his verse. It was characteristic of the spirit of this age, so different from our own, that Southey could say that, in order to earn money, he wrote in verse 'what would otherwise have been better written in prose'.

It was during this period that woman assumed, for the first time, an important place in our literature. Probably the chief reason for this interesting phenomenon lies in the fact that woman was for the first time given some slight chance of education, of entering into the intellectual life of the race; and as is always the case when woman is given anything like a fair opportunity she responded magnificently. A secondary reason may be found in the nature of the age itself, which was intensely emotional. The French Revolution stirred all Europe to its depths, and during the following half century every great movement in literature, as in politics and religion, was characterized by strong emotion; which is all the more noticeable by contrast with the cold, formal, satiric spirit of the early eighteenth century. As woman is naturally more emotional than man, it may well be that the spirit of this emotional age attracted her, and gave her the opportunity to express herself in literature.

Women as Novelists

As all strong emotions tend to extremes, the age produced a new type of novel which seems rather hysterical now, but which in its own day delighted multitudes of readers whose nerves were somewhat excited, and who revelled in 'bogey' stories of supernatural terror. Mrs. Anne Radcliffe (1764-1823) was one of the most successful writers of this school of exaggerated romance. Her novels, with their azure-eyed heroines, haunted castles, trapdoors, bandits, abductions, rescues in the nick of time and a general medley of overwrought joys and horrors,[1] were immensely

---

[1] Mrs Radcliffe's best work is the *Mysteries of Udolpho.* This is the story of a tender heroine shut up in a gloomy castle. Over her broods the terrible shadow of an ancestor's crime. There are the usual 'goose-flesh' accompaniments of haunted rooms, secret doors, sliding panels, mysterious figures behind old pictures, and a subterranean passage leading to a vault, dark and creepy as a tomb. Here the heroine finds a chest with blood-stained papers. By the light of a flickering candle she reads, with chills and shivering, the record of long-buried crimes. At the psychologic moment the little candle suddenly goes out. Then out of the darkness a cold, clammy hand—ugh! Foolish as such stories seem to us now, they show, first, a wild reaction from the skepticism of the preceding age; and second, a development of the mediæval romance of adventure; only the adventure is here inward rather that outward. It faces a ghost instead of

popular, not only with the crowd of novel readers, but also with men of unquestioned literary genius, like Scott and Byron.

In marked contrast to these extravagant stories is the enduring work of Jane Austen, with her charming descriptions of everyday life, and of Maria Edgeworth, whose wonderful pictures of Irish life suggested to Walter Scott the idea of writing his Scottish romances. Two other women who attained a more or less lasting fame were Hannah More, poet, dramatist, and novelist, and Jane Porter, whose *Scottish Chiefs* and *Thaddeus of Warsaw* are still in demand in our libraries. Beside these were Fanny Burney (Madame D'Arblay) and several other writers whose works, in the early part of the nineteenth century, raised woman to the high place in literature which she has ever since maintained.

The Modern Magazines

In this age literary criticism became firmly established by the appearance of such magazines as the *Edinburgh Review* (1802), *The Quarterly Review* (1808), *Blackwood's Magazine* (1817), the *Westminster Review* (1824), *The Spectator* (1828), *The Athenæum* (1828), and *Fraser's Magazine* (1830). These magazines, edited by such men as Francis Jeffrey, John Wilson (who is known to us as Christopher North), and John Gibson Lockhart, who gave us the *Life of Scott,* exercised an immense influence on all subsequent literature. At first their criticisms were largely destructive, as when Jeffrey hammered Scott, Wordsworth, and Byron most unmercifully; and Lockhart could find no good in either Keats or Tennyson; but with added wisdom, criticism assumed its true function of construction. And when these magazines began to seek and to publish the works of unknown writers, like Hazlitt, Lamb, and Leigh Hunt, they discovered the chief mission of the modern magazine, which is to give every writer of ability the opportunity to make his work known to the world.

---

a dragon; and for this work a nun with her beads is better than a knight in armour. So heroines abound, instead of heroes. The age was too educated for mediæval monsters and magic, but not educated enough, to reject ghosts and other bogeys.

1. THE POETS OF ROMANTICISM

William Wordsworth (1770-1850) It was in 1797 that the new romantic movement in our literature assumed definite form. Wordsworth and Coleridge retired to the Quantock Hills, Somerset, and there formed the deliberate purpose to make literature 'adapted to interest mankind permanently', which, they declared, classic poetry could never do. Helping the two poets was Wordsworth's sister Dorothy, with a woman's love for flowers and all beautiful things; and a woman's divine sympathy for human life even in its lowliest forms. Though a silent partner, she furnished perhaps the largest share of the inspiration which resulted in the famous *Lyrical Ballads* of 1798. In their partnership Coleridge was to take up the 'supernatural, or at least romantic'; while Wordsworth was 'to give the charm of novelty to things of everyday—by awakening the mind's attention from the lethargy of custom and directing it to the loveliness and the wonders of the world before us'. The whole spirit of their work is reflected in two poems of this remarkable little volume, 'The Rime of the Ancient Mariner', which is Coleridge's masterpiece, and 'Lines Written a Few Miles above Tintern Abbey', which expresses Wordsworth's poetical creed, and which is one of the noblest and most significant of our poems. That the *Lyrical Ballads* attracted no attention,[1] and was practically ignored by a

William Wordsworth

[1] The *Lyrical Ballads* were better appreciated in America than in England. The first edition was printed here in 1802.

public that would soon go into raptures over Byron's *Childe Harold* and *Don Juan*, is of small consequence. Many men will hurry a mile to see skyrockets, who never notice Orion and the Pleiades from their own doorstep. Had Wordsworth and Coleridge written only this one little book, they would still be among the representative writers of an age that proclaimed the final triumph of Romanticism.

Life of Wordsworth. To understand the life of him who, in Tennyson's words, 'uttered nothing base', it is well to read first *The Prelude,* which records the impressions made upon Wordsworth's mind from his earliest recollection until his full manhood, in 1805, when the poem was completed.[1] Outwardly his long and uneventful life divides itself naturally into four periods: (1) his childhood and youth, in the *Cumberland Hills*, from 1770 to 1787; (2) a period of uncertainty, of storm and stress, including his university life at Cambridge, his travels abroad, and his revolutionary experience, from 1787 to 1797; (3) a short but significant period of finding himself and his work, from 1797 to 1799; (4) a long period of retirement in the northern lake region, where he was born, and where for a full half century he lived so close to nature that her influence is reflected in all his poetry. When one has outlined these four periods he has told almost all that can be told of a life which is marked, not by events, but largely by spiritual experiences.

Wordsworth was born in 1770 at Cockermouth, Cumberland, where the Derwent,

> Fairest of all rivers, loved
> To blend his murmurs with my nurse's song,
> And from his alder shades and rocky falls,
> And from his fords and shallows, sent a voice
> That flowed along my dreams.

It is almost a shock to one who knows Wordsworth only by his calm and noble poetry to read that he was of a moody and violent temper, and that his mother despaired of him alone among her five children. She died when he was but eight years old, but not till she had exerted an influence

[1] *The Prelude* was not published till after Wordsworth's death, nearly half a century later.

which lasted all his life, so that he could remember her as 'the heart of all our learnings and our loves'. The father died some six years later, and the orphan was taken in charge by relatives, who sent him to school at Hawks head, in the beautiful lake region. Here, apparently, the unroofed school of nature attracted him more than the discipline of the classics, and he learned more eagerly from the flowers and hills and stars than from his books; but one must read Wordsworth's own record, in *The Prelude,* to appreciate this. Three things in this poem must impress even the casual reader: first, Wordsworth loves to be alone, and is never lonely, with nature; second, like every other child who spends much time alone in the woods and fields, he feels the presence of some living spirit, real though unseen, and companionable though silent; third, his impressions are exactly like our own, and delightfully familiar. When he tells of the long summer day spent in swimming, basking in the sun, and questing over the hills; or of the winter night when, on his skates, he chased the reflection of a star in the black ice; or of his exploring the lake in a boat, and getting suddenly frightened when the world grew big and strange—in all this he is simply recalling a multitude of our own vague, happy memories of childhood. He goes out into the woods at night to tend his woodcock snares; he runs across another boy's snares, follows them, finds a woodcock caught, takes it, hurries away through the night. And then,

> I heard among the solitary hills
> Low breathings coming after me, and sounds
> Of undistinguishable motion.

That is like a mental photograph. Any boy who has come home through the woods at night will recognize it instantly. Again he tells us of going bird's-nesting on the cliffs:

> Oh, when I have hung
> Above the raven's nest, by knots of grass
> And half-inch fissures in the slippery rock
> But ill-sustained, and almost (so it seemed)
> Suspended by the blast that blew amain,
> Shouldering the naked crag—oh, at that time,
> While on the perilous ridge I hung alone,
> With what strange utterance did the loud dry wind
> Blow through my ear! The sky seemed not a sky
> Of earth—and with what motion moved the clouds!

No man can read such records without finding his own boyhood again, and his own abounding joy of life, in the poet's early impressions.

The second period of Wordsworth's life begins with his university course at Cambridge, in 1787. In the third book of *The Prelude* we find a dispassionate account of student life, with its trivial occupations, its pleasures and general aimlessness. Wordsworth proved to be a very ordinary scholar, following his own genius rather than the curriculum, and looking forward more eagerly to his vacation among the hills than to his examinations. Perhaps the most interesting thing in his life at Cambridge was his fellowship with the young political enthusiasts, whose spirit is expressed in his remarkable poem on the French Revolution—a poem which is better than a volume of history to show the hopes and ambitions that stirred all Europe in the first days of that mighty upheaval. Wordsworth made two trips to France, in 1790 and 1791, seeing things chiefly through the rosy spectacles of the young Oxford Republicans. On his second visit he joined the Girondists, or the moderate Republicans, and only the decision of his relatives, who cut off his allowance and hurried him back to England, prevented his going headlong to the guillotine with the leaders of his party. Two things rapidly cooled Wordsworth's revolutionary enthusiasm, and ended the only dramatic interest of his placid life. One was the excesses of the Revolution itself, and especially the execution of Louis XVI; the other was the rise of Napoleon, and the slavish adulation accorded by France to this most vulgar and dangerous of tyrants. His coolness soon grew to disgust and opposition, as shown by his subsequent poems; and this brought upon him the censure of Shelley, Byron, and other extremists, though it gained the friendship of Scott, who from the first had no sympathy with the Revolution or with the young English enthusiasts.

Of the decisive period of Wordsworth's life, when he was living with his sister Dorothy and with Coleridge at Alfoxden, we have already spoken. The importance of this decision to give himself to poetry is evident when we remember that, at thirty years of age, he was without money or any definite aim or occupation in life. He considered the law, but confessed he had no sympathy for its contradictory precepts and practices; he considered the ministry, but though strongly inclined to the Church, he felt himself not good enough for the sacred office; once he had wanted to be a soldier and serve his country, but had wavered at the prospect of dying of disease in a foreign land and throwing away his life without glory or profit to anybody. An apparent accident, which looks more to us like a special Providence, determined his course. He had taken care of a young friend, Raisley Calvert, who died of consumption and left Wordsworth heir to a few hundred pounds, and to the request that he should give his life to poetry. It was this unexpected gift which enabled Wordsworth to retire from the world and follow his genius. All his life he was poor, and lived in an atmosphere of plain living and high thinking. His poetry brought him almost nothing in the way of money rewards, and it was only by a series of happy accidents that he was enabled to continue his work. One of these accidents was that he became a Tory, and soon accepted the office of a distributor of stamps, and was later appointed poet laureate by the government—which occasioned Browning's famous but ill-considered poem of 'The Lost Leader':

> Just for a handful of silver he left us,
> Just for a riband to stick in his coat.

The last half century of Wordsworth's life, in which he retired to his beloved lake district and lived successively at Grasmere and Rydal Mount, remind one strongly of Browning's long struggle for literary recognition. It was marked by the same steadfast purpose, the same trusted ideal, the same continuous work, and the same tardy recognition by the public. His poetry was mercilessly ridiculed by nearly all the magazine critics, who seized upon the worst of his work as a standard of judgment; and book after book of poems appeared without meeting any success save the approval of a few loyal friends. Without doubt or impatience he continued his work, trusting to the future to recognize and approve it. His attitude here reminds one strongly of the poor old soldier whom he met in the hills,[1] who refused to beg or to mention his long service or the neglect of his country, saying with noble simplicity,

> My trust is in the God of Heaven
> And in the eye of him who passes me.

Such work and patience are certain of their reward, and long before Wordsworth's death he felt the warm sunshine of general approval. The wave of popular enthusiasm for Scott and Byron passed by, as their

---

[1] *The Prelude*, Book IV.

limitations were recognized; and Wordsworth was hailed by critics as the first living poet, and one of the greatest that England had ever produced. On the death of Southey (1843) he was made poet laureate, against his own inclination. The late excessive praise left him quite as unmoved as the first excessive neglect. The steady decline in the quality of his work is due not, as might be expected, to self-satisfaction at success, but rather to his intense conservatism, to his living too much alone and failing to test his work by the standards and judgment of other literary men. He died tranquilly in 1850, at the age of eighty years, and was buried in the churchyard at Grasmere.

Wordsworth's Home at Rydal Mount

Such is the brief outward record of the world's greatest interpreter of nature's message; and only one who is acquainted with both nature and the poet can realize how inadequate is any biography; for the best thing about Wordsworth must always remain unsaid. It is a comfort to know that his life, noble, sincere, 'heroically happy', never contradicted his message. Poetry was his life; his soul was in all his work; and only by reading what he has written can we understand the man.

The Poetry of Wordsworth. There is often a sense of disappointment when one reads Wordsworth for the first time; and this leads us to speak first of two difficulties which may easily prevent a just appreciation of the poet's worth. The first difficulty is in the reader, who is often puzzled by Wordsworth's absolute simplicity. We are so used to stage effects in poetry, that beauty unadorned is apt to escape our notice—like Wordsworth's 'Lucy':

> A violet by a mossy stone,
> Half hidden from the eye;
> Fair as a star, when only one
> Is shining in the sky.

Wordsworth set himself to the task of freeing poetry from all its 'conceits', of speaking the language of simple truth, and of portraying man and nature as they are; and in this good work we are apt to miss the beauty, the passion, the intensity, that hide themselves under his simplest lines. The second difficulty is in the poet, not in the reader. It must be confessed that Wordsworth is not always melodious; that he is seldom graceful, and only occasionally inspired. When he is inspired, few poets can be compared with him; at other times the bulk of his verse is so wooden and prosy that we wonder how a poet could have written it. Moreover he is absolutely without humour, and so he often fails to see the small step that separates the sublime from the ridiculous. In no other way can we explain 'The Idiot Boy', or pardon the serious absurdity of 'Peter Bell' and his grieving jackass.

On account of these difficulties it is well to avoid at first the longer works and begin with a good book of selections.[1] When we read these exquisite shorter poems, with their noble lines that live forever in our memory, we realize that Wordsworth is the greatest poet of nature that our literature has produced. If we go further, and study the poems that impress us, we shall find four remarkable characteristics: (1) Wordsworth is sensitive as a barometer to every subtle change in the world about him. In *The Prelude* he compares himself to an æolian harp, which answers with harmony to every touch of the wind; and the figure is strikingly accurate, as well as interesting, for there is hardly a sight or a sound, from a violet to a mountain and from a bird note to the thunder of the cataract, that is not reflected in some beautiful way in Wordsworth's poetry.

Poems of Nature

(2) Of all the poets who have written of nature there is none that compares with him in the truthfulness of his representation. Burns, like Gray, is apt to read his own emotions into natural

[1] Dowden's Selections from *Wordsworth* is the best of many such collections. See Selections for Reading, and Bibliography, at the end of this chapter.

objects, so that there is more of the poet than of nature even in his mouse and mountain daisy; but Wordsworth gives you the bird and the flower, the wind and the tree and the river, just as they are, and is content to let them speak their own message.

(3) No other poet ever found such abundant beauty in the common world. He had not only sight, but insight, that is, he not only sees clearly and describes accurately, but penetrates to the heart of things and always finds some exquisite meaning that is not written on the surface. It is idle to specify or to quote lines on flowers or stars, on snow or vapour. Nothing is ugly or commonplace in his world; on the contrary, there is hardly one natural phenomenon which he has not glorified by pointing out some beauty that was hidden from our eyes.

(4) It is the *life* of nature which is everywhere recognized; not mere growth and cell changes, but sentient, personal life; and the recognition of this personality in nature characterizes all the world's great poetry. In his childhood Wordsworth regarded natural objects, the streams, the hills, the flowers, even the winds, as his companions; and with his mature belief that all nature is the reflection of the living God, it was inevitable that his poetry should thrill with the sense of a Spirit that 'rolls through all things'. Cowper, Burns, Keats, Tennyson—all these poets give you the outward aspects of nature in varying degrees; but Wordsworth gives you her very life, and the impression of some personal living spirit that meets and accompanies the man who goes alone through the woods and fields. We shall hardly find, even in the philosophy of Leibnitz, or in the nature myths of our Indians, any such impression of living nature as this poet awakens in us. And that suggests another delightful characteristic of Wordsworth's poetry, namely, that he seems to awaken rather than create an impression; he stirs our memory deeply, so that in reading him we live once more in the vague, beautiful wonderland of our own childhood.

Such is the philosophy of Wordsworth's nature poetry. If we search now for his philosophy of human life, we shall find four more doctrines, which rest upon his basal conception that man is not apart from nature, but is the very 'life of her life.' (1) In childhood man is sensitive as a wind harp to all natural influences; he is an epitome of the gladness and beauty of the world. Wordsworth explains this gladness and this sensitiveness to nature by the doctrine that the child comes straight from the Creator of nature:

Poems of Human Life

> Our birth is but a sleep and a forgetting:
> The Soul that rises with us, our life's Star,
> Hath had elsewhere its setting,
> And cometh from afar:
> Not in entire forgetfulness
> And not in utter nakedness,
> But trailing clouds of glory do we come
> From God, who is our home.

In this exquisite ode, which he calls 'Intimations of Immortality from Recollections of Early Childhood' (1807), Wordsworth sums up his philosophy of childhood; and he may possibly be indebted here to the poet Vaughan, who, more than a century before, had proclaimed in 'The Retreat' the same doctrine. This kinship with nature and with God, which glorifies childhood, ought to extend through a man's whole life and ennoble it. This is the teaching of 'Tintern Abbey', in which the best part of our life is shown to be the result of natural influences. According to Wordsworth, society and the crowded unnatural life of cities tend to weaken and pervert humanity; and a return to natural and simple living is the only remedy for human wretchedness.

(2) The natural instincts and pleasures of childhood are the true standards of a man's happiness in this life. All artificial pleasures soon grow tiresome. The natural pleasures, which a man so easily neglects in his work, are the chief means by which we may expect permanent and increasing joy. In 'Tintern Abbey', 'The Rainbow', 'Ode to Duty', and 'Intimations of Immortality' we see

this plain teaching; but we can hardly read one of Wordsworth's pages without finding it slipped in unobtrusively, like the fragrance of a wild flower.

(3) The truth of humanity, that is, the common life which labours and loves and shares the general heritage of smiles and tears, is the only subject of permanent literary interest. Burns and the early poets of the Revival began the good work of showing the romantic interest of common life; and Wordsworth continued it in 'Michael', 'The Solitary Reaper', 'To a Highland Girl', 'Stepping Westward', *The Excursion,* and a score of lesser poems. Joy and sorrow, not of princes or heroes, but 'in widest commonalty spread', are his themes; and the hidden purpose of many of his poems is to show that the keynote of all life is happiness—not an occasional thing, the result of chance or circumstance, but a heroic thing, to be won, as one would win any other success, by work and patience.

(4) To this natural philosophy of man Wordsworth adds a mystic element, the result of his own belief that in every natural object there is a reflection of the living God. Nature is everywhere transfused and illumined by Spirit; man also is a reflection of the divine Spirit; and we shall never understand the emotions roused by a flower or a sunset until we learn that nature appeals through the eye of man to his inner spirit. In a word, nature must be 'spiritually discerned'. In 'Tintern Abbey' the spiritual appeal of nature is expressed in almost every line; but the mystic conception of man is seen more clearly in 'Intimations of Immortality', which Emerson calls 'the high-water mark of poetry in the nineteenth century.' In this last splendid ode Wordsworth adds to his spiritual interpretation of nature and man the alluring doctrine of pre-existence, which has appealed so powerfully to Hindoo and Greek in turn, and which makes of human life a continuous, immortal thing, without end or beginning.

Wordsworth's longer poems, since they contain much that is prosy and uninteresting, may well be left till after we have read the odes, sonnets, and short descriptive poems that have made him famous. As showing a certain heroic cast of Wordsworth's mind, it is interesting to learn that the greater part of his work, including *The Prelude* and *The Excursion,* was intended for a place in a single great poem, to be called *The Recluse,* which should treat of nature, man, and society. *The Prelude,* treating of the growth of a poet's mind, was to introduce the work. The *Home at Grasmere,* which is the first book of *The Recluse,* was not published till 1888, long after the poet's death. *The Excursion* (1814) is the second book of *The Recluse;* and the third was never completed, though Wordsworth intended to include most of his shorter poems in this third part, and so make an immense personal epic of a poet's life and work. It is perhaps just as well that the work remained unfinished. The best of his work appeared in the *Lyrical Ballads* (1798) and in the sonnets, odes, and lyrics of the next ten years; though 'The Duddon Sonnets' (1820), 'To a Skylark' (1825), and 'Yarrow Revisited' (1831) show that he retained till past sixty much of his youthful enthusiasm. In his later years, however, he perhaps wrote too much; his poetry, like his prose, becomes dull and unimaginative; and we miss the flashes of insight, the tender memories of childhood, and the recurrence of noble lines—each one a poem–that constitutes the surprise and the delight of reading Wordsworth.

The Recluse

The outward shows of sky and earth,
    Of hill and valley, he has viewed;
And impulses of deeper birth
    Have come to him in solitude.

In common things that round us lie
    Some random truths he can impart–
The harvest of a quiet eye
    That broods and sleeps on his own heart.

Samuel Taylor Coleridge (1772-1834)

A grief without a pang, void, dark and drear,
    A stifled, drowsy, unimpassioned grief,

Which finds no natural outlet, no relief,
In word, or sigh, or tear.

In the wonderful 'Ode to Dejection', from which the above fragment is taken, we have a single strong impression of Coleridge's whole life—a sad, broken, tragic life, in marked contrast with the peaceful existence of his friend Wordsworth. For himself, during the greater part of his life, the poet had only grief and remorse as his portion; but for everybody else, for the audiences that were charmed by the brilliancy of his literary lectures, for the friends who gathered about him to be inspired by his ideals and conversation, and for all his readers who found unending delight in the little volume which holds his poetry, he had and still has a cheering message, full of beauty and hope and inspiration. Such is Coleridge, a man of grief who makes the world glad.

Life. In 1772 there lived in Ottery St. Mary, Devonshire, a queer little man, the Rev. John Coleridge, vicar of the parish church and master of the local grammar school. In the former capacity he preached profound sermons, quoting to open-mouthed rustics long passages from the Hebrew, which he told them was the very tongue of the Holy Ghost. In the latter capacity he wrote for his boys a new Latin grammar, to mitigate some of the difficulties of traversing that terrible jungle by means of ingenious bypaths and short cuts. For instance, when his boys found the ablative a somewhat difficult case to understand, he told them to think of it as the *quale-quare-quidditive* case, which of course makes its meaning perfectly clear. In both these capacities the elder Coleridge was a sincere man, gentle and kindly, whose memory was 'like a religion' to his sons and daughters. In that same year was born Samuel Taylor Coleridge, the youngest of thirteen children. He was an extraordinarily precocious child, who could read at three years of age, and who, before he was five, had read the Bible and the Arabian Nights, and could remember an astonishing amount from both books. From three to six he attended a 'dame' school; and from six till nine (when his father died and left the family destitute) he was in his father's school, learning the classics, reading an enormous quantity of English books, avoiding novels, and delighting in cumbrous theological and metaphysical treatises. At ten he was sent to the Charity School of

Christ's Hospital, London, where he met Charles Lamb, who records his impression of the place and of Coleridge in one of his famous essays.[1] Coleridge seems to have remained in this school for seven or eight years without visiting his home—a poor, neglected boy, whose comforts and entertainments were all within himself. Just as, when a little child, he used to wander over the fields with a stick in his hand, slashing the tops from weeds and thistles, and thinking himself to be the mighty champion of Christendom against the infidels, so now he would lie on the roof of the school, forgetting the play of his fellows and the roar of the London streets, watching the white clouds drifting over and following them in spirit into all sorts of romantic adventures.

Samuel Taylor Coleridge

At nineteen this hopeless dreamer, who had read more books than an old professor, entered Cambridge as a charity student. He remained for nearly three years, then ran away because of a trifling debt and enlisted in the Dragoons, where he served several months before he was discovered and brought back to the university. He left in 1794 without taking his degree; and presently we find him with the youthful Southey—a kindred spirit, who had been fired to wild enthusiasm by the French Revolution—founding his famous Pantisocracy for the regeneration of human society. 'The Fall of Robespierre', a poem composed by the two enthusiasts, is full of the new revolutionary spirit. The Pantisocracy, on the banks of the Susquehanna, was to be an ideal community, in which the citizens combined farming and literature; and work was to be limited to two hours each day. Moreover, each member of the community was to marry a good woman, and take her with him. The two poets obeyed the latter injunction first, marrying two sisters, and then found that they had no money to pay even their travelling expenses to the new Utopia.

---

[1] See 'Christ's Hospital Five and Thirty Years Ago', in Essays of Elia.

During all the rest of his career a tragic weakness of will takes possession of Coleridge, making it impossible for him, with all his genius and learning, to hold himself steadily to any one work or purpose. He studied in Germany; worked as a private secretary, till the drudgery wore upon his free spirit; then he went to Rome and remained for two years, lost in study. Later he started *The Friend,* a paper devoted to truth and liberty; lectured on poetry and the fine arts to enraptured audiences in London, until his frequent failures to meet his engagements scattered his hearers; was offered an excellent position and a half interest (amounting to some £2000) in the Morning Post and *The Courier,* but declined it, saying 'that I would not give up the country and the lazy reading of old folios for two thousand times two thousand pounds—in short, that beyond £350 a year I considered money a real evil'. His family, meanwhile, was almost entirely neglected; he lived apart, following his own way, and the wife and children were left in charge of his friend Southey. Needing money, he was on the point of becoming a Unitarian minister, when a small pension from two friends enabled him to live for a few years without regular employment.

A terrible shadow in Coleridge's life was the apparent cause of most of his dejection. In early life he suffered from neuralgia, and to ease the pain began to use opiates. The result on such a temperament was almost inevitable. He became a slave to the drug habit; his naturally weak will lost all its directing and sustaining force, until, after fifteen years of pain and struggle and despair, he gave up and put himself in charge of a physician, one Mr. Gillman, of Highgate. Carlyle, who visited him at this time, calls him 'a king of men', but records that 'he gave you the idea of a life that had been full of sufferings, a life heavy-laden, half-vanquished, still swimming painfully in seas of manifold physical and other bewilderment'.

The shadow is dark indeed; but there are gleams of sunshine that occasionally break through the clouds. One of these is his association with Wordsworth and his sister Dorothy, in the Quantock hills, out of which came the famous *Lyrical Ballads* of 1798. Another was his loyal devotion to poetry for its own sake. With the exception of his tragedy *Remorse,* which through Byron's influence was accepted at Drury Lane Theatre, and for which he was paid £400, he received almost nothing for his poetry. Indeed, he seems not to have desired it; for he says: 'Poetry has been to me its own exceeding great reward; it has soothed my afflictions; it has multiplied and refined my enjoyments; it has endeared solitude, and it has given me the habit of wishing to discover the good and the beautiful in all that meets and surrounds me.' One can better understand his exquisite verse after such a declaration. A third ray of sunlight came from the admiration of his contemporaries; for though he wrote comparatively little, he was by his talents and learning a leader among literary men, and his conversations were as eagerly listened to as were those of Dr. Johnson. Wordsworth says of him that, though other men of the age had done some wonderful things, Coleridge was the only wonderful man he had ever known. Of his lectures on literature a contemporary says: 'His words seem to flow as from a person repeating with grace and energy some delightful poem'. And of his conversation it is recorded: 'Throughout a long-drawn summer's day would this man talk to you in low, equable but clear and musical tones, concerning things human and divine; marshalling all history, harmonizing all experiment, probing the depths of your consciousness, and revealing visions of glory and terror to the imagination'.

The last bright ray of sunlight comes from Coleridge's own soul, from the gentle, kindly nature which made men love and respect him in spite of his weaknesses, and which caused Lamb to speak of him humorously as 'an archangel a little damaged'. The universal law of suffering seems to be that it refines and softens humanity; and Coleridge was no exception to the law. In his poetry we find a note of human sympathy, more tender and profound than can be found in Wordsworth or, indeed, in any other of the great English poets. Even in his later poems, when he has lost his first inspiration and something of the splendid imaginative power that makes his work equal to the best of Blake's, we find a soul tender, triumphant, quiet, 'in the stillness of a great peace'. He died in 1834, and was buried in Highgate Church. The last stanza of the boatman's song, in Remorse, serves better to express the world's judgment than any epitaph:

Hark! the cadence dies away
On the quiet moonlit sea;
The boatmen rest their oars and say,
Miserere Domini!

Works of Coleridge. The works of Coleridge naturally divide themselves into three classes—the poetic, the critical, and the philosophical, corresponding to the early, the middle, and the later periods of his career. Of his poetry Stopford Brooke well says: 'All that he did excellently might be bound up in twenty pages, but it should be bound in pure gold'. His early poems show the influence of Gray and Blake, especially of the latter. When Coleridge begins his 'Day Dream' with the line, 'My eyes make pictures when they're shut', we recall instantly Blake's haunting Songs of Innocence. But there is this difference between the two poets—in Blake we have only a dreamer; in Coleridge we have the rare combination of the dreamer and the profound scholar. The quality of this early poetry, with its strong suggestion of Blake, may be seen in such poems as 'A Day Dream', 'The Devil's Thoughts', 'The Suicide's Argument', and 'The Wanderings of Cain'. His later poems, wherein we see his imagination bridled by thought and study, but still running very freely, may best be appreciated in 'Kubla Khan', 'Christabel', and 'The Rime of the Ancient Mariner'. It is difficult to criticize such poems; one can only read them and wonder at their melody, and at the vague suggestions which they conjure up in the mind. 'Kubla Khan' is a fragment, painting a gorgeous Oriental dream picture, such as one might see in an October sunset. The whole poem came to Coleridge one morning when he had fallen asleep over Purchas, and upon awakening he began to write hastily,

> In Xanadu did Kubla Khan
> A stately pleasure-dome decree:
> Where Alph, the sacred river, ran
> Through caverns measureless to man
> Down to a sunless sea.

He was interrupted after fifty-four lines were written, and he never finished the poem.

'Christabel' is also a fragment, which seems to have been planned as the story of a pure young girl who fell under the spell of a sorcerer, in the shape of the woman Geraldine. It is full of a strange melody, and contains many passages of exquisite poetry; but it trembles with a strange, unknown horror, and so suggests the supernatural terrors of the popular hysterical novels, to which we have referred. On this account it is not wholesome reading; though one flies in the face of Swinburne and of other critics by venturing to suggest such a thing.

The Rime of the Ancient Mariner

'The Rime of the Ancient Mariner' is Coleridge's chief contribution to the *Lyrical Ballads* of 1798, and is one of the world's masterpieces. Though it introduces the reader to a supernatural realm, with a phantom ship, a crew of dead men, the overhanging curse of the albatross, the polar spirit, and the magic breeze, it nevertheless manages to create a sense of absolute reality concerning these manifest absurdities. All the mechanisms of the poem, its metre, rhyme, and melody are perfect; and some of its descriptions of the lonely sea have never been equalled. Perhaps we should say suggestions, rather than descriptions; for Coleridge never describes things, but makes a suggestion, always brief and always exactly right, and our own imagination instantly supplies the details. It is useless to quote fragments; one must read the entire poem, if he reads nothing else of the romantic school of poetry.

Among Coleridge's shorter poems there is a wide variety, and each reader must be left largely to follow his own taste. The beginner will do well to read a few of the early poems, to which we have referred, and then try the 'Ode to France', 'Youth and Age', 'Dejection', 'Love Poems', 'Fears in Solitude', 'Religious Musings', 'Work Without Hope', and the glorious 'Hymn Before Sunrise in the Vale of Chamouni'. One exquisite little poem from the Latin, 'The Virgin's Cradle Hymn', and his version of Schiller's *Wallenstein,* show Coleridge's remarkable power as a translator. The latter is one of the best poetical translations in our literature.

Prose Works

Of Coleridge's prose works, the Biographia Literaria, or Sketches of *My Literary Life and Opinions* (1817), his collected *Lectures on Shakespeare* (1849), and *Aids to Reflection* (1825) are the most interesting from a literary viewpoint. The first is an explanation and criticism of Wordsworth's theory of poetry, and contains more sound sense and illuminating ideas on the general subject of poetry than any other book in our language. The *Lectures,* as refreshing as a west wind in midsummer, are remarkable for their attempt to sweep away the arbitrary rules which for two centuries had stood in the way of literary criticism of Shakespeare, in order to study the works themselves. No finer analysis and appreciation of the master's genius has ever been written. In his philosophical work Coleridge introduced the idealistic philosophy of Germany into England. He set himself in line with Berkeley, and squarely against Bentham, Malthus, Mill, and all the materialistic tendencies which were and still are the bane of English philosophy. The *Aids to Reflection* is Coleridge's most profound work, but is more interesting to the student of religion and philosophy than to the readers of literature.

Robert Southey (1774-1843)

Closely associated with Wordsworth and Coleridge is Robert Southey; and the three, on account of their residence in the northern lake district, were referred to contemptuously as the 'Lakers' by the Scottish magazine reviewers. Southey holds his place in this group more by personal association than by his literary gifts. He was born at Bristol, in 1774; studied at Westminster School, and at Oxford, where he found himself in perpetual conflict with the authorities on account of his independent views. He finally left the university and joined Coleridge in his scheme of a Pantisocracy. For more than fifty years he laboured steadily at literature, refusing to consider any other occupation. He considered himself seriously as one of the greatest writers of the day, and a reading of his ballads—which connected him at once with the romantic school—leads us to think that, had he written less, he might possibly have justified his own opinion of himself. Unfortunately he could not wait for inspiration, being obliged to support not only his own family but also, in large measure, that of his friend Coleridge.

Southey gradually surrounded himself with one of the most extensive libraries in England, and set himself to the task of writing something every working day. The results of his industry were one hundred and nine volumes, besides some hundred and fifty articles for the magazines, most of which are now utterly forgotten.

Works of Southey

His most ambitious poems are *Thalaba*, a tale of Arabian enchantment; *The Curse of Kehama*, a medley of Hindu mythology; *Madoc,* a legend of a Welsh prince who discovered the western world; and *Roderick*, a tale of the last of the Goths. All these, and many more, although containing some excellent passages, are on the whole exaggerated and unreal, both in manner and in matter. Southey wrote far better prose than poetry, and his admirable *Life of Nelson* is still often read. Besides these are his *Lives of British Admirals,* his lives of Cowper and Wesley, and his histories of Brazil and of the Peninsular War.

Robert Southey

Southey was made Poet Laureate in 1813, and was the first to raise that office from the low estate into which it had fallen since the death of Dryden. The opening lines of Thalaba, beginning,

> How beautiful is night!
> A dewy freshness fills the silent air,

are still sometimes quoted; and a few of his best known short poems, like 'The Scholar', 'Auld Cloots', 'The Well of St. Keyne',

'The Inchcape Rock', and 'Lodore', will repay the curious reader. The beauty of Southey's character, his patience and helpfulness, make him a worthy associate of the two greater poets with whom he is generally named.

WALTER SCOTT (1771-1832)

We have already called attention to two significant movements of the eighteenth century, which we must for a moment recall if we are to appreciate Scott, not simply as a delightful teller of tales, but as a tremendous force in modern literature. The first is the triumph of romantic poetry in Wordsworth and Coleridge; the second is the success of our first English novelists, and the popularization of literature by taking it from the control of a few patrons and critics and putting it into the hands of the people as one of the forces which mould our modern life. Scott is an epitome of both these movements. The poetry of Wordsworth and Coleridge was read by a select few, but Scott's *Marmion* and *his Lady of the Lake* aroused a whole nation to enthusiasm, and for the first time romantic poetry became really popular. So also the novel had been content to paint men and women of the present, until the wonderful series of Waverley novels appeared, when suddenly, by the magic of this 'Wizard of the North', all history seemed changed. The past, which had hitherto appeared as a dreary region of dead heroes, became alive again, and filled with a multitude of men and women who had the surprising charm of reality. It is of small consequence that Scott's poetry and prose are both faulty; that his poems are read chiefly for the story, rather than for their poetic excellence; and that much of the evident crudity and barbarism of the Middle Ages is ignored or forgotten in Scott's writings. By their vigour, their freshness, their rapid action, and their breezy, out-of-door atmosphere, Scott's novels attracted thousands of readers who else had known nothing of the delights of literature. He is, therefore, the greatest known factor in establishing and in popularizing that romantic element in prose and poetry which has been for a hundred years the chief characteristic of our literature.

Life. Scott was born in Edinburgh, on August 15, 1771. On both his mother's and father's side he was descended from old Border families, distinguished more for their feuds and fighting than for their intellectual attainments. His father was a barrister, a just man, who often lost clients by advising them to be, first of all, honest in their lawsuits. His mother was a woman of character and education, strongly imaginative, a teller of tales which stirred young Walter's enthusiasm by revealing the past as a world of living heroes.

As a child, Scott was lame and delicate, and was therefore sent away from the city to be with his grandmother in the open country at Sandy Knowe, in Roxburghshire, near the Tweed. This grandmother was a perfect treasure-house of legends concerning the old Border feuds. From her wonderful tales Scott developed that intense love of Scottish history and tradition which characterizes all his work.

By the time he was eight years old, when he returned to Edinburgh, Scott's tastes were fixed for life. At the high school he was a fair scholar, but without enthusiasm, being more interested in Border stories than in the textbooks. He remained at school only six or seven years, and then entered his father's office to study law, at the same time attending lectures at the university. He kept this up for some six years without developing any interest in his profession, not even when he passed his examinations and was admitted to the Bar, in 1792. After nineteen years of desultory work, in which he showed far more zeal in gathering Highland legends than in gaining clients, he had won two small legal offices which gave him enough income to support him comfortably. His home, meanwhile, was at Ashestiel on the Tweed, where all his best poetry was written.

Scott's literary work began with the translation from the German of Bürger's romantic ballad of *Lenore* (1796) and of Goethe's Götz von *Berlichingen* (1799); but there was romance enough in his own loved Highlands, and in 1802-1803 appeared three volumes of his *Minstrelsy of the Scottish Border,* which he had been collecting for many years. In 1805, when Scott was 34 years old, appeared his first original work, *The Lay of the Last Minstrel.* Its success was immediate, and when *Marmion* (1808) and *The Lady of the Lake* (1810) aroused Scotland and England to intense enthusiasm, and brought unexpected fame to the author—without in the least spoiling his honest and lovable nature—Scott gladly resolved to abandon the law, in which he had won scant success, and give himself wholly to literature. Unfortunately, however, in order to increase his earnings, he entered secretly into partnership with the firms of Constable and the brothers Ballantyne, as printer-publishers—a sad mistake, indeed, and the cause of that tragedy which closed the life of Scotland's greatest writer.

Walter Scott

The year 1811 is remarkable for two things in Scott's life. In this year he seems to have realized that, notwithstanding the success of his poems, he had not yet 'found himself'; that he was not a poetic genius, like Burns; that in his first three poems he had practically exhausted his material, though he still continued to write verse; and that, if he was to keep his popularity, he must find some other work. The fact that, only a year later, Byron suddenly became the popular favourite, shows how correctly Scott had judged himself and the reading public, which was even more fickle than usual in this emotional age. In that same year, 1811, Scott bought the estate of Abbotsford, on the Tweed, with which place his name is forever associated. Here he began to spend large sums, and to dispense the generous hospitality of a Scotch laird, of which he had been dreaming for years. In 1820 he was made a baronet; and his new title of Sir Walter came nearer to turning his honest head than had all his literary success. His business partnership was kept secret, and during all the years when the Waverley novels were the most popular books in the world, their authorship remained unknown; for Scott deemed it beneath the dignity of his title to earn money by business or literature, and sought to give the impression that the enormous sums spent at Abbotsford in improving the estate and in entertaining lavishly were part of the dignity of the position and came from ancestral sources.

It was the success of Byron's *Childe Harold,* and the comparative failure of Scott's later poems, *Rokeby, The Bridal of Triermain,* and *The Lord of the Isles,* which led our author into the new field, where he was to be without a rival. Rummaging through a cabinet one day in search of some fishing tackle, Scott found the manuscript of a story which he had begun and laid aside nine years before. He read this old story eagerly, as if it had been another's work; finished it within three weeks, and published it without signing his name. The success of this first novel, Waverley (1814), was immediate and unexpected. Its great sales and the general chorus of praise for its unknown author were without precedent; and when *Guy Mannering, The Antiquary, Black Dwarf, Old Mortality, Rob Roy*, and *The Heart of Midlothian* appeared within the next four years, England's delight and wonder knew no bound. Not only at home, but also on the Continent, large numbers of these fresh and fascinating stories were sold as fast as they could be printed.

During the seventeen years which followed the appearance of *Waverley,* Scott wrote on an average nearly two novels per year, creating an unusual number of characters and illustrating many periods of Scotch, English, and French history, from the time of the Crusades to the fall of the Stuarts. In addition to these historical novels, he wrote *Tales of a Grandfather, Demonology* and *Witchcraft,* biographies of Dryden and of Swift, the *Life of Napoleon,* in nine volumes, and a large number of articles for the reviews and magazines. It was an extraordinary amount of literary work, but it was not quite so rapid and spontaneous as it seemed. He had been very diligent in looking up old records, and we must remember that, in nearly all his poems and novels, Scott was drawing upon a fund of legend, tradition, history, and poetry, which he had been gathering for forty years, and which his memory enabled him to produce at will with almost the accuracy of an encyclopaedia.

For the first six years Scott held himself to Scottish history, giving us in nine remarkable novels the whole of Scotland, its heroism, its superb faith and enthusiasm, and especially its clannish loyalty to its hereditary chiefs; giving us also all parties and characters, from Covenanters to Royalists, and from kings to beggars. After reading these nine volumes we know Scotland and Scotchmen as we can know them in no other way. In 1819 he turned abruptly from Scotland, and in *Ivanhoe,* the most popular of his works, showed what a mine of neglected wealth lay just beneath the surface of English history. It is hard to realize now, as we read its rapid, melodramatic action, its vivid portrayal of Saxon and Norman character, and all its picturesque details, that it was written rapidly, at a time when the author was suffering from disease and could hardly repress an occasional groan from finding its way into the rapid dictation. It stands today as the best example of the author's own theory that the will of a man is enough to hold him steadily, against all obstacles, to the task of 'doing what he has a mind to do'. *Kenilworth, Nigel, Peveril, and Woodstock,*

Abbotsford

all written in the next few years, show his grasp of the romantic side of English annals; *Count Robert* and *The Talisman* show his enthusiasm for the heroic side of the Crusaders' nature; and *Quentin Durward* and *Anne of Geierstein* suggest another mine of romance which he discovered in French history.

For twenty years Scott laboured steadily at literature, with the double object of giving what was in him, and of earning large sums to support the lavish display which he deemed essential to a laird of Scotland. In 1826, while he was blithely at work on *Woodstock,* the crash came. Not even the vast earnings of all these popular novels could longer keep the wretched business of Ballantyne on its feet, and the firm failed, after years of mismanagement. Though a silent partner, Scott assumed full responsibility, and at fifty-five years of age, sick, suffering, and with all his best work behind him, he found himself facing a debt of over half a million dollars. The firm could easily have compromised with its creditors; but Scott refused to hear of bankruptcy laws under which he could have taken refuge. He assumed the entire debt as a personal one, and set resolutely to work to pay every penny. Times were indeed changed in England when, instead of a literary genius starving until some wealthy patron gave him a pension, this man, aided by his pen alone, could confidently begin to earn that enormous amount of money. And this is one of the unnoticed results of the popularization of literature. Without a doubt Scott would have accomplished the task, had he been granted only a few years of health. He still lived at Abbotsford, which he had offered to his creditors, but which they generously refused to accept; and in two years, by miscellaneous work, had paid some two hundred thousand dollars of his debt, nearly half of this sum coming from his *Life of Napoleon.* A new edition of the Waverley novels appeared, which was very successful financially, and Scott had every reason to hope that he would soon face the world owing no man a penny, when he suddenly broke under the strain. In 1830 occurred a stroke of paralysis from which he never fully recovered; though after a little time he was again at work, dictating with splendid patience and resolution. He writes in his diary at this time: 'The blow is a stunning one, I suppose, for I scarcely feel it. It is singular, but it comes with as little surprise as if I had a remedy ready, yet God knows I am at sea in the dark, and the vessel leaky'.

It is good to remember that governments are not always ungrateful, and to record that, when it became known that a voyage to Italy might improve Scott's health, the British government promptly placed a naval vessel at the disposal of a man who had led no armies to the slaughter, but had only given pleasure to multitudes of peaceable men and women by his stories. He visited Malta, Naples, and Rome; but in his heart he longed for Scotland, and turned homeward after a few months of exile. The river Tweed, the Scotch hills, the trees of Abbotsford, the joyous clamour of his dogs, brought forth the first exclamation of delight which had passed Scott's lips since he sailed away. He died in September of the same year, 1832, and was buried with his ancestors in the old Dryburgh Abbey.

Works of Scott. Scott's work is of a kind which the critic gladly passes over, leaving each reader to his own joyous and uninstructed opinion. From a literary viewpoint the works are faulty enough, if one is looking for faults; but it is well to remember that they were intended to give delight, and that they rarely fail of their object. When one has read the stirring *Marmion* or the more enduring *Lady of the Lake*, felt the heroism of the Crusaders in *The Talisman*, the picturesqueness of chivalry in *Ivanhoe,* the nobleness of soul of a Scotch peasant girl in *The Heart of Midlothian,* and the quality of Scotch faith in *Old Mortality*, then his own opinion of Scott's genius will be of more value than all the criticisms that have ever been written.

At the outset we must confess frankly that Scott's poetry is not artistic, in the highest sense, and that it lacks the deeply imaginative and suggestive qualities which make a poem the noblest and most enduring work of humanity. We read it now, not for its poetic excellence, but for its absorbing story interest. Even so, it serves an admirable purpose. *Marmion* and *The Lady of the Lake,* which are often the first long poems read by the beginner in literature, almost invariably lead to a deeper interest in the subject; and many readers owe to these poems an introduction to the delights of poetry. They are an excellent beginning, therefore, for young readers, since they are almost certain to hold the attention, and to lead indirectly to an interest in other and better poems. Aside from this, Scott's poetry is marked by vigour and youthful abandon; its interest lies in its vivid pictures, its heroic characters, and especially in its rapid action and succession of adventures, which hold and delight us still, as they held and delighted the first wondering readers. And one finds here and there terse descriptions, or snatches of song and ballad, like the 'Boat Song' and 'Lochinvar', which are among the best known in our literature.

Scott's Poetry

In his novels Scott plainly wrote too rapidly and too much. While a genius of the first magnitude, the definition of genius as 'the infinite capacity for taking pains' hardly belongs to him. For details of life and history, for finely drawn characters, and for tracing the logical consequences of human action, he has usually no inclination. He sketches a character roughly, plunges him into the midst of stirring incidents, and the action of the story carries us on breathlessly to the end. So his stories are largely adventure stories, at the best; and it is this element of adventure and glorious action, rather than the study of character, which makes Scott a perennial favourite of the young. The same element of excitement is what causes mature readers to turn from Scott to better novelists, who have more power to delineate human

Scott's Novels

character, and to create, or discover, a romantic interest in the incidents of everyday life rather than in stirring adventure.[1]

Notwithstanding these limitations, it is well—especially in these days, when we hear that Scott is outgrown—to emphasize four noteworthy things that he accomplished, (1) He created the historical novel;[2] and all novelists of the last century who draw upon history for their characters and events are followers of Scott and acknowledge his mastery.

Scott's Work for Literature

(2) His novels are on a vast scale, covering a very wide range of action, and are concerned with public rather than with private interests. So, with the exception of *The Bride of Lammermoor,* the love story in his novels is generally pale and feeble; but the strife and passions of big parties are magnificently portrayed. A glance over even the titles of his novels shows how the heroic side of history for over six hundred years finds expression in his pages; and all the parties of these six centuries—Crusaders, Covenanters, Cavaliers, Roundheads, Papists, Jews, Gypsies, Rebels—start into life again, and fight or give a reason for the faith that is in them. No other novelist in England, and only Balzac in France, approaches Scott in the scope of his narratives.

(3) Scott was the first novelist in any language to make the scene an essential element in the action. He knew Scotland, and loved it; and there is hardly an event in any of his Scottish novels in which we do not breathe the very atmosphere of the place, and feel the presence of its moors and mountains. The place, morever, is usually so well chosen and described that the action seems almost to be the result of natural environment. Perhaps the most striking illustration of this harmony between scene and incident is found in *Old Mortality,* where Morton approaches the cave of the old Covenanter, and where the spiritual terror inspired by the fanatic's

---

[1] See Scott's criticism of his own work, in comparison with Jane Austen's, p. 439.

[2] Scott's novels were not the first to have an historical basis. For thirty years preceding the appearance of *Waverley,* historical romances were popular; but it was due to Scott's genius that the historical novel became a permanent type of literature. See Cross, *The Development of the English Novel.*

struggle with imaginary fiends is paralleled by the physical terror of a gulf and a roaring flood spanned by a slippery tree trunk. A second illustration of the same harmony of scene and incident is found in the meeting of the arms and ideals of the East and West, when the two champions fight in the burning desert, and then eat bread together in the cool shade of the oasis, as described in the opening chapter of *The Talisman.* A third illustration is found in that fascinating love scene, where Ivanhoe lies wounded, raging at his helplessness, while the gentle Rebecca alternately hides and reveals her love as she describes the terrific assault on the castle, which goes on beneath her window. His thoughts are all on the fight; hers on the man she loves; and both are natural, and both are exactly what we expect under the circumstances. These are but striking examples of the fact that, in all his work, Scott tries to preserve perfect harmony between the scene and the action.

(4) Scott's chief claim to greatness lies in the fact that he was the first novelist to recreate the past; that he changed our whole conception of history by making it to be, not a record of dry facts, but a stage on which living men and women played their parts. Carlyle's criticism is here most pertinent: 'These historical novels have taught this truth—unknown to writers of history: that the bygone ages of the world were actually filled by living men, not by protocols, state papers, controversies, and abstractions of men.' Not only the pages of history, but all the hills and vales of his beloved Scotland are filled with living characters—lords and ladies, soldiers, pirates, gypsies, preachers, schoolmasters, clansmen, bailiffs, dependants—all Scotland is here before our eyes, in the reality of life itself. It is astonishing, with his large numbers of characters, that Scott never repeats himself. Naturally he is most at home in Scotland, and with humble people. Scott's own romantic interest in feudalism caused him to make his lords altogether too lordly; his aristocratic maidens are usually bloodless, conventional, exasperating creatures, who talk like books and pose like figures in an old tapestry. But when he describes characters like Jeanie Deans, in *The Heart of Midlothian,* and the old clansman, Evan

Dhu, in *Waverley,* we know the very soul of Scotch womanhood and manhood.

Perhaps one thing more should be said, or rather repeated, of Scott's enduring work. He is always sane, wholesome, manly, inspiring. We know the essential nobility of human life better, and we are better men and women ourselves, because of what he has written.

GEORGE GORDON, LORD BYRON (1788-1824)

There are two distinct sides to Byron and his poetry, one good, the other bad; and those who write about him generally describe one side or the other in superlatives. Thus one critic speaks of his 'splendid and imperishable excellence of sincerity and strength'; another of his 'gaudy charlatanry, blare of brass, and big bow-wowishness'. As both critics are fundamentally right, we shall not here attempt to reconcile their differences, which arise from viewing one side of the man's nature and poetry to the exclusion of the other. Before his exile from England, in 1816, the general impression made by Byron is that of a man who leads an irregular life, poses as a romantic hero, makes himself out much worse than he really is, and takes delight in shocking not only the conventions but the ideals of English society. His poetry of this first period is generally, though not always, shallow and insincere in thought, and declamatory or bombastic in expression. After his exile, and his meeting with Shelley in Italy, we note a gradual improvement, due partly to Shelley's influence and partly to his own mature thought and experience. We have the impression now of a disillusioned man who recognizes his true character, and who, though cynical and pessimistic, is at least honest in his unhappy outlook on society. His poetry of this period is generally less shallow and rhetorical, and though he still parades his feelings in public, he often surprises us by being manly and sincere. Thus in the third canto of *Childe Harold*, written just after his exile, he says:

In my youth's summer I did sing of one,
The wandering outlaw of his own dark mind;

and as we read on to the end of the splendid fourth canto—with its poetic feeling for nature, and its stirring rhythm that grips and holds the reader like martial music—we lay down the book with profound regret that this gifted man should have devoted so much of his talent to describing trivial or unwholesome intrigues and posing as the hero of his own verses. The real tragedy of Byron's life is that he died just as he was beginning to find himself.

Life. Byron was born in London in 1788, the year preceding the French Revolution. We shall understand him better, and judge him more charitably, if we remember the tainted stock from which he sprang. His father was a dissipated spendthrift of unspeakable morals; his mother was a Scotch heiress, passionate and unbalanced. The father deserted his wife after squandering her fortune; and the boy was brought up by the mother who 'alternately petted and abused' him. In his eleventh year the death of a grand uncle left him heir to Newstead Abbey and to the baronial title of one of the oldest houses in England. He was singularly handsome; and a lameness resulting from a deformed foot lent a suggestion of pathos to his make-up. All this, with his social position, his pseudo-heroic poetry, and his dissipated life—over which he contrived to throw a veil of romantic secrecy—made him a magnet of attraction to many thoughtless young men and foolish women, who made the downhill path both easy and rapid to one whose inclinations led him in that direction. Naturally he was generous, and easily led by affection. He is, therefore, largely a victim of his own weakness and of unfortunate surroundings.

At school at Harrow, and in the university at Cambridge, Byron led an unbalanced life, and was more given to certain sports from which he was not debarred by lameness, than to books and study. His school life, like his infancy, is sadly marked by vanity, violence, and rebellion against every form of authority; yet it was not without its hours of nobility and generosity. Scott describes him as 'a man of real goodness of heart, and the kindest and best feelings, miserably thrown away by his foolish contempt of public opinion'. While at Cambridge, Byron published his first volume of poems, *Hours of Idleness,* in 1807. A severe criticism of the volume in the *Edinburgh Review* wounded Byron's vanity, and threw him into a violent passion, the result of which was the now famous satire called *English Bards and Scotch Reviewers,* in which not only his enemies, but also Scott, Wordsworth, and nearly all the literary men of his day, were satirized in heroic couplets after the manner of Pope's *Dunciad.* It is only just to say that he afterwards made friends with Scott and with others whom he had abused without provocation; and it is interesting to note, in view of his own romantic poetry, that he denounced all masters of romance and accepted the artificial standards of Pope and Dryden. His two favourite books were the Old Testament and a volume of Pope's poetry. Of the latter he says, 'His is the greatest name in poetry— all the rest are barbarians'. In 1809 Byron, when only twenty-one years of age, started on a tour of Europe and the Orient. The poetic results of this trip were the first two cantos of *Childe Harold's Pilgrimage,* with their famous descriptions of romantic scenery. The work made him instantly popular, and his fame overshadowed Scott's completely. As he says himself, 'I awoke one morning to find myself famous', and presently he styles himself 'the grand Napoleon of the realms of rhyme'. The worst element in Byron at this time was his insincerity, his continual posing as the hero of his poetry. His best works were translated, and his fame spread almost as rapidly on the Continent as in England. Even Goethe was deceived, and declared that a man so wonderful in character had never before appeared in literature, and would never appear again. Now that the tinsel has worn off, and we can judge the man and his work dispassionately, we see how easily even the critics of the age were governed by romantic impulses.

George Gordon, Lord Byron

The adulation of Byron lasted only a few years in England. In 1815 he married Miss Milbanke, an English heiress, who abruptly left him a year later. With womanly reserve she kept silence; but the public was not slow to imagine plenty of reasons for the separation. This, together with the fact that men had begun to penetrate the veil of romantic secrecy with which Byron surrounded himself and found a rather brassy idol beneath, turned the tide of public opinion against him. He left England under a cloud of distrust and disappointment, in 1816, and never returned. Eight years were spent abroad, largely in Italy, where he was associated with Shelley until the latter's tragic death in 1822. His house was ever the meeting place for Revolutionists and malcontents calling themselves patriots, whom he trusted too greatly, and with whom he shared his money most generously. Curiously enough, while he trusted men too easily, he had no faith in human society or government, and wrote in 1817: 'I have simplified my politics to an utter detestation of all existing governments'. During his exile he finished *Childe Harold, The Prisoner of Chillon,* his dramas Cain and Manfred, and numerous other works, in some of which, as in *Don Juan,* he delighted in revenging himself upon his countrymen by holding up to ridicule all that they held most sacred.

In 1824 Byron went to Greece to give himself and a large part of his fortune to help that country in its struggle for liberty against the Turks. How far he was led by his desire for posing as a hero, and how far by a certain vigorous Viking spirit that was certainly in him, will never be known. The Greeks welcomed him and made him a leader, and for a few months he found himself in the midst of a wretched squabble of lies, selfishness, insincerity, cowardice, and intrigue, instead of the heroic struggle for liberty which he had anticipated. He died of fever, in Missolonghi, in 1824. One of his last poems, written there on his thirty-sixth birthday, a few months before he died, expresses his own view of his disappointing life:

> My days are in the yellow leaf,
> The flowers and fruits of love are gone:
> The worm, the canker, and the grief
> Are mine alone.

Works of Byron. In reading Byron it is well to remember that he was a disappointed and embittered man, not only in his personal life, but also in his expectation of a general transformation of human society. As he pours out his own feelings, chiefly, in his poetry, he is the most expressive writer of his age in voicing the discontent of a multitude of Europeans who were disappointed at the failure of the French Revolution to produce an entirely new form of government and society.

Hours of Idleness

One who wishes to understand the whole scope of Byron's genius and poetry will do well to begin with his first work, *Hours of Idleness,* written when he was a young man at the university. There is very little poetry in the volume, only a striking facility in rhyme, brightened by the devil-may-care spirit of the Cavalier poets; but as a revelation of the man himself it is remarkable. In a vain and sophomoric preface he declares that poetry is to him an idle experiment, and that this is his first and last attempt to amuse himself in that line. Curiously enough, as he starts for Greece on his last, fatal journey, he again ridicules literature, and says that the poet is a 'mere babbler.' It is this despising of the art which alone makes him famous that occasions our deepest disappointment. Even in his magnificent passages, in a glowing description of nature or of a Hindu woman's exquisite love, his work is frequently marred by a wretched pun, or by some cheap buffoonery, which ruins our first splendid impression of his poetry.

Longer Poems

Byron's later volumes, *Manfred and Cain,* the one a curious, and perhaps unconscious, parody of *Faust,* the other of *Paradise Lost,* are his two best known dramatic works. Aside from the question of their poetic value, they are interesting as voicing Byron's excessive individualism and his rebellion against society. The best known and the most readable of Byron's works are *Maseppa, The Prisoner of Chillon,* and *Childe Harold's Pilgrimage.* The first two cantos of *Childe Harold* (1812) are perhaps more frequently read than any other work of the same author, partly because of their melodious verse, partly because of their descriptions of places along the lines of European travel; but the last two cantos (1816-1818) written after his exile from England, have more sincerity, and are in every way better expressions of Byron's mature genius. Scattered through all his works one finds magnificent descriptions of natural scenery, and exquisite lyrics of love and despair; but they are mixed with such a deal of bombast and rhetoric, together with much that is unwholesome, that the beginner will do well to confine himself to a small volume of well-chosen selections.[1]

Byron is often compared with Scott, as having given to us Europe and the Orient, just as Scott gave us Scotland and its people; but while there is a certain resemblance in the swing and dash of the verses, the resemblance is all on the surface, and the underlying difference between the two poets is as great as that between Thackeray and Bulwer-Lytton. Scott knew his country well—its hills and valleys which are interesting as the abode of living and lovable men and women. Byron pretended to know the secret, unwholesome side of Europe, which generally hides itself in the dark; but instead of giving us a variety of living men, he never gets away from his own unbalanced and egotistical self. All his characters, in *Cain, Manfred, The Corsair, The Giaour, Childe Harold, Don Juan*, are tiresome repetitions of himself—a vain, disappointed, cynical man, who finds no good in life or love or anything. Naturally, with such a disposition, he is entirely incapable of portraying a true woman, to nature alone, especially in her magnificent moods, Byron remains faithful; and his portrayal of the night and the storm and the ocean in *Childe Harold* are unsurpassed in our language.

Percy Bysshe Shelley (1792-1822)

Make me thy lyre, even as the forest is:
    What if my leaves are falling like its own!
The tumult of thy mighty harmonies
    Will take from both a deep, autumnal tone,
Sweet though in sadness. Be thou, spirit fierce,
    My spirit! Be thou me, impetuous one!

In this fragment, from the 'Ode to the West Wind', we have a suggestion of Shelley's own spirit, as reflected in all his poetry. The very spirit of nature, which appeals to us in the wind and the

[1] See Selections for Reading, and Bibliography, at the end of this chapter.

cloud, the sunset and the moonrise, seems to have possessed him, at times, and made him a chosen instrument of melody. At such times he is a true poet, and his work is unrivalled. At other times, unfortunately, Shelley joins with Byron in voicing a vain rebellion against society.

Percy Bysshe Shelley

His poetry, like his life, divides itself into two distinct moods. In one he is the violent reformer, seeking to overthrow our present institutions and to hurry the millennium out of its slow walk into a gallop. Out of this mood come most of his longer poems, like

Queen Mab, Revolt of Islam, Hellas, and *The Witch of Atlas,* which are somewhat violent diatribes against government, priests, marriage, religion, even God as men supposed him to be. In a different mood, which finds expression in *Alastor, Adonais*, and his wonderful lyrics, Shelley is like a wanderer following a vague, beautiful vision, forever sad and forever unsatisfied. In the latter mood he appeals profoundly to all men who have known what it is to follow after an unattainable ideal.

Shelley's Life. There are three classes of men who see visions, and all three are represented in our literature. The first is the mere dreamer, like Blake, who stumbles through a world of reality without noticing it, and is happy in his visions. The second is the seer, the prophet, like Langland, or Wyclif, who sees a vision and quietly goes to work, in ways that men understand, to make the present world a little more like the ideal one which he sees in his vision. The third, who appears in many forms—as visionary, enthusiast, radical, anarchist, revolutionary, call him what you will—sees a vision and straightway begins to tear down all human institutions, which have been built up by the slow toil of centuries, simply because they seem to stand in the way of his dream. To the latter class belongs Shelley, a man perpetually at war with the present world, a martyr and exile, simply because of his inability to sympathize with men and society as they are, and because of his own mistaken judgment as to the value and purpose of a vision.

Shelley was born in Field Place, near Horsham, Sussex, in 1792. On both his father's and his mother's side he was descended from noble old families, famous in the political and literary history of England. From childhood he lived, like Blake, in a world of fancy, so real that certain imaginary dragons and headless creatures of the neighbouring wood kept him and his sisters in a state of fearful expectancy. He learned rapidly, absorbed the classics as if by intuition, and, dissatisfied with ordinary processes of learning, seems to have sought, like Faustus, the acquaintance of spirits, as shown in his 'Hymn to Intellectual Beauty':

> While yet a boy, I sought for ghosts, and sped
>   Through many a listening chamber, cave and ruin,
> And starlight wood, with fearful steps pursuing
>   Hopes of high talk with the departed dead.

Shelley's first public school, kept by a hard-headed Scotch master, with its floggings and its general brutality, seemed to him like a combination of hell and prison; and his active rebellion against existing institutions was well under way when, at twelve years of age, he entered the famous preparatory school at Eton. He was a delicate, nervous, marvellously sensitive boy, of great physical beauty; and, like Cowper, he suffered torments at the hands of his rough school fellows. Unlike Cowper, he was positive, resentful, and brave to the point of rashness; soul and body rose up against tyranny; and he promptly organized a rebellion against the brutal flogging system. 'Mad Shelley' the boys called him, and they chivied him like dogs around a little coon that fights and cries defiance to the end. One finds what he seeks in this world, and it is not strange that Shelley, after his Eton experiences, found causes for rebellion in all existing forms of human society, and that he left school 'to war among man-kind', as he says of himself in the *Revolt of Islam.* His university days are but a repetition of his earlier experiences. While a student at Oxford he read some scraps of Hume's philosophy, and immediately published a pamphlet called 'The Necessity of Atheism.' It was a crude, foolish piece of work, and Shelley distributed it by post to every one to whom it might give offence. Naturally this brought on a conflict with the authorities, but Shelley would not listen to reason or make any explanation, and was expelled from the university in 1811.

Shelley's marriage was even more unfortunate. While living in London, on a generous sister's pocket money, a certain young school- girl, Harriet Westbrook, was attracted by Shelley's crude revolutionary doctrines. She promptly left school, as her own personal part in the general rebellion, and refused to return or even to listen to her parents upon the subject. Having been taught by Shelley, she threw herself upon his protection; and this unbalanced couple were presently married, as they said, 'in deference to anarch custom.' The two infants had already proclaimed a rebellion against the institution of marriage, for which they proposed to substitute the doctrine of elective affinity. For two years they wandered about England, Ireland, and Wales, living on a small allowance from Shelley's father, who had disinherited his son because of his ill-considered marriage. The pair soon separated, and two years later Shelley, having formed a strong friendship with one Godwin—a leader of young enthusiasts and a preacher of anarchy—presently showed his belief in Godwin's theories by eloping with his daughter Mary. It is a sad story, and the details were perhaps better forgotten. We should remember that in Shelley we are dealing with a tragic blend of high-mindedness and light-headedness. Byron wrote of him, 'The most gentle, the most amiable, and the least worldly-minded person I ever met!'

Led partly by the general hostility against him, and partly by his own delicate health, Shelley went to Italy in 1818, and never returned to England. After wandering over Italy he finally settled in Pisa, beloved of so many English poets—beautiful, sleepy Pisa, where one looks out of his window on the main street at the busiest hour of the day, and the only living thing in sight is a donkey, dozing lazily, with his head in the shade and his body in the sunshine. Here his best poetry was written, and here he found comfort in the friendship of Byron, Hunt, and Trelawney, who are forever associated with Shelley's Italian life. He still remained hostile to English social institutions; but life is a good teacher, and that Shelley dimly recognized the error of his rebellion is shown in the increasing sadness of his later poems:

O world, O life, O time!
On whose last steps I climb,
  Trembling at that where I had stood before;
When will return the glory of your prime?
   No more–oh, never more!

Out of the day and night
A joy has taken flight;
  Fresh spring, and summer, and winter hoar,
Move my faint heart with grief, but with delight
   No more–oh, never more!

In 1822, when only thirty years of age, Shelley was drowned while sailing in a small boat off the Italian coast. His body was washed ashore several days later, and was cremated, near Viareggio, by his friends, Byron, Hunt, and Trelawney. His ashes might, with all reverence, have been given to the winds that he loved and that were a symbol of his restless spirit; instead, they found a resting place near the grave of Keats, in the English cemetery at Rome. One rarely visits the spot now without finding English and American visitors standing in silence before the significant inscription, *Cor Cordium.*

Works of Shelley. As a lyric poet, Shelley is one of the supreme geniuses of our literature; and the reader will do well to begin with the poems which show him at his very best. 'The Cloud' 'To a Skylark', 'Ode to the West Wind', 'To Night'—poems like these must surely set the reader to searching among Shelley's miscellaneous works, to find for himself the things 'worthy to be remembered.'

In reading Shelley's longer poems one must remember that there are in this poet two distinct men: one, the wanderer, seeking ideal beauty and forever unsatisfied; the other, the unbalanced reformer, seeking the overthrow of present institutions and the establishment of universal happiness. *Alastor, or the Spirit of Solitude* (1816) is by far the best expression of Shelley's greater mood. Here we see him wandering restlessly through the vast silences of nature, in search of a loved dream-maiden who shall satisfy his love of beauty. Here Shelley is the poet of the moonrise, and of the tender exquisite fancies that can never be expressed. The charm of the poem lies in its succession of dreamlike pictures; but it gives absolutely no impressions of reality. It was written when Shelley, after his long struggle, had begun to realize that the world was too strong for him. *Alastor* is therefore the poet's confession, not simply of failure, but of undying hope in some better thing that is to come.

Alastor

Prometheus Unbound (1818-1820), a lyrical drama, is the best work of Shelley's revolutionary enthusiasm, and the most characteristic of all his poems. Shelley's philosophy (if one may dignify a hopeless dream by such a name) was a curious aftergrowth of the French Revolution, namely, that it is only the existing tyranny of State, Church, and society which keeps man from growth into perfect happiness. Naturally Shelley forgot, like many other enthusiasts, that Church and State and social laws were not imposed upon man from without, but were created by himself to minister to his necessities. In Shelley's poem the hero, Prometheus, represents mankind itself—a just and noble humanity, chained and tortured by Jove, who is here the

Prometheus

personification of human institutions.[1] In due time Demogorgon (which is Shelley's name for Necessity) overthrows the tyrant Jove and releases Prometheus (Mankind), who is presently united to Asia, the spirit of love and goodness in nature, while the earth and the moon join in a wedding song, and everything gives promise that they shall live together happy ever afterwards.

Shelley here looks forward, not back, to the Golden Age, and is the prophet of science and evolution. If we compare his Titan with similar characters in *Faust and Cain,* we shall find this interesting difference—that while Goethe's Titan is cultured and self-reliant, and Byron's stoic and hopeless, Shelley's hero is patient under torture, seeing help and hope beyond his suffering. And he marries Love that the earth may be peopled with superior beings who shall substitute brotherly love for the present laws and conventions of society. Such is his philosophy; but the beginner will read this poem, not chiefly for its thought, but for its youthful enthusiasm, for its marvellous imagery, and especially for its ethereal music. Perhaps we should add here that *Prometheus* is, and probably always will be, a poem for the chosen few who can appreciate its peculiar spiritlike beauty. In its purely pagan conception of the world, it suggests, by contrast, Milton's Christian philosophy in Paradise Regained.

Shelley's revolutionary works, *Queen Mab* (1813), *The Revolt of Islam* (1818), *Hellas* (1821), and *The Witch of Atlas* (1820), are to be judged in much the same way as is *Prometheus Unbound.* They are largely invectives against religion, marriage, kingcraft, and priestcraft, most impractical when considered as schemes for reform, but abounding in passages of exquisite beauty, for which alone they are worth reading. In the drama called *The Cenci* (1819), which is founded upon a morbid Italian story, Shelley for the first and only time descends to reality. The heroine, Beatrice, driven to desperation by the monstrous wickedness of her father, kills him

[1] Shelley undoubtedly took his idea from a lost drama of Æschylus, a sequel to *Prometheus Bound,* in which the great friend of mankind was unchained from a precipice, where he had been placed by the tyrant Zeus.

and suffers the death penalty in consequence. She is the only one of Shelley's characters who seems to us entirely human.

Far different in character is *Epipsychidion* (1821), a rhapsody celebrating Platonic love, the most impalpable, and so one of the most characteristic, of all Shelley's works. It was inspired by a beautiful Italian girl, Emilia Viviani, who was put into a cloister against her will, and in whom Shelley imagined he found his long-sought ideal of womanhood. With this should be read *Adonais* (1821), the best known of all Shelley's longer poems.

Adonais

Adonais is a wonderful threnody, or a song of grief, over the death of the poet Keats. Even in his grief Shelley still preserves a sense of unreality, and calls in many shadowy allegorical figures—Sad Spring, Weeping Hours, Glooms, Splendours, Destinies—all uniting in bewailing the loss of a loved one. The whole poem is a succession of dream pictures, exquisitely beautiful, such as only Shelley could imagine; and it holds its place with Milton's *Lycidas* and Tennyson's *In Memoriam* as one of the three greatest elegies in our language.

Shelley and Wordsworth

In his interpretation of nature Shelley suggests Wordsworth, both by resemblance and by contrast. To both poets all natural objects are symbols of truth; both regard nature as permeated by the great spiritual life which animates all things; but while Wordsworth finds a spirit of thought, and so of communion between nature and the soul of man, Shelley finds a spirit of love, which exists chiefly for its own delight; and so 'The Cloud', 'The Skylark', and 'The West Wind', three of the most beautiful poems in our language, have no definite message for humanity. In his 'Hymn to Intellectual Beauty' Shelley is most like Wordsworth; but in his 'Sensitive Plant', with its fine symbolism and imagery, he is like nobody in the world but himself. Comparison is sometimes an excellent thing; and if we compare Shelley's exquisite 'Lament', beginning 'O world, O life, O time', with Wordsworth's *'Intimations of Immortality'*, we shall perhaps understand both poets better. Both poems recall many happy memories of youth; both express a very real mood of a moment;

but while the beauty of one merely saddens and disheartens us, the beauty of the other inspires us with something of the poet's own faith and hopefulness. In a word, Wordsworth found and Shelley lost himself in nature.

JOHN KEATS (1795-1821)

Keats was not only the last but also the most perfect of the Romanticists. While Scott was merely telling stories, and Wordsworth reforming poetry or upholding the moral law, and Shelley advocating impossible reforms, and Byron voicing his own egoism and the political discontent of the times, Keats lived apart from men and from all political measures, worshipping beauty like a devotee, perfectly content to write what was in his own heart, or to reflect some splendour of the natural world as he saw or dreamed it to be. He had, moreover, the novel idea that poetry exists for its own sake, and suffers loss by being devoted to philosophy or politics or, indeed, to any cause, however great or small. As he says in 'Lamia':

> ... Do not all charms fly
> At the mere touch of cold philosophy?
> There was an awful rainbow once in heaven:
> We know her woof, her texture; she is given
> In the dull catalogue of common things.
> Philosophy will clip an Angel's wings,
> Conquer all mysteries by rule and line,
> Empty the haunted air, and gnomed mine—
> Unweave a rainbow, as it erewhile made
> The tender-person'd Lamia melt into a shade.

Partly because of this high ideal of poetry, partly because he studied and unconsciously imitated the Greek classics and the best works of the Elizabethans, Keats's last little volume of poetry is unequalled by the work of any of his contemporaries. When we remember that all his work was published in three short years, from 1817 to 1820, and that he died when only twenty-five years old, we must judge him to be the most promising figure of the early nineteenth century, and one of the most remarkable in the history of literature.

Life. Keats's life of devotion to beauty and to poetry is all the more remarkable in view of his lowly origin. He was the son of a hostler and stable keeper, and was born in the stable of the Swan and Hoop Inn, London, in 1795. One has only to read the rough stable scenes from our first novelists, or even from Dickens, to understand how little there was in such an atmosphere to develop poetic gifts. Before Keats was fifteen years old both parents died, and he was placed with his brothers and sisters in charge of guardians. Their first act seems to have been to take Keats from school at Enfield, and to bind him as an apprentice to a surgeon at Edmonton. For five years he served his apprenticeship, and for two years more he was surgeon's helper in the hospitals; but though skillful enough to win approval, he disliked his work, and his thoughts were on other things. 'The other day, during a lecture', he said to a friend, 'there came a sunbeam into the room, and with it a whole troop of creatures floating in the ray; and I was off with them to Oberon and fairyland.' A copy of Spenser's *Faery Queen*, which had been given him by Charles Cowden Clark, was the prime cause of his abstraction. He abandoned his profession in 1817, and early in the same year published his first volume of *Poems*. It was modest enough in spirit, as was also his second volume, *Endymion* (1818); but that did not prevent brutal attacks upon the author and his work by the self-constituted critics of *Blackwood's Magazine* and the *Quarterly*. It is often alleged that the poet's spirit and ambition were broken by these attacks;[1] but Keats was a man of strong character, and instead of quarreling with his reviewers, or being crushed by their criticism, he went quietly to work with the idea of producing poetry that should live forever. As Matthew Arnold says, Keats 'had flint and iron in him;' and in his next volume he accomplished his own purpose and silenced unfriendly criticism.

For the three years during which Keats wrote his poetry he lived chiefly in London and in Hampstead, but wandered at times over England and Scotland, living for brief spaces in the Isle of Wight, in Devonshire, and in the Lake district, seeking to recover his own health, and especially to restore that of his brother. His illness began with a severe cold, but soon developed into consumption; and added to this sorrow was another—his love for Fannie Brawne, to whom he was engaged, but

---

[1] This idea is supported by Shelley's poem *Adonais,* and by Byron's parody against the reviewers, beginning. 'Who killed John Keats? I, says the Quarterly'.

whom he could not marry on account of his poverty and growing illness. When we remember all this personal grief and the harsh criticism of literary men, the last small volume, *Lamia, Isabella, The Eve of St. Agnes and Other Poems* (1820), is most significant, as showing not only Keats's wonderful poetic gifts, but also his beautiful and indomitable spirit. Shelley, struck by the beauty and promise of 'Hyperion', sent a generous invitation to the author to come to Pisa and live with him; but *Keats* refused, having little sympathy with Shelley's revolt against society. The invitation had this effect, however, that it turned Keats's thoughts to Italy, whither he soon went in the effort to save his life. He settled in Rome with his friend Severn, the artist, but died soon after his arrival, in February, 1821. His grave, in the Protestant cemetery at Rome, is still an object of pilgrimage to thousands of tourists; for among all our poets there is hardly another whose heroic life and tragic death have so appealed to the hearts of poets and young enthusiasts.

The Work of Keats. 'None but the master shall praise us; and none but the master shall blame' might well be written on the flyleaf of every volume of Keats's poetry; for never was there a poet more devoted to his ideal, entirely independent of success or failure. In strong contrast with his contemporary, Byron, who professed to despise the art that made him famous, Keats lived for poetry alone, and, as Lowell pointed out, a virtue went out of him into everything he wrote. In all his work we have the impression of this intense loyalty to his art; we have the impression also of a profound dissatisfaction that the deed falls so far short of the splendid dream. Thus after reading Chapman's translation of Homer he writes:

> Much have I travelled in the realms of gold,
> And many goodly states and kingdoms seen;
> Round many western islands have I been
> Which bards in fealty to Apollo hold.
> Oft of one wide expanse had I been told
> That deep-browed Homer ruled as his demesne;
> Yet did I never breathe its pure serene
> Till I heard Chapman speak out loud and bold:
> Then felt I like some watcher of the skies
> When a new planet swims into his ken;

Or like stout Cortez when with eagle eyes
He stared at the Pacific—and all his men
Looked at each other with a wild surmise—
Silent, upon a peak in Darien.

In this striking sonnet we have a suggestion of Keats's high ideal, and of his sadness because of his own ignorance, when he published his first little volume of poems in 1817. He knew no Greek; yet Greek literature absorbed and fascinated him, as he saw its broken and imperfect reflection in an English translation. Like Shakespeare, who also was but poorly educated in the schools, he had a marvellous faculty of discerning the real spirit of the classics—a faculty denied to many great scholars, and to most of the 'classic' writers of the preceding century—and so he set himself to the task of reflecting in modern English the spirit of the old Greeks.

The imperfect results of this attempt are seen in his next volume, *Endymion*, which is the story of a young shepherd beloved by a moon goddess. The poem begins with the striking lines:

A thing of beauty is a joy forever;
Its loveliness increases; it will never
Pass into nothingness; but still will keep
A bower quiet for us; and a sleep
Full of sweet dreams, and health, and quiet breathing,

which well illustrate the spirit of Keats's later work, with its perfect finish and melody. It has many quotable lines and passages, and its 'Hymn to Pan' should be read in connection with Wordsworth's famous sonnet beginning, 'The world is too much with us.' The poem gives splendid promise, but as a whole it is rather chaotic, with too much ornament and too little design, like a modern house. That Keats felt this defect strongly is evident from his modest preface, wherein he speaks of *Endymion,* not as a deed accomplished, but only as an unsuccessful attempt to suggest the underlying beauty of Greek mythology.

Keats's third and last volume, *Lamia, Isabella, The Eve of St. Agnes and Other Poems* (1820), is the one with which the reader should begin his acquaintance with this master of English verse. It has only two subjects, Greek mythology and mediæval romance.

Lamia and Other Poems

'Hyperion' is a magnificent fragment, suggesting the first arch of a cathedral that was never finished. Its theme is the overthrow of the Titans by the young sun-god Apollo. Realizing his own immaturity and lack of knowledge, Keats laid aside this work, and only the pleadings of his publisher induced him to print the fragment with his completed poems.

Throughout this last volume, and especially in 'Hyperion', the influence of Milton is apparent, while Spenser is more frequently suggested in reading *Endymion.*

Of the longer poems in the volume, 'Lamia' is the most suggestive. It is the story of a beautiful enchantress, who turns from a serpent into a glorious woman and fills every human sense with delight, until, as a result of the foolish philosophy of old Apollonius, she vanishes forever from her lover's sight. 'The Eve of St. Agnes', the most perfect of Keats's mediæval poems, is not a story after the manner of the metrical romances, but rather a vivid painting of a romantic mood, such as comes to all men, at times, to glorify a workaday world. Like all the work of Keats and Shelley, it has an element of unreality; and when we read at the end,

> And they are gone; aye, ages long ago
> These lovers fled away into the storm,

it is as if we were waking from a dream—which is the only-possible ending to all of Keats's Greek and mediæval fancies. We are to remember, however, that no beautiful thing, though it be intangible as a dream, can enter a man's life and leave him quite the same afterwards. Keats's own word is here suggestive. 'The imagination', he said, 'may be likened to Adam's dream; he awoke and found it true.'

It is by his short poems that Keats is known to the majority of present-day readers. Among these exquisite shorter poems we mention only the four odes, 'On a Grecian Urn', 'To a Nightingale',

'To Autumn', and 'To Psyche.' These are like an invitation to a feast; one who reads them will hardly be satisfied until he knows more of such delightful poetry. Those who study only the 'Ode to a Nightingale' may find four things—a love of sensuous beauty, a touch of pessimism, a purely pagan conception of nature, and a strong individualism—which are characteristic of this last of the romantic poets.

As Wordsworth's work is too often marred by the moralizer, and Byron's by the demagogue, and Shelley's by the reformer, so Keats's work suffers by the opposite extreme of aloofness from every human interest; so much so, that he is often accused of being indifferent to humanity. His work is also criticized as being too effeminate for ordinary readers. Three things should be remembered in this connection. First, that Keats sought to express beauty for its own sake; that beauty is as essential to normal humanity as is government or law; and that the higher man climbs in civilization the more imperative becomes his need of beauty as a reward for his labours. Second, that Keats's letters are as much an indication of the man as is his poetry; and in his letters, with their human sympathy, their eager interest in social problems, their humour, and their keen insight into life, there is no trace of effeminacy, but rather every indication of a strong and noble manhood. The third thing to remember is that all Keats's work was done in three or four years, with small preparation, and that, dying at twenty-five, he left us a body of poetry which will always be one of our most cherished possessions. He is often compared with 'the marvellous boy' Chatterton, whom he greatly admired, and to whose memory he dedicated his *Endymion;* but though both died young, Chatterton was but a child, while Keats was in all respects a man. It is idle to prophesy what he might have done, had he been granted a Tennyson's long life and scholarly training. At twenty-five his work was as mature as was Tennyson's at fifty, though the maturity suggests the too rapid growth of a tropical plant which under the warm rains and the flood of sunlight leaps into life, grows, blooms in a day, and dies.

Keats's Place in Literature

As we have stated, Keats's work was bitterly and unjustly condemned by the critics of his day. He belonged to what was derisively called the cockney school of poetry, of which Leigh Hunt was chief, and Proctor and Beddoes were fellow-workmen. Not even from Wordsworth and Byron, who were ready enough to recommend far less gifted writers, did Keats receive the slightest encouragement. Like young Lochinvar, 'he rode all unarmed and he rode all alone'. Shelley, with his sincerity and generosity, Nvas the first to recognize the young genius, and in his noble *Adonais*—written, alas, like most of our tributes, when the subject of our praise is dead—he spoke the first true word of appreciation, and placed Keats, where he unquestionably belongs, among our greatest poets. The fame denied him in his sad life was granted freely after his death. Most fitly does he close the list of poets of the romantic revival, because in many respects he was the best workman of them all. He seems to have studied words more carefully than did his contemporaries, and so his poetic expression, or the harmony of word and thought, is generally more perfect than theirs. More than any other he lived for poetry, as the noblest of the arts. More than any other he emphasized beauty, because to him, as shown by his 'Grecian Urn', beauty and truth. were one and inseparable. And he enriched the whole romantic movement by adding to its interest in common life the spirit, rather than the letter of the classics and of Elizabethan poetry. For these reasons Keats is, like Spenser, a poet's poet; his work profoundly influenced Tennyson and, indeed, most of the poets of the present era.

II. PROSE WRITERS OF THE ROMANTIC PERIOD

Literary Criticism

Aside from the splendid work of the novel writers—Walter Scott, whom we have considered and Jane Austen, to whom we shall presently return—the early nineteenth century is remarkable for the development of a new and valuable type of critical prose writing. If we except the isolated work of Dryden and of Addison, it is safe to say that literary criticism, in its modern sense, was hardly known in England until about the year 1825. Such criticism as existed seems to us now to have been largely the result of personal opinion or prejudice. Indeed we could hardly expect anything else before some systematic study of our literature as a whole had been attempted. In one age a poem was called good or bad according as it followed or ran counter to socalled classic rules; in another we have the dogmatism of Dr Johnson; in a third the personal judgment of Lockhart and the editors of the *Edinburgh Review* and the *Quarterly,* who so violently abused Keats and the Lake poets in the name of criticism. Early in the nineteenth century there arose a new school of criticism which was guided by knowledge of literature, on the one hand, and by what one might call the fear of God on the other. The latter element showed itself in a profound human sympathy—the essence of the romantic movement—and its importance was summed up by De Quincey when he said, 'Not to sympathize is not to understand.' These new critics, with abundant reverence for past masters, could still lay aside the dogmatism and prejudice which marked Johnson and the magazine editors, and read sympathetically the work of a new author, with the sole idea of finding what he had contributed, or tried to contribute, to the magnificent total of our literature. Coleridge, Hunt, Hazlitt, Lamb, and De Quincey were the leaders in this new and immensely important development; and we must not forget the importance of the new periodicals, like the *London Magazine,* founded in 1820, in which Lamb, De Quincey, and Carlyle found their first real encouragement.

Hunt and Hazlitt

Of Coleridge's *Biographia Literaria* and his *Lectures on Shakespeare* we have already spoken. Leigh Hunt (1784-1859) wrote continuously for more than thirty years, as editor and essayist; and his chief object seems to have been to make good literature known and appreciated. William Hazlitt (1778-1830), in a long series of lectures and essays, treated all reading as a kind of romantic journey into new and pleasant countries. To his work largely, with that of Lamb, was due the new interest in Elizabethan literature, which so strongly influenced Keats's last and best volume of poetry.

For those interested in the art of criticism, and in the appreciation of literature, both Hunt and Hazlitt will well repay study; but we must pass over their work to consider the larger literary interest of Lamb and De Quincey, who were not simply critics of other men's labour, but who also produced some delightful work of their own, which the world has carefully put away among the 'things worthy to be remembered'.

Charles Lamb (1775-1834)

In Lamb and Wordsworth we have two widely different views of the romantic movement; one shows the influence of nature and solitude, the other of society. Lamb was a lifelong friend of Coleridge, and an admirer and defender of the poetic creed of Wordsworth, but while the latter lived apart from men, content with nature and with reading an occasional moral lesson to society, Lamb was born and lived in the midst of the London streets.The city crowd, with its pleasures and occupations, its endless little comedies and tragedies, alone interested him. According to his own account, when he paused in the crowded street tears would spring to his eyes—tears of pure pleasure at the abundance of so much good life; and when he wrote, he simply interpreted that crowded human life of joy and sorrow, as Wordsworth interpreted the woods and waters, without any desire to change or to reform them. He has given us the best pictures we possess of Coleridge, Hazlitt, Landor, Hood, Cowden Clarke, and many more of the interesting men and women of his age; and it is due to his insight and sympathy that the life of those far-off days seems almost as real to us as if we ourselves remembered it. Of all our English essayists he is the most lovable; partly because of his delicate, old-fashioned style and humour, but more because

Charles Lamb

of that cheery and heroic struggle against misfortune which shines like a subdued light in all his writings.

Life. In the very heart of London there is a curious, old-fashioned place known as the Temple—an enormous, rambling, apparently forgotten structure, dusty and still, in the midst of the endless roar of the city streets. Originally it was a chapter house of the Knights Templars, and so suggests to us the spirit of the Crusades and of the Middle Ages; but now the building is given over almost entirely to the offices and lodgings of London lawyers. It is this queer old place which, more than all others, is associated with the name of Charles Lamb. 'I was born', he says, 'and passed the first seven years of my life in the Temple. Its gardens, its halls, its fountain, its river—these are my oldest recollections.' He was the son of a poor clerk, or rather servant, of one of the barristers, and was the youngest of seven children, only three of whom survived infancy. Of these three, John, the elder, was apparently a selfish creature, who took no part in the heroic struggle of his brother and sister. At seven years, Charles was sent to the famous 'Bluecoat' charity school of Christ's Hospital. Here he remained seven years; and here he formed his lifelong friendship for another poor, neglected boy, whom the world remembers as Coleridge.[1]

When only fourteen years old, Lamb left the charity school and was soon at work as a clerk in the South Sea House. Two years later he became a clerk in the famous India House, where he worked steadily for thirty-three years, with the exception of six weeks, in the winter of 1795-1796, spent within the walls of an asylum. In 1796 Lamb's sister Mary, who was as talented and remarkable as Lamb himself, went violently insane and killed her own mother. For a long time after this appalling tragedy she was in an asylum at Hoxton; then Lamb, in 1797, brought her to his own little house, and for the remainder of his life cared for her with a tenderness and devotion which furnishes one of the most beautiful pages in our literary history. At times the malady would return to Mary, giving sure warning of its terrible approach; and then brother and sister might be seen walking silently, hand in hand, to the gates of the asylum, their cheeks wet with tears. One must remember this, as well as Lamb's humble lodgings and the drudgery of his daily work in the big commercial house, if he would appreciate the pathos of 'The Old Familiar Faces', or

---

[1] See 'Christ's Hospital Five and Thirty Years Ago', in *Essays of Elia.*

Christ's Hospital, London

the heroism which shines through the most human and the most delightful essays in our language.

When Lamb was fifty years of age the East India Company, led partly by his literary fame following his first *Essays of Elia,* and partly by his thirty-three years of faithful service, granted him a comfortable pension; and happy as a boy turned loose from school he left India House forever to give himself up to literary work.[1] He wrote to Wordsworth, in April, 1825, 'I came home forever on Tuesday of last week—it was like passing from life into eternity.' Curiously enough Lamb seems to lose power after his release from drudgery, and his last essays, published in 1833, lack something of the grace and charm of his earlier work. He died at Edmonton in 1834; and his gifted sister Mary sank rapidly into the gulf from which his strength and gentleness had so long held her back. No literary man was ever more loved and honoured by a rare circle of friends; and all who knew him bear witness to the simplicity and goodness which any reader may find for himself between the lines of his essays.

Works. The works of Lamb divide themselves naturally into three periods. First, there are his early literary efforts, including the poems signed 'C. L.' in Coleridge's Poems on *Various Subjects* (1796); his

[1] See *Essays of Elia,* 'The Superannuated Man'.

romance *Rosamund Gray* (1798); his poetical drama *John Woodvil* (1802); and various other immature works in prose and poetry. This period comes to an end in 1803, when he gave up his newspaper work, especially the contribution of six jokes, puns, and squibs daily to the *Morning Post* at sixpence apiece. The second period was given largely to literary criticism; and the *Tales from Shakespeare* (1807)—written by Charles and Mary Lamb, the former reproducing the tragedies, and the latter the comedies—may be regarded as his first successful literary venture.

The book was written primarily for children; but so thoroughly had brother and sister steeped themselves in the literature of the Elizabethan period that young and old alike were delighted with this new version of Shakespeare's stories, and the *Tales* are still regarded as the best of their kind in our literature. In 1808 appeared his *Specimens of English Dramatic Poets, Contemporary with Shakespeare.* This carried out the splendid critical work of Coleridge, and was the most noticeable influence in developing the poetic qualities of Keats, as shown in his last volume.

Essays of Elia

The third period includes Lamb's criticisms of life, which are gathered together in his *Essays of Elia* (1823), and his *Last Essays of Elia,* which were published ten years later. These famous essays began in 1820 with the appearance of the new *London Magazine,*[1] and were continued for many years, such subjects as the 'Dissertation on Roast Pig', 'Old China', 'Praise of Chimney Sweepers', 'Imperfect Sympathies', 'A Chapter on Ears', 'Mrs. Battle's Opinions on Whist', 'Mackery End', 'Grace Before Meat', 'Dream Children', and many others being chosen apparently at random, but all leading to a delightful interpretation of the life of London, as it appeared to a quiet little man who

---

[1] In the first essay, 'The South Sea House', Lamb assumed as a joke the name of a former clerk, Elia. Other essays followed, and the name was retained when several successful essays were published in book form, in 1823. In these essays 'Elia' is Lamb himself, and 'Cousin Bridget' is his sister Mary.

walked unnoticed through its crowded streets. In the first and last essays which we have mentioned, 'Dissertation on Roast Pig' and 'Dream Children', we have the extremes of Lamb's humour and pathos.

Lamb's Style

The style of all these essays is gentle, old-fashioned, irresistibly attractive. Lamb was especially fond of old writers and borrowed unconsciously from the style of Burton's *Anatomy of Melancholy* and from Browne's *Religio Medici* and from the early English dramatists. But this style had become a part of Lamb by long reading, and he was apparently unable to express his new thought without using their old quaint expressions. Though these essays are all criticisms or appreciations of the life of his age, they are all intensely personal. In other words, they are an excellent picture of Lamb and of humanity. Without a trace of vanity or self-assertion, Lamb begins with himself, with some purely personal mood or experience, and from this he leads the reader to see life and literature as he saw it. It is this wonderful combination of personal and universal interests, together with Lamb's rare old style and quaint humour, which make the essays remarkable. They continue the best tradition of Addison and Steele, our first great essayists; but their sympathies are broader and deeper, and their humour more delicious than any which preceded them.

THOMAS DE QUINCY (1785-1859)

In De Quincey the romantic element is even more strongly developed than in Lamb, not only in his critical work, but also in his erratic and imaginative life. He was profoundly educated, even more so than Coleridge, and was one of the keenest intellects of the age; yet his wonderful intellect seems always subordinate to his passion for dreaming. Like Lamb, he was a friend and associate of the Lake poets, making his headquarters in Wordsworth's old cottage at Grasmere for nearly twenty years. Here the resemblance ceases, and a marked contrast begins. As a man, Lamb is the most human and lovable of all our essayists; while De Quincey is the most uncanny and incomprehensible. Lamb's modest works breathe the two essential qualities of sympathy and humour; the greater number of De Quincey's essays, while possessing more or less of both these qualities, are characterized chiefly by their brilliant style. Life, as seen through De Quincey's eyes, is nebulous and chaotic, and there is a suspicion of the fabulous in all that he wrote. Even in *The Revolt of the Tartars* the romantic element is uppermost, and in much of De Quincey's prose the element of unreality is more noticeable than in Shelley's poetry. Of his subject-matter, his facts, ideas, and criticisms, we are generally suspicious; but of his style, sometimes stately and sometimes headlong, now gorgeous as an Oriental dream, now musical as Keats's *Endymion,* and always, even in the most violent contrasts, showing a harmony between the idea and the expression such as no other English writer, with the possible exception of Newman, has ever rivalled—say what you will of the marvellous brilliancy of De Quincey's style, you have still only half expressed the truth. It is the style alone which makes these essays immortal.

Life. De Quincey was born in Manchester in 1785. In neither his father, who was a prosperous merchant, nor his mother, who was a quiet, unsympathetic woman, do we see any suggestion of the son's almost uncanny genius. As a child he was given to dreams, more vivid and intense but less beautiful than those of the young Blake, to whom he bears a strong resemblance. In the grammar school at Bath he displayed astonishing ability, and acquired Greek and Latin with a rapidity that frightened his slow tutors. At fifteen he not only read Greek, but spoke it fluently; and one of his astounded teachers remarked, 'That boy could harangue an Athenian mob better than you or I could address an English one.' From the grammar school at Manchester, whither he was sent in 1800, he soon ran away, finding the instruction far below his abilities, and the rough life absolutely intolerable to his sensitive nature. An uncle, just home from India, interceded for the boy lest he be sent back to the school, which he hated; and with an allowance of a guinea a week he started a career of vagrancy, much like that of Goldsmith, living on the open hills, in the huts of shepherds and charcoal burners, in the tents of gypsies, wherever fancy led him. His fear of the Manchester school finally led him to run away to London, where, without money or friends, his life was even more extraordinary than his gypsy wanderings. The details of this vagrancy are best learned in his *Confessions of an English Opium-Eater*, where we meet not simply the facts of his life, but also the confusion of dreams and fancies in the midst of which he wandered like a man lost on the mountains, with storm clouds under his feet hiding the familiar earth. After a year of vagrancy and starvation he was found by his family and allowed to go to Oxford, where his career was marked by the most brilliant and erratic scholarship. When ready for a degree, in 1807, he passed his written tests successfully, but felt a sudden terror at the thought of the oral examination and disappeared from the university, never to return.

It was in Oxford that De Quincey began the use of opium; to relieve the pains of neuralgia, and the habit increased until he was an almost hopeless slave to the drug. Only his extraordinary will power enabled him to break away from the habit, after some thirty years of misery. Some peculiarity of his delicate constitution enabled De Quincey to take enormous quantities of opium, enough to kill several ordinary men; and it was largely opium, working upon a sensitive imagination, which produced his gorgeous dreams, broken by intervals of weakness and profound depression. For twenty years he resided at Grasmere in the companionship of the Lake poets; and here, led by the loss of his small fortune, he began to write, with the idea of supporting his family. In 1821 he published his first famous work, the *Confessions of an English Opium-Eater,* and for nearly forty years afterwards he wrote industriously, contributing to various magazines an astonishing number of essays on a great variety of subjects. Without thought of literary fame, he contributed these articles anonymously; but fortunately, in 1853, he began to collect his own works, and the last of fourteen volumes was published just after his death.

Thomas De Quincey

In 1830, led by his connection with *Blackwood's Magazine,* to which he was the chief contributor, De Quincey removed with his family to

Edinburgh, where his erratic genius and his singularly childlike ways produced enough amusing anecdotes to fill a volume. He would take a room in some place unknown to his friends and family; would live in it for a few years, until he had filled it, even to the bath tub, with books and with his own chaotic manuscripts, allowing no one to enter or disturb his den; and then, when the place became too crowded, he would lock the door and go away and take another lodging, where he repeated the same extraordinary performance. He died in Edinburgh in 1859. Like Lamb, he was a small, boyish figure, gentle, and elaborately courteous. Though excessively shy, and escaping as often as possible to solitude, he was nevertheless fond of society, and his wide knowledge and vivid imagination made his conversations almost as prized as those of his friend Coleridge.

Works. De Quincey's works may be divided into two general classes. The first includes his numerous critical articles, and the second his autobiographical sketches. All his works, it must be remembered, were contributed to various magazines, and were hastily collected just before his death. Hence the general impression of chaos which we get from reading them.

Critical Essays

From a literary viewpoint the most illuminating of De Quincey's critical works is his. *Literary Reminiscences*. This contains brilliant appreciations of Wordsworth, Coleridge, Lamb, Shelley, Keats, Hazlitt, and Landor, as well as some interesting studies of the literary figures of the age preceding. Among the best of his brilliant critical essays are *On the Knocking at the Gate in Macbeth* (1823), which is admirably suited to show the man's critical genius, and *Murder Considered as One of the Fine Arts* (1827), which reveals his grotesque humour. Other suggestive critical works, if one must choose among such a multitude, are his *Letters to a Young Man* (1823), *Joan of Arc* (1847), *The Revolt of the Tartars* (1840), and *The English Mail-Coach* (1849). In the last-named essay the 'Dream Fugue' is one of the most imaginative of all his curious works.

Of De Quincey's autobiographical sketches the best known is his *Confessions of an English Opium-Eater* (1821). This is only partly a record of opium dreams, and its chief interest lies in glimpses it gives us of De Quincey's own life and wanderings. This should be followed by *Suspiria de Profundis* (1845), which is chiefly a record of gloomy and terrible dreams produced by opiates. The most interesting parts of his *Suspiria,* showing De Quincey's marvellous insight into dreams, are those in which we are brought face to face with the strange feminine creations 'Levana', 'Madonna', 'Our Lady of Sighs', and 'Our Lady of Darkness.' A series of nearly thirty articles which he collected in 1853, called *Autobiographic Sketches,* completes the revelation of the author's own life. Among his miscellaneous works may be mentioned, in order to show his wide range of subjects, *Klosterheim,* a novel, *Logic of Political Economy,* the *Essays on Style and Rhetoric, Philosophy of Herodotus,* and his articles on Goethe, Pope, Schiller, and Shakespeare which he contributed to the *Encyclopaedia Britannica.*

Confessions of an Opium Eater, etc.

De Quincey's style is a revelation of the beauty of the English language, and it profoundly influenced Ruskin and other prose writers of the Victorian Age. It has two chief faults—diffuseness, which continually leads De Quincey away from his object, and triviality, which often makes him halt in the midst of a marvellous paragraph to make some light jest or witticism that has some humour but no mirth in it. Notwithstanding these faults, De Quincey's prose is still among the few supreme examples of style in our language. Though he was profoundly influenced by the seventeenth-century writers, he attempted definitely to create a new style which should combine the best elements of prose and poetry. In consequence, his prose works are often, like those of Milton, more imaginative and melodious than much of our poetry. He has been well called 'the psychologist of style', and as such his works will never be popular; but to the few who can appreciate him he will always be an inspiration to better writing. One has a deeper respect for our English language and literature after reading him.

The style of De Quincey

Secondary Writers of Romanticism. One has only to glance back over the authors we have been studying—Wordsworth,

Coleridge, Southey, Byron, Shelley, Keats, Scott, Lamb, De Quincey—to realize the great change which swept over the life and literature of England in a single half century, under two influences which we now know as the French Revolution in history and the Romantic Movement in literature. In life men had rebelled against the too strict authority of state and society; in literature they rebelled even more vigorously against the bonds of classicism, which had sternly repressed a writer's ambition to follow his own ideals and to express them in his own way. Naturally such an age of revolution was essentially poetic—only the Elizabethan Age surpasses it in this respect—and it produced a large number of minor writers, who followed more or less closely the example of its great leaders. Among novelists we have Jane Austen, Frances Burney, Maria Edgeworth, Jane Porter, and Susan Ferrier—all women, be it noted; among the poets, Campbell, Moore, Hogg ('the Ettrick Shepherd'), Mrs. Hemans, Heber, Keble, Hood, and 'Ingoldsby' (Richard Barham); and among miscellaneous writers, Sidney Smith, 'Christopher North' (John Wilson), Chalmers, Lockhart, Leigh Hunt, Hazlitt, Hallam, and Landor. Here is an astonishing variety of writers, and to consider all their claims to remembrance would of itself require a volume. Though these are generally classed as secondary writers, much of their work has claims to popularity, and some of it to permanence. Moore's *Irish Melodies,* Campbell's lyrics, Keble's *Christian Year,* and Jane Porter's *Thaddeus of Warsaw* and *Scottish Chiefs* have still a multitude of readers, where Keats, Lamb, and De Quincey are prized only by the cultured few; and Hallam's historical and critical works are perhaps better known than those of Gibbon, who nevertheless occupies a larger place in our literature. Among all these writers we choose only two, Jane Austen and Walter Savage Landor, whose works indicate a period of transition from the Romantic to the Victorian Age.

Jane Austen (1775-1817)

We have so lately rediscovered the charm and genius of this gifted young woman that she seems to be a novelist of yesterday, rather than the contemporary of Wordsworth and Coleridge; and few even of her readers realize that she did for the English novel precisely what the Lake poets did for English poetry—she refined and simplified it, making it a true reflection of English life. Like the Lake poets, she met with scanty encouragement in her own generation. Her greatest novel, *Pride and Prejudice,* was finished in 1797, a year before the appearance of the famous *Lyrical Ballads* of Wordsworth and Coleridge; but while the latter book was published and found a few appreciative readers, the manuscript of this wonderful novel went begging for sixteen years before it found a publisher. As Wordsworth began with the deliberate purpose of making poetry natural and truthful, so Miss Austen appears to have begun writing with the idea of presenting the life of English country society exactly as it was, in opposition to the romantic extravagance of Mrs. Radcliffe and her school. But there was this difference—that Miss Austen had in large measure the saving gift of humour, which Wordsworth sadly lacked. Maria Edgeworth, at the same time, set a sane and excellent example in her tales of Irish life, *The Absentee* and *Castle Rackrent*; and Miss Austen followed up the advantage with at least six works, which have grown steadily in value until we place them gladly in the first rank of our novels of common life. It is not simply for her exquisite charm, therefore, that we admire her, but also for her influence in bringing our novels back to their true place as an expression of human life. It is due partly, at least, to her influence that a multitude of readers were ready to appreciate Mrs. Gaskell's *Cranford,* and the powerful and enduring work of George Eliot.

Life. Jane Austen's life gives little opportunity for the biographer, unless, perchance, he has something of her own power to show the beauty and charm of commonplace things. She was the seventh child of Rev. George Austen, rector of Steventon, and was born in the parsonage of the village in 1775. With her sisters she was educated at home, and passed her life very quietly, cheerfully, in the doing of small domestic duties, to which love lent the magic lamp that makes all things beautiful. She began to write at an early age, and seems to have done her work on a little table in the family sitting room, in the midst of the family life. When a visitor entered, she would throw a paper or a piece of sewing over her work, and she modestly refused to be known as the author of novels which we now count among our treasured possessions. With the publishers she had little success. *Pride and Prejudice* went begging, as we have said, for sixteen years; and *Northanger Abbey* (1798) was sold for a trivial sum to a publisher, who laid it aside and forgot it, until the appearance and moderate success of Sense and Sensibility in 1811. Then, after keeping the manuscript some fifteen years, he sold it back to the family, who found another publisher.

An anonymous article in the *Quarterly Review,* following the appearance of Emma in 1815, full of generous appreciation of the charm of the new writer, was the beginning of Jane Austen's fame; and it is only within a few years that we have learned that the friendly and discerning critic was Walter Scott. He continued to be her admirer until her early death; but these two, the greatest writers of fiction in their age, were never brought together. Both were home-loving people, and Miss Austen especially was averse to publicity and popularity. She died, quietly as she had lived, at Winchester, in 1817, and was buried in the cathedral. She was a bright, attractive little woman, whose sunny qualities are unconsciously reflected in all her books.

Works. Very few English writers ever had so narrow a field of work as Jane Austen. Like the French novelists, whose success seems to lie in choosing the tiny field that they know best, her works have an exquisite perfection that is lacking in most of our writers of fiction. With the exception of an occasional visit to the watering place of Bath, her whole life was spent in small country parishes, whose simple country people became the characters of her novels. Her brothers were in the navy, and so naval officers furnish the only exciting elements in her stories; but even these alleged heroes lay aside their imposing martial ways and act like themselves and other people. Such was her literary field, in which the chief duties were of the household, the chief pleasures in country gatherings, and the chief interests in matrimony. Life, with its mighty interests, its passions, ambitions, and tragic struggles, swept by like a great river; while the secluded interests of a country parish went round and round quietly, like an eddy behind a sheltering rock. We can easily understand, therefore, the limitations of Jane Austen; but within her own field she is unequalled. Her characters are absolutely true to life, and all her work has the perfection of a delicate miniature painting. The most widely read of her novels is *Pride and Prejudice;* but three others, *Sense and Sensibility, Emma,* and *Mansfield Park,* have slowly won their way to the front rank of fiction. From a literary view point *Northanger Abbey* is perhaps the best; for in it we find that touch of humour and delicate satire with which this gentle little woman combated the grotesque popular novels of the *Udolpho* type. Reading any of these works, one is inclined to accept the hearty endorsement of Sir Walter Scott: 'That young lady has a talent for describing the involvements and feelings and characters of ordinary life which is to me the most wonderful I ever met with. The big bow-wow strain I can do myself, like any now going; but the exquisite touch which renders ordinary commonplace things and characters interesting from the truth of the description and the sentiment, is denied to me. What a pity such a gifted creature died so early!'

WALTER SAVAGE LANDOR (1775-1864)

While Hazlitt, Lamb, De Quincey, and other romantic critics went back to early English literature for their inspiration, Landor shows a reaction from the prevailing Romanticism by his imitation of the ancient classic writers. His life was an extraordinary one and, like his work, abounded in sharp contrasts. On the one hand, there are his egoism, his unncontrollable anger, his perpetual lawsuits, and the last sad tragedy with his children, which suggests *King Lear* and his daughters; on the other hand there is his steady devotion to the classics and to the cultivation of the deep wisdom of the ancients, which suggests Pindar and Cicero. In his works we find the wild extravagance of *Gebir,* followed by the superb classic style and charm of *Pericles and Aspasia.* Such was Landor, a man of high ideals, perpetually at war with himself and the world.

Life. Landor's stormy life covers the whole period from Wordsworth's childhood to the middle of the Victorian Era. He was the son of a physician, and was born at Warwick, in 1775. From his mother he inherited a fortune; but it was soon scattered by large expenditures and law quarrels; and in his old age, refused help by his own children, only Browning's generosity kept Landor from actual want. At Rugby, and at Oxford, his extreme Republicanism brought him into constant trouble; and his fitting out a band of volunteers to assist the Spaniards against Napoleon, in 1808, allies him with Byron and his Quixotic followers. The resemblance to Byron is even more strikingly shown in the poem *Gebir,* published in 1798, a year made famous by the *Lyrical Ballads* of Wordsworth and Coleridge.

A remarkable change in Landor's life is noticeable in 1821, when, at forty-six years of age, after having lost his magnificent estate of Llanthony Abbey, in Glamorganshire, and after a stormy experience in Como, he settled down for a time at Fiesole near Florence. To this period of calm after storm we owe the classical prose works for which he is famous. The calm, like that at the centre of a whirlwind, lasted but a short time, and Landor, leaving his family in great anger, returned to Bath, where he lived alone for more than twenty years. Then, in order to escape a libel suit, the choleric old man fled back to Italy. He died at Florence, in 1864. The spirit of his whole life may be inferred from the defiant farewell which he flung to it:

> I strove with none, for none was worth my strife;
> Nature I loved, and next to Nature Art;
> I warmed both hands before the fire of life;
> It sinks, and I am ready to depart.

Works. Landor's reaction from Romanticism is all the more remarkable in view of his early efforts, such as *Gebir,* a wildly romantic poem, which rivals any work of Byron or Shelley in its extravagance. Notwithstanding its occasional beautiful and suggestive lines, the work was not and never has been successful; and the same may be said of all his poetical works. His first collection of poems was published in 1795, his last a full half century later, in 1846. In the latter volume, *The Hellenics*—which included some translations of his earlier Latin poems, called *Idyllia Heroica*—one has only to read 'The Hamadryad', and compare it with the lyrics of the first volume, in order to realize the astonishing literary vigour of a man who published two volumes, a half century apart, without any appreciable diminution of poetical feeling. In all these poems one is impressed by the striking and original figures of speech which Landor uses to emphasize his meaning.

It is by his prose works, largely, that Landor has won a place in our literature; partly because of their intrinsic worth, their penetrating thought, and severe classic style; and partly because of their profound influence upon the writers of the present age. The most noted of his prose works are his six volumes of *Imaginary Conversations* (1824-1846). For these conversations Landor brings together, sometimes in groups, sometimes in couples, well-known characters, or rather shadows, from the four corners of the earth and from the remotest ages of recorded history. Thus Diogenes talks with Plato, Æsop with a young slave girl in Egypt, Henry VIII with Anne Boleyn in prison, Dante with Beatrice, Leofric with Lady Godiva—all these and many others, from Epictetus to Cromwell, are brought together and speak of life and love and death, each from his own viewpoint. Occasionally, as in the meeting of Henry and Anne Boleyn, the situation is tense and dramatic; but as a rule the characters simply meet and converse in the same quiet strain, which becomes, after much reading, somewhat monotonous. On the other hand, one who reads the *Imaginary Conversations* is lifted at once into a calm and noble atmosphere which braces and inspires him, making him forget petty things, like a view from a hilltop. By its combination of lofty thought and severely classic style the book has won, and deserves, a very high place among our literary records.

The same criticism applies to *Pericles and Aspasia,* which is a series of imaginary letters, telling the experiences of Aspasia, a young lady from Asia Minor, who visits Athens at the summit of its fame and glory, in the great age of *Pericles.* This is, in our judgment, the best worth reading of all Landor's works. One gets from it not only Landor's classic style, but—what is well worth while—a better picture of Greece in the days of its greatness than can be obtained from many historical volumes.

Summary of the Age of Romanticism. This period extends from the war with the colonies, following the Declaration of Independence, in 1776, to the accession of Victoria in 1837, both limits being very indefinite, as will be seen by a glance at the Chronology following. During the first part of the period especially, England was in a continual turmoil, produced by political and economic agitation at home, and by the long wars that covered two continents and the wide sea between them. The mighty changes resulting from these two causes have given this period the name of the Age of Revolution. The storm centre of all the turmoil at home and abroad was the French Revolution, which had a profound influence on the life and literature of all Europe. On the Continent the overthrow of Napoleon at Waterloo (1815) apparently checked the progress of liberty, which had started with the French Revolution,[1] but in England the case was reversed. The agitation for popular liberty, which at one time threatened a revolution, went steadily forward till it resulted in the final triumph of democracy, in the Reform Bill of 1832, and in a number of exceedingly important reforms, such as the extension of manhood suffrage, the removal of the last unjust restrictions against Catholics, the establishment of a national system of schools, followed by a rapid increase in popular education, and the abolition of slavery in all English colonies (1833). To this we must add the changes produced by the discovery of steam and the invention of machinery, which rapidly changed England from an agricultural to a manufacturing nation, introduced the factory system, and caused this period to be known as the Age of Industrial Revolution.

The literature of the age is largely poetical in form, and almost entirely romantic in spirit. For, as we have noted, the triumph of democracy in government is generally accompanied by the triumph of romanticism in literature. At first the literature, as shown especially in the early work of Wordsworth, Byron, and Shelley, reflected the turmoil of the age and the wild hopes of an ideal democracy occasioned by the French Revolution. Later the extravagant enthusiasm subsided, and English writers produced so much excellent literature that the age is often called the Second Creative period, the first being the Age of Elizabeth. The six chief characteristics of the age are: the prevalence of romantic poetry; the creation of the historical novel by Scott; the first appearance of women novelists, such as Mrs. Anne Radcliffe, Jane Porter, Maria Edgeworth, and Jane Austen; the development of literary criticism, in the work of Lamb, De Quincey,

[1] See histories for the Congress of Vienna (1814) and the Holy Alliance (1815)

Coleridge, and Hazlitt; the practical and economic bent of philosophy, as shown in the work of Malthus, James Mill, and Adam Smith; and the establishment of great literary magazines, like the *Edinburgh Review,* the *Quarterly, Blackwood's,* and the *Athenæum.*

In our study we have noted (1) the Poets of Romanticism: the importance of the *Lyrical Ballads* of 1798; the life and work of Wordsworth, Coleridge, Scott, Byron, Shelley, and Keats; (2) the Prose Writers: the novels of Scott; the development of literary criticism; the life and work of the essayists, Lamb, De Quincey, Landor, and of the novelist Jane Austen.

Selections for Reading. Manly's English Poetry and Manly's English Prose (each one vol.) contain good selections from all authors studied. Ward's English Poets (4 vols.), Craik's English Prose Selections (5 vols.), Braithwaite's The Book of Georgian Verse, Page's British Poets of the Nineteenth Century, and Garnett's English Prose from Elizabeth to Victoria, may also be used to advantage. Important works, however, should be read entire in one of the inexpensive school editions given below. (Full titles and publishers may be found in the General Bibliography at the end of this book.)

Wordsworth. Intimations of Immortality, Tintern Abbey, best lyrics and *Sonnets,* in Selections, edited by Dowden (Athenæum Press Series); selections and short poems, edited by M. Arnold, in Golden Treasury Series; Selections, also in Everyman's Library, Riverside Literature Series, Cassell's National Library, etc.

Coleridge. Ancient Mariner, edited by L. R. Gibbs, in Standard English Classics; same poem, in Pocket Classics, Eclectic English Classics, etc.; Poems, edited by J. M. Hart, in Athenæum Press (announced, 1909); Selections, Golden Book of Coleridge, in Everyman's Library; Selections from Coleridge and Campbell, in Riverside Literature; Prose Selections (Ginn and Company, also Holt); Lectures on Shakespeare, in Everyman's Library, Bohn's Standard Library, etc.

Scott. Lady of the Lake, Marmion, Ivanhoe, The Talisman, Guy Mannering, Quentin Durward. Numerous inexpensive editions of Scott's best poems and novels in Standard English Classics, Pocket Classics, Cassell's National Library, Eclectic English Classics, Everyman's Librắry, etc.; thus, Lady of the Lake, edited by Edwin Ginn, and Ivanhoe, edited by W. D. Lewis, both in Standard English Classics; Marmion, edited by G. B. Acton, and The Talisman, edited by F. Treudly, in Pocket Classics, etc.

Byron. Mazeppa and The Prisoner of Chillon, edited by S. M. Tucker, in Standard English Classics; short poems, Selections from Childe Harold, etc., in Canterbury Poets, Riverside Literature, Holt's English Readings, Pocket Classics, etc.

Shelley. To a Cloud, To a Skylark, West Wind, Sensitive Plant, Adonais, etc., all in Selections from Shelley, edited by Alexander, in Athenæum Press Series; Selections, edited by Woodberry, in Belles Lettres Series; Selections, also in Pocket Classics, Heath's English Classics, Golden Treasury Series, etc.

Keats. Ode on a Grecian Urn, Eve of St. Agnes, Hyperion, Lamia, To a Nightingale, etc., in Selections from Keats, in Athenæum Press; Selections also in Muses' Library, Riverside Literature, Golden Treasury Series, etc.

Lamb. Essays: Dream Children, Old China, Dissertation on Roast Pig, etc., edited by Wauchope, in Standard English Classics; various essays also in Camelot Series, Temple Classics, Everyman's Library, etc. Tales from Shakespeare, in Home and School Library (Ginn and Company); also in Riverside Literature, Pocket Classics, Golden Treasury, etc.

De Quincey. The English Mail-Coach and Joan of Arc, in Standard English Classics, etc.; Confessions of an English Opium-Eater, in Temple Classics, Morley's Universal Library, Everyman's Library, Pocket Classics, etc.; Selections, edited by M. H. Turk, in Athenæum Press; Selections, edited by B. Perry (Holt).

Landor. Selections, edited by W. Clymer, in Athenæum Press; *Pericles* and Aspasia, in Camelot Series; Imaginary Conversations, selected (Ginn and Company); the same, 2 vols., in Dutton's Universal Library; selected poems, in Canterbury Poets; selections, prose and verse, in Golden Treasury Series.

Jane Austen. Pride and Prejudice, in Everyman's Library, Pocket Classics, etc.

Bibliography.[1] ***History.*** *Textbook,* Montgomery, pp. 323-357; Cheyney, 576-632. *General Works.* Green, X, 2-4, Traill, Gardiner, Macaulay, etc. *Special Works.* Cheyney's Industrial and Social History of England; Warner's Landmarks of English Industrial History; Hassall's Making of the British Empire; Macaulay's William Pitt; Trevelyan's Early Life of Charles James Fox; Morley's Edmund Burke; Morris's Age of Queen Anne and the Early Hanoverians.

---

[1] For ful titles and publishers of general reference books, see General Bibliography at end of this book.

Literature. *General Works.* Mitchell, Courthope, Garnett and Gosse, Taine (see General Bibliography). *Special Works.* Beers's English Romanticism in the Nineteenth Century; A. Symons's The Romantic Movement in English Poetry; Dowden's The French Revolution and English Literature, also Studies in Literature, 1789-1877; Hancock's The French Revolution and the English Poets; Herford's The Age of Wordsworth (Handbooks of English Literature); Mrs. Oliphant's Literary History of England in the End of the Eighteenth and Beginning of the Nineteenth Centuries; Saintsbury's History of Nineteenth Century Literature; Masson's Wordsworth, Shelley, Keats, and Other Essays; Poets and Poetry of the Nineteenth Century, vols. 1-3; Gates's Studies and Appreciations; S. Brooke's Studies in Poetry; Rawnsley's Literary Associations of the English Lakes (2 vols.).

Wordsworth. Texts: Globe, Aldine, Cambridge editions, etc.; Poetical and Prose Works, with Dorothy Wordsworth's Journal, edited by Knight, Eversley Edition (London and New York, 1896); Letters of the Wordsworth Family, edited by Knight, 3 vols. (Ginn and Company); Poetical Selections, edited by Dowden, in Athenæum Press; various other selections, in Golden Treasury, etc.; Prose Selections, edited by Gayley (Ginn and Company). Life: Memoirs, 2 vols., by Christopher Wordsworth; by Knight, 3 vols.; by Myers (English Men of Letters); by Elizabeth Wordsworth; Early Life (a Study of the Prelude) by E. Legouis, translated by J. Matthews; Raleigh's Wordsworth; N.C. Smith's Wordsworth's Literary Criticism; Rannie's Wordsworth and His Circle. Criticism: Herford's The Age of Wordsworth; Masson's Wordsworth, Shelley, and Keats; Magnus's Primer of Wordsworth; Wilson's Helps to the Study of Arnold's Wordsworth; Essays, by Lowell, in Among My Books; by M. Arnold, in Essays in Criticism; by Hutton, in Literary Essays; by L. Stephen, in Hours in a Library, and in Studies of a Biographer; by Bagehot, in Literary Studies; by Hazlitt, in The Spirit of the Age; by Pater, in Appreciations; by De Quincey, in Essays on the Poets; by Fields, in Yesterdays with Authors; by Shairp, in Studies in Poetry and Philosophy. See also Knight's Through the Wordsworth Country, and Rawnsley's Literary Associations of the English Lakes.

Coleridge. Texts: Complete Works, edited by Shedd, 7 vols. (New York 1884); Poems, Globe, Aldine, and Cambridge editions, in Athenæum Press (announced, 1909), Muses' Library, Canterbury Poets, etc.; Biographia Literaria, in Everyman's Library; the same, in Clarendon Press; Prose Selections, Lectures on Shakespeare, etc. (see Selections for Reading, above);

Letters, edited by E.H. Coleridge (London, 1895). Life: by J.D. Campbell; by Traill (English Men of Letters); by Dykes; by Hall Caine (Great Writers Series); see also Coleridge's Biographia Literaria, and Lamb's essay, Christ's Hospital, in Essays of Elia. Criticism: Brandl's Coleridge and the English Romantic Movement. Essays, by Shairp, in Studies in Poetry and Philosophy; by Woodberry, in Makers of Literature; by J. Forster, in Great Teachers; by Dowden, in New Studies; by Swinburne, in Essays and Studies; by Brooke, in Theology in the English Poets; by Saintsbury, in Essays in English Literature; by Lowell in Democracy and Other Essays; by Hazlitt, and by Pater (see Wordsworth, above). See also Beers's English Romanticism; Carlyle's chapter on Coleridge, in Life of John Sterling.

Southey. Texts: Poems, edited by Dowden (Macmillan); Poetical Works (Crowell); Selections in Canterbury Poets; Life of Nelson, in Everyman's Library, Temple Classics, Morley's Universal Library, etc. Life: by Dowden (English Men of Letters). Essays, by L. Stephen, in Studies of a Biographer; by Hazlitt and Saintsbury (see above).

Scott. Texts: Numerous good editions of novels and poems. For single works, see Selections for Reading, above. Life: by Lockhart, 5 vols. (several editions; best by Pollard, 1900); by Hutton (English Men of Letters); by A. Lang, in Literary Lives; by C. D. Yonge (Great Writers); by Hudson; by Saintsbury (Famous Scots Series). Criticism: Essays, by Stevenson, Gossip on Romance, in Memories and Portraits; by Shairp, in Aspects of Poetry; by Swinburne, in Studies in Prose and Poetry; by Carlyle, in Miscellaneous Essays; by Hazlitt, Bagehot, L. Stephen, Brooke, and Saintsbury (see Coleridge and Wordsworth, above).

Byron. Texts: Complete Works, Globe, Cambridge Poets, and Oxford editions; Selections, edited by M. Arnold, in Golden Treasury (see also Selections for Reading, above); Letters and Journals of Byron, edited by Moore (unreliable). Life: by Noel (Great Writers); by Nichol (English Men of Letters); The Real Lord Byron, by J. C. Jeaffreson; Trelawny's Recollections of Shelley and Byron. Criticism: Hunt's Lord Byron and His Contemporaries; Essays, by Morley, Macaulay, Hazlitt, Swinburne, and M. Arnold.

Shelley. Texts: Centenary Edition, edited by Woodberry, 4 vols.; Globe and Cambridge Poets editions; Essays and Letters, in Camelot Series (see Selections for Reading, above). Life: by Symonds (English Men of Letters); by Dowden, 2 vols.; by Sharp (Great Writers); by T. J. Hogg, 2 vols.; by W. M. Rossetti. Criticism: Salt's A Shelley Primer; Essays, by Dowden, in Transcripts and Studies; by M. Arnold, Woodberry, Bagehot, Forster, L.

Stephen, Brooke, De Quincey, and Hutton (see Coleridge and Wordsworth, above).

Keats. Texts: Complete Works, edited by Forman, 4 vols. (London, 1883); Cambridge Poets Edition, with Letters, edited by H. E. Scudder (Houghton, Mifflin); Aldine Edition, with Life, edited by Lord Houghton (Macmillan); Selected Poems, with introduction and notes by Arlo Bates (Ginn and Company); Poems, also in Everyman's Library, Muses' Library, Golden Treasury, etc.; Letters, edited by S. Colvin, in Eversley Edition. Life: by Forman, in Complete Works; by Colvin (English Men of Letters); by W. M. Rossetti (Great Writers); by A. E. Hancock. Criticism: H. C. Shelley's Keats and His Circle; Masson's Wordsworth, Shelley, Keats, and Other Essays; Essays, by M. Arnold, in Essays in Criticism, also in Ward's English Poets, vol. 4; by Hudson, in Studies in Interpretation; by Lowell, in Among My Books, or Literary Essays, vol. 2; by Brooke, De Quincey, and Swinburne (above).

Lamb. Texts: Complete Works and Letters, edited by E. V. Lucas, 7 vols. (Putnam); the same, edited by Ainger, 6 vols. (London, 1883-1888); Essays of Elia, in Standard English Classics, etc. (see Selections for Reading); Dramatic Essays, edited by B. Matthews (Dodd, Mead); Specimens of English Dramatic Poets, in Bohn's Library. Life: by E. V. Lucas, 2 vols.; by Ainger (English Men of Letters); by Barry Cornwall; Talfourd's Memoirs of Charles Lamb. Criticism: Essays, by De Quincey, in Biographical Essays; by F. Harrison, in Tennyson, Ruskin, Mill, and Other Literary Estimates; by Pater, and Woodberry (see Wordsworth and Coleridge, above). See also Fitzgerald's Charles Lamb, his Friends, his Haunts, and his Books.

De Quincey. Texts: Collected Writings, edited by Masson, 14 vols. (London, 1889-1891); Confessions of an Opium-Eater, etc. (see Selections for Reading). Life: by Masson (English Men of Letters); Life and Writings, by H. A. Page, 2 vols.; Hogg's De Quincey and his Friends; Findlay's Personal Recollections of De Quincey; see also De Quincey's Autobiographical Sketches, and Confessions. Criticism: Essays, by Saintsbury, in Essays in English Literature; by Masson, in Wordsworth, Shelley, Keats, and Other Essays; by L. Stephen, in Hours in a Library. See also Minto's Manual of English Prose Literature.

Landor. Texts: Works, with Life by Forster, 8 vols. (London, 1876); Works, edited by Crump (London, 1897); Letters, etc., edited by Wheeler (London, 1897 and 1899); Imaginary Conversations, etc. (see Selections for Reading). Life: by Colvin (English Men of Letters); by Forster. Criticism:

Essays, by De Quincey, Woodberry, L. Stephen, Saintsbury, Swinburne, Dowden (see above). See also Stedman's Victorian Poets.

Jane Austen. Texts: Works, edited by R. B. Johnson (Dent); various other editions of novels; Letters, edited by Woolsey (Roberts). Life: Austen-Leigh's Memoir of Jane Austen; Hill's Jane Austen, her Home and her Friends; Milton's Jane Austen and her Times. Life, by Goldwin Smith; by Maiden (Famous Women Series); by O. F. Adams. Criticism: Pollock's Jane Austen; Pellew's Jane Austen's Novels; A. A. Jack's Essay on the Novel as Illustrated by Scott and Miss Austen; H. H. Bonnell's Charlotte Brontë, George Eliot, and Jane Austen; Essay, by Howells, in Heroines of Fiction.

Maria Edgeworth. Texts: Tales and Novels, New Langford Edition, 10 vols. (London, 1893) various editions of novels (Dent, etc.); The Absentee, and Castle Rackrent, in Morley's Universal Library. Life: by Helen Zimmerman; Memoir, by Hare.

Mrs. Anne Radcliffe. Romances, with introduction by Scott, in Ballantynes' Novelists Library (London, 1824); various editions-of-Udolpho, etc.; Saintsbury's Tales of Mystery, vol. i. See Beers's English Romanticism.

Moore. Poetical Works, in Canterbury Poets, Chandos Classics, etc.; Selected poems, in Golden Treasury; Gunning's Thomas Moore, Poet and Patriot; Symington's Life and Works of Moore. Essay, by Saintsbury.

Campbell. Poems, Aldine edition; Selections, in Golden Treasury. Life, by Hadden.

Hazlitt. Texts: Works, edited by Henley, 12 vols. (London, 1902); Selected Essays, in Temple Classics, Camelot Series, etc. Life: by Birrell (English Men of Letters); Memoirs, by W. C. Hazlitt. Essays, by Saintsbury; by L. Stephen.

Leigh Hunt. Texts: Selected essays, in Camelot Series, also in Cavendish Library (Warne); Stories from the Italian Poets (Putnam). Life: by Monkhouse (Great Writers). Essays, by Macaulay; by Saintsbury; by Hazlitt. See also Mrs. Field's A Shelf of Old Books.

Suggestive Questions. (NOTE. In a period like the Age of Romanticism, the poems and essays chosen for special study vary so widely that only a few general questions on the selections for reading are attempted.)

1. Why is this period of Romanticism (1789-1837) called the Age of Revolution? Give some reasons for the influence of the French Revolution on English literature, and illustrate from poems or essays which you have read. Explain the difference between Classicism and Romanticism. Which of these two types of literature do you prefer?

2. What are the general characteristics of the literature of this period? What two opposing tendencies are illustrated in the novels of Scott and Jane Austen? in the poetry of Byron and Wordsworth?

3. *Wordsworth.* Tell briefly the story of Wordsworth's life, and name some of his best poems. Why do the Lyrical Ballads (1798) mark an important literary epoch? Read carefully, and make an analysis of the 'Intimations of Immortality'; of 'Tintern Abbey.' Can you explain what political conditions are referred to in Wordsworth's 'Sonnet on Milton'? in his 'French Revolution'? Does he attempt to paint a picture in his sonnet on Westminster Bridge, or has he some other object in view? What is the central teaching of the 'Ode to Duty'? Compare Wordsworth's two Skylark poems with Shelley's. Make a brief comparison between Wordsworth's *Sonnets* and those of Shakespeare and of Milton, having in mind the thought, the melody, the view of nature, and the imagery of the three poets. Quote from Wordsworth's poems to show his belief that nature is conscious; to show the influence of nature on man; to show his interest in children; his sensitiveness to sounds; to illustrate the chastening influence of sorrow. Make a brief comparison between the characters of Wordsworth's 'Michael' and of Burns's 'The Cotter's Saturday Night.' Compare Wordsworth's point of view and method, in the three poems 'To a Daisy', with Burns's view, as expressed in his famous lines on the same subject.

4. *Coleridge.* What are the general characteristics of Coleridge's life? What explains the profound sympathy for humanity that is reflected in his poems? For what, beside his poems, is he remarkable? Can you quote any passages from his poetry which show the influence of Wordsworth? What are the characters in 'The Ancient Mariner'? In what respect is this poem romantic? Give your own reasons for its popularity. Does the thought or the style of this poem impress you? If you have read any of the Lectures on *Shakespeare,* explain why Coleridge's work is called romantic criticism.

5. *Scott.* Tell the story of Scott's life, and name his chief poems and novels. Do you recall any passage from his poetry which suggests his own heroism? Why was he called 'the wizard of the North'? What is the general character of his poetry? Compare Marmion with one of the old ballads, having in mind the characters, the dramatic interest of the story, and the style of writing. In what sense is he the creator of the historical novel? Upon what does he depend to hold the reader's attention? Compare

him, in this respect, with Jane Austen. Which of his characters impress you as being the most lifelike? Name any novels of the present day which copy Scott or show his influence. Read Ivanhoe and the *Lady of the Lake;* make a brief analysis of each work, having in mind the style, the plot, the dramatic interest, the use of adventure, and the truth to nature of the different characters.

6. *Byron.* Why is Byron called the revolutionary poet? (Illustrate, if possible, from his poetry.) What is the general character of his work? In what kind of poetry does he excel? (Quote from Childe Harold to illustrate your opinion.) Describe the typical Byronic hero. Can you explain his great popularity at first, and his subsequent loss of influence? Why is he still popular on the Continent? Do you find more of thought or of emotion in his poetry? Compare him, in this respect, with Shelley; with Wordsworth. Which is the more brilliant writer, Byron or Wordsworth? Which has the more humour? Which has the healthier mind? Which has the higher ideal of poetry? Which is the more inspiring and helpful? Is it fair to say that Byron's quality is power, not charm?

7. *Shelley.* What are the chief characteristics of Shelley's poetry? Is it most remarkable for its thought, form, or imagery? What poems show the influence of the French Revolution? What subjects are considered in 'Lines written among the Euganean Hills'? What does Shelley try to teach in 'The Sensitive Plant'? Compare Shelley's view of nature, as reflected in 'The Cloud' or 'The West Wind', with Wordsworth's view, as reflected in 'The Prelude', 'Tintern Abbey', 'Daffodils', etc. To what class of poems does 'Adonais' belong? What is the subject of the poem? Name others of the same class. How does Shelley describe himself in this poem? Compare Shelley's 'Adonais' and Milton's 'Lycidas' with regard to the view of life after death as expressed in the poems. What kinds of scenes does Shelley like best to describe? Compare his characters with those of Wordsworth; of Byron. Do you recall any poem in which he writes of ordinary people or of ordinary experiences?

8. *Keats.* What is the essence of Keats's poetical creed, as expressed in the 'Ode on a Grecian Urn'? What are the remarkable elements in his life and work? What striking difference do you find between his early poems and those of Shelley and Byron? What are the chief subjects of his verse? What poems show the influence of the classics? of Elizabethan literature? Can you explain why his work has been called literary poetry? Keats and Shelley are generally classed together. What similarities do you find in their

poems? Give some reasons why Keats introduces the old Bedesman in 'The Eve of Saint Agnes.' Name some of the literary friends mentioned in Keats's poetry. Compare Keats's characters with those of Wordsworth; of Byron. Does Keats ever remind you of Spenser? In what respects? Is your personal preference for Wordsworth, Byron, Shelley, or Keats? Why?

9. *Lamb.* Tell briefly the story of Lamb's life and name his principal works. Why is he called the most human of essayists? His friends called him 'the last of the Elizabethans.' Why? What is the general character of the *Essays of Elia?* How is the personality of Lamb shown in all these essays? Cite any passage showing Lamb's skill in portraying people. Make a brief comparison between Lamb and Addison, having in mind the subjects treated, the style, the humour, and the interest of both essayists. Which do you prefer, and why?

10. *De Quincey.* What are the general characteristics of De Quincey's essays? Explain why he is called the psychologist of style. What accounts for a certain unreal element in all his work. Read a passage from *The English Mail-Coach,* or from *Joan of Arc,* or from *Levana, Our Lady of Sorrows,* and comment freely upon it, with regard to style, ideas, interest, and the impression of reality or unreality which it leaves.

11. *Landor.* In what respect does Landor show a reaction from Romanticism? What qualities make Landor's poems stand out so clearly in the memory? Why, for instance, do you think Lamb was so haunted by 'Rose Aylmer'? Quote from Landor's poems to illustrate his tenderness, his sensitiveness to beauty, his power of awakening emotion, his delicacy of characterization. Do you find the same qualities in his prose? Can you explain why much of his prose seems like a translation from the Greek? Compare a passage from the *Imaginary Conversations* with a passage from Gibbon or Johnson, to show the difference between the classic and the pseudo-classic style. Compare one of Landor's characters, in *Imaginary Conversations,* with the same character in history.

12. *Jane Austen.* How does Jane Austen show a reaction from Romanticism? What important work did she do for the novel? To what kind of fiction was her work opposed? In what does the charm of her novels consist? Make a brief comparison between Jane Austen and Scott (as illustrated in *Pride and Prejudice* and *Ivanhoe*), having in mind the subject, the characters, the manner of treatment, and the interest of both narratives. Do Jane Austen's characters have to be explained by the author, or do they explain themselves? Which method calls for the greater literary skill?

What does Jane Austen say about Mrs. Radcliffe, in *Northanger Abbey?* Does she make any other observations on eighteenth-century novelists?

CHRONOLOGY

End of the Eighteenth and Beginning of the Nineteenth Century

HISTORY	LITERATURE
1760-1820. George III	
	1770-1850. Wordsworth
	1771-1832. Scott
1789-1799. French Revolution	
	1796-1816. Jane Austen's novels
	1798. Lyrical Ballads of Wordsworth and Coleridge
1800. Union of Great Britain and Ireland	
1802. Colonization of Australia	1802. Scott's Minstrelsy of the Scottish Border
1805. Battle of Trafalgar	1805-1817. Scotts poems
	1807. Wordsworth's Intimations of Immortality. Lamb's Tales from Shakespeare
1807. Abolition of slave trade	
1808-1814. Peninsular War	
	1809-1818. Byron's Childe Harold
1812. Second war with United States	1810-1813. Coleridge's Lectures on Shakespeare
1814. Congress of Vienna	1814-1831. Waverley Novels
1815. Battle of Waterloo	
	1816. Shelley's Alastor
	1817. Coleridge's Biographia Literaria
	1817-1820. Keats's poems
	1818-1820. Shelley's Prometheus
1819. First Atlantic steamship	
1820. George IV (*d.* 1830)	1820. Wordsworth's Duddon Sonnets
	1820-1833. Lamb's Essays of Elia
	1821. De Quincey's Confessions

History	Literature
	1824-1846. Landor's Imaginary Conversations.
1826. First Temperance Society 1829. Catholic Emancipation Bill 1830. William IV (*d.* 1837) First railway	1830. Tennyson's first poems
	1831. Scott's last novel
1832. Reform Bill 1833. Emancipation of slaves	1833. Carlyle's Sartor Resartus Browning's Pauline
1834. System of national education 1837. Victoria (*d.* 1901)	
	1853-1861. De Quincey's Collected Essays

Chapter 11

THE VICTORIAN AGE (1850-1900)

THE MODERN PERIOD OF PROGRESS AND UNREST

When Victoria became queen, in 1837, English literature seemed to have entered upon a period of lean years, in marked contrast with the poetic fruitfulness of the romantic age which we have just studied. Coleridge, Shelley, Keats, Byron, and Scott had passed away, and it seemed as if there were no writers in England to fill their places. Wordsworth had written, in 1835,

> Like clouds that rake, the mountain summits,
> Or waves that own no curbing hand,
> How fast has brother followed brother,
> From sunshine to the sunless land!

In these lines is reflected the sorrowful spirit of a literary man of the early nineteenth century who remembered the glory that had passed away from the earth. But the leanness of these first years is more apparent than real. Keats and Shelley were dead, it is true, but already there had appeared three disciples of these poets who were destined to be far more widely, read than were their masters. Tennyson had been publishing poetry since 1827, his first poems appearing almost simultaneously with the last work of Byron, Shelley, and Keats; but it was not until 1842, with the publication of his collected poems, in two volumes, that England recognized in him one of her great literary leaders. So also Elizabeth Barrett had been writing since 1820, but not till twenty years later did her poems become deservedly popular; and Browning had published his *Pauline* in 1833, but it was not until 1846, when he published the last of the series called *Bells and Pomegranates,* that the reading public began to appreciate his power and originality. Moreover, even as romanticism seemed passing away, a group of great prose writers—Dickens, Thackeray, Carlyle, and Ruskin—had already begun to proclaim the literary glory of a new age, which now seems to rank only just below the Elizabethan and the Romantic periods.

Historical Summary. Amid the multitude of social and political forces of this great age, four things stand out clearly. First, the long struggle of the Anglo-Saxons for personal liberty is definitely settled, and democracy becomes the established order of the day. The king, who appeared in an age of popular weakness and ignorance, and the peers, who came with the Normans in triumph, are both stripped of their power and left as figureheads of a past civilization. The last vestige of personal government and of the divine right of rulers disappears; the House of Commons becomes the ruling power in England; and a series of new reform bills rapidly extend the suffrage, until the whole body of English people choose for themselves the men who shall represent them.

Democracy

Second, because it is an age of democracy, it is an age of popular education, of religious tolerance, of growing brotherhood, and of profound social unrest. The slaves had been freed in 1833; but in the middle of the century England awoke to the fact that slaves are not necessarily negroes, stolen in Africa to be sold like cattle in the marketplace, but that multitudes of men, women, and little children in the mines and factories were victims of a more terrible industrial and social slavery. To free these slaves also, the unwilling victims of our unnatural competitive methods, has been the growing purpose of the Victorian Age until the present day.

Social Unrest

Third, because it is an age of democracy and education, it is an age of comparative peace. England begins to think less of the pomp and false glitter of fighting, and more of its moral evils, as the nation realizes that it is the common people who

The Ideal of Peace

bear the burden and the sorrow and the poverty of war, while the privileged classes reap most of the financial and political rewards. Moreover, with the growth of trade and of friendly foreign relations, it becomes evident that **the social equality for which England was contending** at home belongs to the whole race of men; that brotherhood is universal, not insular; that a question of justice is never settled by fighting; and that war is generally unmitigated horror and barbarism. Tennyson, who came of age when the great Reform Bill occupied attention, expresses the ideals of the Liberals of his day who proposed to spread the gospel of peace,

> Till the war-drum throbb'd no longer, and the battle-flags were
> furled In the Parliament of Man, the Federation of the world.

Arts and Sciences

Fourth, the Victorian Age is especially remarkable because of its rapid progress in all the arts and sciences and in mechanical inventions. A glance at any record of the industrial achievements of the nineteenth century will show how vast they are, and it is unnecessary to repeat here the list of the inventions, from spinning looms to steamboats, and from matches to electric lights. All these material things, as well as the growth of education, have their influence upon the life of a people, and it is inevitable that they should react upon its prose and poetry; though as yet we are too much absorbed in our sciences and mechanics to determine accurately their influence upon literature. When these new things shall by long use have became familiar as country roads, or have been replaced by newer and better things, then they also will have their associations and memories, and a poem on the railroads may be as suggestive as Wordsworth's sonnet on Westminster Bridge; and the busy, practical working men who today throng our streets and factories may seem, to a future and greater age, as quaint and poetical as to us seem the slow toilers of the Middle Ages.

Literary Characteristics. When one is interested enough to trace the genealogy of Victoria he finds, to his surprise, that in her veins flowed the blood both of William the Conqueror and of Cerdic, the first Saxon king of England; and this seems to be symbolic of the literature of her age, which embraces

An Age of Prose

the whole realm of Saxon and Norman life—the strength and ideals of the one, and the culture and refinement of the other. The romantic revival had done its work, and England entered upon a new free period, in which every form of literature, from pure romance to gross realism, struggled for expression. At this day it is obviously impossible to judge the age as a whole; but we are getting far enough away from the early half of it to notice certain definite characteristics. First, though the age produced many poets, and two who deserve to rank among the greatest, nevertheless this is emphatically an age of prose. And since the number of readers has increased a thousandfold with the spread of popular education, it is the age of the newspaper, the magazine, and the modern novel—the first two being the story of the world's daily life, and the last our pleasantest form of literary entertainment, as well as our most successful method of presenting modern problems and modern ideals. The novel in this age fills a place which the drama held in the days of Elizabeth; and never before, in any age or language, has the novel appeared in such numbers and in such perfection.

Moral Purpose

The second marked characteristic of the age is that literature, both in prose and in poetry, seems to depart from the purely artistic standard, of art for art's sake, and to be actuated by a definite moral purpose. Tennyson, Browning, Carlyle, Ruskin—who and what were these men if not the teachers of England, not vaguely but definitely, with superb faith in their message, and with the conscious moral purpose to uplift and to instruct? Even the novel breaks away from Scott's romantic influence, and first studies life as it is, and then points out what life may and ought to be. Whether we read the fun and sentiment of Dickens, the social miniatures of Thackeray, or the psychological studies of George Eliot, we find in almost every case a definite purpose to sweep away error and to reveal the underlying truth of human life. So the novel sought to do for society in this age precisely what Lyell and Darwin sought to do for science, that is, to find the truth, and to show how it might be used to uplift humanity. Perhaps for this reason the Victorian Age is emphatically an age of realism rather than of romance—not the realism of Zola and Ibsen, but a deeper realism which strives to tell the whole truth, showing moral and physical diseases as they are, but holding up health and hope as the normal conditions of humanity.

Idealism

It is somewhat customary to speak of this age as an age of doubt and pessimism, following the new conception of man and of the universe which was formulated by science under the name of Evolution. It is spoken of also as a prosaic age, lacking in great ideals. Both these criticisms seem to be the result of judging a large thing when we are too close to it to get its true proportions, just as Cologne Cathedral, one of the world's most perfect structures, seems to be a shapeless pile of stone when we stand too close beneath its mighty walls and buttresses. Tennyson's immature work, like that of the minor poets, is sometimes in a doubtful or despairing strain; but his *In Memoriam* is like the rainbow after storm; and Browning seems better to express the spirit of his age in the strong, manly faith of 'Rabbi Ben Ezra', and in the courageous optimism of all his poetry. Stedman's *Victorian Anthology* is, on the whole, a most inspiring book of poetry. It would be hard to collect more varied cheer from any age. And the great essayists, like Macaulay, Carlyle, Ruskin, and the great novelists, like Dickens, Thackeray, George Eliot, generally leave us with a larger charity and with a deeper faith in our humanity.

So also the judgment that this age is too practical for great ideals may be only a description of the husk that hides a very full ear of corn. It is well to remember that Spenser and Sidney judged their own age (which we now consider to be the greatest in our literary history) to be altogether given over to materialism, and to be incapable of literary greatness. Just as time has made us smile at their blindness, so the next century may correct our judgment of this as a material age, and looking upon the enormous growth of charity and brotherhood among us, and at the literature which expresses our faith in men, may judge the

Victorian Age to be, on the whole, the noblest and most inspiring in the history of the world.

THE POETS OF THE VICTORIAN AGE

ALFRED TENNYSON (1809-1892)

O young Mariner,
You from the haven
Under the sea-cliff,
You that are watching
The gray Magician
With eyes of wonder,
I am Merlin,
And *I* am dying,
I am Merlin
Who follow The Gleam.

....

O young Mariner,
Down to the haven
Call your companions,
Launch your vessel,
And crowd your canvas,
And, ere it vanishes
Over the margin,
After it, follow it,
Follow The Gleam.

One who reads this haunting poem of 'Merlin and The Gleam' finds in it a suggestion of the spirit of the poet's whole life—his devotion to the ideal as expressed in poetry, his early romantic impressions, his struggles, doubts, triumphs, and his thrilling message to his race. Throughout the entire Victorian period Tennyson stood at the summit of poetry in England. Not in vain was he appointed laureate at the death of Wordsworth, in 1850; for, almost alone among those who have held the office, he felt the importance of his place, and filled and honoured it. For nearly half a century Tennyson was not only a man and a poet; he was a voice, the voice of a whole people, expressing in exquisite melody their doubts and their faith, their griefs and their triumphs. In the wonderful variety of his verse he suggests all the qualities of England's greatest poets. The dreaminess of Spenser, the majesty of Milton, the natural simplicity of Wordsworth, the fantasy of Blake and Coleridge, the melody of Keats and Shelley, the narrative vigour of Scott and Byron—all these striking qualities are evident on successive pages of Tennyson's poetry. The only thing lacking is the dramatic power of the Elizabethans. In reflecting the restless spirit of this progressive age Tennyson is as remarkable as Pope was in voicing the artificiality of the early eighteenth century. As a poet, therefore, who expresses not so much a personal as a national spirit, he is probably the most representative literary man of the Victorian era.

Life. Tennyson's life is a remarkable one in this respect, that from beginning to end he seems to have been dominated by a single impulse, the impulse of poetry. He had no large or remarkable experiences, no wild oats to sow, no great successes or reverses, no business cares or public offices. For sixty-six years, from the appearance of the *Poems by Two Brothers,* in 1827, until his death in 1892, he studied and practised his art continually and exclusively. Only Browning, his fellow-worker, resembles him in this; but the differences in the two men are worldwide. Tennyson was naturally shy, retiring, indifferent to men, hating noise and publicity, loving to be alone with nature, like Wordsworth. Browning was sociable, delighting in applause, in society, in travel, in the noise and bustle of the big world.

Tennyson was born in the rectory of Somersby, Lincolnshire, in 1809. The sweet influences of his early natural surroundings can be better understood from his early poems than from any biography. He was one of the twelve children of the Rev. George Clayton Tennyson, a scholarly clergyman, and his wife Elizabeth Fytche, a gentle, lovable woman, 'not learned, save in gracious household ways', to whom the poet pays a son's loyal tribute near the close of The Princess. It is interesting to note that most of these children were poetically inclined, and that two of the brothers, Charles and Frederick, gave far greater promise than did Alfred.

When seven years old the boy went to his grandmother's house at Louth, in order to attend a famous grammar school at that place. Not even a man's memory, which generally makes light of hardship and glorifies early experiences, could ever soften Tennyson's hatred of school life. His complaint was not so much at the roughness of the boys, which had so frightened Cowper, as at the brutality of the teachers, who put over the school door a wretched Latin inscription translating Solomon's barbarous advice about the rod and the child. In these psychologic days, when the child is more important than the curriculum, and when we teach girls and boys rather than Latin and arithmetic, we read with wonder Carlyle's description of his own schoolmaster, evidently a type of his kind, who 'knew of the human soul thus much, that it had a faculty called memory, and could be acted on through the muscular integument by appliance of birch rods.' After four years of most unsatisfactory school life, Tennyson returned home, and was fitted for the university by his scholarly father. With his brothers he wrote many verses, and his first efforts appeared in a little volume called *Poems by Two Brothers,* in 1827. The next year he entered Trinity College, Cambridge, where he became the centre of a brilliant circle of friends, chief of whom was the young poet Arthur Henry Hallam.

At the university Tennyson soon became known for his poetical ability, and two years after his entrance he gained the prize of the Chancellor's Medal for a poem called 'Timbuctoo', the subject, needless to say, being chosen by the chancellor. Soon after winning this honour Tennyson published his first signed work, called *Poems Chiefly Lyrical* (1830), which, though it seems somewhat crude and disappointing to us now, nevertheless contained the germ of all his later poetry. One of the most noticeable things in this volume is the influence which Byron evidently exerted over the poet in his early days; and it was perhaps due largely to the same romantic influence that Tennyson and his friend Hallam presently sailed away to Spain, with the idea of joining the army of insurgents against King Ferdinand. Considered purely as a revolutionary venture, this was something of a fiasco, suggesting the noble Duke of York and his ten thousand men—'he marched them up a hill, one day; and he marched them down again.' From a literary viewpoint, however, the experience was not without its value. The deep impression which the wild beauty of the Pyrenees made upon the young poet's mind is reflected clearly in the poem 'Œnone.'

Alfred Tennyson

After the Portrait by George Frederic Watts

In 1831 Tennyson left the university without taking his degree. The reasons for this step are not clear; but the family was poor, and poverty may have played a large part in his determination. His father died a few months later; but, by a generous arrangement with the new rector, the family retained the rectory at Somersby, and here, for nearly six years, Tennyson lived in a retirement which strongly suggests Milton at Horton. He read and studied widely, cultivated an intimate acquaintance with nature, thought deeply on the problems suggested by the Reform Bill which was then agitating England, and during his leisure hours wrote poetry. The first fruits of this retirement appeared, late in 1832, in a wonderful little volume bearing the simple name Poems. As the work of a youth only twenty-three, this book is remarkable for the variety and melody of its verse. Among its treasures we still read with delight 'The Lotos Eaters', 'Palace of Art', 'A Dream of Fair Women', 'The Miller's Daughter', 'Œnone', and 'The Lady of Shalott'; but the critics of the Quarterly, who had brutally condemned his earlier work, were again unmercifully severe. The effect of this harsh criticism upon a sensitive nature was most unfortunate; and when his friend Hallam died, in 1833, Tennyson was plunged into a period of gloom and sorrow. The sorrow may be read in the exquisite little poem beginning, 'Break, break, break, On thy cold gray stones, O Sea!' which was his first published elegy for his friend; and the depressing influence of the harsh and unjust criticism is suggested in 'Merlin and The Gleam', which the reader will understand only after he has read Tennyson's biography.

For nearly ten years after Hallam's death Tennyson published nothing, and his movements are hard to trace as the family went here and there, seeking peace and a home in various parts of England. But though silent, he continued to write poetry, and it was in these sad wandering days that he began his immortal *In Memoriam* and his *Idylls of the King.* In 1842 his friends persuaded him to give his work to the world, and with some hesitation he published his Poems. The success of this work was almost instantaneous, and we can appreciate the favour with which it was received when we read the noble blank verse of 'Ulysses' and 'Morte d'Arthur', the perfect little song of grief for Hallam which we have already mentioned, and the exquisite idylls like 'Dora' and 'The Gardener's Daughter', which aroused even Wordsworth's enthusiasm and brought from him a letter saying that he had been trying all his life to write such an

English pastoral as 'Dora' and had failed. From this time forward Tennyson, with increasing confidence in himself and his message, steadily maintained his place as the best known and best loved poet in England.

The year 1850 was a happy one for Tennyson. He was appointed poet laureate, to succeed Wordsworth; and he married Emily Sellwood,

> Her whose gentle will has changed my fate
> And made my life a perfumed altar flame,

whom he had loved for thirteen years, but whom his poverty had prevented him from marrying. The year is made further remarkable by the publication of *In Memoriam,* probably the most enduring of his poems, upon which he had worked at intervals for sixteen years. Three years later, with the money that his work now brought him, he leased the house Farringford, in the Isle of Wight, and settled in the first permanent home he had known since he left the rectory at Somersby.

For the remaining forty years of his life he lived, like Wordsworth, 'in the stillness of a great peace', writing steadily, and enjoying the friendship of a large number of people, some distinguished, some obscure, from the kindly and sympathetic Victoria to the servants on his own farm. All of these he called with equal sincerity his friends, and to each one he was the same man, simple, strong, kindly, and noble. Carlyle describes him as 'a fine, large-featured, dim-eyed, bronze-coloured, shaggy-headed man,—most restful, brotherly, solid-hearted.' Loving solitude and hating publicity as he did, the numerous tourists from both sides of the ocean, who sought him out in his retreat and insisted upon seeing him, made his life at times intolerable. Influenced partly by the desire to escape such popularity, he bought land and built for himself a new house, Aldworth, in Surrey, though he made his home in Farringford for the greater part of the year.

His labour during these years and his marvellous freshness and youthfulness of feeling are best understood by a glance at the contents of his complete works. Inferior poems, like *The Princess,* which was written in the first flush of his success, and his dramas, which were written against the advice of his best friends, may easily be criticised; but the bulk of his verse shows an astonishing originality and vigour to the very end. He died very quietly at Aldworth, with his family about him in the moonlight, and beside him a volume of Shakespeare, open at the dirge in *Cymbeline:*

Fear no more the heat o' the sun,
    Nor the furious winter's rages;
Thou thy worldly task hast done,
    Home art gone, and ta'en thy wages.

The strong and noble spirit of his life is reflected in one of his best known poems, 'Crossing the Bar', which was written in his eighty-first year, and which he desired should be placed at the end of his collected works:

Sunset and evening star,
    And one clear call for me!
And may there be no moaning of the bar,
    When I put out to sea,

But such a tide as, moving, seems asleep,
    Too full for sound and foam,
When that which drew from out the boundless deep
    Turns again home.

Twilight and evening bell,
    And after that the dark!
And may there be no sadness of farewell,
    When I embark;

For tho' from out our bourne of Time and Place
    The flood may bear me far,
I hope to see my Pilot face to face
    When I have crost the bar.

Works. At the outset of our study of Tennyson's works it may be well to record two things, by way of suggestion. First, Tennyson's poetry is not so much to be studied as to be read and appreciated; he is a poet to have open on one's table, and to enjoy as one enjoys his daily exercise. And second, we should by all means begin to get acquainted with Tennyson in the days of our youth. Unlike Browning, who is generally appreciated by more mature minds, Tennyson is for enjoyment, for inspiration, rather than for instruction. Only youth can fully appreciate him; and youth, unfortunately, except in a few rare, beautiful cases, is something which does not dwell with us long after our school days. The secret of poetry, especially of Tennyson's poetry, is to be eternally young, and, like Adam in Paradise, to find every morning a new world, fresh, wonderful, inspiring, as if just from the hands of God.

Early Poems and Dramas

Except by the student, eager to understand the whole range of poetry in this age, Tennyson's earlier poems and his later dramas may well be omitted. Opinions vary about both; but the general judgment seems to be that the earlier poems show too much of Byron's influence, and their crudeness suffers by comparison with the exquisitely finished work of Tennyson's middle life. Of dramatic works he wrote seven, his great ambition being to present a large part of the history of England in a series of dramas. Becket was one of the best of these works and met with considerable favour on the stage; but, like all the others, it indicates that Tennyson lacked the dramatic power and the humour necessary for a successful playwright.

The Princess and Maud

Among the remaining poems there is such a wide variety that every reader must be left largely to follow his own delightful choice.[1] Of the Poems of 1842 we have already mentioned those best worth reading. *The Princess, a Medley* (1847), a long poem of over three thousand lines of blank verse, is Tennyson's answer to the question of woman's rights and woman's sphere, which was then, as in our own day, strongly agitating the public mind. In this poem a baby finally solves the problem which philosophers have pondered ever since men began to think connectedly about human society. A few exquisite songs, like 'Tears, Idle Tears', 'Bugle Song', and 'Sweet and Low', form the most delightful part of this poem, which in general is hardly up to the standard of the poet's later work. *Maud* (1855) is what is

[1] An excellent little volume for the beginner is Van Dyke's 'Poems by Tennyson', which shows the entire range of the poet's work from his earliest to his latest years (See Selections for Reading, at the end of this chapter.)

called in literature a monodrama, telling the story of a lover who passes from morbidness to ecstasy, then to anger and murder, followed by insanity and recovery. This was Tennyson's favourite, and among his friends he read aloud from it more than from any other poem. Perhaps if we could hear Tennyson read it, we should appreciate it better; but, on the whole, it seems overwrought and melodramatic. Even its lyrics, like 'Come into the Garden, Maud', which make this work a favourite with young lovers, are characterized by 'prettiness' rather than by beauty or strength.

In Memoriam

Perhaps the most loved of all Tennyson's works is *In Memoriam*, which, on account of both its theme and its exquisite workmanship is 'one of the few immortal names that were not born to die.' The immediate occasion of this remarkable poem was Tennyson's profound personal grief at the death of his friend Hallam. As he wrote lyric after lyric, inspired by this sad subject, the poet's grief became less personal, and the greater grief of humanity mourning for its dead and questioning its immortality took possession of him. Gradually the poem became an expression, first, of universal doubt, and then of universal faith—a faith which rests ultimately not on reason or philosophy but on the soul's instinct for immortality. The immortality of human love is the theme of the poem, which is made up of over one hundred different lyrics. The movement takes us through three years, rising slowly from poignant sorrow and doubt to a calm peace and hope, and ending with a noble hymn of courage and faith—a modest courage and a humble faith, love-inspired—which will be a favourite as long as saddened men turn to literature for consolation. Though Darwin's greatest books had not yet been written, science had already overturned many old conceptions of life; and Tennyson, who lived apart and thought deeply on all the problems of his day, gave this poem to the world as his own answer to the doubts and questionings of men. This universal human interest, together with its exquisite form and melody, makes the poem, in popular favour at least, the supreme threnody, or elegiac poem, of our literature; though Milton' *Lycidas* is, from the critical viewpoint, undoubtedly a more artistic work.

Sir Galahad

After the Painting by George Frederic Watts

Idylls of the King

The Idylls of the King ranks among the greatest of Tennyson's later works. Its general subject is the Celtic legends of King Arthur and his knights of the Round Table, and the chief source of its material is Malory's *Morte d'Arthur.* Here, in this mass of beautiful legends, is certainly the subject of a great national epic; yet after four hundred years, during which many poets have used the material, the great epic is still unwritten. Milton and Spenser, as we have already noted, considered this material carefully; and Milton alone, of all English writers, had perhaps the power to use it in a great epic. Tennyson began to use these legends in his *Morte d'Arthur* (1842); but the epic idea probably occurred to him later, in 1856, when he began 'Geraint and Enid', and he added the stories of 'Vivien', 'Elaine', 'Guinevere', and other heroes and heroines at intervals, until 'Balin', the last of the *Idylls,* appeared in 1885. Later these works were gathered together and arranged with an attempt at unity. The result is in no sense an epic poem, but rather a series of single poems loosely connected by a thread of interest in Arthur, the central personage, and in his unsuccessful attempt to found an ideal kingdom.

English Idyls

Entirely different in spirit is another collection of poems called *English Idyls,*[1] which began in the Poems of 1842, and which Tennyson intended should reflect the ideals of widely different types of English life. Of these varied poems, 'Dora', 'The Gardener's Daughter', 'Ulysses', 'Locksley Hall' and 'Sir Galahad' are the best; but all are worthy of study. One of the most famous of this series is 'Enoch Arden' (1864), in which Tennyson turns from mediæval knights, from lords, heroes, and fair ladies, to find the material for true poetry among the lowly people that make up the bulk of English life. Its rare melody, its sympathy for common life, and its revelation of the beauty and heroism which hide in humble men and women everywhere, made

[1] Tennyson made a distinction in spelling between the *Idylls of the King,* and the *English Idyls,* like 'Dora'.

this work an instant favourite. Judged by its sales alone, it was the most popular of his works during the poet's lifetime.

Tennyson's later volumes, like the *Ballads* (1880) and *Demeter* (1889), should not be overlooked, since they contain some of his best work. The former contains stirring war songs, like 'The Defence of Lucknow', and pictures of wild passionate grief, like 'Rizpah'; the latter is notable for 'Romney's Remorse', a wonderful piece of work; 'Merlin and The Gleam', which expresses the poet's lifelong ideal; and several exquisite little songs, like 'The Throstle', and 'The Oak', which show how marvellously the aged poet retained his youthful freshness and inspiration. Here certainly is variety enough to give us long years of literary enjoyment; and we need hardly mention miscellaneous poems, like 'The Brook' and 'The Charge of the Light Brigade', which are known to every schoolboy; and 'Wages' and 'The Higher Pantheism', which should be read by every man who thinks about the old, old problem of life and death.

Characteristics of Tennyson's Poetry. If we attempt to sum up the quality of Tennyson, as shown in all these works, the task is a difficult one; but three things stand out more or less plainly. First, Tennyson is essentially the artist. No other in his age studied the art of poetry so constantly or with such singleness of purpose; and only Swinburne rivals him in melody and the perfect finish of his verse. Second, like all the great writers of his age, he is emphatically a teacher, often a leader. In the preceding age, as the result of the turmoil produced by the French Revolution, lawlessness was more or less common, and individuality was the rule in literature. Tennyson's theme, so characteristic of his age, is the reign of order—of law in the physical world, producing evolution, and of law in the spiritual world, working out the perfect man. *In Memoriam, Idylls of the King, The Princess*—here are three widely different poems; yet the theme of each, so far as poetry is a kind of spiritual philosophy and weighs its words before it utters them, is the orderly development of law in the natural and in the spiritual world.

This certainly is a new doctrine in poetry, but the message does not end here. Law implies a source, a method, and object.

Tennyson, after facing his doubts honestly and manfully, finds law even in the sorrows and losses of humanity. He gives this law an infinite and personal source, and finds the supreme purpose of all law to be a revelation of divine love. All earthly love, therefore, becomes an image of the heavenly. What first perhaps attracted readers to Tennyson, as to Shakespeare, was the character of his women—pure, gentle, refined beings, whom we must revere as our Anglo-Saxon forefathers revered the women they loved. Like Browning, the poet had loved one good woman supremely, and her love made clear the meaning of all life. The message goes one step farther. Because law and love are in the world, faith is the only reasonable attitude toward life and death, even though we understand them not. Such, in a few words, seems to be Tennyson's whole message and philosophy.

Tennyson's Message

If we attempt now to fix Tennyson's permanent place in literature, as the result of his life and work, we must apply to him the same test that we applied to Milton and Wordsworth, and, indeed, to all our great poets, and ask with the German critics, 'What new thing has he said to the world or even to his own country?' The answer is, frankly, that we do not yet know surely; that we are still too near Tennyson to judge him impersonally. This much, however, is clear. In a marvellously complex age, and amid a hundred great men, he was regarded as a leader. For a full half century he was the voice of England, loved and honoured as a man and a poet, not simply by a few discerning critics, but by a whole people that do not easily give their allegiance to any one man. And that, for the present, is Tennyson's sufficient eulogy.

Robert Browning (1812-1889)

How good is man's life, the mere living! how fit to employ
All the heart and the soul and the senses for ever in joy!

In this new song of David, from Browning's *Saul*, we have a suggestion of the astonishing vigour and hope that characterize all the works of Browning, the one poet of the age who, after thirty years of continuous work, was finally recognized and placed beside Tennyson, and whom future ages may judge to be a greater poet—perhaps, even, the greatest in our literature since Shakespeare.

The chief difficulty in reading Browning is the obscurity of his style, which the critics of half a century ago held up to ridicule. Their attitude towards the poet's early work may be inferred from Tennyson's humorous criticism of Sordello. It may be remembered that the first line of this obscure poem is, 'Who will may hear Sordello's story told'; and that the last line is, 'Who would has heard Sordello's story told.' Tennyson remarked that these were the only lines in the whole poem that he understood, and that they were evidently both lies. If we attempt to explain this obscurity, which puzzled Tennyson and many less friendly critics, we find that it has many sources. First, the poet's thought is often obscure, or else so extremely subtle that language expresses it imperfectly—

Thoughts hardly to be packed
Into a narrow act,
Fancies that broke through language and escaped.

Browning's Obscurity

Second, Browning is led from one thing to another by his own mental associations, and forgets that the reader's associations may be of an entirely different kind. Third, Browning is careless in his English, and frequently clips his speech, giving us a series of ejaculations. As we do not quite understand his processes of thought, we must stop between the ejaculations to trace out the connections. Fourth, Browning's allusions are often far-fetched, referring to some odd scrap of information which he has picked up in his wide reading, and the ordinary reader finds it difficult to trace and understand them. Finally, Browning wrote too much and revised too little. The time which he should have given to making one thought clear was used in expressing other thoughts that flitted through his head like a flock of swallows. His field was the individual soul, never exactly alike in any two men, and he sought to express the hidden motives and principles which govern individual action. In this field he is like a miner delving underground, sending up masses of mingled earth and ore; and the reader must sift all this material to separate the gold from the dross.

Here, certainly, are sufficient reasons for Browning's obscurity; and we must add the word that the fault seems unpardonable, for the simple reason that Browning shows himself capable, at times, of writing directly, melodiously, and with noble simplicity.

Robert Browning

So much for the faults, which must be faced and overlooked before one finds the treasure that is hidden in Browning's poetry. Of all the poets in our literature, no other is so completely, so consciously, so magnificently a teacher of men. He feels his mission of faith and courage in a world of doubt and timidity. For thirty years he faced indifference or ridicule, working bravely and cheerfully the while, until he made the world recognize and follow him. The spirit of his whole life is well expressed in his *Paracelsus,* written when he was only twenty-two years old:

Browning as a teacher

I see my way as birds their trackless way.
I shall arrive—what time, what circuit first,
I ask not; but unless God send his hail
Or blinding fireballs, sleet or stifling snow,
In some time, his good time, I shall arrive;
He guides me and the bird. In his good time.

He is not, like so many others, an entertaining poet. One cannot read him after dinner, or when settled in a comfortable easy-chair. One must sit up, and think, and be alert when he reads Browning. If we accept these conditions, we shall probably find that Browning is the most stimulating poet in our language. His influence upon our life is positive and tremendous. His strength, his joy of life, his robust faith, and his invincible optimism enter into us, making us different and better men after reading him. And perhaps the best thing he can say of Browning is that his thought is slowly but surely taking possession of all well-educated men and women.

Life. Browning's father was outwardly a business man, a clerk for fifty years in the Bank of England; inwardly he was an interesting combination of the scholar and the artist, with the best tastes of both. His mother was a sensitive, musical woman, evidently very lovely in character, the daughter of a German shipowner and merchant who had settled in Scotland. She was of Celtic descent, and Carlyle describes her as the true type of a Scottish gentlewoman. From his neck down, Browning was the typical Briton—short, stocky, large-chested, robust; but even in the lifeless portrait his face changes as we view it from different angles. Now it is like an English businessman, now like a German scientist, and now it has a curious suggestion of Uncle Remus—these being, no doubt, so many different reflections of his mixed and unremembered ancestors.

He was born in Camberwell, on the outskirts of London, in 1812. From his home and from his first school, at Peckham, he could see London; and the city lights by night and the smoky chimneys by day had the same powerful fascination for the child that the woods and fields and the beautiful country had for his friend Tennyson. His schooling was short and desultory, his education being attended to by private tutors and by his father, who left the boy largely to follow his own inclination. Like the young Milton, Browning was fond of music, and in many of his poems, especially in 'Abt Vogler' and 'A Toccata of Galuppi's', he interprets the musical temperament better, perhaps, than any other writer in our literature. But unlike Milton, through whose poetry there runs a great melody, music seems to have had no consistent effect upon his verse, which is often so jarring that one must wonder how a musical ear could have endured it.

Like Tennyson, this boy found his work very early, and for fifty years hardly a week passed that he did not write poetry. He began at six to produce verses, in imitation of Byron; but fortunately this early work has been lost. Then he fell under the influence of Shelley, and his first known work, *Pauline* (1833), must be considered as a tribute to Shelley and his poetry. Tennyson's earliest work, *Poems by Two Brothers,* had been published and well paid for, five years before; but Browning could find no publisher who would even consider Pauline, and the work was published by means of money furnished by an indulgent relative. This poem received scant notice from the reviewers, who had pounced like hawks on a dovecote upon Tennyson's first two modest volumes. Two years later appeared *Paracelsus,* and then his tragedy *Strafford* was put upon the stage; but not till *Sordello* was published, in 1840, did he attract attention enough to be denounced for the obscurity and vagaries of his style. Six years later, in 1846, he suddenly became famous, not because he finished in that year his *Bells and Pomegranates* (which is Browning's symbolic name for 'poetry and thought' or 'singing and sermonizing'), but because he eloped with the best known literary woman in England, Elizabeth Barrett, whose fame was for many years, both before and after her marriage, much greater than Browning's, and who was at first considered superior to Tennyson. Thereafter, until his own work compelled attention, he was known chiefly as the man who married Elizabeth Barrett. For years this lady had been an almost helpless invalid, and it seemed a quixotic thing when Browning, having failed to gain her family's consent to the marriage, carried her off romantically. Love and Italy proved better than her physicians, and for fifteen years Browning and his wife lived an ideally happy life in Pisa and in Florence. The exquisite romance of their love is preserved in Mrs. Browning' *Sonnets from the Portuguese,* and in the volume of Letters recently published—wonderful letters, but so tender and intimate that it seems almost a sacrilege for inquisitive eyes to read them.

Mrs. Browning died in Florence in 1861. The loss seemed at first too much to bear, and Browning fled with his son to England. For the remainder of his life he lived alternately in London and in various parts of Italy, especially at the Palazzo Rezzonico, in Venice, which is now an object of pilgrimage to almost every tourist who visits the beautiful city. Wherever he went he mingled with men and women, sociable, well dressed, courteous, loving crowds and popular applause, the very reverse of his friend Tennyson. His earlier work had been much better appreciated in America than in England; but with the publication of *The Ring and the Book,* in 1868, he was at last recognized by his countrymen as one of the greatest of English poets. He died in Venice, on December 12, 1889, the same day that saw the publication of his last work, *Asolando.* Though Italy offered him an honoured resting place, England claimed him for her own, and he lies buried beside Tennyson in Westminster Abbey. The spirit of his whole life is magnificently expressed in his own lines, in the Epilogue of his last book:

> One who never turned his back, but marched breast forward,
> Never doubted clouds would break,
> Never dreamed, tho' right were worsted, wrong would triumph,
> Held we fall to rise, are baffled to fight better,
> Sleep to wake.

Works. A glance at even the titles which Browning gave to his best known volumes–*Dramatic Lyrics* (1842), *Dramatic Romances and Lyrics* (1845), *Men and Women* (1855), *Dramatis Personæ* (1864)—will suggest how strong the dramatic element is in all his work. Indeed, all his poems may be divided into three classes—pure dramas, like *Strafford* and *A Blot in the 'Scutcheon;* dramatic narratives, like *Pippa Passes,* which are dramatic in form, but were not meant to be acted; and dramatic lyrics, like *The Last Ride Together,* which are short poems expressing some strong personal emotion, or describing some dramatic episode in human life, and in which the hero himself generally tells the story.

Browning and Shakespeare

Though Browning is often compared with Shakespeare, the reader will understand that he has very little of Shakespeare's dramatic talent. He cannot bring a group of people together and let the actions and words of his characters show us the comedy and tragedy of human life. Neither can the author be disinterested, satisfied, as Shakespeare was, with life itself, without drawing any moral conclusions. Browning has always a moral ready, and insists upon giving us his own views of life, which Shakespeare never does. His dramatic power lies in depicting what he himself calls the history of a soul. Sometimes, as in *Paracelsus,* he endeavours to trace the progress of the human spirit. More often he takes some dramatic moment in life, some crisis in the ceaseless struggle between good and evil, and describes with wonderful insight the hero's own thoughts and feelings; but he almost invariably tells us how, at such and such a point, the good or the evil in his hero must inevitably have triumphed. And generally, as in 'My Last Duchess', the speaker adds a word here and there, aside from the story, which unconsciously shows the kind of man he is. It is this power of revealing the soul from within that causes Browning to fascinate those who study him long enough. His range is enormous, and brings all sorts and conditions of men under analysis. The musician in 'Abt Vogler', the artist in 'Andrea del Sarto', the early Christian in 'A Death in the Desert', the Arab horseman in 'Mutéykeh', the sailor in 'Hervé Riel', the mediæval knight in 'Childe Roland', the Hebrew in 'Saul', the Greek in 'Balaustion's Adventure', the monster in 'Caliban', the immortal dead in 'Karshish'—all these and a hundred more histories of the soul show Browning's marvellous versatility. It is this great range of sympathy with many different types of life that constitutes Browning's chief likeness to Shakespeare, though otherwise there is no comparison between the two men.

First Period of Work

If we separate all these dramatic poems into three main periods—the early, from 1833 to 1841; the middle, from 1841 to 1868; and the late, from 1868 to 1889—the work of the beginner will be much more easily designated. Of his early soul studies, *Pauline* (1833), *Paracelsus* (1835), and *Sordello* (1840), little need be said here, except perhaps this: that if we begin with these works, we shall probably never read anything else by Browning. And that were a pity. It is better to leave these obscure works until his better poems have so attracted us to Browning that we will cheerfully endure his worst faults for the sake of his undoubted virtues. The same criticism applies, though in less degree, to his first drama, *Strafford* (1837), which belongs to the early period of his work.

The merciless criticism which greeted *Sordello* had a wholesome effect on Browning, as is shown in the better work of his second period. Moreover, his new power was developing rapidly, as may be seen by comparing the eight numbers of his famous *Bells and Pomegranates* series (1841-1846) with his earlier work. Thus, the first number of this wonderful series, published in 1841, contains *Pippa Passes,* which is, on the whole, the most perfect of his longer poems; and another number contains *A Blot in the 'Scutcheon,* which is the most readable of his dramas. Even a beginner must be thrilled by the beauty and the power of these two works. Two other noteworthy dramas of the period are *Colombe's Birthday* (1844) and *In a Balcony* (1855), which, however, met with scant appreciation on the stage, having too much subtle analysis and too little action to satisfy the public. Nearly all his best lyrics, dramas, and dramatic poems belong to this middle period of labour; and when *The Ring and the Book* appeared, in 1868, he had given to the world the noblest expression of his poetic genius.

Second period

In the third period, beginning when Browning was nearly sixty years old, he wrote even more industriously than before, and published on an average nearly a volume of poetry a year. Such volumes as *Fifine at the Fair, Red Cotton NightCap Country, The Inn Album, Jocoseria,* and many others, show how Browning gains steadily in the power of revealing the hidden springs of human action; but he often rambles most tiresomely, and in general his work loses in sustained interest. It is perhaps significant that most of his best work was done under Mrs. Browning's influence.

Third Period

What to Read. Of the short miscellaneous poems there is such an unusual variety that one must hesitate a little in suggesting this or that to the beginner's attention. 'My Star', 'Evelyn Hope', 'Wanting is—What?' 'Home Thoughts from Abroad', 'Meeting at Night', 'One Word More' (an exquisite tribute to his dead wife), 'Prospice' (Look Forward); songs from Pippa Passes; various love poems like 'By the Fireside' and 'The Last Ride Together'; the inimitable 'Pied Piper', and the ballads like 'Hervé Riel' and 'How They Brought the Good News',—these are a mere suggestion, expressing only the 'writer's personal preference; but a glance at the contents of Browning's volumes will reveal scores of other poems, which another writer might recommend as being better in themselves or more characteristic of Browning.[1]

Among Browning's dramatic soul studies there is also a very wide choice. 'Andrea del Sarto' is one of the best, revealing as it does the strength and the weakness of 'the perfect painter', whose love for a soulless woman with a pretty face saddens his life and hampers his best work. Next in importance to 'Andrea' stands 'An Epistle', reciting the experiences of Karshish, an Arab physician, which is one of the best examples of Browning's peculiar method of presenting the truth. The half-scoffing, half-earnest, and wholly bewildered state of this Oriental scientist's mind is clearly indicated between the lines of his letter to his old master. His description of Lazarus, whom he meets by chance, and of the state of mind of one who, having seen, the glories of immortality, must live again in the midst of the jumble of trivial and stupendous things which constitute our life, forms one of the most original and suggestive poems in our literature. 'My Last Duchess' is a short but very keen analysis of the soul of a selfish man, who reveals his character unconsciously by his words of praise concerning his dead wife's picture. In 'The Bishop Orders his Tomb' we have another extraordinarily interesting revelation of the mind of a vain and worldly man, this time a churchman, whose words tell you far more than he dreams about his own character. 'Abt Vogler', undoubtedly one of Browning's finest poems, is the study of a musician's soul. 'Muléykeh' gives us the soul of an Arab, vain and proud of his fast horse, which was never beaten in a race. A rival steals the horse and rides away upon her back; but, used as she is to her master's touch, she will not show her best pace to the stranger. Muléykeh rides up furiously; but instead of striking the thief from his saddle, he boasts about his peerless mare, saying that if a certain spot on her neck were touched

Soul Studies

---

[1] An excellent little book for the beginner is Lovett's *Selections from Browning.* (See Selections for Reading, at the end of this chapter.)

with the rein, she could never be overtaken. Instantly the robber touches the spot, and the mare answers with a burst of speed that makes pursuit hopeless. Muléykeh has lost his mare; but he has kept his pride in the unbeaten one, and is satisfied. 'Rabbi Ben Ezra', which refuses analysis, and which must be read entire to be appreciated, is perhaps the most quoted of all Browning's works, and contains the best expression of his own faith in life, both here and hereafter. All these wonderful poems are, again, merely a suggestion. They indicate simply the works to which one reader turns when he feels mentally vigorous enough to pick up Browning. Another list of soul studies, citing 'A Toccata of Galuppi's', 'A Grammarian's Funeral', 'Fra Lippo Lippi', 'Saul', 'Cleon', 'A Death in the Desert', and 'Soliloquy of the Spanish Cloister', might, in another's judgment, be more interesting and suggestive.

Among Browning's longer poems there are two, at least, that well deserve our study. *Pippa Passes,* aside from its rare poetical qualities, is a study of unconscious influence. The idea of the poem was suggested to Browning while listening to a gypsy girl singing in the woods near his home; but he transfers the scene of the action to the little mountain town of Asolo, in Italy. Pippa is a little silk weaver, who goes out in the morning to enjoy her one holiday of the whole year. As she thinks of her own happiness she is vaguely wishing that she might share it, and do some good. Then, with her childish imagination, she begins to weave a little romance in which she shares in the happiness of the four greatest and happiest people in Asolo. It never occurs to her that perhaps there is more of misery than of happiness in the four great ones of whom she dreams; and so she goes on her way singing,

Pippa Passes

The year's at the spring
And day's at the morn;
Morning's at seven;
The hillside's dew-pearled;
The lark's on the wing;
The snail's on the thorn:

God's in his heaven—
All's right with the world!

Fate wills it that the words and music of her little songs should come to the ears of four different groups of people at the moment when they are facing the greatest crises of their lives, and turn the scale from evil to good. But Pippa knows nothing of this. She enjoys her holiday, and goes to bed still singing, entirely ignorant of the good she has done in the world. With one exception, it is the most perfect of all Browning's works. At best it is not easy, nor merely entertaining reading; but it richly repays whatever hours we spend in studying it.

The Ring and the Book

The Ring and the Book is Browning's masterpiece. It is an immense poem, twice as long as Paradise Lost, and longer by some two thousand lines than the Iliad; and before we begin the undoubted task of reading it, we must understand that there is no interesting story or dramatic development to carry us along. In the beginning we have an outline of the story, such as it is—a horrible story of Count Guido's murder of his beautiful young wife; and Browning tells us in detail just when and how he found a book containing the record of the crime and the trial. There the story element ends, and the symbolism of the book begins. The title of the poem is explained by the habit of the old Etruscan goldsmiths who, in making one of their elabourately chased rings, would mix the pure gold with an alloy, in order to harden it. When the ring was finished, acid was poured upon it; and the acid ate out the alloy, leaving the beautiful design in pure gold. Browning purposes to follow the same plan with his literary material, which consists simply of the evidence given at the trial of Guido in Rome, in 1698. He intends to mix a poet's fancy with the crude facts, and create a beautiful and artistic work.

The result of Browning's purpose is a series of monologues, in which the same story is retold nine different times by the different actors in the drama. The count, the young wife, the suspected priest, the lawyers, the Pope who presides at the trial—each tells he story, and each unconsciously reveals the depths of his own ature in the recital. The most interesting of the characters are Guido, the husband, who changes from bold defiance to abject ear; Caponsacchi, the young priest, who aids the wife in her flight rom her brutal husband, and is unjustly accused of false motives; 'ompilia, the young wife, one of the noblest characters in literature, it in all respects to rank with Shakespeare's great heroines; and he Pope, a splendid figure, the strongest of all Browning's nasculine characters. When we have read the story, as told by nese four different actors, we have the best of the poet's work, nd of the most original poem in our language.

Browning's Place and Message. Browning's place in our terature will be better appreciated by comparison with his friend Tennyson, whom we have just studied. In one respect, at least, these poets are in perfect accord. Each finds in love the supreme purpose and meaning of life. In ther respects, especially in their methods of approaching the truth, ne two men are the exact opposites. Tennyson is first the artist nd then the teacher; but with Browning the message is always the nportant thing, and he is careless, too careless, of the form in which it is expressed. Again, Tennyson is under the influence of ne romantic revival, and chooses his subjects daintily; but 'all's sh' that comes to Browning's net. He takes comely and ugly ubjects with equal pleasure, and aims to show that truth lies hidden n both the evil and the good. This contrast is all the more striking when we remember that Browning's essentially scientific attitude was taken by a man who refused to study science. Tennyson, whose work is always artistic, never studied art, but was devoted to the ciences; while Browning, whose work is seldom artistic in form, nought that art was the most suitable subject for a man's study.

rowning and ennyson

The two poets differ even more widely in their respective nessages. Tennyson's message reflects the growing order of the age, and is summed up in the word 'law.' In his view, the individual will must be suppressed; the self must ways be subordinate. His resignation is at times almost Oriental

rowning's essage

in its fatalism, and occasionally it suggests Schopenhauer in it mixture of fate and pessimism. Browning's message, on the othe hand, is the triumph of the individual will over all obstacles; th self is not subordinate but supreme. There is nothing Oriental nothing doubtful, nothing pessimistic in the whole range of hi poetry. His is the voice of the Anglo-Saxon, standing up in th face of all obstacles and saying, 'I can and I will'. He is, therefore far more radically English than is Tennyson; and it may be fo this reason that he is the more studied, and that, while yout delights in Tennyson, manhood is better satisfied with Browning Because of his invincible will and optimism, Browning is a present regarded as the poet who has spoken the strongest wor of faith to an age of doubt. His energy, his cheerful courage, hi faith in life and in the development that awaits us beyond th portals of death, are like a bugle-call to good living. This sum up his present influence upon the minds of those who hav learned to appreciate him. Of the future we can only say tha both at home and abroad, he seems to be gaining steadily i appreciation as the years go by.

MINOR POETS OF THE VICTORIAN AGE

Elizabeth Barrett. Among the minor poets of the past centur Elizabeth Barrett (Mrs. Browning) occupies perhaps the highe place in popular favour. She was born at Coxhoe Hall, near Durhar in 1806; but her childhood and early youth were spent i Herefordshire, among the Malvern Hills made famous by *Pie Ploughman.* In 1835 the Barrett family moved to London, wher Elizabeth gained a literary reputation by the publication of *T Seraphim and Other Poems* (1838). Then illness and the shock cause by the tragic death of her brother, in 1840, placed her frail life i danger, and for six years she was confined to her own room. Th innate strength and beauty of her spirit here showed itself strong in her daily study, her poetry, and especially in her interest in th social problems which sooner or later occupied all the Victoria writers. 'My mind to me a kingdom is' might well have been writte over the door of the room where this delicate suffered in loneliness and in silence.

In 1844 Miss Barrett published her Poems, which, though somewhat impulsive and overwrought, met with remarkable public favour. Such poems as 'The Cry of the Children', which voices the protest of humanity against child labour, appealed tremendously to the readers of the age, and this young woman's fame as a poet temporarily overshadowed that of Tennyson and Browning. Indeed, as late as 1850, when Wordsworth died, she was seriously considered for the position of poet laureate, which was finally given to Tennyson. A reference to Browning, in 'Lady Geraldine's Courtship', is supposed to have first led the poet to write to Miss Barrett in 1845. Soon afterwards he visited the invalid; they fell in love almost at first sight, and the following year, against the wishes of her father—who was evidently a selfish old tyrant—Browning carried her off and married her. The exquisite romance of their love is reflected in Mrs. Browning's *Sonnets from the Portuguese* (1850). This is a noble and inspiring book of love poems; and Stedman regards the opening sonnet, 'I thought once how Theocritus had sung', as equal to any in our language.

For fifteen years the Brownings lived an ideally happy life at Pisa, and at Casa Guidi, Florence, sharing the same poetical ambitions. And love was the greatest thing in the world—

> How do I love thee? Let me count the ways.
> I love thee to the depth and breadth and height
> My soul can reach, when feeling out of sight
> For the ends of Being and ideal Grace.
> I love thee to the level of everyday's
> Most quiet need, by sun and candlelight.
> I love thee freely, as men strive for Right;
> I love thee purely, as they turn from Praise;
> I love thee with the passion put to use
> In my old griefs, and with my childhood's faith;
> I love thee with a love I seemed to lose
> With my lost saints—I love thee with the breath

Smiles, tears, of all my life!—and, if God choose,
I shall but love thee better after death.

Mrs. Browning entered with whole-souled enthusiasm into the aspirations of Italy in its struggle against the tyranny of Austria; and her *Casa Guidi Windows* (1851) is a combination of poetry and politics, both, it must be confessed, a little too emotional. In 1856 she published *Aurora Leigh,* a novel in verse, having for its hero a young social reformer, and for its heroine a young woman, poetical and enthusiastic, who strongly suggests Elizabeth Barrett herself. It emphasizes in verse precisely the same moral and social ideals which Dickens and George Eliot were proclaiming in all their novels. Her last two volumes were *Poems before Congress* (1860), and *Last Poems,* published after her death. She died suddenly in 1861 and was buried in Florence. Browning's famous line, 'O lyric love, half angel and half bird', may well apply to her frail life and aërial spirit.

Mrs. Browning

Rossetti. Dante Gabriel Rossetti (1828-1882), the son of an exiled Italian painter and scholar, was distinguished both as a painter and as a poet. He was a leader in the Pre-Raphaelite movement[1] and published

---

[1] This term, which means simply Italian painters before Raphæl, is generally applied to an artistic movement in the middle of the nineteenth century. The term was first used by a brotherhood of German artists who worked together in the convent of San Isodoro, in Rome, witih the idea of restoring art to its mediæval purity and simplicity. The term now generally refers to a company of seven young men—Dante Gabriel Rossetti and his brother William, William Holman Hunt, John Everett Millais, James Collinson, Frederick George Stevens, and Thomas Woolner—who formed the Pre-Raphælite brotherhood in England in 1848. Their official literary organ was called *The Germ,* in which much of the early work of Morris and Rossetti appeared. They took for their models the early Italian painters who, they declared, were 'simple, sincere, and religious'.

in the first numbers of *The Germ* his 'Hand and Soul', a delicate prose study, and his famous 'The Blessed Damozel', beginning,

> The blessed damozel leaned out
> From the gold bar of Heaven;
> Her eyes were deeper than the depth
> Of waters stilled at even;
> She had three lilies in her hand,
> And the stars in her hair were seven.

These two early works, especially 'The Blessed Damozel', with its simplicity and exquisite spiritual quality, are characteristic of the ideals of the Pre-Raphælites.

In 1860, after a long engagement, Rossetti married Elizabeth Siddal, a delicate, beautiful English girl, whom he has immortalized both in his pictures and in his poetry. She died two years later, and Rossetti never entirely recovered from the shock. At her burial he placed in her coffin the manuscripts of all his unpublished poems, and only at the persistent demands of his friends did he allow them to be exhumed and printed in 1870. The publication of this volume of love poems created a sensation in literary circles, and Rossetti was hailed as one of the greatest of living poets. In 1881 he published his *Ballads and Sonnets,* a remarkable volume containing, among other poems, 'The Confession', modelled after Browning; 'The Ballad of Sister Helen', founded on a mediæval superstition; 'The King's Tragedy', a masterpiece of dramatic narrative; and 'The House of Life', a collection of one hundred and one sonnets reflecting the poet's love and loss. This last collection deserves to rank with Mrs. Browning's *Sonnets from the Portuguese* and with Shakespeare's *Sonnets,* as one of the three great cycles of love poems in our language. It has been well said that

---

Their purpose was to encourage simplicity and naturalness in art and literature; and one of their chief objects, in the face of doubt and materialism, was to express the 'wonder, reverence, and awe' which characterizes mediæval art. In its return to the mysticism and symbolism of the mediæval age, this Pre-Raphælitism suggests the contemporary Oxford or Tractarian movement in religion. (See footnote, p. 554.)

both Rossetti and Morris paint pictures as well in their poems as on their canvases, and this pictorial quality of their verse is its chief characteristic.

Morris. William Morris (1834-1896) is a most interesting combination of literary man and artist. In the latter capacity, as architect, designer, and manufacturer of furniture, carpets, and wallpaper, and as founder of the Kelmscott Press for artistic printing and bookbinding, he has laid us all under an immense debt of gratitude. From boyhood he had steeped himself in the legends and ideals of the Middle Ages, and his best literary work is wholly mediæval in spirit. *The Earthly Paradise* (1868-1870) is generally regarded as his masterpiece. This delightful collection of stories in verse tells of a roving band of Vikings, who are wrecked on the fabled island of Atlantis, and who discover there a superior race of men having the characteristics of ideal Greeks. The Vikings remain for a year, telling stories of their own Northland, and listening to the classic and Oriental tales of their hosts. Morris's interest in Icelandic literature is further shown by his *Sigurd the Volsung,* an epic founded upon one of the old sagas, and by his prose romances, *The House of the Wolfings, The Story of the Glittering Plain,* and *The Roots of the Mountains.* Later in life he became deeply interested in socialism, and two other romances, *The Dream of John Ball* and *News from Nowhere,* are interesting as modern attempts at depicting an ideal society governed by the principles of More's *Utopia.*

Swinburne. Algernon Charles Swinburne (1837-1909) is, chronologically, the last of the Victorian poets. As an artist in technique—having perfect command of all old English verse forms and a remarkable faculty for inventing new—he seems at the present time to rank among the best in our literature. Indeed, as Stedman says, 'before his advent we did not realize the full scope of English verse.' This refers to the melodious and constantly changing form rather than to the content of Swinburne's poetry. At the death of Tennyson, in 1892, he was undoubtedly the greatest living poet, and only his liberal opinions, his scorn of royalty and of conventions, and the prejudice aroused by the pagan spirit of his early work prevented his appointment as poet laureate. He has written a very large number of poems, dramas, and essays in literary criticism; but we are still too near to judge of the permanence of his work or of his place in literature. Those who would read and estimate his work for themselves will do well to begin with a volume of selected poems, especially those which show his love of the sea and his exquisite appreciation of child life. His *Atalanta in Calydon* (1864), a beautiful lyric drama modelled on the Greek tragedy, is generally regarded as his masterpiece. In all his work Swinburne carries Tennyson's love of melody to an extreme, and often sacrifices sense to sound. His poetry is always musical, and, like music, appeals almost exclusively to the emotions.

We have chosen, somewhat arbitrarily, these four writers—Mrs. Browning, D. G. Rossetti, Morris, and Swinburne—as representative of the minor poets of the age; but there are many others who are worthy of study—Arthur Hugh Clough and Matthew Arnold,[1] who are often called the poets of skepticism, but who in reality represent a reverent seeking for truth through reason and human experience; Frederick William Faber, the Catholic mystic, author of some exquisite hymns; and the scholarly John Keble, author of *The Christian Year,* our best known book of devotional verse; and among the women poets, Adelaide Procter, Jean Ingelow, and Christina Rossetti, each of whom had a large, admiring circle of readers. It would be a hopeless task at the present time to inquire into the relative merits of all these minor poets. We note only their careful workmanship and exquisite melody, their wide range of thought and feeling, their eager search for truth, each in his own way, and especially the note of freshness and vitality which they have given to English poetry.

---

[1] Arnold was one of the best known poets of the age,but because he has exerted a deeper influence on our literature as a critic, we have reserved him for special study among the essayists. (See p. 545.)

II. THE NOVELISTS OF THE VICTORIAN AGE

CHARLES DICKENS (1812-1870)

When we consider Dickens's life and work, in comparison with that of the two great poets we have been studying, the contrast is startling. While Tennyson and Browning were being educated for the life of literature, and shielded most tenderly from the hardships of the world, Dickens, a poor, obscure, and suffering child, was helping to support a shiftless family by pasting labels on blacking bottles, sleeping under a counter like a homeless cat, and once a week timidly approaching the big prison where his father was confined for debt. In 1836 his *Pickwick* was published, and life was changed as if a magician had waved his wand over him. While the two great poets were slowly struggling for recognition, Dickens, with plenty of money and too much fame, was the acknowledged literary hero of England, the idol of immense audiences which gathered to applaud him wherever he appeared. And there is also this striking contrast between the novelist and the poets—that while the whole tendency of the age was toward realism, away from the extremes of the romanticists and from the oddities and absurdities of the early novel writers, it was precisely by emphasizing oddities and absurdities, by making caricatures rather than characters, that Dickens first achieved his popularity.

Life. In Dickens's early life we see a stern but unrecognized preparation for the work that he was to do. Never was there a better illustration of the fact that a boy's early hardship and suffering are sometimes only divine messengers disguised, and that circumstances which seem only evil are often the source of a man's strength and of the influence which he is to wield in the world. He was the second of eight poor children, and was born at Landport in 1812. His father, who is supposed to be the original of Mr. Micawber, was a clerk in a navy office. He could never make both ends meet, and after struggling with debts in his native town for many years, moved to London when Dickens was nine years old.

The debts still pursued him, and after two years of grandiloquent misfortune he was thrown into the poor-debtors' prison. His wife, the original of Mrs. Micawber, then set up the famous Boarding Establishment for Young Ladies; but, in Dickens's words, no young ladies ever came. The only visitors were creditors, and they were quite ferocious. In the picture of the Micawber family, with its tears and smiles and general shiftlessness, we have a suggestion of Dickens's own family life.

At eleven years of age the boy was taken out of school and went to work in the cellar of a blacking factory. At this time he was, in his own words, a 'queer small boy', who suffered as he worked; and we can appreciate the boy and the suffering more when we find both reflected in the character of David Copperfield. It is a heartrending picture, this sensitive child working from dawn till dark for a few pennies, and associating with toughs and waifs in his brief intervals of labour; but we can see in it the sources of that intimate knowledge of the hearts of the poor and outcast which was soon to be reflected in literature and to startle all England by its appeal for sympathy. A small legacy ended this wretchedness, bringing the father from the prison and sending the boy to Wellington House Academy—a worthless and brutal school, evidently, whose head master was, in Dickens's words, a most ignorant fellow and a tyrant. He learned little at this place, being interested chiefly in stories, and in acting out the heroic parts which appealed to his imagination; but again his personal experience was of immense value, and resulted in his famous picture of Dotheboys Hall, in *Nicholas Nickleby,* which helped largely to mitigate the evils of private schools in England. Wherever he went, Dickens was a marvellously keen observer, with an active imagination which made stories out of incidents and characters that ordinary men would have hardly noticed. Moreover he was a born actor, and was at one time the leading spirit of a band of amateurs who gave entertainments for charity all over England. These three things, his keen observation, his active imagination, and the actor's spirit which animated him, furnish a key to his life and writings.

When only fifteen years old, he left the school and again went to work, this time as clerk in a lawyer's office. By night he studied shorthand, in order to fit himself to be a reporter—this in imitation of his father, who was now engaged by a newspaper to report the speeches in Parliament. Everything that Dickens attempted seems to have been done with vigour and intensity, and within two years we find him reporting important speeches, and writing out his notes as the heavy coach lurched and rolled through the mud of country roads on its dark way to London town. It was largely during this period that he gained his extraordinary knowledge of inns and stables and 'horsey' persons, which is reflected in his novels. He also grew ambitious, and began to write on his own account. At the age of twenty-one he dropped his first little sketch 'stealthily, with fear and trembling, into a dark letterbox, in a dark office up a dark court in Fleet Street.' The name of this first sketch was 'Mr. Minns and his Cousin', and it appeared with other stories in his first book, *Sketches by Boz,* in 1835. One who reads these sketches now, with their intimate knowledge of the hidden life of London, can understand Dickens's first newspaper success perfectly. His best known work, *Pickwick,* was published serially in 1836-1837, and Dickens's fame and fortune were made. Never before had a novel appeared so full of vitality and merriment. Though crude in design, a mere jumble of exaggerated characters and incidents, it fairly bubbled over with the kind of humour in which the British public delights, and it still remains, after three quarters of a century, one of our most care-dispelling books.

The remainder of Dickens's life is largely a record of personal triumphs. *Pickwick* was followed rapidly by *Oliver Twist, Nicholas Nickleby, Old Curiosity Shop,* and by many other works which seemed to indicate that there was no limit to the new author's invention of odd, grotesque, uproarious, and sentimental characters. In the intervals of his novel writing he attempted several times to edit a weekly paper; but his power lay in other directions, and with the exception of *Household Words,* his journalistic ventures were not a marked success. Again the actor came to the surface, and after managing a company of amateur actors successfully, Dickens began to give dramatic readings from his own works. As he was already the most popular writer in the English language, these readings were very successful. Crowds thronged to hear him, and his journeys became a continuous ovation. Money poured into his pockets from his novels and from his readings, and he bought for himself a home, Gadshill Place, which he had always desired, and which is forever associated with his memory. Though he spent the greater part of his time and strength in travel at this period, nothing is more characteristic of the man than the intense energy with which he turned from his lecturing to his novels, and then, for relaxation, gave himself up to what he called the magic lantern of the London streets.

In 1842, while still a young man, Dickens was invited to visit the United States and Canada, where his works were even better known than in England, and where he was received as the guest of the nation and treated with every mark of honor and appreciation. At this time America

Charles Dickens

After the portrait by Daniel Maclise

was, to most Europeans, a kind of huge fairyland, where money sprang out of the earth, and life was happy as a long holiday. Dickens evidently shared this rosy view, and his romantic expectations were naturally disappointed. The crude, unfinished look of the big country seems to have roused a strong prejudice in his mind, which was not overcome at the time of his second visit, twenty-five years later, and which brought forth the harsh criticism of his *American Notes* (1842) and of *Martin Chuzzlewit* (1843-1844). These two unkind books struck a false note, and Dickens began to lose something of his great popularity. In addition he had spent money beyond his income. His domestic life, which had been at first very happy, became more and more irritating, until he separated from his wife in 1858. To get inspiration, which seemed for a time to have failed, he journeyed to Italy, but was disappointed. Then he turned back to the London streets, and in the five years from 1848 to 1853 appeared *Dombey and Son, David Copperfield,* and *Bleak House*—three remarkable novels, which indicate that he had rediscovered his own power and genius. Later he resumed the public readings, with their public triumph and applause, which soon came to be a necessity to one who craved popularity as a hungry man craves bread. These excitements exhausted Dickens, physically and spiritually, and death was the inevitable result. He died in 1870, over his unfinished *Edwin Drood,* and was buried in Westminster Abbey.

Dickens's Work in View of his Life. A glance through even this unsatisfactory biography gives us certain illuminating suggestions in regard to all of Dickens's work. First, as a child, poor and lonely, longing for love and for society, he laid the foundation for those heart-rending pictures of children, which have moved so many readers to unaccustomed tears. Second, as clerk in a lawyer's office and in the courts, he gained his knowledge of an entirely different side of human life. Here he learned to understand both the enemies and the victims of society, between whom the harsh laws of that day frequently made no distinction. Third, as a reporter, and afterwards as manager of various newspapers, he learned the trick of racy writing, and of knowing to a nicety what would suit the popular taste. Fourth, as an actor, always an actor in spirit, he seized upon every dramatic possibility, every tense situation, every peculiarity of voice and gesture in the people whom he met, and reproduced these things in his novels, exaggerating them in the way that most pleased his audience.

When we turn from his outward training to his inner disposition we find two strongly marked elements. The first is his excessive imagination, which made good stories out of incidents that ordinarily pass unnoticed, and which described the commonest things—a street, a shop, a fog, a lamp-post, a stagecoach–with a wealth of detail and of romantic suggestion that makes many of his descriptions like lyric poems. The second element is his extreme sensibility, which finds relief only in laughter and tears. Like shadow and sunshine these follow one another closely throughout all his books.

Dickens and his Public

Remembering these two things, his training and disposition, we can easily foresee the kind of novel he must produce. He will be sentimental, especially over children and outcasts; he will excuse the individual in view of the faults of society; he will be dramatic or melodramatic; and his sensibility will keep him always close to the public, studying its tastes and playing with its smiles and tears. If pleasing the public be in itself an art, then Dickens is one of our greatest artists. And it is well to remember that in pleasing his public there was nothing of the hypocrite or demagogue in his make-up. He was essentially a part of the great drifting panoramic crowd that he loved. His sympathetic soul made all their joys and griefs his own. He fought against injustice; he championed the weak against the strong; he gave courage to the faint, and hope to the weary in heart; and in the love which the public gave him in return he found his best reward. Here is the secret of Dickens's unprecedented popular success, and we may note here a very significant parallel with Shakespeare. The great differencet in the genius and work of the two men does not change the fact that each won success largely because he studied and pleased his public.

General Plan of Dickens's Novels. An interesting suggestion comes to us from a study of the conditions which led to Dickens's first three novels. *Pickwick* was written, at the suggestion of an editor, for serial publication. Each chapter was to be accompanied by a cartoon by Seymour (a comic artist of the day), and the object was to amuse the public, and, incidentally, to sell the paper. The result was a series of characters and scenes and incidents which for vigour and boundless fun have never been equalled in our language. Thereafter, no matter what he wrote, Dickins was labelled a humorist. Like a certain American writer of our own generation, everything he said, whether for a feast or a funeral, was supposed to contain a laugh. In a word, he was the victim of his own book. Dickens was keen enough to understand his danger, and his next novel, *Oliver Twist,* had the serious purpose of mitigating the evils under which the poor were suffering. Its hero was a poor child, the unfortunate victim of society; and, in order to draw attention to the real need, Dickens exaggerated the woeful condition of the poor, and filled his pages with sentiment which easily slipped over into sentimentality. This also was a popular success, and in his third novel, *Nicholas Nickleby,* and indeed in most of his remaining works, Dickens combined the principles of his first two books, giving us mirth on the one hand, injustice and suffering on the other; mingling humour and pathos, tears and laughter, as we find them in life itself. And in order to increase the lights and shadows in his scenes, and to give greater dramatic effect to his narrative, he introduced odious and lothsome characters, and made vice more hateful by contrasting it with innocence and virtue.

His Characters

We find, therefore, in most of Dickens's novels three or four widely different types of character: first, the innocent little child, like Oliver, Joe, Paul, Tiny Tim, and Little Nell, appealing powerfully to the child love in every human heart; second, the horrible or grotesque foil, like Squeers, Fagin, Quilp, Uriah Heep, and Bill Sykes; third, the grandiloquent or broadly humorous fellow, the fun maker, like Micawber and Sam Weller; and fourth, a tenderly or powerfully drawn figure, like Lady Dedlock of *Bleak House,* and Sydney Carton of *A Tale of Two Cities,* which rise to the dignity of true characters. We note also that most of Dickens's novels belong decidely to the class of purpose or problem novels. Thus *Bleak House* attacks 'the law's delays'; *Little Dorrit,* the injustice which persecutes poor debtors; *Nicholas Nickleby,* the abuses of charity schools and brutal schoolmasters; and *Oliver Twist,* the unnecessary degradation and suffering of the poor in English workhouses. Dickens's serious purpose was to make the novel the instrument of morality and justice, and whatver we may think of the exaggeration of his characters, it is certain that his stories did more to correct the general selfishness and injustice of society toward the poor than all the works of other literary men of his age combined.

The Limitations of Dickens. Any severe criticism of Dickens as a novelist must seem, at first glance, unkind and unnecessary. In almost every house he is a welcome guest, a personal friend who has beguiled many an hour with his stories, and who has furnished us much good laughter and a few good tears. Moreover, he has always a cheering message. He emphasizes the fact that this is an excellent world; that some errors have crept into it, due largely to thoughtlessness, but that they can be easily remedied by a little human sympathy. That is a most welcome creed to an age overburdened with social problems; and to criticise our cheery companion seems as discourteous as to speak unkindly of a guest who has just left our home. But we must consider Dickens not merely as a friend, but as a novelist, and apply to his work the same standards of art which we apply to other writers; and when we do this we are sometimes a little disappointed. We must confess that his novels, while they contain many realistic details, seldom give the impression of reality. His characters, though we laugh or weep or shudder at them, are sometimes only caricatures, each one an exaggeration of some peculiarity, which suggest Ben Jonson's *Every Man in His Humour.* It is Dickens's art to give his heroes sufficient reality to make them suggest certain types of men and women whom we know; but in reading him we find ourselves often in the mental state of a man who is watching through a microscope the swarming life of a water drop. Here are lively, bustling, extraordinary creatures, some beautiful, some grotesque, but all far apart from the life that we know in daily experience. It is certainly not the reality of these characters, but rather the genius of the author in managing them, which interests us and holds our attention. Notwithstanding this criticism, which we would gladly have omitted, Dickens is excellent reading, and his novels will continue to be popular just so long as men enjoy a wholesome and absorbing story.

What to Read. Aside from the reforms in schools and prisons and workhouses which Dickens accomplished, he has laid us all, rich and poor alike, under a debt of gratitude. After the year 1843 the one literary work which he never neglected was to furnish a Christmas story for his readers; and it is due in some measure to the help of these stories, brimming over with good cheer, that Christmas has become in all English-speaking countries a season of gladness, of gift giving at home, and of remembering those less fortunate than ourselves, who are still members of a common brotherhood. If we read nothing else of Dickens, once a year, at Christmas time, we should remember him and renew our youth by reading one of his holiday stories—*The Cricket on the Hearth, The Chimes,* and above all the unrivalled *Christmas Carol.* The latter especially will be read and loved as long as men are moved by the spirit of Christmas.

Of the novels, *David Copperfield* is regarded by many as Dickens's masterpiece. It is well to begin with this novel, not simply for the unusual interest of the story, but also for the glimpse it gives us of the author's own boyhood and family. For pure fun and hilarity *Pickwick* will always be a favourite; but for artistic finish, and for the portrayal of one great character, Sydney Carton, nothing else that Dickens wrote is comparable to *A Tale of Two Cities.*

Tale of Two Cities

Here is an absorbing story, with a carefully constructed plot, and the action moves swiftly to its thrilling, inevitable conclusion. Usually Dickens introduces several pathetic or grotesque or laughable characters besides the main actors, and records various unnecessary dramatic episodes for their own sake; but in *A Tale of Two Cities* everything has its place in the development of the main story. There are, as usual, many characters—Sydney Carton, the outcast, who lays down his life for the happiness of one whom he loves; Charles Darnay, an exiled young French noble; Dr. Manette, who has been 'recalled to life' from a frightful imprisonment, and his gentle daughter Lucie, the heroine; Jarvis Lorry, a lovable, old-fashioned clerk in the big banking house; the terrible Madame Defarge, knitting calmly at the door of her wine shop and recording, with the ferocity of a tiger licking its chops, the names of all those who are marked for vengeance; and a dozen others, each well drawn, who play minor parts in the tragedy. The scene is laid in London and Paris, at the time of the French Revolution; and, though careless of historical details, Dickens reproduces the spirit of the Reign of Terror so well that *A Tale of Two Cities* is an excellent supplement to the history of the period. It is written in Dickens's usual picturesque style, and reveals his usual imaginative outlook on life and his fondness for fine sentiments and dramatic episodes. Indeed, all his qualities are here shown, not brilliantly or garishly, as in other novels, but subdued and softened, like a shaded light, for artistic effect.

Those who are interested in Dickens's growth and methods can hardly do better than to read in succession his first three novels, *Pickwick, Oliver Twist,* and *Nicholas Nickleby,* which, as we have indicated, show clearly how he passed from fun to serious purpose, and which furnish in combination the general plan of all his later works. For the rest, we can only indicate those which, in our personal judgment, seem best worth reading—*Bleak House, Dombey and Son, Our Mutual Friend,* and *Old Curiosity Shop*—but we are not yet far enough away from the first popular success of these works to determine their permanent value and influence.

William Makepeace Thackeray (1811-1863)

As the two most successful novelists of their day, it is natural for us, as it was for their personal friends and admirers, to compare Dickens and Thackeray with respect to their life and work, and their attitude toward the world in which they lived. Dickens, after a desperately hard struggle in his boy-hood, without friends or higher education, comes into man-hood cheery, self-confident, energetic, filled with the joy of his work; and in the world, which had at first treated him so harshly, he finds good everywhere, even in the jails and in the slums, simply because he is looking for it. Thackeray, after a boyhood spent in the best of English schools, with money, friends, and comforts of every kind, faces life timidly, distrustfully, and dislikes the literary work which makes him famous. He has a gracious and lovable personality, is kind of heart, and reveres all that is pure and good in life; yet he is almost cynical toward the world which uses him so well, and finds shams, deceptions, vanities everywhere, because he looks for them. One finds what one seeks in this world, but it is perhaps significant that Dickens sought his golden fleece among plain people, and Thackeray in high society. The chief difference between the two novelists, however, is not one of environment but of temperament. Put Thackeray in a workhouse, and he will still find material for another *Book of Snobs;* put Dickens in society, and he cannot help finding undreamed-of possibilities among bewigged and be-powdered high lords and ladies. For Dickens is romantic and emotional, and interprets the world largely through his imagination; Thackeray is the realist and moralist, who judges solely by observation and reflection. He aims to give us a true picture of the society of his day, and as he finds it pervaded by intrigues and snobbery he proceeds to satirize it and point out its moral evils. In his novels he is influenced by Swift and Fielding, but he is entirely free from the bitterness of the one and the coarseness of the other, and his satire is generally softened by a noble tenderness. Taken together, the novels of Dickens and Thackeray give us a remarkable picture of all classes of English society in the middle of the nineteenth century.

Life. Thackeray was born in 1811, in Calcutta, where his father held a civil position under the Indian government. When the boy was five years old his father died, and the mother returned with her child to England.

Presently she married again, and Thackeray was sent to the famous Charterhouse school, of which he has given us a vivid picture in *The Newcomes.* Such a school would have been a veritable heaven to Dickens, who at this time was tossed about between poverty and ambition; but Thackeray detested it for its rude manners, and occasionally referred to it as the 'Slaughterhouse.' Writing to his mother he says: 'There are three hundred and seventy boys in the school. I wish, there were only three hundred and sixty-nine.'

In 1829 Thackeray entered Trinity College, Cambridge, but left after less than two years, without taking a degree, and went to Germany and France where he studied with the idea of becoming an artist. When he became of age, in 1832, he came into possession of a comfortable fortune, returned to England, and settled down in the Temple to study law. Soon he began to dislike the profession intensely, and we have in *Pendennis* a reflection of his mental attitude toward the law and the young men who studied it. He soon lost his fortune, partly by gambling and speculation, partly by unsuccessful attempts at running a newspaper, and at twenty-two began for the first time to earn his own living, as an artist and illustrator. An interesting meeting between Thackeray and Dickens at this time (1836) suggests the relative importance of the two writers. Seymour, who was illustrating the *Pickwick Papers,* had just died, and Thackeray called upon Dickens with a few drawings and asked to be allowed to continue the illustrations. Dickens was at this time at the beginning of his great popularity. The better literary artist, whose drawings were refused, was almost unknown, and had to work hard for more than ten years before he received recognition. Disappointed by his failure as an illustrator, he began his literary career by writing satires on society for *Fraser's Magazine.* This was the beginning of his success; but though the *Yellowplush Papers, The Great Hoggarty Diamond, Catherine, The Fitz Boodlers, The Book of Snobs,*

William Makepeace Thackeray

Barry Lyndon, and various other immature works made him known to a few readers of Punch and of *Fraser's Magazine,* it was not till the publication of *Vanity Fair* (1847-1848) that he began to be recognized as one of the great novelists of his day. All his earlier works are satires, some upon society, others upon the popular novelists—Bulwer, Disraeli, and especially Dickens—with whose sentimental heroes and heroines he had no patience whatever. He had married, meanwhile, in 1836, and for a few years was very happy in his home. Then disease and insanity fastened upon his young wife, and she was placed in an asylum. The whole afterlife of our novelist was darkened by this loss worse than death. He became a man of the clubs, rather than of his own home, and though his wit and kindness made him the most welcome of clubmen, there was an undercurrent of sadness in all that he wrote. Long afterwards he said that, though his marriage ended in shipwreck, he 'would do it over again; for behold Love is the crown and completion of all earthly good'.

After the moderate success of *Vanity Fair,* Thackeray wrote the three novels of his middle life upon which his fame chiefly rests—*Pendennis* in 1850, *Henry Esmond* in 1852, and *The Newcomes* in 1855. Dickens's great popular success as a lecturer and dramatic reader had led to a general desire on the part of the public to see and to hear literary men, and Thackeray, to increase his income, gave two remarkable courses of lectures, the first being *English Humorists of the Eighteenth Century,* and the second *The Four Georges*—both courses being delivered with gratifying success in England and especially in America. Dickens, as we have seen, was disappointed in America and vented his displeasure in outrageous criticism; but Thackeray, with his usual good breeding, saw only the best side of his generous entertainers, and in both his public and private utterances emphasized the virtues of the new land, whose restless energy seemed to fascinate him. Unlike Dickens, he had no confidence in himself when he faced an audience, and like most literary men he disliked lecturing, and soon gave it up. In 1860 he became editor of the *Cornhill Magazine,* which prospered in his hands, and with a comfortable income he seemed just ready to do his best work for the world (which has always believed that he was capable of even better things than he ever wrote) when he died suddenly in 1863. His body lies buried in Kensal Green, and only a bust does honour to his memory in Westminster Abbey.

Works of Thackeray. The beginner will do well to omit the earlier satires of Thackeray, written while he was struggling to earn a living from the magazines, and open *Henry Esmond* (1852), his most perfect novel, though not the most widely known and read. The fine historical and literary flavour of this story is one of its most marked characteristics, and only one who knows something of the history and literature of the eighteenth century can appreciate its value. The hero, Colonel Esmond; relates his own story, carrying the reader through the courts and camps of Queen Anne's reign, and giving the most complete and accurate picture of a past age that has ever appeared in a novel. Thackeray is, as we have said, a realist, and he begins his story by adopting the style and manner of a scholarly gentleman of the period he is describing. He has an extraordinary knowledge of eighteenth-century literature, and he reproduces its style in detail, going so far as to insert in his narrative an alleged essay from the *Tatler*. And so perfectly is it done that it is impossible to say wherein it differs from the style of Addison and Steele.

Henry Esmond

In his matter also Thackeray is realistic, reflecting not the pride and pomp of war, which are largely delusions, but its brutality and barbarism, which are all too real; painting generals and leaders, not as the newspaper heroes to whom we are accustomed, but as moved by intrigues, petty jealousies, and selfish ambitions; showing us the great Duke of Marlborough not as the military hero, the idol of war-crazed multitudes, but as without personal honour, and governed by despicable avarice. In a word, Thackeray gives us the 'back stairs' view of war, which is, as a rule, totally neglected in our histories. When he deals with the literary men of the period, he uses the same frank realism, showing us Steele and Addison and other leaders, not with halos about their heads, as popular authors, but in slippers and dressing gowns, smoking a pipe in their own rooms, or else growing tipsy and hilarious in the taverns—just as they appeared in daily life. Both

Realism of Esmond

in style and in matter, therefore, *Esmond* deserves to rank as probably the best historical novel in our language.

The plot of the story is, like most of Thackeray's plots, very slight, but perfectly suited to the novelist's purpose.

The Plot of Esmond

The plans of his characters fail; their ideals grow dim; there is a general disappearance of youthful ambitions. There is a love story at the centre; but the element of romance, which furnishes the light and music and fragrance of love, is inconspicuous. The hero, after ten years of devotion to a young woman, a paragon of beauty, finally marries her mother, and ends with a few pious observations concerning Heaven's mercy and his own happy lot. Such an ending seems disappointing, almost bizarre, in view of the romantic novels to which we are accustomed; but we must remember that Thackeray's purpose was to paint life as he saw it, and that in life men and things often take a different way from that described in romances. As we grow acquainted with Thackeray's characters, we realize that no other ending was possible to his story, and conclude that his plot, like his style, is perhaps as near perfection as a realistic novelist can ever come.

Vanity Fair

Vanity Fair (1847–1848) is the best known of Thackeray's novels. It was his first great work, and was intended to express his own views of the social life about him, and to protest against the overdrawn heroes of popular novels. He takes for his subject that Vanity Fair to which Christian and Faithful were conducted on their way to the Heavenly City, as recorded in *Pilgrim's Progress.* In this fair there are many different booths, given over to the sale of 'all sorts of vanities', and as we go from one to another we come in contact with 'juggling, cheats, games, plays, fools, apes, knaves, rogues, and that of every kind.' Evidently this is a picture of one side of social life; but the difference between Bunyan and Thackeray is simply this—that Bunyan made Vanity Fair a small incident in a long journey, a place through which most of us pass on our way to better things; while Thackeray, describing high society in his own day, makes it a place of long sojourn, wherein his characters spend the greater part of their lives.

Thackeray styles this work 'a novel without a hero.' The whole action of the story, which is without plot or development, revolves about two women—Amelia, a meek creature of the milk-and-water type, and Becky Sharp, a keen, unprincipled intriguer, who lets nothing stand in the way of her selfish desire to get the most out of the fools who largely constitute society. On the whole, it is the most powerful but not the most wholesome of Thackeray's works.

In his second important novel, Pendennis (1849-1850), we have a continuation of the satire on society begun in *Vanity Fair.* This novel, which the beginner should read after *Esmond,* is interesting to us for two reasons—because it reflects more of the details of Thackeray's life than all his other writings, and because it contains one powerfully drawn character who is a perpetual reminder of the danger of selfishness. The hero is 'neither angel nor imp', in Thackeray's words, but the typical young man of society, whom he knows thoroughly, and whom he paints exactly as he is—a careless, good-natured but essentially selfish person, who goes through life intent on his own interests. *Pendennis* is a profound moral study, and the most powerful arraignment of well-meaning selfishness in our literature, not even excepting George Eliot's *Romola,* which it suggests.

Pendennis

Two other novels, *The Newcomes* (1855) and *The Virginians* (1859), complete the list of Thackeray's great works of fiction. The former is a sequel to *Pendennis,* and the latter to *Henry Esmond;* and both share the general fate of sequels in not being quite equal in power or interest to their predecessors. *The Newcomes,* however, deserves a very high place—some critics, indeed, placing it at the head of the author's works. Like all Thackeray's novels, it is a story of human frailty; but here the author's innate gentleness and kindness are seen at their best, and the hero is perhaps the most genuine and lovable of all his characters.

The Newcomes

Thackeray is known in English literature as an essayist as well as a novelist. His *English Humorists* and *The Four Georges* are among the finest essays of the nine-teenth century. In the former especially,

Thackeray's Essays

Thackeray shows not only a wide knowledge but an extraordinary understanding of his subject. Apparently this nineteenth-century writer knows Addison, Fielding, Swift, Smollett, and other great writers of the past century almost as intimately as one knows his nearest friend; and he gives us the fine flavour of their humour in a way which no other writer, save perhaps Larnb, has ever rivalled.[1] *The Four Georges* is in a vein of delicate satire, and presents a rather unflattering picture of four of England's rulers and of the courts in which they moved. Both these works are remarkable for their exquisite style, their gentle humour, their keen literary criticisms, and for the intimate knowledge and sympathy which makes the people of a past age live once more in the written pages.

General Characteristics. In treating of Thackeray's view of life, as reflected in his novels, critics vary greatly, and the following summary must be taken not as a positive judgment but only as an attempt to express the general impression of his works on an uncritical reader. He is first of all a realist, who paints life as he sees it. As he says himself, 'I have no brains above my eyes; I describe what I see.' His pictures of certain types, notably the weak and vicious elements of society, are accurate and true to life, but they seem to play too large a part in his books, and have perhaps too greatly influenced his general judgment of humanity. An excessive sensibility, or the capacity for fine feelings and emotions, is a marked characteristic of Thackeray, as it is of Dickens and Carlyle. He is easily offended, as they are, by the shams of society; but he cannot find an outlet, as Dickens does, in laughter and tears, and he is too gentle to follow Carlyle in violent denunciations and prophecies. He turns to satire—influenced, doubtless, by eighteenth-century literature which he knew so well,

[1] It should be pointed out that the *English Humorists* is somewhat too highly coloured to be strictly accurate. In certain cases also, notably that of Steele, the reader may well object to Thackeray' patronizing attitude toward his subject.

and in which satire played too large a part.[1] His satire is never personal, like Pope's, or brutal, like Swift's, and is tempered by kindness and humour; but it is used too freely, and generally lays too much emphasis on faults and foibles to be considered a true picture of any large class of English society.

Thackeray as a Moralist

Besides being a realist and satirist, Thackeray is essentially a moralist, like Addison, aiming definitely in all his work at producing a moral impression. So much does he revere goodness, and so determined is he that his Pendennis or his Becky Sharp shall be judged at their true value, that he is not content, like Shakespeare, to be simply an artist, to tell an artistic tale and let it speak its own message; he must explain and emphasize the moral significance of his work. There is no need to consult our own conscience over the actions of Thackeray's characters; the beauty of virtue and the ugliness of vice are evident on every page.

His Style

Whatever we may think of Thackeray's matter, there is one point in which critics are agreed—that he is master of a pure and simple English style. Whether his thought be sad or humorous, commonplace or profound, he expresses it perfectly, without effort or affectation. In all his work there is a subtle charm, impossible to describe, which gives the impression that we are listening to a gentleman. And it is the ease, the refinement, the exquisite naturalness of Thackeray's style that furnishes a large part of our pleasure in reading him.

Mary Ann Evans, George Eliot (1819-1880)

In nearly all the writers of the Victorian Age we note, on the one hand, a strong intellectual tendency to analyze the problems of life, and on the other a tendency to teach, that is, to explain to men the method by which these problems may be solved. The novels especially seem to lose sight of the purely artistic ideal of writing, and to aim definitely at moral instruction. In George Eliot

[1] See pp. 260-261.

both these tendencies reach a climax. She is more obviously, more consciously a preacher and moralizer than any of her great contemporaries.

Though profoundly religious at heart, she was largely occupied by the scientific spirit of the age; and finding no religious creed or political system satisfactory, she fell back upon duty as the supreme law of life. All her novels aim, first, to show in individuals the play, of universal moral forces, and second, to establish the moral law as the basis of human society. Aside from this moral teaching, we look to George Eliot for the reflection of country life in England, just as we look to Dickens for pictures of the city streets, and to Thackeray for the vanities of society. Of all the women writers who have helped and are still helping to place our English novels at the head of the world's fiction, she holds at present unquestionably the highest rank.

Life. Mary Ann (or Marian) Evans, known to us by her pen name of George Eliot, began to write late in life, when nearly forty years of age, and attained the leading position among living English novelists in the ten years between 1870 and 1880, after Thackeray and Dickens had passed away. She was born at Arbury Farm, Warwickshire, some twenty miles from Stratford-on-Avon, in 1819. Her parents were plain, honest folk, of the farmer class, who brought her up in the somewhat strict religious manner of those days. Her father seems to have been a man of sterling integrity and of practical English sense—one of those essentially noble characters who do the world's work silently and well, and who by their solid worth obtain a position of influence among their fellow-men.

A few months after George Eliot's birth the family moved to another home, in the parish of Griff, where her childhood was largely passed. The scenery of the Midland counties and many details of her own family life are reflected in her earlier novels. Thus we find her and her brother, as Maggie and Tom Tulliver, in *The Mill on the Floss;* her aunt, as Dinah Morris, and her mother, as Mrs. Poyser, in *Adam Bede.* We have a suggestion of her father in the hero of the latter novel, but the picture is more fully drawn as Caleb Garth, in *Middlemarch.* For a few years she studied at two private schools for young ladies, at Nuneaton and Coventry; but the death of her mother called her, at seventeen years of age, to take entire charge of the household. Thereafter her education was gained wholly by miscellaneous reading. We have a suggestion of her method in one of her early letters, in which she says: 'My mind presents an assemblage of disjointed specimens of history, ancient and modern; scraps of poetry picked up from Shakespeare, Cowper, Wordsworth, and Milton; newspaper topics, morsels of Addison and Bacon, Latin verbs, geometry, entomology, and chemistry; reviews and metaphysics, all arrested and petrified and smothered by the fast-thickening everyday accession of actual events, relative anxieties, and household cares and vexations.'

When Mary was twenty-one years old the family again moved, this time to Foleshill Road, near Coventry. Here she became acquainted with the family of Charles Bray, a prosperous ribbon manufacturer, whose house was a gathering place for the freethinkers of the neighbourhood. The effect of this liberal atmosphere upon Miss Evans, brought up in a narrow way, with no knowledge of the world, was to unsettle many of her youthful convictions. From a narrow, intense dogmatism, she went to the other extreme of radicalism; then (about 1860) she lost all sympathy with the freethinkers, and, being instinctively religious, seemed to be groping after a definite faith while following the ideal of duty. This spiritual struggle, which suggests that of Carlyle, is undoubtedly the cause of that gloom and depression which hang, like an English fog, over much of her work; though her biographer, Cross, tells us that she was not by any means a sad or gloomy woman.

Mary Ann Evans, George Eliot

In 1849 Miss Evans's father died, and the Brays took her abroad for a tour of the continent. On her return to England she wrote several liberal articles for the *Westminster Review,* and presently was made assistant editor of that magazine. Her residence in London at this time marks a turning point in her career and the real beginning of her literary life. She made strong friendships with Spencer, Mill, and other scientists of the day, and through Spencer met George Henry Lewes, a miscellaneous writer, whom she afterwards married.

Under his sympathetic influence she began to write fiction for the magazines, her first story being 'Amos Barton' (1857), which was later included in the *Scenes of Clerical Life* (1858). Her first long novel, *Adam Bede,* appeared early in 1859 and met with such popular favour that to the end of her life she despaired of ever again repeating her triumph. But the unexpected success proved to be an inspiration, and she completed *The Mill on the Floss* and began *Silas Marner* during the following year. Not until the great success of these works led to an insistent demand to know the author did the English public learn that it was a woman, and not an English clergyman, as they supposed, who had suddenly jumped to the front rank of living writers.

Up to this point George Eliot had confined herself to English country life, but now she suddenly abandoned the scenes and the people with whom she was most familiar in order to write an historical novel. It was in 1860, while travelling in Italy, that she formed 'the great project' of *Romola*—a mingling of fiction and moral philosophy, against the background of the mighty Renaissance movement. In this she was writing of things of which she had no personal knowledge, and the book cost her many months of hard and depressing labour. She said herself that she was a young woman when she began the work, and an old woman when she finished it. *Romola* (1862–1863) was not successful with the public, and the same may be said of *Felix Holt the Radical* (1866) and *The Spanish Gypsy* (1868). The last-named work was the result of the author's ambition to write a dramatic poem which should duplicate the lesson of *Romola;* and for the purpose of gathering material she visited Spain, which she had decided upon as the scene of her poetical effort. With the publication of *Middlemarch* (1871-1872) George Eliot came back again into popular favour, though this work is less spontaneous, and more laboured and pedantic, than her earlier novels. The fault of too much analysis and moralizing was even more conspicuous in *Daniel Deronda* (1876), which she regarded as her greatest book. Her life during all this time was singularly uneventful, and the chief milestones along the road mark the publication of her successive novels.

During all the years of her literary success her husband Lewes had been a most sympathetic friend and critic, and when he died, in 1878, the loss seemed to be more than she could bear. Her letters of this period are touching in their loneliness and their craving for sympathy. Later she astonished everybody by marrying John Walter Cross, much younger than herself, who is known as her biographer. 'Deep down below there is a river of sadness, but—I am able to enjoy my newly re-opened life', writes this woman of sixty, who, ever since she was the girl whom we know as Maggie Tulliver, must always have some one to love and to depend upon. Her new interest in life lasted but a few months, for she died in December of the same year (1880). One of the best indications of her strength and her limitations is her portrait, with its strong masculine features, suggesting both by resemblance and by contrast that wonderful portrait of Savonarola which hangs over his old desk in the monastery at Florence.

Works of George Eliot. These are conveniently divided into three groups, corresponding to the three periods of her life. The first group includes all her early essays and miscellaneous work, from her translation of Strauss's *Leben Jesu,* in 1846, to her union with Lewes in 1854. The second group includes *Scenes of Clerical Life, Adam Bede, Mill on the Floss,* and *Silas Marner,* all published between 1858 and 1861. These four novels of the middle period are founded on the author's own life and experience; their scenes are laid in the country, and their characters are taken from the stolid people of the Midlands, with whom George Eliot had been familiar since childhood. They are probably the author's most enduring works. They have a naturalness, a spontaneity, at times a flash of real humour, which are lacking in her later novels; and they show a rapid development of literary power which reaches a climax in *Silas Marner.*

The novel of Italian life, *Romola* (1862-1863), marks a transition to the third group, which includes three more novels—*Felix Holt* (1866), *Middlemarch* (1871-1872), *Daniel Deronda* (1876)—the ambitious dramatic poem *The Spanish Gypsy* (1868), and a collection of miscellaneous essays called *The Impressions of Theophrastus Such* (1879). The general impression of these works is not so favourable as that produced by the novels of the middle period. They are more laboured and less interesting; they contain much deep reflection and analysis of character, but less observation, less delight in picturing country life as it is, and very little of what we call inspiration. We must add, however, that this does not express a unanimous literary judgment, for critics are not wanting who assert that *Daniel Deronda* is the highest expression of the author's genius.

General Character

The general character of all these novels may be described, in the author's own term, as psychologic realism. This means that George Eliot sought to do in her novels what Browning attempted in his poetry; that is, to represent the inner struggle of a soul, and to reveal the motives, impulses, and hereditary influences which govern human action. Browning generally stops when he tells his story, and either lets you draw your own conclusion or else gives you his in a few striking lines. But George Eliot is not content until she has minutely explained the motives of her characters and the moral lesson to be learned from them. Moreover, it is the development of a soul, the slow growth or decline of moral power, which chiefly interests her. Her heroes and heroines differ radically from those of Dickens and Thackeray in this respect—that when we meet the men and women of the latter novelists, their characters are already formed, and we are reasonably sure what they will do under given circumstances. In George Eliot's novels the characters develop gradually as we come to know them. They go from weakness to strength, or from strength to weakness, according to the works that they do and the thoughts that they cherish. In *Romola*, for instance, Tito, as we first meet him, may be either good or bad, and we know not whether he will finally turn to the right hand or to the left. As time passes, we see him degenerate steadily because he follows his selfish impulses, while *Romola,* whose character is at first only faintly indicated, grows into beauty and strength with every act of self-renunciation.

Moral Teaching

In these two characters, Tito and Romola, we have an epitome of our author's moral teaching. The principle of law was in the air during the Victorian era, and we have already noted how deeply Tennyson was influenced by it. With George Eliot law is like fate; it overwhelms personal freedom and inclination. Moral law was to her as inevitable, as automatic, as gravitation. Tito's degeneration, and the sad failure of Dorothea and Lydgate in *Middlemarch,* may be explained as simply as the fall of an apple, or as a bruised knee when a man loses his balance. A certain act produces a definite moral effect on the individual; and character is the added sum of all the acts of a man's life—just as the weight of a body is the sum of the weights of many different atoms which constitute it. The matter of rewards and punishments, therefore, needs no final judge or judgment, since these things take care of themselves automatically in a world of inviolable moral law.

Perhaps one thing more should be added to the general characteristics of George Eliot's novels—they are all rather depressing. The gladsomeness of life, the sunshine of smiles and laughter, is denied her. It is said that once, when her husband remarked that her novels were all essentially sad, she wept, and answered that she must describe life as she had found it.

What to Read. George Eliot's first stories are in some respects her best, though her literary power increases during her second period, culminating in *Silas Marner,* and her psychological analysis is more evident in *Daniel Deronda.* On the whole, it is an excellent way to begin with the freshness and inspiration of the *Scenes of Clerical Life* and read her books in the order in which they were written. In the first group of novels *Adam Bede* is the most natural, and probably interests more readers than all the others combined. *The Mill on the Floss* has a larger personal interest, because it reflects much of George Eliot's history and the scenes and the friends of her early life. The lack of proportion in this story, which gives rather too much space to the girl-and-boy experiences, is naturally explained by the tendency in every man and woman to linger over early memories.

Silas Marner is artistically the most perfect of George Eliot's novels, and we venture to analyze it as typical of her ideals and methods. We note first the style, which is heavy and a little self-conscious, lacking the vigour and picturesqueness of Dickens, and the grace and naturalness of Thackeray. The characters are the common people of the Midlands, the hero being a linen weaver, a lonely outcast who hoards and gloats over his hard-earned money, is robbed, thrown into utter despair, and brought back to life and happiness by the coming of

Silas Marner

an abandoned child to his fire. In the development of her story the author shows herself, first, a realist, by the naturalness of her characters and the minute accuracy with which she reproduces their ways and even the accents of their speech; second, a psychologist, by the continual analysis and explanation of motives; third, a moralist, by showing in each individual the action and reaction of universal moral forces, and especially by making every evil act bring inevitable punishment to the man who does it. Tragedy, therefore, plays a large part in the story; for, according to George Eliot, tragedy and suffering walk close behind us, or lurk at every turn in the road of life. Like all her novels, *Silas Marner* is depressing. We turn away from even the wedding of Eppie—which is just as it should be—with a sense of sadness and incompleteness. Finally, as we close the book, we are conscious of a powerful and enduring impression of reality. Silas, the poor weaver; Godfrey Cass, the well-meaning, selfish man; Mr. Macey, the garrulous, and observant parish clerk; Dolly Winthrop, the kind-hearted country-woman who cannot understand the mysteries of religion and so interprets God in terms of human love—these are real people, whom having once met we can never forget.

Romola

Romola has the same general moral theme as the English novels; but the scenes are entirely different, and opinion is divided as to the comparative merit of the work. It is a study, a very profound study of moral development in one character and of moral degeneracy in another. Its characters and its scenes are both Italian, and the action takes place during a critical period of the Renaissance movement, when Savonarola was at the height of his power in Florence. Here is a magnificent theme and a superb background for a great novel, and George Eliot read and studied till she felt sure that she understood the place, the time, and the people of her story. *Romola* is therefore interesting reading, in many respects the most interesting of her works. It has been called one of our greatest historical novels; but as such it has one grievous fault. It is not quite true to the people or even to the locality which it endeavours to represent. One who reads it here, in a new and different land, thinks only of the story and of the novelist's power; but one who reads it on the spot which it describes, and amidst the life which it pictures, is continually haunted by the suggestion that George Eliot understood neither Italy nor the Italians. It is this lack of harmony with Italian life itself which caused Morris and Rossetti and even Browning, with all his admiration for the author, to lay aside the book, unable to read it with pleasure or profit. In a word, Romola is a great moral study and a very interesting book; but the characters are not Italian, and the novel as a whole lacks the strong reality which marks George Eliot's English studies.

MINOR NOVELISTS OF THE VICTORIAN AGE

In the three great novelists just considered we have an epitome of the fiction of the age, Dickens using the novel to solve social problems, Thackeray to paint the life of society as he saw it, and George Eliot to teach the fundamental principles of morality. The influence of these three writers is reflected in all the minor novelists of the Victorian Age. Thus, Dickens is reflected in Charles Reade, Thackeray in Anthony Trollope and the Brontë sisters, and George Eliot's psychology finds artistic expression in George Meredith. To these social and moral and realistic studies we should add the element of romance, from which few of our modern novelists can long escape. The nineteenth century, which began with the romanticism of Walter Scott, returns to its first love, like a man glad to be home, in its delight over Blackmore's *Lorna Doone* and the romances of Robert Louis Stevenson.

Charles Reade. In his fondness for stage effects, for picturing the romantic side of common life, and for using the novel as the instrument of social reform, there is a strong suggestion of Dickens in the work of Charles Reade (1814-1884). Thus his *Peg Woffington* is a study of stage life from behind the scenes; *A Terrible Temptation* is a study of social reforms and reformers; and *Put yourself in his*

Place is the picture of a workingman who struggles against the injustice of the trade unions. His masterpiece, *The Cloister and the Hearth* (1861), one of our best historical novels, is a somewhat labourious study of student and vagabond life in Europe in the days of the German Renaissance. It has small resemblance to George Eliot's *Romola*, whose scene is laid in Italy during the same period; but the two works may well be read in succession, as the efforts of two very different novelists of the same period to restore the life of an age long past.

Anthony Trollope. In his realism, and especially in his conception of the novel as the entertainment of an idle hour, Trollope (1815-1882) is a reflection of Thackeray. It would be hard to find a better duplicate of Becky Sharp, the heroine of *Vanity Fair*, for instance, than is found in Lizzie Eustace, the heroine of *The Eustace Diamonds*. Trollope was the most industrious and systematic of modern novelists writing a definite amount each day, and the wide range of his characters suggests the *Human Comedy* of Balzac. His masterpiece is *Barchester Towers* (1857). This is a study of life in a cathedral town, and is remarkable for its minute pictures of bishops and clergymen, with their families and dependents. It would be well to read this novel in connection with The Warden (1855), *The Last Chronicle of Barset* (1867), and other novels of the same series, since the scenes and characters are the same in all these books, and they are undoubtedly the best expression of the author's genius. Hawthorne says of his novels: 'They precisely suit my taste—solid and substantial, and—just as real as if some giant had hewn a great lump out of the earth and put it under a glass case, with all the inhabitants going about their daily business and not suspecting that they were being made a show of.'

Charlotte Brontë. We have another suggestion of Thackeray in the work of Charlotte Brontë (1816-1855). She aimed to make her novels a realistic picture of society, but she added to Thackeray's realism the element of passionate and somewhat unbalanced romanticism. The latter element was partly the expression of Miss Brontë's own nature, and partly the result of her lonely and grief-stricken life, which was darkened by a succession of family tragedies. It will help us to understand her work if we remember that both Charlotte Brontë and her sister Emily[1] turned to literature because they found their work as governess and teacher unendurable, and sought to relieve the loneliness and sadness of their own lot by creating a new world of the imagination. In this new world, however, the sadness of the old remains, and all the Brontë novels have behind them an aching heart. Charlotte Brontë's best known work is *Jane Eyre* (1847), which, with all its faults, is a powerful and fascinating study of elemental love and hate, reminding us vaguely of one of Marlowe's tragedies. This work won instant favour with the public, and the author was placed in the front rank of living novelists. Aside from its value as a novel, it is interesting, in many of its early passages, as the reflection of the author's own life and experience. *Shirley* (1849) and *Villette* (1853) make up the trio of novels by which this gifted woman is generally remembered.

Bulwer Lytton. Edward Bulwer Lytton (1803-1873) was an extremely versatile writer, who tried almost every kind of novel known to the nineteenth century. In his early life he wrote poems and dramas, under the influence of Byron; but his first notable work, *Pelham* (1828), one of the best of his novels, was a kind of burlesque on the Byronic type of gentleman. As a study of contemporary manners in high society, *Pelham* has a suggestion of Thackeray, and the resemblance is more noticeable in other novels of the same type, such as *Ernest Maltravers* (1837), *The Caxtons* (1848-1849), *My Novel* (1853), and *Kenelm Chillingly* (1873). We have a suggestion of Dickens in at least two of Lytton's novels, *Paul Clifford* and *Eugene Aram,* the heroes of which are criminals, pictured as the victims rather than as the oppressors of society.

---

[1] Emily Brontë (1818-1848) was only a little less gifted than her famous sister. Her best known work is *Wuthering Heights* (1847), a strong but morbid novel of love and suffering. Matthew Arnold said of her that, 'for the portrayal of passion, vehemence, and grief', Emily Brontë had no equal save Byron. An exquisite picture of Emily is given in Charlotte Brontë's novel Shirley.

Lytton essayed also, with considerable popular success, the romantic novel in *The Pilgrims of the Rhine* and *Zanoni,* and tried the ghost story in *The Haunted and the Haunters.* His fame at the present day rests largely upon his historical novels, in imitation of Walter Scott, *The Last Days of Pompeii* (1834), *Rienzi* (1835), and *Harold* (1848), the last being his most ambitious attempt to make the novel the supplement of history. In all his novels Lytton is inclined to sentimentalism and sensationalism, and his works, though generally interesting, seem hardly worthy of a high place in the history of fiction.

Kingsley. Entirely different in spirit are the novels of the scholarly clergyman, *Charles Kingsley* (1819-1875). His works naturally divide themselves into three classes. In the first are his social studies and problem novels, such as *Alton Locke* (1850), having for its hero a London tailor and poet, and *Yeast* (1848), which deals with the problem of the agricultural labourer. In the second class are his historical novels, *Hereward the Wake, Hypatia,* and *Westward Ho! Hypatia* is a dramatic story of Christianity in contact with paganism, having its scene laid in Alexandria at the beginning of the fifth century. *Westward Ho*! (1855), his best known work, is a stirring tale of English conquest by land and sea in the days of Elizabeth. In the third class are his various miscellaneous works, not the least of which is *Water-Babies,* a fascinating story of a chimney sweep, which mothers read to their children at bedtime—to the great delight of the round-eyed little listeners under the counterpane.

Mrs. Gaskell. Mrs. Elizabeth Gaskell (1810-1865) began, like Kingsley, with the idea of making the novel the instrument of social reform. As the wife of a clergyman in Manchester, she had come in close contact with the struggles and ideals of the industrial poor of a great city, and she reflected her sympathy as well as her observation in *Mary Barton* (1848) and in *North and South* (1855). Between these two problem novels she published her masterpiece, *Cranford,* in 1853. The original of this country village, which is given over to spinsters, is undoubtedly Knutsford, in Cheshire, where Mrs. Gaskell had spent her childhood. The sympathy, the keen observation, and the gentle humour with which the small affairs of a country village are described make *Cranford* one of the most delightful stories in the English language. We are indebted to Mrs. Gaskell also for the *Life of Charlotte Brontë,* which is one of our best biographies.

Blackmore. Richard Doddridge Blackmore (1825–1900) was a prolific writer, but he owes his fame almost entirely to one splendid novel, *Loma Doone,* which was published in 1869. The scene of this fascinating romance is laid in Exmoor in the seventeenth century. The story abounds in romantic scenes and incidents; its descriptions of natural scenery are unsurpassed; the rhythmic language is at times almost equal to poetry; and the whole tone of the book is wholesome and refreshing. Altogether it would be hard to find a more delightful romance in any language, and it well deserves the place it has won as one of the classics of our literature. Other works of Blackmore which will repay the reader are *Clara Vaitglian* (1864), his first novel, *The Maid of Sker* (1872), *Springhaven* (1887), *Perlycross* (1894), and *Tales from the Telling House* (1896); but none of these, though he counted them his best work, has met with the same favour as *Lorna Doone.*

Meredith. So much does George Meredith (1828-1909) belong to our own day that it is difficult to think of him as one of the Victorian novelists. His first notable work, *The Ordeal of Richard Feverel,* was published in 1859, the same year as George Eliot's *Adam Bede;* but it was not till the publication of *Diana of the Crossways* in 1885, that his power as a novelist was widely recognized. He resembles Browning not only in his condensed style, packed with thought, but also in this respect—that he laboured for years in obscurity, and after much of his best work was published and apparently forgotten he slowly won the leading place in English fiction. We are still too near him to speak of the permanence of his work, but a casual reading of any of his novels suggests a comparison and a contrast with George Eliot. Like her, he is a realist and a psychologist; but while George Eliot uses tragedy to teach a moral lesson, Meredith depends more upon comedy, making vice not terrible but ridiculous. For the hero or heroine of her novel George Eliot invariably takes an individual, and shows in each one the play of universal moral forces. Meredith constructs a type-man as a hero, and makes this type express his purpose and meaning. So his characters seldom speak naturally, as George Eliot's do; they are more like Browning's characters in packing a whole paragraph into a single sentence or an exclamation. On account of his enigmatic style and his psychology, Meredith will never be popular; but by thoughtful men and women he will probably be ranked among our greatest writers of fiction. The simplest and easiest of his novels for a beginner is *The Adventures of Henry Richmond* (1871). Among the best of his works, besides the two mentioned above, are *Beauchamp's Career* (1876) and *The Egoist* (1879). The latter is, in our personal judgment, one of the strongest and most convincing novels of the Victorian Age.

Hardy. Thomas Hardy (1840-1928) seems, like Meredith, to belong to the present rather than to a past age, and an interesting comparison may be drawn between these two novelists. In style, Meredith is obscure and difficult, while Hardy is direct and simple, aiming at realism in all things. Meredith makes man the most important phenomenon in the universe; and the struggles of men are brightened by the hope of victory. Hardy makes man an insignificant part of the world, struggling against powers greater than himself—sometimes against systems which he cannot reach or influence, sometimes against a kind of grim world-spirit who delights in making human affairs go wrong. He is, therefore, hardly a realist, but rather a man blinded by pessimism; and his novels, though generally powerful and sometimes fascinating, are not pleasant or wholesome reading. From the reader's viewpoint some of his earlier works, like the idyllic love story *Under the Greenwood Tree* (1872) and *A Pair of Blue Eyes* (1873), are the most interesting. Hardy became noted, however, when he published *Far from the Madding Crowd,* a book which, when it appeared anonymously in the *Cornhill Magazine* (1874), was generally attributed to George Eliot, for the simple reason that no other novelist was supposed to be capable of writing it. *The Return of the Native* (1878) and *The Woodlanders* are generally regarded as Hardy's masterpieces; but two novels of our own day, *Tess of the D'Ubervilles* (1891) and *Jude the Obscure* (1895), are better expressions of Hardy's literary art and of his gloomy philosophy.

Stevenson. In pleasing contrast with Hardy is Robert Louis Stevenson (1850-1894), a brave, cheery, wholesome spirit, who has made us all braver and cheerier by what he has written. Aside from their intrinsic value, Stevenson's novels are interesting in this respect—that they mark a return to the pure romanticism of Walter Scott. The novel of the nineteenth century had, as we have shown, a very definite purpose. It aimed not only to represent life but to correct it, and to offer a solution to pressing moral and social problems. At the end of the century Hardy's gloom in the face of modern social conditions became oppressive, and Stevenson broke away from it into that land of delightful romance in which youth finds an answer to all its questions. Problems differ, but youth is ever the same, and therefore Stevenson will probably be regarded by future generations as one of our most enduring writers. To his life, with its 'heroically happy' struggle, first against poverty, then against physical illness, it is impossible to do justice in a short article. Even a longer biography is inadequate, for Stevenson's spirit, not the incidents of his life, is the important thing; and the spirit has no biographer. Though he had written much better work earlier, he first gained fame by his *Treasure Island* (1883), an absorbing story of pirates and of a hunt for buried gold. *Dr. Jekyll and Mr. Hyde* (1886) is a profound ethical parable, in which, however, Stevenson leaves the psychology and the minute analysis of character to his readers, and makes the story the chief thing in his novel. *Kidnapped* (1886), *The Master of Ballantrae* (1889), and *David Balfour* (1893) are novels of adventure, giving us vivid pictures of Scotch life. Two romances left unfinished by his early death in Samoa are *The Weir of Hermiston* and *St. Ives.* The latter was finished by Quiller-Couch in 1897; the former is happily just as Stevenson left it, and though unfinished is generally regarded as his masterpiece. In addition to these novels, Stevenson wrote a large number of essays, the best of which are collected in *Virginibus Puerisque, Familiar Studies of Men and Books,* and *Memories and*

Portraits. Delightful sketches of his travels are found in *An Inland Voyage* (1878), *Travels with a Donkey* (1879), *Across the Plains* (1892), and *The Amateur Emigrant* (1894). *Underwoods* (1887) is an exquisite little volume of poetry, and *A Child's Garden of Verses* is one of the books that mothers will always keep to read to their children.

In all his books Stevenson gives the impression of a man at play rather than at work, and the reader soon shares in the happy spirit of the author. Because of his beautiful personality, and because of the love and admiration he awakened for himself in multitudes of readers, we are naturally inclined to exaggerate his importance as a writer. However that may be, a study of his works shows him to be a consummate literary artist. His style is always simple, often perfect, and both in his manner and in his matter he exercises a profound influence on the writers of the present generation.

III. ESSAYISTS OF THE VICTORIAN AGE

THOMAS BABINGTON MACAULAY (1800-1859)

Macaulay is one of the most typical figures of the nineteenth century. Though not a great writer, if we compare him with Browning or Thackeray, he was more closely associated than any of his literary contemporaries with the social and political struggles of the age. While Carlyle was proclaiming the gospel of labour, and Dickens writing novels to better the condition of the poor, Macaulay went vigorously to work on what he thought to be the most important task of the hour, and by his brilliant speeches did perhaps more than any other single man to force the passage of the famous Reform Bill. Like many of the Elizabethans, he was a practical man of affairs rather than a literary man, and though we miss in his writings the imagination and the spiritual insight which stamp the literary genius, we have the impression always of a keen, practical, honest mind, which looks at present problems in the light of past experience. Moreover, the man himself, with his marvellous mind, his happy spirit, and his absolute integrity of character, is an inspiration to better living.

Life. Macaulay was born at Rothley Temple, Leicestershire, in 1800. His father, of Scotch descent, was at one time governor of the Sierra Leone colony for liberated negroes, and devoted a large part of his life to the abolition of the slave trade. His mother, of Quaker parentage, was a brilliant, sensitive woman, whose character is reflected in that of her son. The influence of these two, and the son's loyal devotion to his family, can best be read in Trevelyan's interesting biography.

As a child, Macaulay is strongly suggestive of Coleridge. At three years of age he began to read eagerly; at five he 'talked like a book'; at ten he had written a compendium of universal history, besides various hymns, verse romances, arguments for Christianity, and one ambitious epic poem. The habit of rapid reading, begun in childhood, continued throughout his life, and the number and variety of books which he read is almost incredible. His memory was phenomenal. He could repeat long poems and essays after a single reading; he could quote not only passages but the greater part of many books, including *Pilgrim's Progress, Paradise Lost,* and various novels like *Clarissa.* Once, to test his memory, he recited two newspaper poems which he had read in a coffee house forty years before, and which he had never thought of in the interval.

At twelve years of age this remarkable boy was sent to a private school at Little Shelford, and at eighteen he entered Trinity College, Cambridge. Here he made a reputation as a classical scholar and a brilliant talker, but made a failure of his mathematics. In a letter to his mother he wrote: 'Oh for words to express my abomination of that science... Discipline of the mind! Say rather starvation, confinement, torture, annihilation!' We quote this as a commentary on Macaulay's later writings, which are frequently lacking in the exactness and the logical sequence of the science which he detested.

After his college course Macaulay studied law, was admitted to the bar, devoted himself largely to politics, entered Parliament in 1830, and almost immediately won a reputation as the best debater and the most eloquent speaker of the Liberal or Whig party. Gladstone says of him: 'Whenever he arose to speak it was a summons like a trumpet call to fill the benches.' At the time of his election he was poor, and the loss of his father's property threw upon him the support of his brothers and sisters; but he took up the burden with cheerful courage, and by his own efforts soon placed himself and his family in comfort. His political progress was rapid, and was due not to favouritism or intrigue, but to his ability, his hard work, and his sterling character. He was several times elected to Parliament, was legal adviser to the Supreme Council of India, was a member of the cabinet, and declined many offices for which other men labour a lifetime. In 1857 his great ability and services to his country were recognized by his being raised to the peerage with the title of Baron Macaulay of Rothley.

Thomas Babington Macaulay

Macaulay's literary work began in college with the contribution of various ballads and essays to the magazines. In his later life practical affairs claimed the greater part of his time, and his brilliant essays were written in the early morning or late at night. His famous *Essay on Milton* appeared in the *Edinburgh Review* in 1825. It created a sensation, and Macaulay, having gained the ear of the public, never once lost it during the twenty years in which he was a contributor to the magazines. His *Lays of Ancient Rome* appeared in 1842, and in the following year three volumes of his collected *Essays*. In 1847 he lost his seat in Parliament, temporarily, through his zealous efforts in behalf of religious toleration; and the loss was most fortunate, since it gave him opportunity to begin his *History of England*—a monumental work which he had been planning for many years. The first two volumes appeared in 1848, and their success can be compared only to that of the most popular novels. The third and fourth volumes of the *History* (1855) were even more successful, and Macaulay was hard at work on the remaining volumes when he died, quite suddenly, in 1859. He was buried, near Addison, in the Poets' Corner of Westminster Abbey. A paragraph from one of his letters, written at the height of his fame and influence, may give us an insight into his life and work:

I can truly say that I have not, for many years, been so happy as I am at present... I am free. I am independent. I am in Parliament, as honourably seated as man can be. My family is comfortably off. I have leisure for literature, yet I am not reduced to the necessity of writing for money. If

I had to choose a lot from all that there are in human life, I am not sure that I should prefer any to that which has fallen to me. I am sincerely and thoroughly contented.

Works of Macaulay. Macaulay is famous in literature for his essays, for his martial ballads, and for his *History of England.* His first important work, the *Essay on Milton* (1825), is worthy of study not only for itself, as a critical estimate of the Puritan poet, but as a key to all Macaulay's writings. Here, first of all, is an interesting work, which, however much we differ from the author's opinion, holds our attention and generally makes us regret that the end comes so soon. The second thing to note is the historical flavor of the essay. We study not only Milton, but also the times in which he lived, and the great movements of which he was a part. History and literature properly belong together, and Macaulay was one of the first writers to explain the historical conditions which partly account for a writer's work and influence. The third thing to note is Macaulay's enthusiasm for his subject—an enthusiasm which is often partisan, but which we gladly share for the moment as we follow the breathless narrative. Macaulay generally makes a hero of his man, shows him battling against odds, and the heroic side of our own nature awakens and responds to the author's plea. The fourth, and perhaps most characteristic thing in the essay is the style, which is remarkably clear, forceful, and convincing. Jeffrey, the editor of the *Edinburgh Review,* wrote enthusiastically when he received the manuscript, 'The more I think, the less I can conceive where you picked up that style.' We still share in the editor's wonder; but the more we think, the less we conceive that such a style could be picked up. It was partly the result of a well-stored mind, partly of unconscious imitation of other writers, and partly of that natural talent for clear speaking and writing which is manifest in all Macaulay's work.

Essay on Milton

In the remaining essays we find the same general qualities which characterize Macaulay's first attempt. They cover a wide range of subjects, but they may be divided into two general classes, the literary or critical, and the historical. Of the literary essays the best are those on Milton, Addison, Goldsmith, Byron, Dryden, Leigh Hunt, Bunyan, Bacon, and Johnson. Among the best known of the historical essays are those on Lord Clive, Chatham, Warren Hastings, Hallam's Constitutional History, Von Ranke's History of the Papacy, Frederick the Great, Horace Walpole, William Pitt, Sir William Temple, Machiavelli, and Mirabeau. Most of these were produced in the vigour of young manhood, between 1825 and 1845, while the writer was busy with practical affairs of state. They are often one-sided and inaccurate, but always interesting, and from them a large number of busy people have derived their first knowledge of history and literature.

Other Essays

The best of Macaulay's poetical work is found in the *Lays of Ancient Rome* (1842), a collection of ballads in the style of Scott, which sing of the old heroic days of the Roman republic. The ballad does not require much thought or emotion. It demands clearness, vigour, enthusiasm, action; and it suited Macaulay's genius perfectly. He was, however, much more careful than other ballad writers in making his narrative true to tradition. The stirring martial spirit of these ballads, their fine workmanship, and their appeal to courage and patriotism made them instantly popular. Even today, after more than fifty years, such ballads as those on Virginius and Horatius at the Bridge are favourite pieces in many school readers.

Lays of Ancient Rome

The *History of England,* Macaulay's masterpiece, is still one of the most popular historical works in the English language. Originally it was intended to cover the period from the accession of James II, in 1685, to the death of George IV, in 1830. Only five volumes of the work were finished, and so thoroughly did Macaulay go into details that these five volumes cover only sixteen years. It has been estimated that to complete the work on the same scale would require some fifty volumes and the labour of one man for over a century.

History of England

In his historical method Macaulay suggests Gibbon. His own knowledge of history was very great, but before writing he read numberless pages, consulted original documents, and visited the scenes which he intended to describe. Thackeray's remark, that 'Macaulay reads twenty books to write a sentence and travels one hundred miles to make a line of description', is, in view of his industry, a well-warranted exaggeration.

As in his literary essays, he is fond of making heroes, and he throws himself so heartily into the spirit of the scene he is describing that his word pictures almost startle us by their vivid reality. The story of Monmouth's rebellion, for instance, or the trial of the seven bishops, is as fascinating as the best chapters of Scott's historical novels.

While Macaulay's search for original sources of information suggests the scientific historian, his use of his material is much more like that of a novelist or playwright. In his essay on Machiavelli he writes: 'The best portraits are perhaps those in which there is a slight mixture of caricature, and we are not certain that the best histories are not those in which a little of the exaggeration of fictitious narrative is judiciously employed. Something is lost in accuracy, but much is gained in effect.'[1] Whether this estimate of historical writing be true or false, Macaulay employed it in his own work and made his narrative as absorbing as a novel. To all his characters he gives the reality of flesh and blood, and in his own words he 'shows us over their houses and seats us at their tables.' All that is excellent, but it has its disadvantages. In his admiration for heroism, Macaulay makes some of his characters too good and others too bad. In his zeal for details he misses the importance of great movements, and of great leaders who are accustomed to ignore details; and in his joy of describing events he often loses sight of underlying causes. In a word, he is without historical insight, and his work, though fascinating, is seldom placed among the reliable histories of England.

---

[1] *Essays,* Riverside edition, I, 318.

General Characteristics. To the reader who studies Macaulay's brilliant essays and a few chosen chapters of his *History,* three things soon become manifest. First, Macaulay's art is that of a public speaker rather than that of a literary man. He has a wonderful command of language, and he makes his meaning clear by striking phrases, vigorous antitheses, anecdotes, and illustrations. His style is so clear that 'he who runs may read', and from beginning to end he never loses the attention of his readers. Second, Macaulay's good spirits and enthusiasm are contagious. As he said himself, he wrote 'out of a full head', chiefly for his own pleasure or recreation; and one who writes joyously generally awakens a sense of pleasure in his readers. Third, Macaulay has 'the defect of his qualities'. He reads and remembers so much that he has no time to think or to form settled opinions. As Gladstone said, Macaulay is 'always conversing or recollecting or reading or composing, but reflecting never.' So he wrote his brilliant *Essay on Milton,* which took all England by storm, and said of it afterward that it contained 'scarcely a paragraph which his mature judgment approved.' Whether he speaks or writes, he has always before him an eager audience, and he feels within him the born orator's power to hold and fascinate. So he gives loose rein to his enthusiasm, quotes from a hundred books, and in his delight at entertaining us forgets that the first quality of a critical or historical work is to be accurate, and the second to be interesting.

THOMAS CARLYLE (1795-1881)

In marked contrast with Macaulay, the brilliant and cheerful essayist, is Thomas Carlyle, the prophet and censor of the nineteenth century. Macaulay is the practical man of affairs, helping and rejoicing in the progress of his beloved England. Carlyle lives apart from all practical interests, looks with distrust on the progress of his age, and tells men that truth, justice, and immortality are the only worthy objects of human endeavour. Macaulay is delighted with material comforts; he is most at home in brilliant and fashionable company; and he writes, even when ill and suffering, with unfailing hopefulness and good nature. Carlyle is like a Hebrew prophet just in from the desert, and the burden of his message is, 'Woe to them that are at ease in Zion!' Both men are, in different ways, typical of the century, and somewhere between the two extremes—the practical, helpful activity of Macaulay and the spiritual agony and conflict of Carlyle—we shall find the measure of an age which has left the deepest impress upon our own.

Life of Carlyle. Carlyle was born at Ecclefechan, Dumfriesshire, in 1795, a few months before Burns's death, and before Scott had published his first work. Like Burns, he came of peasant stock—strong, simple, God-fearing folk, whose influence in Carlyle's later life is beyond calculation. Of his mother he says, 'She was too mild and peaceful for the planet she lived in'; and of his father, a stone mason, he writes, 'Could I write my books as he built his houses, walk my way so manfully through this shadow world, and leave it with so little blame, it were more than all my hopes.'

Of Carlyle's early school life we have some interesting glimpses in *Sartor Resartus*. At nine years he entered the Annan grammar school, where he was bullied by the older boys, who nicknamed him Tom the Tearful. For the teachers of those days he has only ridicule, calling them 'hide-bound pedants', and he calls the school by the suggestive German name of *Hinterschlag Gymnasium*. At the wish of his parents, who intended Carlyle for the ministry, he endured this hateful school life till 1809, when he entered Edinburgh University. There he spent five miserable years, of which his own record is: 'I was without friends, experience, or connection in

University of Edinburgh

the sphere of human business, was of sly humour, proud enough and to spare, and had begun my long curriculum of dyspepsia.' This nagging illness was the cause of much of that irritability of temper which frequently led him to scold the public, and for which he has been harshly handled by unfriendly critics.

The period following his university course was one of storm and stress for Carlyle. Much to the grief of the father whom he loved, he had given up the idea of entering the ministry. Wherever he turned, doubts like a thick fog surrounded him—doubts of God, of his fellow-men, of human progress, of himself. He was poor, and to earn an honest living was his first problem. He tried successively teaching school, tutoring, the study of law, and writing miscellaneous articles for the *Edinburgh Encyclopaedia.* All the while he was fighting his doubts, living, as he says, 'in a continual, indefinite, pining fear.' After six or seven years of mental agony, which has at times a suggestion of Bunyan's spiritual struggle, the crisis came in 1821, when Carlyle suddenly shook off his doubts and found himself. 'All at once', he says in *Sartor,* 'there arose a thought in me, and I asked myself: "What *Art* thou afraid of? Wherefore like a coward dost thou forever pip and whimper, and go cowering and trembling? Despicable biped! What is the sum total of the worst that lies before thee? Death? Well, Death; and say the pangs of Tophet too, and all that the Devil and Man may, will, or can do against thee! Hast thou not a heart; canst thou not suffer whatsoever it be; and, as a Child of Freedom, though outcast, trample Tophet itself under thy feet, while it consumes thee? Let it come then; I will meet it and defy it!" And as I so thought, there rushed like a stream of fire over my whole soul; and I shook base Fear away from me forever. This struggle between fear and faith, and the triumph of the latter, is recorded in two remarkable chapters, 'The Everlasting No' and 'The Everlasting Yea', of *Sartor Resartus.*

Carlyle now definitely resolved on a literary life, and began with any work that offered a bare livelihood. He translated Legendre's *Geometry* from the French, wrote numerous essays for the magazines, and continued his study of German while making translations from that language. His translation of Goethe's *Wilhelm Meister* appeared in 1824, his *Life of Schiller* in 1825, and his *Specimens of German Romance* in 1827. He began at this time a correspondence with Goethe, his literary hero, which lasted till the German poet's death in 1832. While still busy with 'hack work', Carlyle,

Thomas Carlyle
After the portrait by James McNeill Whistler

in 1826, married Jane Welsh, a brilliant and beautiful woman, whose literary genius almost equalled that of her husband. Soon afterwards, influenced chiefly by poverty, the Carlyles retired to a farm, at Craigenputtoch (Hawks' Hill), a dreary and lonely spot, far from friends and even neighbours. They remained here six years, during which time Carlyle wrote many of his best essays, and *Sartor Resartus,* his most original work. The latter went begging among publishers for two years, and was finally published serially in *Eraser's Magazine,* in 1833-1834. By this time Carlyle had begun to attract attention as a writer, and, thinking that one who made his living by the magazines should be in close touch with the editors, took his wife's advice and moved to London 'to seek work and bread.' He settled in Cheyne Row, Chelsea—a place made famous by More, Erasmus, Bolingbroke, Smollett, Leigh Hunt, and many lesser lights of literature—and began to enjoy the first real peace he had known since childhood. In 1837 appeared *The French Revolution,* which first made Carlyle famous; and in the same year, led by the necessity of earning money, he began the series of lectures—*German Literature* (1837), *Periods of European Culture* (1838), *Revolutions of Modern Europe* (1839), *Heroes and Hero Worship* (1841)—which created a sensation in London. 'It was', says Leigh Hunt, 'as if some Puritan had come to life again, liberalized by German philosophy and his own intense reflection and experience.'

Though Carlyle set himself against the spirit of his age, calling the famous Reform Bill a 'progress into darkness', and democracy 'the rule of the worst rather than the best', his rough sincerity was unquestioned, and his remarks were more quoted than those of any other living man. He was supported, moreover, by a rare circle of friends—Edward Irving, Southey, Sterling, Landor, Leigh Hunt, Dickens, Mill, Tennyson, Browning, and, most helpful of all, Emerson, who had visited Carlyle at Craigenputtoch in 1833. It was due largely to Emerson's influence that Carlyle"s works were better appreciated, and brought better financial rewards, in America than in England.

Carlyle's fame reached its climax in the monumental *History of Frederick the Great* (1858-1865), published after thirteen years of solitary toil, which, in his own words, 'made entire devastation of home life and happiness.' The proudest moment of his life was when he was elected to succeed Gladstone as lord rector of Edinburgh University, in 1865, the year in which *Frederick the Great* was finished. In the midst of his triumph, and while he was in Scotland to deliver his inaugural address, his happiness was suddenly destroyed by the death of his wife—a terrible blow, from which he never recovered. He lived on for fifteen years, shorn of his strength and interest in life; and his closing hours were like the dull sunset of a November day. Only as we remember his grief and remorse at the death of the companion who had shared his toil but not his triumph, can we understand the sorrow that pervades the pages of his *Reminiscences.* He died in 1881, and at his own wish was buried, not in Westminster Abbey, but among his humble kinsfolk in Ecclefechan. However much we may differ from his philosophy or regret the harshness of his minor works, we shall probably all agree in this sentiment from one of his own letters—that the object of all his struggle and writing was 'that men should find out and believe the truth, and match their lives to it.'

Works of Carlyle. There are two widely different judgments of Carlyle as a man and a writer. The first, which is founded largely on his minor writings, like *Chartism, Latter Day Pamphlets,* and *Shooting Niagara,* declares that he is a misanthrope and dyspeptic with a barbarous style of writing; that he denounces progress, democracy, science, America, Darwin—everybody and everything that he does not understand; that his literary opinions are largely prejudices; that he began as a prophet and ended as a scold; and that in denouncing shams of every sort he was something of a sham himself, since his practice was not in accord with his own preaching. The second judgment, which is founded upon *Heroes and Hero Worship, Cromwell,* and *Sartor Resartus,* declares that these works are the supreme manifestation of genius; that their rugged, picturesque style makes others look feeble or colourless by comparison; and that the author is the greatest teacher, leader, and prophet of the nineteenth century.

Somewhere between these two extremes will be found the truth about Carlyle. We only note here that, while there are some grounds for the first unfavourable criticism, we are to judge an author by his best rather than by his worst work; and that a man's aims as well as his accomplishments must be taken into consideration. As it is written, 'Whereas it was in thine heart to build an house unto my name, thou didst well that it was in thine heart.' Whatever the defects of Carlyle and his work, in his heart he was always planning a house or temple to the God of truth and justice.

Carlyle's important works may be divided into three general classes—critical and literary essays, historical works, and *Sartor Resartus,* the last being in a class by itself, since there is nothing like it in literature. To these should be added a biography, the admirable *Life of John Sterling,* and Carlyle's *Letters* and *Reminiscences,* which are more interesting and suggestive than some of his better known works. We omit here all consideration of translations, and his intemperate denunciations of men and institutions in *Chartism, Latter-Day Pamphlets,* and other essays, which add nothing to the author's fame or influence.

Of the essays, which are all characterized by Carlyle's zeal to get at the heart of things, and to reveal the soul rather than the works of a writer, the best are those on 'Burns', 'Scott', 'Novalis', 'Goethe', 'Characteristics', 'Signs of the Times', and 'Boswell's Life of Johnson.'[1] In the famous *Essay on Burns,* which is generally selected for special study, we note four significant things: (1) Carlyle is peculiarly well fitted for his task, having many points in common with his hero. (2) In most of his work Carlyle, by his style and mannerisms and positive opinions, generally attracts our attention away from his subject; but in this essay he shows himself capable of forgetting himself for a moment. To an unusual extent he sticks to his subject, and makes us think of Burns rather than of Carlyle. The style, though unpolished, is fairly simple and readable, and is free from the breaks, crudities, ejaculations, and general 'nodulosities' which disfigure much of his work. (3) Carlyle has an original and interesting theory of biography and criticism. The object of criticism is to show the man himself, his aims, ideals, and outlook on the universe; the

Essay on Burns

[1] The student should remember that Carlyle's literary opinions, though very positive, are to be received with caution. Sometimes, indeed, they are so one-sided and prejudiced that they are more valuable as a revelation of Carlyle himself than as a study of the author he is considering.

object of biography is 'to show what and how produced was the effect of society upon him; what and how produced was his effect on society.' (4) Carlyle is often severe, even harsh, in his estimates of other men, but in this case the tragedy of Burns's 'life of fragments' attracts and softens him. He grows enthusiastic and—a rare thing for Carlyle—apologizes for his enthusiasm in the striking sentence, 'We love Burns, and we pity him; and love and pity are prone to magnify.' So he gives us the most tender and appreciative of his essays, and one of the most illuminating criticisms of Burns that has appeared in our language.

Heroes and Hero Worship

The central idea of Carlyle's historical works is found in his *Heroes and Hero Worship* (1841), his most widely read book. 'Universal history', he says, 'is at bottom the history of the great men who have worked here.' To get at the truth of history we must study not movements but men, and read not state papers but the biographies of heroes. His summary of history as presented in this work has six divisions: (1) The Hero as Divinity, having for its general subject Odin, the 'type Norseman', who, Carlyle thinks, was some old heroic chief, afterwards defied by his countrymen; (2) The Hero as Prophet, treating of Mahomet and the rise of Islam; (3) The Hero as Poet, in which Dante and Shakespeare are taken as types; (4) The Hero as Priest, or religious leader, in which Luther appears as the hero of the Reformation, and Knox as the hero of Puritanism; (5) The Hero as Man of Letters, in which we have the curious choice of Johnson, Rousseau, and Burns; (6) The Hero as King, in which Cromwell and Napoleon appear as the heroes of reform by revolution.

It is needless to say that Heroes is not a book of history; neither is it scientifically written in the manner of Gibbon. With science in any form Carlyle had no patience; and he miscalculated the value of that patient search for facts and evidence which science undertakes before building any theories, either of kings or cabbages. The book, therefore, abounds in errors; but they are the errors of carelessness and are perhaps of small consequence. His misconception of history, however, is more serious. With the modern idea of history, as the growth of freedom among all classes, he has no sympathy. The progress of democracy was to him an evil thing, a 'turning of the face towards darkness and anarchy.' At certain periods, according to Carlyle, God sends us geniuses, sometimes as priests or poets, sometimes as soldiers or statesmen; but in whatever guise they appear, these are our real rulers. He shows, moreover, that whenever such men appear, multitudes follow them, and that a man's following is a sure index of his heroism and kingship.

Whether we agree with Carlyle or not, we must accept for the moment his peculiar view of history, else Heroes can never open its treasures to us. The book abounds in startling ideas, expressed with originality and power, and is pervaded throughout by an atmosphere of intense moral earnestness. The more we read it, the more we find to admire and to remember.

French Revolution

Carlyle's *French Revolution* (1837) is to be taken more seriously as a historical work; but here again his hero worship comes to the front, and his book is a series of flashlights thrown upon men in dramatic situations, rather than a tracing of causes to their consequences. The very titles of his chapters—'Astræa Redux', 'Windbags', 'Broglie the War God'—do violence to our conception of history, and are more suggestive of Carlyle's individualism than of French history. He is here the preacher rather than the historian; his text is the eternal justice; and his message is that all wrongdoing is inevitably followed by vengeance. His method is intensely dramatic. From a mass of historical details he selects a few picturesque incidents and striking figures, and his vivid pictures of the storming of the Bastille, the rush of the mob to Versailles, the death of Louis XVI, and the Reign of Terror, seem like the work of an eyewitness describing some terrible catastrophe. At times, as it portrays Danton, Robespierre, and the great characters of the tragedy, Carlyle's work is suggestive of an historical play of Shakespeare; and again, as it describes the rush and riot of men led by elemental passion, it is more like a great prose epic. Though not a reliable history in any sense, it is one of the most dramatic and stirring narratives in our language.

Two other historical works deserve at least a passing notice. The *History of Frederick the Great* (1858-1865), in six volumes, is a colossal picture of the life and times of the hero of the Prussian Empire. *Oliver Cromwell's Letters and Speeches* is, in our personal judgment, Carlyle's best historical work. His idea is to present the very soul of the great Puritan leader. He gives us, as of first importance, Cromwell's own words, and connects them by a commentary in which other men and events are described with vigour and vividness. Cromwell was one of Carlyle's greatest heroes, and in this case he is most careful to present the facts which occasion his own enthusiasm. The result is, on the whole, the most lifelike picture of a great historical character that we possess. Other historians had heaped calumny upon Cromwell till the English public regarded him with prejudice and horror; and it is an indication of Carlyle's power that by a single book he revolutionized England's opinion of one of her greatest men.

Oliver Cromwell

Carlyle's *Sartor Resartus* (1834), his only creative work, is a mixture of philosophy and romance, of wisdom and nonsense—a chaotic jumble of the author's thoughts, feelings, and experiences during the first thirty-five years of his life. The title, which means 'The Tailor Patched-up', is taken from an old Scotch song. The hero is Diogenes Teufelsdroeckh, a German professor at the University of Weissnichtwo (don't know where); the narrative concerns this queer professor's life and opinions; and the central thought of the book is the philosophy of clothes, which are considered symbolically as the outward expression of spirit. Thus, man's body is the outward garment of his soul, and the universe is the visible garment of the invisible God. The arrangement of *Sartor* is clumsy and hard to follow. In order to leave himself free to bring in everything he thought about, Carlyle assumed the position of one who was translating and editing the old professor's manuscripts, which are supposed to consist of numerous sheets stuffed into twelve paper bags, each labelled with a sign of the zodiac. The editor pretends to make order out of this chaos; but he is free to jump from one subject to another and to

Sartor Resartus

state the most startling opinion by simply using quotation marks and adding a note that he is not responsible for Teufelsdroeckh's crazy notions—which are in reality Carlyle's own dreams and ideals. Partly because of the matter, which is sometimes incoherent, partly because of the style, which, though picturesque, is sometimes confused and ungrammatical, Sartor is not easy reading; but it amply repays whatever time and study we give to it. Many of its passages are more like poetry than prose; and one cannot read such chapters as 'The Everlasting No', 'The Everlasting Yea', 'Reminiscences', and 'Natural Supernaturalism', and be quite the same man afterwards; for Carlyle's thought has entered into him, and he walks henceforth more gently, more reverently through the world, as in the presence of the Eternal.

General Characteristics. Concerning Carlyle's style there are almost as many opinions as there are readers. This is partly because he impresses different people in widely different ways, and partly because his expression varies greatly. At times he is calm, persuasive, grimly humorous, as if conversing; at other times, wildly exclamatory, as if he were shouting and waving his arms at the reader. We have spoken of Macaulay's style as that of the finished orator, and we might reasonably speak of Carlyle's as that of the exhorter, who cares little for methods so long as he makes a strong impression on his hearers. 'Every sentence is alive to its finger tips', writes a modern critic; and though Carlyle often violates the rules of grammar and rhetoric, we can well afford to let an original genius express his own intense conviction in his own vivid and picturesque way.

Carlyle's Style

Carlyle's message may be summed up in two imperatives—labour, and be sincere. He lectured and wrote chiefly for the upper classes who had begun to think, somewhat sentimentally, of the conditions of the labouring men of the world; and he demanded for the latter, not charity or pity, but justice and honour. All labour, whether of head or hand, is divine; and labour alone justifies a man as a son of earth and heaven. To society, which Carlyle thought to be occupied wholly

His Message

with conventional affairs, he came with the stamp of sincerity, calling upon men to lay aside hypocrisy and to think and speak and live the truth. He had none of Addison's delicate satire and humour, and in his fury at what he thought was false he was generally unsympathetic and often harsh; but we must not forget that Thackeray—who knew society much better than did Carlyle—gave a very unflattering picture of it in *Vanity Fair* and *The Book of Snobs.* Apparently the age needed plain speaking, and Carlyle furnished it in scripture measure. Harriet Martineau, who knew the world for which Carlyle wrote, summed up his influence when she said that he had 'infused into the mind of the English nation—sincerity, earnestness, healthfulness, and courage.' If we add to the above message Carlyle's conceptions of the world as governed by a God of justice who never forgets, and of human history as 'an inarticulate Bible', slowly revealing the divine purpose, we shall understand better the force of his ethical appeal and the profound influence he exercised on the moral and intellectual life of the past century.

JOHN RUSKIN (1819-1900)

In approaching the study of Ruskin we are to remember, first of all, that we are dealing with a great and good man, who is himself more inspiring than any of his books. In some respects he is like his friend Carlyle, whose disciple he acknowledged himself to be; but he is broader in his sympathies, and in every way more hopeful, helpful, and humane. Thus, in the face of the drudgery and poverty of the competitive system, Carlyle proposed, with the grim satire of Swift's 'Modest Proposal', to organize an annual hunt in which successful people should shoot the unfortunate, and to use the game for the support of the army and navy. Ruskin, facing the same problem, wrote: 'I will endure it no longer quietly; but henceforward, with any few or many who will help, do my best to abate this misery.' Then, leaving the field of art criticism, where he was the acknowledged leader, he begins to write of labour and justice; gives his fortune in charity, in establishing schools and libraries; and founds his St. George's Guild of workingmen, to put in practice the principles of brotherhood and cooperation for which he and Carlyle contended. Though his style marks him as one of the masters of English prose, he is generally studied not as a literary man but as an ethical teacher, and we shall hardly appreciate his works unless we see behind every book the figure of the heroically sincere man who wrote it.

Life. Ruskin was born in London, in 1819. His father was a prosperous wine merchant who gained a fortune in trade, and who spent his leisure hours in the company of good books and pictures. On his tombstone one may still read this inscription written by Ruskin: 'He was an entirely honest merchant and his memory is to all who keep it dear and helpful. His son, whom he loved to the uttermost and taught to speak truth, says this of him.' Ruskin's mother, a devout and somewhat austere woman, brought her son up with Puritanical strictness, not forgetting Solomon's injunction that 'the rod and reproof give wisdom.'

Of Ruskin's early years at Herne Hill, on the outskirts of London, it is better to read his own interesting record in Praterita. It was in some respects a cramped and lonely childhood, but certain things which strongly moulded his character are worthy of mention. First, he was taught by word and example in all things to speak the truth, and he never forgot the lesson. Second, he had few toys, and spent much time in studying the leaves, the flowers, the grass, the clouds, even the figures and colors of the carpet, and so laid the foundation for that minute and accurate observation which is manifest in all his writings. Third, he was educated first by his mother, then by private tutors, and so missed the discipline of the public schools. The influence of this lonely training is evident in all his work. Like Carlyle, he is often too positive and dogmatic—the result of failing to test his work by the standards of other men of his age. Fourth, he was obliged to read the Bible every day and to learn long passages verbatim. The result of this training was, he says, 'to make every word of the Scriptures familiar to my ear in habitual music.' We can hardly read a page of his later work without finding some reflection of the noble simplicity or vivid imagery of the sacred records. Fifth, he travelled much with his father and mother, and his innate love of nature was intensified by what he saw on his leisurely journeys through the most beautiful parts of England and the Continent.

Ruskin entered Christ Church College, Oxford, in 1836, when only seventeen years old. He was at this time a shy, sensitive boy, a lover of nature and of every art which reflects nature, but almost entirely ignorant of the ways of boys and men. An attack of consumption, with which he had long been threatened, caused him to leave Oxford in 1840, and for nearly two years he wandered over Italy searching for health and cheerfulness, and gathering materials for the first volume of *Modern Painters,* the book that made him famous.

Ruskin's literary work began in childhood, when he was encouraged to write freely in prose and poetry. A volume of poems illustrated by his own drawings was published in 1859, after he had won fame as a prose writer, but, save for the drawings, it is of small importance. The first volume of *Modern Painters* (1843) was begun as a heated defence of the artist Turner, but it developed into an essay on art as a true picture of nature, 'not only in her outward aspect but in her inward spirit.' The work, which was signed simply 'Oxford Graduate', aroused a storm of mingled approval and protest; but however much critics warred over its theories of art, all were agreed that the unknown author was a master of descriptive prose. Ruskin now made frequent trips to the art galleries of the Continent, and produced four more volumes of *Modern Painters* during the next seventeen years. Meanwhile he wrote other books—*Seven Lamps of Architecture* (1849), *Stones of Venice* (1851-1853), *Pre-Raphaelitism,* and numerous lectures and essays, which gave him a place in the world of art similar to that held by Matthew Arnold in the world of letters. In 1869 he was appointed professor of art at Oxford, a position which greatly increased his prestige and influence, not only among students but among a great variety of people who heard his lectures and read his published works. *Lectures on*

John Ruskin

Art, Aratra Pentelici (lectures on sculpture), *Ariadne Florentina* (lectures on engraving), *Michael Angelo and Tintoret, The Art of England, Val d'Arno* (lectures on Tuscan art), *St. Mark's Rest* (a history of Venice), *Mornings in Florence* (studies in Christian art, now much used as a guidebook to the picture galleries of Florence), *The Laws of Fiesole* (a treatise on drawing and painting for schools), *Academy of Fine Arts in Venice, Pleasures of England*—all these works on art show Ruskin's literary industry. And we must also record *Love's Meinie* (a study of birds), *Proserpina* (a study of flowers), *Deucalion* (a study of waves and stones), besides various essays on political economy which indicate that Ruskin, like Arnold, had begun to consider the practical problems of his age.

At the height of his fame, in 1860, Ruskin turned for a time from art, to consider questions of wealth and labour—terms which were used glibly by the economists of the age without much thought for their fundamental meaning. 'There is no wealth but life', announced Ruskin—'life, including all its powers of love, of joy, and of admiration. That country is the richest which nourishes the greatest number of noble and happy human beings.' Such a doctrine, proclaimed by Goldsmith in his *Deserted Village,* was regarded as a pretty sentiment, but coming from one of the greatest leaders and teachers of England it was like a bombshell. Ruskin wrote four essays establishing this doctrine and pleading for a more socialistic form of government in which reform might be possible. The essays were published in the *Cornhill Magazine,* of which Thackeray was editor, and they aroused such a storm that the publication was discontinued. Ruskin then published the essays in book form, with the title *Unto This Last,* in 1862. *Munera Pulveris* (1862) was another work in which the principles of capital and labour and the evils of the competitive system were discussed in such a way that the author was denounced as a visionary or a madman. Other works of this practical period are *Time and Tide, Fors Clavigera, Sesame* and *Lilies,* and the *Crown of Wild Olive.*

The latter part of Ruskin's life was a time of increasing sadness, due partly to the failure of his plans, and partly to public attacks upon his motives or upon his sanity. He grew bitter at first, as his critics ridiculed or denounced his principles, and at times his voice is as querulous as that of Carlyle. We are to remember, however, the conditions under which he struggled. His health had been shattered by successive attacks of disease;

he had been disappointed in love; his marriage was unhappy; and his work seemed a failure. He had given nearly all his fortune in charity, and the poor were more numerous than ever before. His famous St. George's Guild was not successful, and the tyranny of the competitive system seemed too deeply rooted to be overthrown. On the death of his mother he left London and, in 1879, retired to Brantwood, on Coniston Lake, in the beautiful region beloved of Wordsworth. Here he passed the last quiet years of his life under the care of his cousin, Mrs. Severn, the 'angel of the house', and wrote, at Professor Norton's suggestion, *Præterita,* one of his most interesting books, in which he describes the events of his youth from his own viewpoint. He died quietly in 1900, and was buried, as he wished, without funeral pomp or public ceremony, in the little churchyard at Coniston.

Works of Ruskin. There are three little books which, in popular favour, stand first on the list of Ruskin's numerous works—*Ethics-of-the-Dust,* a series of Lectures to Little Housewives, which appeals most to women; *Crown of Wild Olive,* three lectures on Work, Traffic, and War, which appeals to thoughtful men facing the problems of work and duty; and *Sesame and Lilies,* which appeals to men and women alike. The last is the most widely known of Ruskin's works and the best with which to begin our reading.

Sesame and Lilies

The first thing we notice in *Sesame and Lilies* is the symbolical title. 'Sesame', taken from the story of the robbers' cave in the *Arabian Nights,* means a secret word or talisman which unlocks a treasure house. It was intended, no doubt, to introduce the first part of the work, called 'Of Kings' Treasuries', which treats of books and reading. 'Lilies', taken from Isaiah as a symbol of beauty, purity, and peace, introduces the second lecture, 'Of Queens' Gardens', which is an exquisite study of woman's life and education. These two lectures properly constitute the book, but a third is added, on 'The Mystery of Life.' The last begins in a monologue upon his own failures in life, and is pervaded by an atmosphere of sadness, sometimes of pessimism, quite different from the spirit of the other two lectures.

Though the theme of the first lecture is books, Ruskin manages to present to his audience his whole philosophy of life. He gives us, with a wealth of detail, a description of what constitutes a real book; he looks into the meaning of words, and teaches us how to read, using a selection from Milton's *Lycidas* as an illustration. This study of words gives us the key with which we are to unlock 'Kings' Treasuries', that is, the books which contain the precious thoughts of the kingly minds of all ages. He shows the real meaning and end of education, the value of labour and of a purpose in life; he treats of nature, science, art, literature, religion; he defines the purpose of government, showing that soul-life, not money or trade, is the measure of national greatness; and he criticizes the general injustice of his age, quoting a heart-rending story of toil and suffering from the newspapers to show how close his theory is to daily needs. Here is an astonishing variety in a small compass; but there is no confusion. Ruskin's mind was wonderfully analytical, and one subject develops naturally from the other.

Kings' Treasuries

In the second lecture, 'Of Queens' Gardens', he considers the question of woman's place and education, which Tennyson had attempted to answer in *The Princess.* Ruskin's theory is that the purpose of all education is to acquire power to bless and to redeem human society; and that in this noble work woman must always play the leading part. He searches all literature for illustrations, and his description of literary heroines, especially of Shakespeare's perfect women, is unrivalled. Ruskin is always at his best in writing of women or for women, and the lofty idealism of this essay, together with its rare beauty of expression, makes it, on the whole, the most delightful and inspiring of his works.

Of Queens' Gardens

Among Ruskin's practical works the reader will find in *Fors Clavigera,* a series of letters to workingmen, and *Unto This Last,* four essays on the principles of political economy, the substance of his economic teachings. In the latter work, starting with the proposition that our present competitive system centres about the idea of wealth, Ruskin tries to find out what wealth is; and the pith of his teaching is this—that men are of more account than money; that a man's real wealth is found in

Unto This Last

his soul; not in his pocket; and that the prime object of life and labour is 'the producing of as many as possible full-breathed, bright-eyed, and happy-hearted human creatures.' To make this ideal practical, Ruskin makes four suggestions: (1) that training schools be established to teach young men and women three things—the laws and practice of health, habits of gentleness and justice, and the trade or calling by which they are to live; (2) that the government establish farms and workshops for the production of all the necessaries of life, where only good and honest work shall be tolerated and where a standard of work and wages shall be maintained; (3) that any person out of employment shall be received at the nearest government school: if ignorant he shall be educated, and if competent to do any work he shall have the opportunity to do it; (4) that comfortable homes be provided for the sick and for the aged, and that this be done in justice, not in charity. A labourer serves his country as truly as does a soldier or a statesman, and a pension should be no more disgraceful in one case than in the other.

Works on Art

Among Ruskin's numerous books treating of art, we recommend the Seven *Lamps of Architecture* (1849), *Stones of Venice* (1851-1853), and the first two volumes of *Modern Painters* (1843-1846). With Ruskin's art theories, which, as Sydney Smith prophesied, 'worked a complete revolution in the world of taste', we need not concern ourselves here. We simply point out four principles that are manifest in all his work: (1) that the object of art, as of every other human endeavour, is to find and to express the truth; (2) that art, in order to be true, must break away from conventionalities and copy nature; (3) that morality is closely allied with art, and that a careful study of any art reveals the moral strength or weakness of the people that produced it; (4) that the main purpose of art is not to delight a few cultured people but to serve the daily uses of common life. 'The giving brightness to pictures is much', he says, 'but the giving brightness to life is more.' In this attempt to make art serve the practical ends of life, Ruskin is allied with all the great writers of the period, who use literature as the instrument of human progress.

General Characteristics. One who reads Ruskin is in a state of mind analogous to that of a man who goes through a picture gallery, pausing now to admire a face or a landscape for its own sake, and again to marvel at the technical skill of the artist, without regard to his subject. For Ruskin is a great literary artist and a great ethical teacher, and we admire one page for its style, and the next for its message to humanity. The best of his prose, which one may find in the descriptive passages of *Præterita* and *Modern Painters,* is written in a richly ornate style, with a wealth of figures and allusions, and at times a rhythmic, melodious quality which makes it almost equal to poetry. Ruskin had a rare sensitiveness to beauty in every form, and more, perhaps, than any other writer in our language, he has helped us to see and appreciate the beauty of the world around us.

Ethical Teaching

As for Ruskin's ethical teaching, it appears in so many forms and in so many different works that any summary must appear inadequate. For a full half century he was 'the apostle of beauty' in England, and the beauty for which he pleaded was never sensuous or pagan, as in the Renaissance, but always spiritual, appealing to the soul of man rather than to his eyes, leading to better work and better living. In his economic essays Ruskin is even more directly and positively ethical. To mitigate the evils of the unreasonable competitive system under which we labour and sorrow; to bring master and man together in mutual trust and helpfulness; to seek beauty, truth, goodness as the chief ends of life, and, having found them, to make our characters correspond; to share the best treasures of art and literature with rich and poor alike; to labour always, and, whether we work with hand or head, to do our work in praise of something that we love—this sums up Ruskin's purpose and message. And the best of it is that, like Chaucer's country parson, he practiced his doctrine before he preached it.

MATTHEW ARNOLD (1822-1888)

In the world of literature Arnold has occupied for many years an authoritative position as critic and teacher, similar to that held by

Ruskin in the world of art. In his literary work two very different moods are manifest. In his poetry he reflects the doubt of an age which witnessed the conflict between science and revealed religion. Apparently he never passed through any such decisive personal struggle as is recorded in *Sartor Resartus,* and he has no positive conviction such as is voiced in 'The Everlasting Yea.' He is beset by doubts which he never settles, and his poems generally express sorrow or regret or resignation. In his prose he shows the cavalier spirit—aggressive, light-hearted, self-confident. Like Carlyle, he dislikes shams, and protests against what he calls the barbarisms of society; but he writes with a light touch, using satire and banter as the better part of his argument. Carlyle denounces with the zeal of a Hebrew prophet, and lets you know that you are hopelessly lost if you reject his message. Arnold is more like the cultivated Greek; his voice is soft, his speech suave, but he leaves the impression, if you happen to differ with him, that you must be deficient in culture. Both these men, so different in spirit and methods, confronted the same problems, sought the same ends, and were dominated by the same moral sincerity.

Life. Arnold was born in Laleham, in the valley of the Thames, in 1822. His father was Dr. Thomas Arnold, headmaster of Rugby, with whom many of us have grown familiar by reading *Tom Brown's School Days.* After fitting for the university at Winchester and at Rugby, Arnold entered Balliol College, Oxford, where he was distinguished by winning prizes in poetry and by general excellence in the classics. More than any other poet Arnold reflects the spirit of his university. 'The Scholar-Gipsy' and 'Thyrsis' contain many references to Oxford and the surrounding country, but they are more noticeable for their spirit of aloofness—as if Oxford men were too much occupied with classic dreams and ideals to concern themselves with the practical affairs of life.

After leaving the university Arnold first taught the classics at Rugby; then, in 1847, he became private secretary to Lord Lansdowne, who appointed the young poet to the position of inspector of schools under the government. In this position Arnold worked patiently for the next thirty-five years, travelling about the country, examining teachers, and correcting endless examination papers. For ten years (1857-1867) he was professor of poetry at Oxford, where his famous lectures *On Translating Homer* were given. He made numerous reports on English and foreign schools, and was three times sent abroad to study educational methods on the Continent. From this it will be seen that Arnold led a busy, often a laborious life, and we can appreciate his statement that all his best literary work was done late at night, after a day of drudgery. It is well to remember that, while Carlyle was preaching about labour, Arnold laboured daily; that his work was cheerfully and patiently done; and that after the day's work he hurried away, like Lamb, to the Elysian fields of literature. He was happily married, loved his home, and especially loved children, was free from all bitterness and envy, and, notwithstanding his cold manner, was at heart sincere, generous, and true. We shall appreciate his work better if we can see the man himself behind all that he has written.

Arnold's literary work divides itself into three periods, which we may call the poetical, the critical, and the practical. He had written poetry since his schooldays, and his first volume, *The Strayed Reveller and Other Poems,* appeared anonymously in 1849. Three years later he published *Empedocles on Etna and other Poems;* but only a few copies of these volumes were sold, and presently both were withdrawn from circulation. In 1853-1855 he published his signed Poems, and twelve years later appeared his last volume of poetry. Compared with the early work of Tennyson, these works met with little favour, and Arnold practically abandoned poetry in favor of critical writing.

The chief works of his critical period are the lectures *On Translating Homer* (1861) and the two volumes of *Essays in Criticism* (1865-1888), which made Arnold one of the best known literary men in England. Then, like Ruskin, he turned to practical questions, and his *Friendship's Garland* (1871) was intended to satirize and perhaps reform the great middle class of England, whom he called the Philistines. *Culture and Anarchy,* the most characteristic work of his practical period, appeared in 1869. These were followed by four books on religious subjects—*St. Paul and Protestantism* (1870), *Literature and Dogma* (1873), *God and the Bible* (1875), and *Last Essays on Church and Religion* (1877). *The Discourses in America* (1885) completes the list of his important works. At the height of his fame and influence he died suddenly, in 1888, and was buried in the churchyard at Laleham. The spirit of his whole life is well expressed in a few lines of one of his own early sonnets:

One lesson, Nature, let me learn of thee,
One lesson which in every wind is blown,
One lesson of two duties kept at one
Though the loud world proclaim their enmity—
Of toil unsever'd from tranquillity;
Of labour, that in lasting fruit outgrows
Far noisier schemes, accomplish'd in repose,
Too great for haste, too high for rivalry.

Works of Matthew Arnold. We shall better appreciate Arnold's poetry if we remember two things: First, he had been taught in his home a simple and devout faith in revealed religion, and in college he was thrown into a world of doubt and questioning. He faced these doubts honestly, reverently—in his heart longing to accept the faith of his fathers, but in his head demanding proof and scientific exactness. The same struggle between head and heart, between reason and intuition, goes on today, and that is one reason why Arnold's poetry, which wavers on the borderland between doubt and faith, is a favourite with many readers. Second, Arnold, as shown in his essay on *The Study of Poetry,* regarded poetry as 'a criticism of life under the conditions fixed for such criticism by the laws of poetic truth and poetic beauty.' Naturally, one who regards poetry as a 'criticism' will write very differently from one who regards poetry as the natural language of the soul. He will write for the head rather than for the heart, and will be cold and critical rather than enthusiastic. According to Arnold, each poem should be a unit, and he protested against the tendency of English poets to use brilliant phrases and figures of speech which only detract attention from the poem as a whole. For his models he went to Greek poetry, which he regarded as 'the only sure guidance to what is sound and true in poetical art.' Arnold is, however, more indebted than he thinks to English masters, especially to Wordsworth and Milton, whose influence is noticeable in a large part of his poetry.

His Poetry

Of Arnold's narrative poems the two best known are *Balder Dead* (1855), an incursion into the field of Norse mythology which is suggestive of Gray, and *Sohrab and Rustum* (1853), which takes us into the field of legendary Persian history. The theme of the latter poem is taken from the *Shah-Namah* (Book of Kings) of the Persian poet Firdausi, who lived and wrote in the eleventh century.

Sohrab and Rustrum

Briefly, the story is of one Rustem or Rustum, a Persian Achilles, who fell asleep one day when he had grown weary of hunting. While he slept a band of robbers stole his favourite horse, Ruksh. In trailing the robbers Rustum came to the palace of the king of Samengan, where he was royally welcomed, and where he fell in love with the king's daughter, Temineh, and married her. But he was of a roving, adventurous disposition, and soon went back to fight among his own people, the Persians. While he was gone his son Sohrab was born, grew to manhood, and became the hero of the Turan army. War arose between the two peoples, and two hostile armies were encamped by the Oxus. Each army chose a champion, and Rustum and Sohrab found themselves matched in mortal combat between the lines. At this point Sohrab, whose chief interest in life was to find his father, demanded to know if his enemy were not Rustum; but the latter was disguised and denied his identity. On the first day of the fight Rustum was overcome, but his life was spared by a trick and by the generosity of Sohrab. On the second day Rustum prevailed, and mortally wounded his antagonist. Then he recognized his own son by a gold bracelet which he had long ago given to his wife Temineh. The two armies, rushing into battle, were stopped by the sight of father and son weeping in each-other's arms. Sohrab died, the war ceased, and Rustum went home to a life of sorrow and remorse.

Using this interesting material, Arnold produced a poem which has the rare and difficult combination of classic reserve and romantic feeling. It is written in blank verse, and one has only to read the first few lines to see that the poet is not a master of his instrument. The lines are seldom harmonious, and we must frequently change the accent of common words, or lay stress on unimportant particles, to show the rhythm. Arnold frequently copies Milton, especially in his repetition of ideas and phrases; but the poem as a whole is lacking in Milton's wonderful melody.

The classic influence on *Sohrab and Rustum* is especially noticeable in Arnold's use of materials. Fights are short; grief is long; therefore the poet gives few lines to the combat, but lingers over the son's joy at finding his father, and the father's quenchless sorrow at the death of his son. The last lines especially, with their 'passionate grief set to solemn music', make this poem one of the best, on the whole, that Arnold has written. And the exquisite ending, where the Oxus, unmindful of the trivial strifes of men, flows on sedately to join 'his luminous home of waters' is most suggestive of the poet's conception of the orderly life of nature, in contrast with the doubt and restlessness of human life.

Miscellaneous Poems

Next in importance to the narrative poems are the elegies, 'Thyrsis', 'The Scholar-Gipsy', 'Memorial Verses', 'A Southern Night', 'Obermann', 'Stanzas from the Grande Chartreuse', and 'Rugby Chapel.' All these are worthy of careful reading, but the best is 'Thyrsis', a lament for the poet Clough, which is sometimes classed with Milton's *Lycidas* and Shelley's *Adonais.* Among the minor poems the reader will find the best expression of Arnold's ideals and methods in 'Dover Beach', the love lyrics entitled 'Switzerland', 'Requiescat', 'Shakespeare', 'The Future', 'Kensington Gardens', 'Philomela', 'Human Life', 'Callicles's Song', 'Morality', and 'Geist's Grave'—the last being an exquisite tribute to a little dog which, like all his kind, had repaid our scant crumbs of affection with a whole life's devotion.

Essays in Criticism

The first place among Arnold's prose works must be given to the *Essays in Criticism,* which raised the author to the front rank of living critics. His fundamental idea of criticism appeals to us strongly. The business of criticism, he says, is neither to find fault nor to display the critic's own learning or influence; it is to know 'the best which has been thought and said in the world', and by using this knowledge to create a current of fresh and free thought. If a choice must be made among these essays, which are all worthy of study, we would suggest 'The Study of Poetry', 'Wordsworth', 'Byron', and 'Emerson.' The last-named essay, which is found in the *Discourses in America,* is hardly a satisfactory estimate of Emerson, but its singular charm of manner and its atmosphere of intellectual culture make it perhaps the most characteristic of Arnold's prose writings.

Among the works of Arnold's practical period there are two which may be taken as typical of all the rest. *Literature and Dogma* (1873) is, in general, a plea for liberality in religion. Arnold would have us read the Bible, for instance, as we would read any other great work, and apply to it the ordinary standards of literary criticism.

Culture and Anarchy

Culture and Anarchy (1869) contains most of the terms—culture, sweetness and light, Barbarian, Philistine, Hebraism, and many others—which are now associated with Arnold's work and influence. The term 'Barbarian' refers to the aristocratic classes, whom Arnold thought to be essentially crude in soul, notwithstanding their good clothes and superficial graces. 'Philistine' refers to the middle classes—narrow-minded and self-satisfied people, according to Arnold, whom he satirizes with the idea of opening their minds to new ideas. 'Hebraism' is Arnold's term for moral education. Carlyle had emphasized the Hebraic or moral element in life, and Arnold undertook to preach the Hellenic or intellectual element, which welcomes new ideas, and delights in the arts that reflect the beauty of the world. 'The uppermost idea with Hellenism', he says, 'is to see things as they are; the uppermost idea with Hebraism is conduct and obedience.' With great clearness, sometimes with great force, and always with a play of humour and raillery aimed at the 'Philistines', Arnold pleads for both these elements in life which together aim at 'Culture', that is, at moral and intellectual perfection.

General Characteristics. Arnold's influence in our literature may be summed up, in a word, as intellectual rather than inspirational. One cannot be enthusiastic over his poetry, for the simple reason that he himself lacked enthusiasm. He is, however, a true reflection of a very real mood of the past century, the mood of doubt and sorrow; and a future generation may give him a higher place than he now holds as a poet. Though marked by 'the elemental note of sadness', all Arnold's poems are distinguished by clearness, simplicity, and the restrained emotion of his classic models.

As a prose writer the cold intellectual quality, which mars his poetry by restraining romantic feeling, is of first importance, since it leads him to approach literature with an open mind and with the single desire to find 'the best which has been thought and said in the world.' We cannot yet speak with confidence of his rank in literature; but by his crystal-clear style, his scientific spirit of inquiry and comparison, illumined here and there by the play of humour, and especially by his broad sympathy and intellectual culture, he seems destined to occupy a very high place among the masters of literary criticism.

John Henry Newman (1801-1890)

Any record of the prose literature of the Victorian era, which includes the historical essays of Macaulay and the art criticism of Ruskin, should contain also some notice of its spiritual leaders. For there was never a time when the religious ideals that inspire the race were kept more constantly before men's minds through the medium of literature.

Among the religious writers of the age the first place belongs unquestionably to Cardinal Newman. Whether we consider him as a man, with his powerful yet gracious personality, or as a religious reformer, who did much to break down old religious prejudices by showing the underlying beauty and consistency of the Roman church, or as a prose writer whose style is as near perfection as we have ever reached, Newman is one of the most interesting figures of the whole nineteenth century.

Life. Three things stand out clearly in Newman's life: first, his unshaken faith in the divine companionship and guidance; second, his desire to find and to teach the truth of revealed religion; third, his quest of an authoritative standard of faith, which should remain steadfast through the changing centuries and amid all sorts and conditions of men. The first led to that rare and beautiful spiritual quality which shines in all his work; the second to his frequent doctrinal and controversial essays; the third to his conversion to the Catholic church, which he served as priest and teacher for the last forty-five years of his life. Perhaps we should add one more characteristic—the practical bent of his religion; for he was never so busy with study or controversy that he neglected to give a large part of his time to gentle ministration among the poor and needy.

He was born in London, in 1801. His father was an English banker; his mother, a member of a French Huguenot family, was a thoughtful, devout woman, who brought up her son in a way which suggests the mother of Ruskin. Of his early training, his reading of doctrinal and argumentative works, and of his isolation from material things in the thought that there were 'two and only two absolute and luminously self-evident beings in the world', himself and his Creator, it is better to read his own record in the *Apologia,* which is a kind of spiritual biography.

At the age of fifteen Newman had begun his profound study of theological subjects. For science, literature, art, nature—all the

Quadrangle of Oriel College, Oxford

broad interests which attracted other literary men of his age—he cared little, his mind being wholly occupied with the history and doctrines of the Christian church, to which he had already devoted his life. He was educated first at the school in Ealing, then at Oxford, taking his degree in the latter place in 1820. Though his college career was not more brilliant than that of many unknown men, his unusual ability was recognized and he was made a fellow of Oriel College, retaining the fellowship, and leading a scholarly life for over twenty years. In 1824 he was ordained in the Anglican church, and four years later was chosen vicar of St. Mary's, at Oxford, where his sermons made a deep impression on the cultivated audiences that gathered from far and near to hear him.

A change is noticeable in Newman's life after his trip to the Mediterranean in 1832. He had begun his life as a Calvinist, but while in Oxford, then the centre of religious unrest, he described himself as 'drifting in the direction of Liberalism.' Then study and bereavement and an innate mysticism led him to a profound sympathy with the mediæval Church. He had from the beginning opposed Catholicism; but during his visit to Italy, where he saw the Roman church at the centre of its power and splendour, many of his prejudices were overcome. In this enlargement of his spiritual horizon Newman was greatly influenced by his friend Hurrell Froude, with whom he made the first part of the journey. His poems of this period (afterwards collected in the *Lyra Apostolica),* among which is the famous 'Lead, Kindly Light', are noticeable for their radiant spirituality; but one who reads them carefully sees the beginning of that mental struggle which ended in his leaving the church in which he was born. Thus he writes of the Catholic church, whose services he had attended as 'one who in a foreign land receives the gifts of a good Samaritan':

O that thy creed were sound!
For thou dost soothe the heart, thou church of Rome,
By thy unwearied watch and varied round
Of service, in thy Saviour's holy home.
I cannot walk the city's sultry streets,
But the wide porch invites to still retreats,
Where passion's thirst is calmed, and care's
unthankful gloom.

On his return to England, in 1833, he entered into the religious struggle known as the Oxford or Tractarian Movement,[1] and speedily became its acknowledged leader. Those who wish to follow this attempt at religious

[1] The Oxford movement in religion has many points of resemblance to the Pre-Raphaelite movement in art. Both protested against the materialism of the age, and both went back for their models to the Middle Ages. Originally the movement was intended to bring new life to the Anglican church by a revival

reform, which profoundly affected the life of the whole English church, will find it recorded in the *Tracts for the Times,* twenty-nine of which were written by Newman, and in his Parochial and *Plain Sermons* (1837-1843). After nine years of spiritual conflict Newman retired to Littlemore, where, with a few followers, he led a life of almost monastic seclusion, still striving to reconcile his changing belief with the doctrines of his own church. Two years later he resigned his charge at St. Mary's and left the Anglican communion—not bitterly, but with a deep and tender regret. His last sermon at Littlemore on 'The Parting of Friends' still moves us profoundly, like the cry of a prophet torn by personal anguish in the face of duty. In 1845 he was received into the Catholic church, and the following year, at Rome, he joined the community of St. Philip Neri, 'the saint of gentleness and kindness', as Newman describes him, and was ordained to the Roman priesthood.

By his preaching and writing Newman had exercised a strong influence over his cultivated English hearers, and the effect of his conversion was tremendous. Into the theological controversy of the next twenty years we have no mind to enter. Through it all Newman retained his serenity, and, though a master of irony and satire, kept his literary power always subordinate to his chief aim, which was to establish the truth as he saw it. Whether or not we agree with his conclusions, we must all admire the spirit of the man, which is above praise or criticism. His most widely read work, *Apologia Pro Vita Sua* (1864), was written in answer to an unfortunate attack by Charles Kingsley, which would long since have been forgotten had it not led to this remarkable book. In 1854 Newman was appointed rector of the Catholic University in Dublin, but after four years returned to England and founded a Catholic school at Edgbaston.

---

of the doctrine and practices of an earlier period. Recognizing the power of the press, the leaders, chose literature for their instrument of reform, and by their *Tracts for the Times* they became known as Tractarians. To oppose liberalism and to restore the doctrine and authority of the early Church was the centre of their teaching. Their belief might be summed up in one great article of the Creed, with all that it implies—'I believe in one Catholic and Apostolic Church'. The movement began at Oxford with Keble's famous sermon on 'National Apostasy', in 1833; but Newman was the real leader of the movement, which practically ended when he entered the Catholic church in 1845.

In 1879 he was made cardinal by Pope Leo XIII. The grace and dignity of his life, quite as much as the sincerity of his *Apologia,* had long since disarmed criticism, and at his death, in 1890, the thought of all England might well be expressed by his own lines in 'The Dream of Gerontius':

> I had a dream. Yes, some one softly said,
> 'He's gone', and then a sigh went round the room;
> And then I surely heard a priestly voice
> Cry Subvenite; and they knelt in prayer.

Works of Newman. Readers approach Newman from so many different motives, some for doctrine, some for argument, some for a pure prose style, that it is difficult to recommend the best works for the beginner's use. As an expression of Newman's spiritual struggle the *Apologia Pro Vita Sua* is perhaps the most significant. This book is not light reading and one who opens it should understand clearly the reasons for which it was written. Newman had been accused of insincerity, not only by Kingsley but by many other men, in the public press. His retirement to solitude and meditation at Littlemore had been outrageously misunderstood, and it was openly charged that his conversion was a cunningly devised plot to win a large number of his followers to the Catholic church. This charge involved others, and it was to defend them, as well as to vindicate himself, that Newman wrote the *Apologia.* The perfect sincerity with which he traced his religious history, showing that his conversion was only the final step in a course he had been following since boyhood, silenced his critics and revolutionized public opinion concerning himself and the church which he had joined. As the revelation of a soul's history, and as a model of pure, simple, unaffected English, this book, entirely apart from its doctrinal teaching, deserves a high place in our prose literature.

Apologia Pro Vita Sua

In Newman's doctrinal works, the *Via Media,* the *Grammar of Assent,* and in numerous controversial essays the student of literature will have little interest. Much more significant are his sermons, the unconscious reflection of a rare spiritual nature, of which Professor Shairp said: 'His power shows itself clearly in the new and unlooked-for way in which he touched into life old truths, moral or spiritual—And as he spoke, how the old truth became new! and how it came home with a meaning never felt before! He laid his finger how gently yet how powerfully on some inner place in the hearer's heart, and told him things about himself he had never known till then. Subtlest truths, which would have taken philosophers pages of circumlocution and big words to state, were dropped out by the way in a sentence or two of the most transparent Saxon.' Of greater interest to the general reader are *The Idea of a University,* discourses delivered at Dublin, and his two works of fiction, *Loss and Gain,* treating of a man's conversion to Catholicism, and *Callista,* which is, in his own words, 'an attempt to express the feelings and mutual relations of Christians and heathens in the middle of the third century.' The latter is, in our judgment, the most readable and interesting of Newman's works. The character of Callista, a beautiful Greek sculptor of idols, is powerfully delineated; the style is clear and transparent as air, and the story of the heroine's conversion and death makes one of the most fascinating chapters in fiction, though it is not the story so much as the author's unconscious revelation of himself that charms us. It would be well to read this novel in connection with Kingsley's *Hypatia,* which attempts to reconstruct the life and ideals of the same period.

Callista

Newman's poems are not so well known as his prose, but the reader who examines the *Lyra Apostolica* and *Verses on Various Occasions* will find many short poems that stir a religious nature profoundly by their pure and lofty imagination; and future generations may pronounce one of these poems, 'The Dream of Gerontius', to be Newman's most enduring work. This poem aims to reproduce the thoughts and feelings of a man whose soul is just quitting the body, and who is just beginning a new and greater life. Both in style and in thought 'The Dream' is a powerful and original poem and is worthy of attention not only for itself but, as a modern critic suggests, 'as a revelation of that high spiritual purpose which animated Newman's life from beginning to end.'

Poems

Of Newman's style it is as difficult to write as it would be to describe the dress of a gentleman we had met, who was so perfectly dressed that we paid no attention to his clothes. His style is called transparent, because at first we are not conscious of his manner; and unobtrusive, because we never think of Newman himself, but only of the subject he is discussing. He is like the best French prose writers in expressing his thought with such naturalness and apparent ease that, without thinking of style, we receive exactly the impression which he means to convey. In his sermons and essays he is wonderfully simple and direct; in his controversial writings, gently ironical and satiric, and the satire is pervaded by a delicate humour; but when his feelings are aroused he speaks with poetic images and symbols, and his eloquence is like that of the Old Testament prophets. Like Ruskin's, his style is modelled largely on that of the Bible, but not even Ruskin equals him in the poetic beauty and melody of his sentences. On the whole he comes nearer than any other of his age to our ideal of a perfect prose writer.

Newman's style

Other Essayists of the Victorian Age. We have selected the above five essayists, Macaulay, Carlyle, Arnold, Newman, and Ruskin, as representative writers of the Victorian Age; but there are many others who well repay our study. Notable among these are John Addington Symonds, author of *The Renaissance in Italy,* undoubtedly his greatest work, and of many critical essays; Walter Pater, whose *Appreciations* and numerous other works mark him as one of our best literary critics; and Leslie Stephen, famous for his work on the monumental *Dictionary of National Biography,* and for his *Hours in a Library,* a series of impartial and excellent criticisms, brightened by the play of an original and delightful humur.

Critical Writers

Among the most famous writers of the age are the scientists, Lyell, Darwin, Huxley, Spencer, Tyndall, and Wallace—a wonderful group of men whose works, though they hardly belong to our present study, have exercised an incalculable influence on our life and literature. Darwin's *Origin of Species* (1859), which apparently established the theory of evolution, was an epoch-making book. It

The Scientists

revolutionized not only our conceptions of natural history, but also our methods of thinking on all the problems of human society. Those who would read a summary of the greatest scientific discovery of the age will find it in Wallace's *Darwinism*—a most interesting book, written by the man who claims, with Darwin, the honour of first announcing the principle of evolution. And, from a multitude of scientific works, we recommend also to the general reader Huxley's *Autobiography* and his *Lay Sermons, Addresses, and Reviews,* partly because they are excellent expressions of the spirit and methods of science, and partly because Huxley as a writer is perhaps the clearest and the most readable of the scientists.

The Spirit of Modern Literature. As we reflect on the varied work of the Victorian writers, three marked characteristics invite our attention. First, our great literary men, no less than our great scientists, have made truth the supreme object of human endeavour. All these eager poets, novelists, and essayists, questing over so many different ways, are equally intent on discovering the truth of life. Men as far apart as Darwin and Newman are strangely alike in spirit, one seeking truth in the natural, the other in the spiritual history of the race. Second, literature has become the mirror of truth; and the first requirement of every serious novel or essay is to be true to the life or the facts which it represents. Third, literature has become animated by a definite moral purpose. It is not enough for the Victorian writers to create or attempt an artistic work for its own sake; the work must have a definite lesson for humanity. The poets are not only singers, but leaders; they hold up an ideal, and they compel men to recognize and follow it. The novelists tell a story which pictures human life, and at the same time call us to the work of social reform, or drive home a moral lesson. The essayists are nearly all prophets or teachers, and use literature as the chief instrument of progress and education. Among them all we find comparatively little of the exuberant fancy, the romantic ardour, and the boyish gladness of the Elizabethans. They write books not primarily to delight the artistic sense, but to give bread to the hungry and water to the thirsty in soul. Milton's famous sentence, 'A good book is the precious life-blood of a master spirit', might be written across the whole Victorian era. We are still too near these writers to judge how far their work suffers artistically from their practical purpose; but this much is certain—that whether or not they created immortal works, their books have made the present world a better and a happier place to live in. And that is perhaps the best that can be said of the work of any artist or artisan.

Summary of the Victorian Age. The year 1830 is generally placed at the beginning of this period, but its limits are very indefinite. In general we may think of it as covering the reign of Victoria (1837-1901). Historically the age is remarkable for the growth of democracy following the Reform Bill of 1832; for the spread of education among all classes; for the rapid development of the arts and sciences; for important mechanical inventions; and for the enormous extension of the bounds of human knowledge by the discoveries of science.

At the accession of Victoria the romantic movement had spent its force; Wordsworth had written his best work; the other romantic poets, Coleridge, Shelley, Keats, and Byron, had passed away; and for a time no new development was apparent in English poetry. Though the Victorian Age produced two great poets, Tennyson and Browning, the age, as a whole, is remarkable for the variety and excellence of its prose. A study of all the great writers of the period reveals four general characteristics: (1) Literature in this Age has come very close to daily life, reflecting its practical problems and interests, and is a powerful instrument of human progress. (2) The tendency of literature is strongly ethical; all the great poets, novelists, and essayists of the age are moral teachers. (3) Science in this age exercises an incalculable influence. On the one hand it emphasizes truth as the sole object of human endeavour; it has established the principle of law throughout the universe; and it has given us an entirely new view of life, as summed up in the word 'evolution', that is, the principle of growth or development from simple to complex forms. On the other hand, its first effect seems to be to discourage works of the imagination. Though the age produced an incredible number of books, very few of them belong among the great creative works of literature. (4) Though the age is generally characterized as practical and materialistic, it is significant that nearly all the writers whom the nation delights to honour vigorously attack materialism, and exalt a purely ideal conception of life. On the whole, we are inclined to call this an idealistic age fundamentally, since love, truth, justice, brotherhood—all great ideals—are emphasized as the chief ends of life, not only by its poets but also by its novelists and essayists.

In our study we have considered: (1) The Poets; the life and works of Tennyson and Browning; and the chief characteristics of the minor poets, Elizabeth Barrett (Mrs. Browning), Rossetti, Morris, and Swinburne. (2) The Novelists; the life and works of Dickens, Thackeray, and George Eliot; and the chief works of Charles Reade, Anthony Trollope, Charlotte Brontë, Bulwer-Lytton, Kingsley, Mrs. Gaskell, Blackmore, George Meredith, Hardy, and Stevenson. (3) The Essayists; the life and works of Macaulay, Matthew Arnold, Carlyle, Newman, and Ruskin. These were selected, from among many essayists and miscellaneous writers, as most typical of the Victorian Age. The great scientists, like Lyell, Darwin, Huxley, Wallace, Tyndall, and Spencer, hardly belong to our study of literature, though their works are of vast importance; and we omit the works of living writers who belong to the present rather than to the past century.

Selections for Reading. Manly's English Poetry and Manly's English Prose (Ginn and Company) contain excellent selections from all authors of this period. Many other collections, like Ward's English Poets, Garnett's English Prose from Elizabeth to Victoria, Page's British Poets of the Nineteenth Century, and Stedman's A Victorian Anthology, may be used to advantage. All important works may be found in the convenient and inexpensive school editions given below. (For full titles and publishers see the General Bibliography.)

Tennyson. Short poems, and selections from Idylls of the King, In Memoriam, Enoch Arden, and The Princess. These are found in various school editions, Standard English Classics, Pocket Classics, Riverside Literature Series, etc. Poems by Tennyson, selected and edited with notes by Henry Van Dyke (Athenæum Press Series), is an excellent little volume for beginners.

Browning. Selections, edited by R.M. Lovett, in Standard English Classics. Other school editions in Everyman's Library, Belles Lettres Series, etc.

Elizabeth Barrett Browning. Selections, edited by Elizabeth Lee, in Standard English Classics. Selections also in Pocket Classics, etc.

Matthew Arnold. Sohrab and Rustum, edited by Trent and Brewster, in Standard English Classics. The same poem in Riverside Literature Series, etc. Selections in Golden Treasury Series, etc. Poems, students' edition (Crowell). Essays in Everyman's Library, etc. Prose selections (Holt, Allyn & Bacon, etc.).

Dickens. Tale of Two Cities, edited by J.W. Linn, in Standard English Classics. A Christmas Carol, David Copperfield, and Pickwick Papers. Various good school editions of these novels in Everyman's Library, etc.

Thackeray. Henry Esmond, edited by H.B. Moore, in Standard English Classics. The same novel, in Everyman's Library, Pocket Classics, etc.

George Eliot. Silas Marner, edited by R. Adelaide Witham, in Standard English Classics. The same novel, in Pocket Classics, etc.

Carlyle. Essay on Burns, edited by C.L. Hanson, in Standard English Classics, and Heroes and Hero Worship, edited by A. MacMechan, in Athenæum Press Series. Selections, edited by H.W. Boynton (Allyn & Bacon). Various other inexpensive editions, in Pocket Classics, Eclectic English Classics, etc.

Ruskin. Sesame and Lilies, edited by Lois G. Hufford, in Standard English Classics. Other editions in Riverside Literature, Everyman's Library, etc. Selected Essays and Letters, edited by Hufford, in Standard English Classics. Selections, edited by Vida D. Scudder (Sibley); edited by C.B. Tinker, in Riverside Literature.

Macaulay. Essays on Addison and Milton, edited by H.A. Smith, in Standard English Classics. Same essays, in Cassell's National Library, Riverside Literature, etc. Lays of Ancient Rome, in Standard English Classics, Pocket Classics, etc.

Newman. Selections, with introduction by L.E. Gates (Holt); Selections from prose and poetry, in Riverside Literature. The Idea of a University, in Manly's English Prose.

Bibliography. (Note. For full titles and publishers of general reference books, see General Bibliography.) ***History***. Textbook, Montgomery, pp. 357-383; Cheyney, pp. 632-643. *General Works.* Gardiner, and Traill. *Special Works.* McCarthy's History of Our Own Times; Bright's History of England, vols. 4-5; Lee's Queen Victoria; Bryce's Studies in Contemporary Biography.

Literature. *General Works.* Garnett and Gosse, Taine. *Special Works.* Harrison's Early Victorian Literature; Saintsbury's A History of Nineteenth Century Literature; Walker's The Age of Tennyson; same author's The Greater Victorian Poets; Morley's Literature of the Age of Victoria; Stedman's Victorian Poets; Mrs. Oliphant's Literary History of England in the Nineteenth Century; Beers's English Romanticism in the Nineteenth Century; Dowden's Victorian Literature, in Transcripts and Studies; Brownell's Victorian Prose Masters.

Tennyson. Texts: Cabinet edition (London, 1897) is the standard. Various good editions, Globe, Cambridge Poets, etc. Selections in Athenæum Press (Ginn and Company). Life: Alfred Lord Tennyson, a Memoir by his son, is the standard; by Lyall (in English Men of Letters); by Horton; by Waugh. See also Anne T. Ritchie's Tennyson and His Friends; Napier's The Homes and Haunts of Tennyson; Rawnsley's Memories of the Tennysons. Criticism: Brooke's Tennyson, his Art and his Relation to Modern Life; A. Lang's Alfred Tennyson; Van Dyke's The Poetry of Tennyson; Sneath's The Mind of Tennyson; Gwynn's A Critical Study of Tennyson's Works; Luce's Handbook to Tennyson's Works; Dixon's A Tennyson Primer; Masterman's Tennyson as a Religious Teacher; Collins's The Early Poems of Tennyson; Macallum's Tennyson's Idylls of the King and the Arthurian Story; Bradley's Commentary on In Memoriam; Bagehot's Literary Studies, vol. 2; Brightwell's Concordance; Shepherd's Bibliography. Essays: By F. Harrison, in Tennyson, Ruskin, Mill, and Other Literary Estimates; by Stedman, in Victorian Poets; by Hutton, in Literary Essays; by Dowden, in Studies in Literature; by Gates, in Studies and Appreciations; by Forster, in Great Teachers; by Forman, in Our Living Poets. See also Myers's Science and a Future Life.

Browning. Texts: Cambridge and Globe editions, etc. Various editions of selections. (See Selections for Reading, above.) Life: by W. Sharp (Great Writers); by Chesterton (English Men of Letters); Life and Letters, by Mrs. Sutherland Orr; by Waugh, in Westminster Biographies (Small & Maynard). Criticism: Symons's An Introduction to the Study of Browning; same title, by Corson; Mrs. Orr's Handbook to the Works of Browning; Nettleship's Robert Browning; Brooke's The Poetry of Robert Browning; Cooke's Browning Guide Book; Revell's Browning's Criticism of Life; Berdoe's Browning's Message to his Times; Berdoe's Browning Cyclopedia. Essays: by Hutton, Stedman, Dowden, Forster (for titles, see Tennyson, above); by Jacobs, in Literary Studies; by Chapman, in Emerson and Other Essays; by Cooke, in Poets and Problems; by Birrell, in Obiter Dicta.

Elizabeth Barrett Browning. Texts: Globe and Cambridge editions, etc.; various editions of selections. Life: by J. H. Ingram; see also Bayne's Two Great Englishmen. Kenyon's Letters of E. B. Browning. Criticism: Essays, by Stedman, in Victorian Poets; by Benson, in Essays.

Matthew Arnold. Texts: Poems, Globe edition, etc. See Selections for Reading, above. Life: by Russell; by Saintsbury; by Paul (English Men of Letters); Letters, by Russell. Criticism: Essays by Woodberry, in Makers of Literature; by Gates, in Three Studies in Literature; by Hutton, in Modern Guides of English Thought; by Brownell, in Victorian Prose Masters; by F. Harrison (see Tennyson, above).

Dickens. Texts: numerous good editions of novels. Life: by J. Forster; by Marzials (Great Writers); by Ward (English Men of Letters); Langton's The Childhood and Youth of Dickens. Criticism: Gissing's Charles Dickens; Chesterton's Charles Dickens; Kitton's The Novels of Charles Dickens; Fitzgerald's The History of Pickwick. Essays by F. Harrison (see above); by Bagehot, in Literary Studies; by Lilly, in Four English Humorists; by A. Lang, in Gadshill edition of Dickens's works.

Thackeray. Texts: numerous good editions of novels and essays. Life: by Melville; by Merivale and Marzials (Great Writers); by A. Trollope (English Men of Letters); by L. Stephen, in Dictionary of National Biography. See also Crowe's Homes and Haunts of Thackeray; Wilson's Thackeray in the United States. Criticism: Essays, by Lilly, in Four English Humorists; by Harrison, in Studies in Early Victorian Literature; by Scudder, in Social Ideals in English Letters; by Brownell, in Victorian Prose Masters.

George Eliot. Texts: numerous editions. Life: by L. Stephen (English Men of Letters); by O. Browning (Great Writers); by her husband, J.W. Cross. Criticism: Cooke's George Eliot, a Critical Study of her Life and Writings. Essays: by J. Jacobs, in Literary Studies; by H. James, in Partial Portraits; by Dowden, in Studies in Literature; by Hutton, Harrison, Brownell, Lilly (see above). See also Parkinson's Scenes from the George Eliot Country.

Carlyle. Texts: various editions of works. Heroes, and Sartor Resartus, in Athenæum Press (Ginn and Company); Sartor, and Past and Present, 1 vol. (Harper); Critical and Miscellaneous Essays, 1 vol. (Appleton); Letters and Reminiscences, edited by C. E. Norton, 6 vols. (Macmillan). Life: by Garnett (Great Writers); by Nichol (English Men of Letters); by Froude, 2 vols. (very full, but not trustworthy). See also Carlyle's Reminiscences and Correspondence, and Craig's The Making of Carlyle. Criticism: Masson's Carlyle Personally and in his Writings. Essays: by Lowell, in My Study Windows; by Harrison, Brownell, Hutton, Lilly (see above).

Ruskin. Texts: Brantwood edition, edited by C.E. Norton; various editions of separate works. Life: by Harrison (English Men of Letters);

by Collingwood, 2 vols.; see also Ruskin's Præterita. Criticism: Mather's Ruskin, his Life and Teaching; Cooke's Studies in Ruskin; Waldstein's The Work of John Ruskin; Hobson's John Ruskin, Social Reformer; Mrs. Meynell's John Ruskin; Sizeranne's Ruskin and the Religion of Beauty, translated from the French; White's Principles of Art; W. M. Rossetti's Ruskin, Rossetti, and Pre-Raphaelitism. Essays: by Robertson, in Modern Humanists; by Saintsbury, in Corrected Impressions; by Brownell, Harrison, Forster (see above).

Macaulay. Texts: Complete works, edited by his sister, Lady Trevelyan (London, 1866); various editions of separate works (see Selections for Reading, above). Life: Life and Letters, by Trevelyan, 2 vols.; by Morrison (English Men of Letters). Criticism: Essays, by Bagehot, in Literary Studies; by L. Stephen, in Hours in a Library; by Saintsbury, in Corrected Impressions; by Harrison, in Studies in Early Victorian Literature; by Matthew Arnold.

Newman. Texts: Uniform edition of important works (London, 1868-1881); Apologia (Longmans); Selections (Holt, Riverside Literature, etc.). Life: Jennings's Cardinal Newman; Hutton's Cardinal Newman; Early Life, by F. Newman; by Waller and Barrow, in Westminster Biographies. See also Church's The Oxford Movement; Fitzgerald's Fifty Years of Catholic Life and Progress. Criticism: Essays, by Donaldson, in Five Great Oxford Leaders; by Church, in Occasional Papers, vol. 2; by Gates, in Three Studies in Literature; by Jacobs, in Literary Studies; by Hutton, in Modern Guides of English Thought; by Lilly, in Essays and Speeches; by Shairp, in Studies in Poetry and Philosophy. See also Hutton's Cardinal Newman.

Rossetti. Works, 2 vols. (London, 1901). Selections, in Golden Treasury Series. Life: by Knight (Great Writers); by Shairp; Hall Caine's Recollections of Dante Gabriel Rossetti; Cary's The Rossettis; Marillier's Rossetti; Wood's Rossetti and the Pre-Raphaelite Movement; W.M. Hunt's Pre-Raphaelitism and the Pre-Raphaelite Brotherhood. Criticism: Tirebuck's Rossetti, his Work and Influence. Essays: by Swinburne, in Essays and Studies; by Forman, in Our Living Poets; by Pater, in Ward's English Poets; by F.W.H. Myers, in Essays Modern.

Morris. Texts: Story of the Glittering Plain, House of the Wolfings, etc. (Reeves & Turner); Early Romances, in Everyman's Library; Sigurd the Volsung, in Camelot Series; Socialistic writings (Humboldt Publishing Co.). Life: by Mackail; by Cary; by Vallance. Criticism: Essays, by Symons, in Studies in Two Literatures; by Dawson, in Makers of Modern English;

by Saintsbury, in Corrected Impressions. See also Nordby's Influence of Old Norse Literature.

Swinburne. Texts: Complete works (Chatto and Windus); Poems and Ballads (Lovell); Selections (Rivington, Belles Lettres Series, etc.). Life: Wratislaw's Algernon Charles Swinburne, a Study. Criticism: Essays, by Forman, Saintsbury (see above); by Lowell, in My Study Windows; see also Stedman's Victorian Poets.

Charles Reade. Texts: Cloister and the Hearth, in Everyman's Library; various editions of separate novels. Life: by C. Reade. Criticism: Essay, by Swinburne, in Miscellanies.

Anthony Trollope. Texts: Royal edition of principal novels (Philadelphia, 1900); Barchester Towers, etc., in Everyman's Library. Life: Autobiography (Harper, 1883). Criticism: H.T. Peck's Introduction to Royal edition, vol. 1. Essays: by H. James, in Partial Portraits; by Harrison, in Early Victorian Literature. See also Cross, The Development of the English Novel.

Charlotte and Emily Brontë. Texts: Works, Haworth edition, edited by Mrs. H. Ward (Harper); Complete works (Dent, 1893); Jane Eyre, Shirley, and Wuthering Heights, in Everyman's Library. Life of Charlotte Brontë: by Mrs. Gaskell; by Shorter; by Birrell (Great Writers). Life of Emily Brontë: by Robinson. See also Leyland's The Brontë Family. Criticism: Essays, by L. Stephen, in Hours in a Library; by Gates, in Studies and Appreciations; by Harrison, in Early Victorian Literature; by G.B. Smith, in Poets and Novelists. See also Swinburne's A Note on Charlotte Brontë.

Bulwer-Lytton. Texts: Works, Knebsworth edition (Routledge); various editions of separate works; Last Days of Pompeii, etc., in Everyman's Library. Life: by his son, the Earl of Lytton; by Cooper; by Ten Brink. Criticism: Essay, by W. Senior, in Essays in Fiction.

Mrs. Gaskell. Various editions of separate works; Cranford, in Standard English Classics, etc. Life: see Dictionary of National Biography. Criticism: see Saintsbury's Nineteenth-Century Literature.

Kingsley. Texts: Works, Chester edition; Hypatia, Westward Ho! etc., in Everyman's Library. Life: Letters and Memories, by his wife; by Kaufmann. Criticism: Essays, by Harrison, in Early Victorian Literature; by L. Stephen, in Hours in a Library.

Stevenson. Texts: Works (Scribner); Treasure Island, in Everyman's Library; Master of Ballantrae, in Pocket Classics; Letters, edited by Colvin (Scribner). Life: by Balfour; by Baildon; by Black; by Cornford. See also Simpson's Edinburgh Days; Fraser's In Stevenson's Samoa; Osborne and Strong's Memories of Vailima. Criticism: Raleigh's Stevenson; Alice

Brown's Stevenson. Essays: by H. James, in Partial Portraits; by Chapman, in Emerson and Other Essays.

Hardy. Texts: Works (Harper). Criticism: Macdonnell's Thomas Hardy; Johnson's The Art of Thomas Hardy. See also Windle's The Wessex of Thomas Hardy; and Dawson's Makers of English Fiction.

George Meredith. Texts: Novels and Selected Poems (Scribner). Criticism: Le Gallienne's George Meredith; Hannah Lynch's George Meredith. Essays: by Henley, in Views and Reviews; by Brownell, in Victorian Prose Masters; by Monkhouse, in Books and Plays. See also Bailey's The Novels of George Meredith; Curie's Aspects of George Meredith; and Cross's The Development of the English Novel.

Suggestive Questions. (NOTE. The best questions are those which are based upon the books, essays, and poems read by the pupil. As the works chosen for special study vary greatly with different teachers and classes, we insert here only a few questions of general interest.)

1. What are the chief characteristics of Victorian literature? Name the chief writers of the period in prose and poetry. What books of this period are, in your judgment, worthy to be placed among the great works of literature? What effect did the discoveries of science have upon the literature of the age? What poet reflects the new conception of law and evolution? What historical conditions account for the fact that most of the Victorian writers are ethical teachers?

2. *Tennyson.* Give a brief sketch of Tennyson's life, and name his chief works. Why is he, like Chaucer, a national poet? Is your pleasure in reading Tennyson due chiefly to the thought or the melody of expression? Note this figure in 'The Lotos Eaters':

> Music that gentlier on the spirit lies
> Than tired eyelids upon tired eyes.

What does this suggest concerning Tennyson's figures of speech in general? Compare 'Locksley Hall' with 'Locksley Hall Sixty Years After.' What differences do you find in thought, in workmanship, and in poetic enthusiasm? What is Tennyson's idea of faith and immortality as expressed in In Memoriam?

3. *Browning.* In what respects is Browning like Shakespeare? What is meant by the optimism of his poetry? Can you explain why many thoughtful persons prefer him to Tennyson? What is Browning's creed as expressed in 'Rabbi Ben Ezra'? Read 'Fra Lippo Lippi' or 'Andrea del

Sarto', and tell what is meant by a dramatic monologue. In 'Andrea' what is meant by the lines,

> Ah, but a man's reach should exceed his grasp,
> Or what's a heaven for?

4. *Dickens.* What experiences in Dickens's life are reflected in his novels? What are his favorite types of character? What is meant by the exaggeration of Dickens? What was the serious purpose of his novels? Make a brief analysis of the *Tale of Two Cities,* having in mind the plot, the characters, and the style, as compared with Dickens's other novels.

5. *Thackeray.* Read *Henry Esmond* and explain Thackeray's realism. What is there remarkable in the style of this novel? Compare it with Ivanhoe as a historical novel. What is the general character of Thackeray's satire? What are the chief characteristics of his novels? Describe briefly the works which show his great skill as a critical writer.

6. *George Eliot.* Read *Silas Marner* and make a brief analysis, having in mind the plot, the characters, the style, and the ethical teaching of the novel. Is the moral teaching of George Eliot convincing; that is, does it suggest itself from the story, or is it added for effect? What is the general impression left by her books? How do her characters compare with those of Dickens and Thackeray?

7. *Carlyle.* Why is Carlyle called a prophet, and why a censor? Read the Essay on Burns and make an analysis, having in mind the style, the idea of criticism, and the picture which this essay presents of the Scotch poet. Is Carlyle chiefly interested in Burns or in his poetry? Does he show any marked appreciation of Burns's power as a lyric poet? What is Carlyle's idea of history as shown in *Heroes and Hero Worship?* What experiences of his own life are reflected in *Sartor Resartus?* What was Carlyle's message to his age? What is meant by a 'Carlylese' style?

8. *Macaulay.* In what respects is Macaulay typical of his age? Compare his view of life with that of Carlyle. Read one of the essays, on Milton or Addison, and make an analysis, having in mind the style, the interest, and the accuracy of the essay. What useful purpose does Macaulay's historical knowledge serve in writing his literary essays? What is the general character of Macaulay's *History of England?* Read a chapter from Macaulay's History, another from Carlyle's *French Revolution,* and compare the two. How does each writer regard history and historical writing? What differences do

you note in their methods? What are the best qualities of each work? Why are both unreliable?

9. *Arnold.* What elements of Victorian life are reflected in Arnold's poetry?

How do you account for the coldness and sadness of his verses? Read Sohrab and Rustum and write an account of it, having in mind the story, Arnold's use of his material, the style, and the classic elements in the poem. How does it compare in melody with the blank verse of Milton or Tennyson? What marked contrasts do you find between the poetry and the prose of Arnold?

10. *Ruskin.* In what respects is Ruskin 'the prophet of modern society'? Read the first two lectures in *Sesame and Lilies* and then give Ruskin's views of labour, wealth, books, education, woman's sphere, and human society. How does he regard the commercialism of his age? What elements of style do you find in these lectures? Give the chief resemblances and differences between Carlyle and Ruskin.

11. Read Mrs. Gaskell's *Cranford* and describe it, having in mind the style, the interest, and the characters of the story. How does it compare, as a picture of country life, with George Eliot's novels?

12. Read Blackmore's *Lorna Doone* and describe it (as in the question above). What are the romantic elements in the story? How does it compare with Scott's romances in style, in plot, in interest, and in truthfulness to life?

CHRONOLOGY

Ninteenth Century

History	Literature
	1825. Macaulay's Essay on Milton
	1826. Mrs. Browning's early poems
1830. William IV	1830. Tennyson's Poems, Chiefly Lyrical
1832. Reform Bill	
	1833. Browning's Pauline
	1833-1834. Carlyle's Sartor Resartus
	1836-1865. Dickens's novels
1837. Victoria (*d.* 1901)	1837. Carlyle's French Revolution
	1843. Macaulay's essays

History	Literature
1844. Morse's Telegraph	1843-1860. Ruskin's Modern Painters
1846. Repeal of Corn Laws	
	1847-1859. Thackeray's important novels
	1847-1857. Charlotte Brontë's novels
	1848-1861. Macaulay's History
	1853. Kingsley's Hypatia Mrs. Gaskell's Cranford
1854. Crimean War	
	1853-1855. Matthew Arnold's poems
	1856. Mrs. Browning's Aurora Leigh
1857. Indian Mutiny	
	1858-1876. George Eliot's novels
	1859-1888. Tennyson's Idylls of the King
	1859. Darwin's Origin of Species
	1864. Newman's Apologia Tennyson's Enoch Arden
	1865-1888. Arnold's Essays in Criticism
1867. Dominion of Canada established	
	1868. Browning's Ring and the Book
	1869. Blackmore's Lorna Doone
1870. Government schools established	1879. Meredith's The Egoist
1880. Gladstone prime minister	
	1883. Stevenson's Treasure Island
	1885. Ruskin's Præterita begun
1887. Queen's jubilee	
	1889. Browning's last work, Asolando
	1892. Death of Tennyson
1901. Edward VII	

CHAPTER 12

TWENTIETH-CENTURY LITERATURE

What have I done for you,
        England, my England,
What is there I would not do,
        England my own?
With your glorious eyes austere
As the Lord were walking near,
Whispering terrible things and dear
As the song on your bugles blown, England,
Round the world on your bugles blown.

Henley, 'England, My England'

Three centuries ago Robert Burton, then a famous writer, looked with troubled eyes on the enormous complexity of his age, saying:

I have new books every day, whole catalogues of volumes of all sorts. New paradoxes, opinions, heresies, controversies in philosophy and religion. Now come tidings of weddings, entertainments, jubilees, embassies, sports, plays; then again, as in a new-shipped scene, treasons, tricks, robberies, enormous villainies, deaths, funerals, discoveries, expeditions. Now comical, then tragical matters.

Viewed from this time-distance the many writers who reflected this complexity have sunk to the same featureless level. Looming above them, like crests of a mountain range on the horizon, we see one high peak named Milton, two lower peaks named Bunyan and Dryden, and to left or right a sunny or a gloomy hill named Browne or Donne or Lovelace or Herbert or Izaak Walton. And who will be the Milton or the Dryden of this present age, with its hundreds of books where readers of Puritan-and-Cavalier times had but one, and its scores of ready poets, novelists, and playwrights to reflect its kaleidoscopic changes?

To ask the question is to know that contemporary history cannot possibly be written. The best one can do is to wander clear-eyed through its maze of literature, stopping here or there to point out a poem or play or novel that seems to be important because it is so near, and to say with Montaigne at the end of the survey, 'I have here gathered a posy of other men's flowers, and only the thread that binds them is mine own.'

Background of History

The long and progressive reign of Queen Victoria came to a climax in the Diamond Jubilee Year (1897), a time of peace and plenty when the British Empire seemed to be at the summit of its power and security. Of the discord that soon followed we shall here note only two factors which had large influence on contemporary English literature.

Imperialism

The first disturbing factor was imperialism, the reawakening of a dominating spirit which had seemingly been put to sleep by the proclamation of an Imperial Federation. Its coming was heralded by the Boer War in South Africa, through which Britain blundered to what was hoped to be an era of peace and goodwill. Other nations promptly made such hope a vain whistling in the wind. Germany demanded her larger 'place in the sun' and began warlike preparation for a future 'push to the East'. France enlarged her huge empire in Africa and Indo-China. Italy began a career of disaster by her first attack on Abyssinia. Japanese war lords, inflated by victory over Russia, began a career of conquest which aimed to make Japan master of Asia and the East

Indies. Pacific islands that had for ages slept peacefully were turned into frowning naval stations. Five nations began to dismember China by seizing treaty ports and claiming special concessions in trade. Even the United States, aroused by an easy triumph in the Spanish War, started on an imperialistic adventure by taking control of the Philippines, thus making an implacable enemy of Japan, which had covetous eyes on the same prize.

Only a nation that enters on a dangerous course with eyes wide open has any chance of a safe way out, and the imperialistic nations were all alike blind. An inevitable result was the First World War and the greater horror of a Second World War, the two calamities being different acts of the same tragedy of imperialism, separated only by a breathing spell.

Social Unrest

Another factor that influenced literature for the worse was a widespread demand for social reform of every kind; not slow and orderly reform, which is progress, but immediate and intemperate reform, which breeds a spirit of rebellion and despair. Before the Victorian age had come to an end, English literature appeared to have lost touch with healthy English life. Many writers, as if alternating between chills and fever, echoed the sorrowful cry of James Thomson in his *City of Dreadful Night,* or babbled of 'art for art's sake' with Oscar Wilde, Aubrey Beardsley, and other decadents in *The Yellow Book*. Groom, in his survey of the period, notes that writers had mostly a critical attitude toward morals and religion, Church and State, as relics from 'the dead hand of Puritan beliefs'. Small wonder that German and Japanese warmongers regarded Englishmen as a decadent race when the same or a worse opinion was daily read in the novels of Samuel Butler and nightly heard in the plays of Bernard Shaw.

Suddenly came the First World War, and lo! in a time of trial Englishmen were the same breed that ever they had been, with the same courage, the same ideals, the same faith in themselves and their country. Rupert Brooke, who had himself been among the decadents, voiced the return to health in two superb poems, beginning 'Now God be thanked who hash matched us with this hour', and

> If I should die, think only this of me:
> That there's some corner of a foreign field
> That is for ever England.

Literary Reactions

Imperialism had its outstanding advocate in Kipling, who with drum and trumpet called upon England to 'take up the White Man's burden' by dominating all 'lesser breeds without the law'. No other prominent writer of his day was ever quite so dogmatic; no other so cocksure that his was the only message worthy of attention.

Social reform had its advocates by the score, not in censorious essays only, following the example of Carlyle, but also in fiction, in verse, and especially in drama. One unexpected literary feature of the age was the enthusiasm for stage plays that rolled like a tide over the whole English-speaking world. In the Elizabethan age, still called the age of drama, London had five playhouses, and there was not another in the kingdom. Early in the present century new stages appeared like mushrooms after a warm rain; nearly every city had its Provincial Theatre, as well as a number of regular playhouses, and there was hardly a town in England or America without its 'drama-study group' or a college without its 'drama workshop'. Nearly all successful novelists wrote plays also, and most of them used the stage as an instrument of social reform.

On the surface, at least, the contrast between Victorian and post-Victorian literature is rather startling. Tennyson and Kipling serve as excellent examples, since they were in turn acclaimed wherever English is spoken, one for his worldwide idealism, the other for his intolerance of everything outside the British pale. Dickens, the outstanding Victorian novelist, was a man of colossal optimism; and Hardy, most 'finished' novelist of the age following, was sunk in the deeps of pessimism. Poets of the Victorian age, as reflected in Stedman's *Victorian Anthology* (1899), leave a general impression of beauty, of faith, and therefore of cheerfulness. Housman, finest of poetic craftsmen in the age following, sees life as 'a fool's errand to the grave', and portrays himself as part of the procession on a spring morning:

> Yonder see the morning blink:
> The sun is up, and up must I
> To wash and dress and eat and drink,
> And look at things, and talk and think
> And work, and God knows why.

RUDYARD KIPLING (1865-1936)

Kipling's early and most impressionable years were spent in Bombay, India, where his parents were part of a tiny colony of the British born-and-bred, like an island in a foreign sea. They were the sahibs, the ruling race, to whom imperialism was a religion not to be questioned. Through the crowded streets passed a motley multitude of natives, of many different tribes and tongues, all with strange customs and beliefs. Around the city, as around every village, stretched the trackless jungle, where men and beasts and creeping things were imagined to be swayed by brutality and terror. Other influences were at work in Kipling; but these four—the glory of imperialism, the assumed superiority of the British, the darkly mysterious natives, and the imaginary 'law of the jungle'—dominated much the greater part of his literary work.

A Meteoric Career

As a boy he was sent 'home' to England, where he received a little formal education in what the English call a public school, and what would here be called a private 'prep' school. His experience and impressions were later recorded in *Stalky and Co.,* a ruffianly book glorifying the crude jokes and mock heroism of young barbarians. Returning to India, he became a reporter, first for a local newspaper, then as a footloose observer at a frontier military post. No sooner had his verse and prose (written for newspaper readers and reprinted as *Departmental Ditties* and *Plain Tales from the Hills)* made him known than he headed for London, bent on a literary career. Magazines bought his work, American magazines especially, and with the proceeds he toured the English-speaking world with a reporter's eye for novelty and a genius for dramatizing every colourful place or event in swinging verse or up-to-the-minute prose. Everywhere he was the journalist, the newspaper man; but it was soon apparent that he was also a very clever craftsman. By his skilful use of words in presenting a vivid picture to the eye or creating an impression of wonder or fear in the mind, he became at twenty-five the best-known living writer in the world. For a few years he lived with his American wife in Vermont, where he scorned or criticized or quarrelled with his neighbours in intervals of writing *Captains Courageous, The Jungle Book, The Seven Seas,* and *Many Inventions. The* remainder of his long life was spent in a quiet Sussex villages, where he wrote voluminously but with decreasing effect. The vast audience he had won by the originality of his early work stood by him to the end, sadly recognizing that his storytelling had lost its novelty and was at best merely ingenious. In 1907 he received the Nobel Prize for Literature.

Underwood & Underwood

Rudyard Kipling

Kipling's Verse. There is in most of Kipling's verse a balladlike quality, that is, the impression of a story being told without loss of words. One of the best is his 'Ballad of East and West', with its memorable lines:

> But there is neither East nor West, Border, nor Breed, nor Birth,
> When two strong men stand face to face, though they come from
> the ends of the earth.

Two others of the same type are 'Gunga Din' and 'Fuzzy Wuzzy', which are written in exaggerated Cockney dialect and would be much better if written in unaffected English. Most formally perfect is 'Danny Deever', beginning with a dirgelike measure and ending with the quickstep played after a military execution.

Of the ballads published in *Departmental Ditties* the obvious thing to be said is that they should all have gone to the bonfire. *Barrack-Room Ballads* is a little better in spots, but the 'spots' are far between. Notable among them is 'Mandalay', which has now the queer effect of making us realize how quickly times have changed, and the imperialistic Empire with them. When this 'Mandalay' was unexpectedly revived during the Japanese conquest of Burma (1943), one seemed to be reading of 'old, unhappy, far-off things' that could never be the same again.

Ballads and Lyrics

Kipling's lyric and narrative verse runs the whole gamut from good poetry to poor trash. Notable among poems of the imperialistic type are 'Recessional', written when the gorgeous Diamond Jubilee came to an end, and 'For All We Have and Are', which commemorated England's entrance into the First World War. So ready was Kipling to speak for the nation on any occasion—as when he wrote the cockney-dialect poem 'Lord Roberts' at the passing of a great soldier, or 'Things and the Man' to celebrate a trouble-making Joseph Chamberlain—that many English voices were raised to insist that he should be the poet laureate. But this official versemaker must know the virtue of silence, especially when foreign relations are strained, and Kipling had no grace to hold his tongue. By airing his arrogant opinions he offended Russia with his 'Truce of the Bear', Germany by 'The Rowers', Ireland by 'The Ballad of the Red Earl', the United States by 'An American', Canada by 'Our Lady of the Snows', and democracy everywhere by 'A Servant When He Reigneth'.

Among the best of his lyric verses are 'The Bell Buoy', 'The Feet of the Young Men', 'The Love Song of Har Dyal', 'Mother o' Mine', and 'Shiv and the Grasshopper'. The last-named, an English version of a Hindu lullaby, represents what is probably the oldest form of poetry and the most widespread, because there is hardly a man anywhere, savage or civilized, who lacks the cherished memory of a mother singing in the twilight.

Kipling's Prose. To read the exquisite 'Without Benefit of Clergy' and then one of the dreary short stories collected in *A Diversity of Creatures* is to understand why critics commonly say that Kipling's enduring work was mostly done in his youth. Two excellent examples of his tales of British India are 'The Tomb of His Ancestors' and 'The Man Who Was.' Others, such as 'The Mark of the Beast', indicate how skilfully he tried his hand on a Gothic tale of mystery and horror. Soldiers Three is a collection of short stories dealing with the extravagant adventures of an Irish soldier and his cockney pals. Most dreamlike of all and, as some think, the most perfect is a novelette called *The Brushwood Boy.*

Among the longer tales, *Captains Courageous* deals with a spoiled boy who fell overboard from a liner and found his manhood when picked up by a schooner from the Gloucester fishing fleet. *Kim,* reflecting the experiences of a boy who wandered over India with a holy man, was supposed to be a realistic portrayal of native life; but to read it as such is to fill one's head with pleasant delusions. Best of all is The Jungle Book. Not all the stories are successful; for those of Arctic life are as out of place as a fur coat would be in the jungle, but only those that deal with the hero Mowgli and, for good measure, 'Rikki Tikki Tavi' and 'Toomai of the Elephants'.

The Jungle Book

One should begin the reading of these animal tales with 'Tiger Tiger', telling how a baby was saved from a man-eating tiger by a mother wolf, who brought him up to run with the pack. If you think the idea is fantastically impossible, know that in 1912 a shewolf stole two Hindu babies at different times; that they ran on all fours with the pack for over seven years; that they were then rescued and tenderly cared for in a missionary hospital, and that at their death, eight years later, they had begun to talk and act like human beings. The adventures of Mowgli, as the mother wolf called him, a name meaning 'little frog', were much more romantic in that he became leader of the pack and friend or master of all jungle animals that speak the English language.

This fascinating *Jungle Book* suggests an odd grouping of Kipling's characters into the less real, the more real, and the wholly real, the oddity being that reality is found where least we expect it. When his men and women talk we are skeptical, thinking they are too clever or too sophisticated to be natural. His machines speak a little more naturally, as in 'The Ship That Found Herself'; but not until his animals talk do we surrender to his romantic spell. Instinctively we look askance at Mulvaney or Mrs Hawksbee or Cottar, finding one stagy, another artificial, a third illusory; but we welcome brave Little Frog and grumbling old Baloo as good companions on life's highway. Because these characters are here to stay, many regard the Mowgli stories as the most enduring of Kipling's work in verse or prose.

Representative Novelists

Outstanding among fiction writers devoted to social reform is one astonishing figure with the revolutionary idea that in this scientific age the novelist should quit storytelling and write prescriptions. Speaking for himself, but using the editorial 'we' to assume a modesty which was no part of his character, he announced:

> The novel is to be the social mediator, the vehicle of understanding, the instrument of self-expression, the parade of morals and the exchange of manners, the factory of custom, the criticism of laws and institutions and social dogmas and ideas... We are going to write about the whole of human life. We are going to deal with political questions and religious questions and finance and politics and precedence and pretentiousness and decorum and indecorum, until a thousand pretences and ten thousand impostures shrivel in the cold clear light of our elucidations. We are going to...

At this point we interrupt the pronunciamento to ask,Who is this medicine man that so confidently proposes to cure all the ills of misguided humanity? How did he prepare himself for such a mighty work of healing, and how would he accomplish it?

HERBERT G. WELLS (1866-1946)

In the story of his life, *An Experiment in Autobiography* (1934), Wells tells us, rather boastfully, that he was 'born a cockney'. On many another page of the same record is the unconscious reflection of a man who has no idea of beauty or humour or reverence or goodness, not even of good taste. In his cockney world view human society is made up of shams, pretences, impostures, but is not hopelessly lost so long as he remains to do his work of redemption. To a scanty education of the common-school kind he added three years at the Normal School of Science at Kensington; but two of the years were wasted, he said, because the professors did not know their subject or how to teach it. Thereafter he let no occasion pass to remind his readers that he was 'scientifically trained'.

His Method

Beyond question, he took himself very seriously, and it is a tribute to his writing skill that many accepted him at his own valuation. In a busy age that has too few hours for leisure, readers want their ideas of education or religion or philosophy or science in capsule form, and Wells was their prophet. His typical method was, first, to arrange the 'ten thousand impostures' of society in related groups, and then do away with them one after another by a novel wherein a grain of amateurish science served, like a yeast cake, to leaven a mass of speculative opinions. Business impostures were thus slain by *Tono-Bungay,* moral impostures by The *New Machiavelli,* educational impostures by *Joan and Peter,* theological impostures by *The Soul of a Bishop.*

Of history Wells knew as little as of theology; yet confidently he wrote a voluminous *Outline of History* to prove that democracy is everywhere a sham, and that the only hope of nations is a World State to be ruled by supermen. As if the present were a field too small for his curative genius, he deals with the illimitable future in *A Year of Prophesying* and a dozen more novels that offer a troubled world but one alternative: we must take the proffered medicine or perish, and the time is short. Such is the doleful burden of *The Shape of Things to Come* (1933).

Personal taste is the only guide in making a selection from the Wellsian mass of preaching, prophecy, and prescription, with its fifty-one volumes of fiction and fifty-two volumes of what he calls 'philosophy and history', which are far from being the whole of it. Some readers may like his early sensational tales of the Jules Verne kind, such as *The Time Machine* (1895), which takes us back into the past or forward into the future, as we will. *Mr Britling Sees it Through* (1916) is a realistic portrayal of English society in the dark days of the First World War. Most readable of all, because most human and least 'scientific', is *The Wheels of Chance* (1896), which deals with the adventures of a poor clerk off on his bicycle for a holiday.

John Galsworthy (1867-1933)

Galsworthy was like Wells in his absorption in social problems, but in other respects a contrast—a finely cultured gentleman, a lover of solitude who refused the proffered honour of knighthood, and a craftsman who tried to make his every novel or play a finished work of art. Wells wrote as if firing a machine gun at the reader; Galsworthy, as if speaking with an equal in a cultivated prose style. One was confident he could remedy social ills by a scientific nostrum; the other, looking upon the masses of humanity as mostly victims of their own ignorance or folly, was content to reflect a social problem which we must somehow endure because there is no solution.

© Underwood & Underwood

John Galsworthy

Several of Galsworthy's early novels, written over the pseudonym 'John Sinjohn', failed to find a publisher, and to read them now, in a 'complete' edition, is to understand why they were rejected. After fifteen more years of training he wrote The Man of Property (1906), which raised him to the front rank of living novelists. In this first successful work he created a new type of fiction by 'balancing', as he said, the virtues and vices of his hero, Soames Forsyte, against the vices and virtues of other members of the same family—a method to which he held in his subsequent novels and plays. He never learned to tell a good story; but in stressing the development of character as the prime purpose of fiction he won the approval of critics who hold the same debatable theory.

Forsyte Saga

In his next novel he carried out his theme by portraying a second generation of Forsytes, and so became father of a school of fiction writers whose heroes or heroines are the progenitors of the characters of a succession of later stories, as if the family and not the individual were the unit of society. Still in love with his brain child, he told of other Forsyte generations, and collected them all in *The Forsyte Saga* (1922). A good way to get acquainted with his work is to begin with *The Man of Property,* dealing with middle-class Victorian society, and follow it with *Flowering Wilderness,* which reflects, with less than usual of his good taste, a younger generation 'disillusioned' by the First World War. The best single selection from his thirty volumes of fiction may be *Indian Summer of a Forsyte,* which is commonly regarded as his masterpiece.

Galsworthy Plays. The impression of a scene in a play, which one often gets from reading a chapter of any Galsworthy novel, is probably due to this author's habit of writing fiction in the morning and drama in the afternoon. Another of his habits was to turn an old novel into a new play by changing names, shifting scenes, and substituting dialogue for narrative. Thus his *Island Pharisees* (1904) reappeared as The Pigeon (1922), which dramatized a problem well known to charitable societies the world over. On one side is a group of ne'er-do-wells who insist on their right to go to the devil in their own way; on the other, a few earnest but misguided people who try to change these wild sheep into tame sheep, or, as one of them said, 'try to make rooks look white by washing their skins.'

Galsworthy's thirty plays are nearly all of the problem type. His favourite method is to stage two contrasting individuals, as in *Justice,* or two contrasting groups, as in *Loyalties,* and let the audience weigh their conflicting claims as in a balance. In explanation he wrote: 'Every grouping of life has its inherent moral; and the business of the dramatist is to bring that moral poignantly to the light of day.' Plot or story element was to him of no consequence. 'Take care of character', he said, 'and action and dialogue will take care of themselves.' He was a conscientious dramatist, one of the rare few who have scorned the old stage tricks that Roman comedians first used for their effect on the audience. In presenting different groups he tried to deal fairly with all classes. His sympathy for the unfortunate often led him to dramatize them as victims of social injustice where another sees them as victims of their own folly or carelessness. When in one of his prefaces he declared, 'The play is a picture of the human herd in its attitude toward an offender, heads lowered, horns pointed', he was out of tune with both nature and the stage that 'holds a mirror up to nature', and proved it by his own play, *Escape* (1926), wherein the human herd displayed its proverbial sympathy for the underdog.

The Play of Balance

All such problem plays are, at best, of momentary interest, their stage life being commonly as brief as a dance of mayflies in the spring sunshine; but Galsworthy's are of abiding interest to drama-study groups because of his mastery of technique. *Justice* (1910) and *The Silver Box* (1909) are good examples of his earlier work. and *Loyalties* (1922) of his failure to hold an even balance between two groups by permitting his realism to stray over the border of sentimentality.

James M. Barrie (1860-1937)

From a little Scottish village Barrie came to Nottingham in search of literary work, and found it on.a local newspaper. To the end of his long life he was by instinct a journalist, forever on the lookout for something he could 'sell' to the public, as Stevenson pointed out when he said, 'There's a journalist at his elbow—and there's the risk'. This does not mean or imply that Barrie was not also a literary genius, but only that his genius was thrifty. His thrift brought him wealth; his genius made him, next to Kipling, the most widely read author in the English-speaking world.

Of the man himself or of his intimate thoughts and opinions it is idle to write because, despite a deal of biographical and critical material, we simply do not know him. If friends ever penetrated the shell of his disguise, they have kept the secret well. With interviewers, who on rare occasion were permitted to meet him, he invariably played a game of hide-and-seek. Nor does a study of his work give us any sure indication of what lay behind his talk or his silence or his impishness. On the surface he is by turns playful, humorous, whimsical, pathetic, sentimental. Below this glitter is an undercurrent of satire, at times of cynicism, as if he were thinking, 'What fools these mortals be!' From the surface comes the prevalent impression that he was at heart a child; from the undercurrent, a hint that he assumed a childlike pose of innocence in order to fool multitudinous readers of the sentimental kind by giving them what they liked.

Lizzie C. Smith

James M. Barrie

Barrie's Fiction. He began by writing sketches of the dour folk of Kirriemuir, his native village, only to learn that he bored readers by his realism. Then he turned to romance, and found himself on the road to fame and fortune. From his mother, whom he immortalized in the biography *Margaret Ogilvy,* he received an honest account of the Scottish peasantry, of their poverty, their loyalty, their terrible theology. When they reappeared in his *Window in Thrums* (1889) or his *Auld Licht Idylls* they were the heroes or heroines of romantic tales that his mother called 'perfect blether', and that a host of readers welcomed as the work of a magician. Unexpectedly he had discovered a new field, as novel as the field

Kipling had found in India, and so became the father of a new school of fiction. Why it should be called the 'kailyard' (cabbage patch) school is still a mystery.

Barrie touched the height of his fame with *The Little Minister* (1891), a novel with a melodramatic ending, portraying a young minister who scandalized his church folk by falling in love with a gypsy girl. In truly romantic fashion the gypsy turned out to be a highborn lady of whom the church folk could be proud. This immensely popular novel was followed by *Sentimental Tommy* and its sequel *Tommy and Grizel*. It is said that criticism of these two works, one a disappointment to his readers, the other a bore, turned Barrie away from fiction. A more probable explanation is that when *The Little Minister* was dramatized and staged to crowded houses on both sides of the Atlantic, bringing the surprised author a larger royalty than he received for the original work, it dawned upon him that the novel was a far less profitable field than the theatre.

Barrie's Plays. Greek tragedies, like English miracle plays, were the retelling of well-known stories, and for that reason the audience, knowing how the plot must work out, could give attention wholly to the acting. The dramatization of *The Little Minister* was thus a revival to the many who had read the story, and it opened a new way to fortune at a time when drama-study groups were everywhere awaiting the latest stage novelty. Other contemporary dramatists—Pinero, Jones, Galsworthy, Shaw, and the rest—immediately published every play that had even a moderately successful run on the stage; but Barrie refused to follow the crowd until his dramatic work had ended. Then he earned the gratitude of literary historians by giving half of it to the bonfire. The better half, consisting of sixteen long plays and twenty-two one-act plays, he revised again and again, adding supplementary scenes or characters and sprinkling the text with descriptive notes on the action, before publishing them as the Complete Edition of 1929. Thus appeared a new type, called 'the drama-novel', which in Barrie's hands became the most readable of its kind in modern literature.

Of the long plays the greatest favourite at the time was *Peter Pan,* with its boy hero who would not grow up, and its scene a mixture of the present world with ancient Fairyland. Probably the most enduring as a stage comedy is *The Admirable Crichton.* In this play a shipwrecked family of the upper class find, to its amazement, that the butler is the only one who knows what to do when people are cast away on a desert island. So the servant reverses the traditional human roles by becoming the master. One of the most fascinating plays is *Dear Brutus,* dramatizing the wish of almost every man that he might have the chance to live his life over again. As a drama-novel it is good reading, of its kind; as a stage play it is impossible because it is hard to act, and because no theatre can reproduce the Elfland scene through which characters move like shadows from another world.

The Play of Dreams

Among the other plays Quality Street has the old-fashioned charm of such characters as we meet in Mrs Gaskell's Cranford, of happy memory, and *The Old Lady Shows Her Medals* is pure sentiment made visible. In the latter, as in most of the other one-act plays, Barrie has no interest in the great ones of the earth, who are the heroes or heroines of old romance. His sympathy is with children who have no toys, with grown people who have lost money or friends or lovers and who suffer proudly in silence, dreaming, like the Maud Muller of Whittier's ballad, of what might have been. His rare genius in the history of modern drama is that he, almost alone, can stage a winsome dream and give it human reality.

JOSEPH CONRAD (1857-1924)

Admirers of Teodor Jozef Konrad Korzeniowski, who adopted the simpler name on becoming a British citizen, are of the kind called 'few but select', many of whom regard him as the most artistic of modern novelists. Uncritical readers are puzzled by such high praise until they learn that, more than any other storyteller's, his work is largely a reflection of his own personality. That is an elusive quality, at best, and puzzling in this case because the personality is foreign and Slavic and uncommonly introspective.

Annan

Joseph Conrad

Conrad was born of aristocratic Polish parents in the Ukraine,where his father was imprisoned and his mother banished by the Tsar's officials. As an orphan he was educated by French tutors, from whose Gallic vanity came the idea that, as he said, 'French is the only modern language fit for literature.' At nineteen he went to sea on a square-rigger, and by twenty years of devotion to his sailor craft won the high rating of master mariner in the British merchant marine. During all that time he never met one of his own countrymen. Like the ancient mariner of Coleridge, he often felt

Alone, alone, all, all alone,
Alone on a wide, wide sea.

In speaking, as he did, of 'the loneliness that surrounds every human soul' he unconsciously told what manner of man he was and what he must write. In all probability he had read Hawthorne; certainly he was like the American novelist in brooding over life as a solitude encompassed by mystery, and in portraying human events as important only in their effect on character. The scene of his story, usually the sea or a lonely island of the South Pacific, is always in harmony with his sombre theme. His characters are rather shadowy, like strangers met in a foreign port, each with a story in his face, a story that can be only half told.

One quality of Conrad's work has been strangely misunderstood by those who place him among the realists of modern fiction. Of it he said, as recorded by James Maddox Ford in *Return to Yesterday* (1932), 'My task is, by the power of the

Two Qualities

written word, to make you hear, to make you feel, above all to make you see.' That would be sheer realism if Conrad had kept his eye steadily upon an external object; but that is what he seldom did. He was again like Hawthorne in portraying the effect that an object makes upon him who observes it. So he became a master of impressionism, which is poles apart from realism. To compare his descriptions of the sea with those of Cooper, who also was a sailorman, is to note the interesting difference. Conrad, in *The Nigger of the Narcissus,* looks within to portray the effect of the lonely sea on his characters. Cooper, in *The Red Rover,* looks out with the ever-youthful eyes of a sailor to portray the sea itself.

Another outstanding quality of Conrad's fiction is the ideal of personal honour which runs through it like a guiding thread of gold. When he pits a man against the hostile influences of the Tsarist regime in *Under Western Eyes,* or against the hostility of the unquiet sea in *Lord Jim,* the one test by which the man stands or falls is loyalty to his fellow men. That is a hard test, but beyond challenge, as if Conrad were saying, with Kant, 'I will not in my own person violate the dignity of humanity.' He is thus a profound moralist, but again with a difference. Unlike Thackeray, who followed his revered master, Addison, by interrupting his tale to preach morality, Conrad is content to let a character speak for himself by his actions, and to save his soul or lose it by loyalty or disloyalty to a moral ideal.

One hesitates to recommend this or that novel, because Conrad is not easy reading, and not for the many. Few will agree with his own judgment that *The Nigger of the Narcissus* (1898), portraying a tremendous voyage around Cape Horn, was his masterpiece; but the preface to that novel is an excellent summary of his artistic theory of fiction. One of his best characters is found in *Under Western Eyes* (1911), a novel dealing with life in the Ukraine under the Tsar's domination. *Almayeris Folly* and *An Outcast of the Islands* (1896) deal with characters stranded in some forgotten South Sea port. *Typhoon,* which gives its title to a collection of short stories, is notable for a superb description of a storm at sea. *Victory* is a departure from the author's alleged realism in that it verges on melodrama, and his one happy story is *A Point of Honour.*

ARNOLD BENNETT (1867-1931)

Bennett is an excellent example of the 'popular' novelists who are scorned by critics, but who win much larger audiences than do novelists whom the critics highly recommend. He was earning a scant living, as clerk in a lawyer's office when a newspaper offered £ 20 for the best condensation of a novel that many were then reading. Carelessly he tried for the prize, and won it, and was off to a running start on a literary career. He accepted frankly the fact that multitudes who read fiction 'just to pass the time' regard novelty as the chief literary virtue, and for them he produced an incredible amount of what he called 'frolics, fantasies and diversions'. Setting himself a stint of a thousand words a day, he wrote books to make money, as another man manufactures a patent medicine, and succeeded so well that at the height of his fame he was paid at the rate of two shillings for every word.

Five Towns Novels

It was an inspiration, no less, when this clever craftsman had the idea of dropping his trash long enough to put real men and women into fiction. He had grown up in a forgotten corner of England, the Five Towns of the pottery district, in Staffordshire, where the inhabitants clung to their old ways, thinking them better than the new, as no doubt some of them were. The resultant *Old Wives Tale* (1908) portraying the contrasting destinies of two sisters, one of whom eloped and the other stayed at home, won an instant and well-deserved success. Among the thousands who read it were critics who frankly voiced their surprise at finding figs where they expected only thistles. Enlightened by his triumph, Bennett planned a series of Five Towns stories, in the latest literary fashion set by Galsworthy in the Forsyte novels. His next work, *Clayhanger* (1910), was an even better portrayal of Five Towns characters; but *Hilda Lessways* was inferior, and the light that Bennett had seen went out like a candle flame in These Twain. In a score more novels lie produced nothing but trash mingled with sensationalism. To read his *Truth about an*

Author (1903), a sketchy and untrustworthy autobiography, is to meet a writer who would never know the difference between good literature and bad because of his conviction that whatever glitters must be gold. To read his *Clayhanger* is to conclude, sadly, that he might have been a great novelist.

SAMUEL BUTLER (1835-1902)

Butler was the literary 'bad boy' of the Victorians, whom he scandalized almost as badly as his namesake had scandalized the Puritans, and for the same reason—because he understood neither their idealism nor the moral earnestness from which it sprang. The earlier Samuel delayed printing his *Hudibras* for fear of consequences to himself; the later Samuel refused to publish his work, scornfully asking, 'What is the use of addressing people who will not listen?' So it happened that he was not widely known or even 'discovered' until the Victorian age had passed into history.

One of Butler's minor works, *The Authoress of the Odyssey*, satirized classical scholarship, and its theories about the authorship of the Odyssey and the Iliad, by proving that the epics of Homer were written by a woman who had a low opinion of braggart Greek heroes, as well she might. One of his few novels, Erewhon (a title made by rearranging the letters of 'nowhere') originated in Wordsworth's famous lines in the 'Intimations of Immortality':

> Our birth is but a sleep and a forgetting;
> The Soul that rises with us, our life's Star,
> Hath had elsewhere its setting,
> And cometh from afar.

From this poetic start, which is not expressed, he proceeds to humiliate humanity by telling how its children all lead a happy pre-existence, with liberty to continue it; how their curiosity is aroused by hearing strange tales about the world, and how only the silly ones elect to be born. Thus by implication he explains why human society is forever enmeshed in a net of foolishness.

Only one other satirist, Jonathan Swift, could have written such a satire, and Butler was his pupil, as detached, as coldly analytical, and almost as powerful as his master. This appeared in *The Way of All Flesh* (1903), a novel on which Butler worked twelve years, but which he refused to print until he was dying. It carries an autobiographical story through three generations in order to prove that family life is a prison where parents are the tyrannical keepers; that school education is a humbug; that moral and religious ideas have no foundation; that children should as soon as possible be sent into the world with the only two essential things, money and liberty to spend it as they please. This is not the whole accounting, but enough to suggest Butler's fundamental idea that the only sensible person in the parable of the Prodigal Son was the prodigal. Naturally we ask, Why should he or any man draw such a sordid picture of contemporary life?

The Way of All Flesh

One answer is that, as Swift had a touch of madness, so his disciple had a warped personality which made him see humanity in an evil light. Another, which comes as a vague hint from his interesting *NoteBooks* (1912), is that he was a keenly observant man who, in the role of the devil's advocate, would test every belief by assuming that the opposite is true. In either case *The Way of All Flesh,* judged as a piece of literature, is the most notable of modern satires in having a satanic power to make sensitive readers doubt truth by giving falsehood an appearance of plausibility.

Romantic Realism

From the satire of Butler to the gaiety of Locke is like passing from darkness to sunlight. While some novelists were copying the crass realism of Zola and other advocates of the theory that disease is the normal condition of humanity, others, like Locke and De Morgan, proved the superiority of romantic realism, a new literary term which is hard to define but easy to understand. For example, Jane Austen, in *Pride and Prejudice,* was a realist in dealing with ordinary characters in their everyday life. Walter Scott, in *The Heart of Midlothian,* was a romantic realist in that he portrayed humble characters in extraordinary or adventurous situations.

William J. Locke, an architect who worked by day and found relaxation by writing at night, had the genius to discover lovable characters in unexpected places. This was abundantly proved by *The Beloved Vagabond,* portraying a footloose fiddler who was to become one of the bestknown figures of contemporary fiction. His next novel, *Septimus* (1909), created another memorable character in the person of a hare-brained inventor, and surprised a host of readers by a play of humour that ranged from delicate wit to explosive hilarity. To read either novel is to feel the charm of a writer who knows how to tell a story, and who apparently has a song in his heart while telling it. The theme of all other of his novels, however eccentric they may appear, is that the one sure way to help a troubled world is the way of selfsacrifice. A fine reflection of his philosophy of life may be found between the lines of his *Three Wise Men.*

Locke

A surprising thing about William Frend de Morgan is that he had passed his sixtieth birthday and was confined to an invalid's room when he began to write fiction. His first work, *Joseph Vance* (1906), was no sooner in print, after several publishers had rejected the manuscript, than it was welcomed by a multitude of readers. This story of a boy of the streets, which he called 'an ill-written autobiography', is still notable as the precursor of a whole new school of autobiographical novels. It was followed by a companion piece and better story, *Alice for-Short,* portraying a poor girl on her upward way to womanhood. The theme is what Browning would have called 'a spark in the clod', a spark which turns to pure flame and burns away all dross. To read either novel is to be reminded of Dickens, with whom De Morgan had two things in common—the same hearty love of life, and the same unplanned method of plunging into the middle of a story, trusting heaven or human nature to bring it to a good end.

De Morgan

From the wide field of romantic realism we select three more novels, very different one from another, which are alike in that they are modelled on English rather than on French or Russian fiction. *The Divine Fire* (1904), by May Sinclair, has an emotional intensity to recall the best work of Charlotte

Three Novels

Brontë. That the author had studied her model appears in *The Three Brontës,* an intimate biography of the sisters whose work has for a full century been acclaimed by readers who like fiction with a thrill to it. *Joanna Godden* (1921), by Sheila Kaye-Smith, is a clear reflection of English country folk in the manner of Hardy and George Eliot, but without the pessimism of the one or the moralizing of the other. *The Good Companions* (1929), by J.B. Priestley, dealing with the haps and mishaps of a company of stage players on a tour of the English countryside would bring Dickens to mind if one could imagine that genius without exaggeration or sentimentality. By its sheer narrative power it recalls the fact, now almost buried under a flood of problem novels, that the prime object of a novelist is to tell a story.

A Modern Miscellany

The most striking feature of contemporary literature is that fiction, which began long ago when some children said, 'Tell us a story', is now regarded by many apologists as the most inclusive of all arts. As one of them said:

> The art of the novel embraces every sort of mental interest. Among those of fine natural endowment who approach it with sincerity and full strength are the best writers now living. The very fire of life glows in this art; its possibilities are beyond prediction, for fiction is the greatest educational force in the modern world.[1]

While many thus write novels to educate or reform us, as many more remain true to an older ideal. If fiction be indeed an art, they say, it should first of all give us wholesome pleasure; and these novelists who please us have a hundred readers where the others have only one or two.

The oldest stories, which we call epics, were every one a tale of brave adventure. That their kind is still alluring was made evident toward the close of the Victorian age by Rider Haggard, whose absorbing tales—*King Solomon's Mines, Allan*

Tales of Adventure

[1]Abridged from an essay by Eden Phillpotts, author of *Widecombe Fair* and more than fifty other novels that made him famous a few years ago and are now forgotten.

Quartermain, and the rest—still have power to keep readers wide awake when a problem novel makes them think more of their beds. Since his day the adventure story has been vastly improved by adding to the call of danger the literary quality of a finished romance. To take but one of many such romances, Jeffery Farnol won an immense audience by his *Black Bartlemy's Treasure* (1920), which includes also *Martin Conisby's Vengeance,* because the two form a connected pirate story. The author is even better in his historical romances, such as *Gyfford of Weare;* and best of all when he takes to the open road, as in *The High Adventure,* to meet in this prosaic age with all sorts of wayfarers and find in them some admirable quality or alluring oddity.

Mystery Stories

Mystery stories, a new version of the old Gothic romance, have won larger and larger audiences ever since Conan Doyle invented a famous character of fiction in Sherlock Holmes, the detective. It is the critical fashion to jeer at such 'popular' tales and to deny that they are either novels or literature; but that is a mere prejudice. The unnumbered readers who turn to a well-written mystery story for rest or relaxation or 'escape' when the day's work is done are of all classes, old and young, wise and simple. They read for enjoyment alone, and their literary taste may be quite as good as that of readers who acclaim our latest fantasy, the psycho-analytical novel.

While many novelists and dramatists portray modern society as a disease to be cured, it is refreshing to find one whose only purpose is to amuse his readers. Such is P. G.Wodehouse, who won his standing as the 'funny man' of contemporary literature with *A Damsel in Distress, Fish Preferred,* and a score more of the same kind. His typical method is to bring a varied company together in a country house, where they promptly fall into such a *Comedy of Errors* as only Puck or a lunatic might devise. With the solemn air of a philosopher he analyzes the situation, salting his analysis with tags of poetry and tatters of slang. When suspense rises to a climax and most of the company are on the verge of insanity, he deftly unravels the plot and brings his comedy to a happy end. It is all sheer nonsense, to be sure, but the nonsense of a fun-making genius. Sorrowfully we add that he apparently fell from grace, and certainly lost his large audience, during the Second World War.

Representative Poets

Several hundred volumes of verse have lately been written by symbolists, imagists, impressionists, traditionalists, and what not, but among them all there is none to hold for a day the rank of national poet that Tennyson held for half a life-time. Criticism of such an output, so huge, so varied, and so near, is further handicapped by the fact that many contemporary poets are merely experimental in trying to do an old thing in a new way.

The Younger Poets

This conclusion is manifest in the work of our 'younger poets', a title which at frequent intervals passes like a flaming torch from one group to another. At the present writing (1945) these younger poets as represented by Spender, Auden, MacNeice, and a few others—have apparently abandoned the traditional idea of Keats, that poetry is a reflection of beauty, in the conviction that the time has come for ugliness to have its poetic day. They look out upon an industrial world wherein are no blossomy meadows, no blue sky or singing birds or enraptured lovers, but only factories, smoke, noise, telegraph wires, workmen hurrying to their jobs; and from such an outlook they try to make a new kind of poetry. Certainly they write verse, often of good quality; but do they ever sing?

The question is fundamental because only a poem that sings has any enduring value. For poetry, if you would personify it, is the old nurse that sang to the world's childhood, and still sings. Her lyrics or ballads rise naturally from a heart touched by emotion, to find lodgment and welcome in other hearts that feel a like emotion. Housman, who for the moment holds a high rank among recent poets, voiced the same idea when he said, 'It is the peculiar function of poetry not to transmit thought but to transfuse emotion, that is, to set up in the reader a vibration corresponding to what was felt by the writer.' He spoke subjectively, for himself, but Noyes, the poet of a great promise that was not fulfilled, spoke objectively, for his readers, in saying that the function of poetry is 'to give rhythmic utterance to the thoughts and emotions of a people'.

Poets that Pass. There was a poet who was acclaimed as the worthy successor to Tennyson, and with good reason, because his early volumes seemed to combine the best qualities of two great poets, having the simplicity of Wordsworth and the romantic feeling of Keats. For his verse he was knighted, just as Tennyson had been raised to the peerage before him; but he refused the proffered honour of poet laureate for the reason, as he said, that a poet must be free to express beauty or truth as he sees it, and not as the Foreign Office expects him to see it. In the summer of 1935 our newspapers recorded the passing of this 'dean of English poets', and the news was sad because he had died neglected in a village whose very name was strange. An impressive chapter might be written of this one poet, highly honoured by one generation, and so easily forgotten that to speak now of Sir William Watson is commonly to hear the query, Who was he?

William Watson

Watson is symbolic of many another who won a temporary fame—Hardy, for example, who wrote good verse after he abandoned fiction because of sharp criticism; or Stephen Phillips, who wrote the most poetic dramas that have appeared in a lifetime; or Robert Bridges, poet laureate, acclaimed for his 'faultless poetic taste'; or Francis Thompson, who was called 'the Catholic Shelley' after Alice Meynell (another poet) had rescued him from the gutter; or William Ernest Henley, who wrote the superb national hymn quoted at the beginning of this chapter, and immortalized himself by his 'Invictus', beginning 'Out of the night that troubles me'; or Wilfrid Gibson, the poet of everday English life; or Walter de la Mare, whose poems of childhood won and deserved wide recognition; or Rupert Brooke, Siegfried Sassoon, and other poets of the First World War, a conflict in marked contrast with another and greater upheaval which has not yet produced a widely read poet or even a memorable poem. To make an end of our long list,

Austin Dobson, Sir Henry Newbolt, and Helen Parry Eden are but three of many more whose ephemeral but happy relations with their audience suggest Longfellow's lines:

> Ships that pass in the night, and speak each other in passing,
> Only a signal shown, and a distant voice in the darkness.

JOHN MASEFIELD (1878-1967)

Masefield, the present poet laureate, is a rugged kind of 'scop', or saga singer, who would have been at home in a viking ship, but who for forty years has found poetry in the seamy side of civilization. His subjects are mostly folk of the unfortunate or 'underprivileged' class, for whom he sings because, he says, 'To simple people poetry is a gift of the gods which fills out and makes radiant this life of ours;' which is but repeating in English what Bede said in Latin of the songs of Cædmon thirteen centuries ago. One's first and last impression of Masefield is that he is at heart a poet, a singer, but lacks the supreme 'gift', or whatever it may be, that enables a poet to give adequate expression to his deep feeling.

As a boy in Herefordshire, near the Welsh border, Masefield would run away from home to join in the songs, dances, and folk plays of villagers whom the world had forgotten. The same gypsy strain took him to sea, where he spent some tough years as a foremost hand and learned to be a sailorman the hard way. Next he was an odd-job man in New York, and a little later a hack writer in London. A volume of Chaucer which chance put into his hands was the turning point of his life. With the reading of it came a resolve to dedicate himself to poetry, and from that day to this Chaucer has been his revered master. When the First World War broke out, he played a man's part, either at the front or in charge of a hospital ship or as the eloquent voice of England's propaganda in America. Still later, as official historian of the war, he wrote *Gallipoli,* a superb prose story of that heroic but unsuccessful attempt to capture the Dardanelles. To read it is to make even his admirers think that he might have won a greater reputation as a prose writer.

His first books of verse—*The Everlasting Mercy, The Widow in the Bye Street,* and *Dauber,* the last-named telling of an artist who went to sea in order to learn how to paint it, and who was done to death by a heartless crew—were scornfully dismissed by critics as 'an attempt to put brutality into verse'. There were good grounds for the stricture; but Masefield stoutly defended his work, saying, in effect, that poetry should be a reflection of common life and written in the common tongue, even when that tongue is foul or brutal. The first part of the saying may be true; the rest is a denial not only of poetry itself but of Masefield's own verse, which with the years grew steadily in refinement without losing its force or clarity. Those who read poetry for its own sake might well leave these early works to the end, and little of value will be missed by forgetting to return to them.

Crude Early Works

Underwood & Underwood

John Masefield

What to Read. To get acquainted with Masefield, read, in his *Collected Poems* (1932), three lyrics wherein he unconsciously tells us of himself and his subject. 'The Seekers' reveals his philosophy or attitude toward the world by portraying humanity on its way to a City of God where beauty dwells and radiant people meet, but never getting to the end of the road. 'A Consecration' outlines his chosen subject—not the great ones of earth but such humble men and women as he has met on sea or land. 'A Biography' looks back to recall what he has most valued in life, and what 'golden moments' he keeps among his cherished memories. If a single selection is to be made from his twenty-nine books of verse, read *A Letter from Pontus and Other Verse* (1936). The alleged 'letter' is what Browning would have called a dramatic monologue, spoken by Horace, a poet exiled from his beloved Rome. Though the subject is thus Roman and classical, every line is such as could be written only by a modern Englishman who speaks the tongue of the common people. Other of the poems are likewise far from being beautiful or melodious, if compared with the work of Keats or Shelley; but they are English to the core, and so reflect Masefield's outstanding quality—his intensely English spirit.

Next in order are a few selections from *Salt Water Ballads* (1902), the first poems since Anglo-Saxon days to be written by a sailor, though they hardly prove what Masefield said:

> It has not been done, the sea, not yet been done
> From the inside, by one who really knows.

Notable among his *Selected Poems* (1922) are 'Beauty', 'Her Heart', and 'Being Her Friend'; a few gypsy songs, such as 'The Tewkesbury Road' and 'The Vagabond', and especially 'Cargoes', which in three short stanzas symbolizes as many civilizations. 'August, 1914', written in commemoration of England's entrance into the First World War, is typical of the best poems produced by the conflict, and is rarely beautiful in its reflection not of waving flags or marching men but of quiet English fields that in times present, as in times past, are as lovely as remembered faces to men who leave them to answer the call of country.

Among his long narrative poems *Right Royal* is the tale of a horse race, *King Cole* takes us afoot with a travelling circus, and *Midsummer Night* retells some of the old Arthurian legends. Longest and, even to the author's admirers, hardest to read is *Reynard the Fox,* which attempts to repeat what Chaucer did in his *Canterbury Tales,* that is, to portray a cross section of contemporary English life.

Reynard the Fox

Chaucer selected for his masterpiece the most picturesque feature of his own age, a pilgrimage, and was content to individualize 'nine and twenty in a companye'. Masefield selected a very picturesque feature of our later day, a fox hunt, but failed to limit his company. In the first part of the narrative he tries to individualize a score of huntsmen, twice as many horses and hounds, and a motley crowd of countryfolk, who are attracted to a 'meet' as children to a circus parade. In the second part he tells a great deal of vulpine history, much of it at variance with natural history. In the third part he portrays a very long chase from the viewpoint of the hunted animal, and by this time the reader's interest flags or goes to sleep. One explanation may be that Masefield tries to put too many characters or events into the forefront of his picture, without making any artistic selection of his materials. The inevitable result, as with most overlong narratives in verse, is an impression not of a finished and readable poem but of a *few* lines of good poetry scattered like wildflowers over a barren landscape.

ALFRED NOYES (1880-1958)

'Anglers and poets must be born so', said Izaak Walton; but the poetry of Noyes, like the fly which the angler uses as bait, is mostly of the made' kind. Evidently he had no natural talent for singing, such as we find in the work of Burns or of Whittier, and no inhibiting idea that poetry is a gift that only the gods can bestow. To him poetry was a tonic, not hard to compound, to which people respond as naturally as to sunshine or fresh air. That is why, as a student at Oxford, he studied poetry in order to learn the secret of its appeal to men of all lands and times. Deliberately then he not only chose poetry as a profession but proved, by making a good living, that it can be a paying profession. So he became, more than any other writer, representative of an age which is supposed to be incurably prosaic, industrial, mechanical, but which responds as readily as any other to the charm of singing words. On the practical side, for he looks and acts more like a business man than a poet, he uses verse not to reflect the social trend of his age but as an influence to set the trend in forward motion. As he said, to quote his idea rather than his precise words:

> The basis of all poetry is a sense of rhythm, and because it is an un-changeable part of human nature, as strong in the civilized man as in the savage, whoever gives rhythmic expression to the thought and emotion of a people will unite them, as no statesman or philosopher can, in a common fellowship of understanding.

In other words, there is nothing like a song to make men forget their differences and remember their common humanity. Such was the idea of Housman when lately he said that the function of poetry is to transfuse emotion; and such the idea that John Skinner put into rollicking verse three centuries ago:

> Come gie's a sang Montgomery cried,
> And lay your disputes all aside;
> What signifies for folks to chide
>   At what's been done afore them?
> Let Whig and Tory all agree,
> Whig and Tory, Whig and Tory,
> Let Whig and Tory now agree
>   To drop their whip-mig-morum.
> Let Whig and Tory all agree
> To spend the night in mirth and glee,
> And cheerful sing, along wi' me,
>   The reel o'Tullochgorum.

What to Read. One of Noyes's early poems, 'The Barrel Organ', is typical of all his best work in that it tells, by implication, what a harmonizing influence rhythm can be in a discordant world. Because his theme is not some wandering minstrel in the form of an organ-grinder but minstrelsy itself, he lifts a tune above the clatter of London streets to show its effect on all who hear it—the same effect that one sees in the brightened faces and dancing feet of children when a hurdygurdy sends a melody like a breath of springtime into a crowded tenement district. Here or there the rhythm changes as if to reflect the sad or happy feeling of different hearers, and the repeated line 'Come down to Kew in lilac time' has the haunting suggestion of a melody that rises not from the barrel organ but from the heart of the audience, like a memory of happy days. The final impression, after reflection, is of a vanished age when someone on the village green raised a song in which others joined, an age when poetry and folk song were the same thing and the only expression of a community spirit.

A good companion piece is 'Newspaper Boy', which is the ballad not of any particular newsboy but of the response of a crowd to his street cries. Among other short poems, 'A Tramp Transfigured' reflects the author's purpose to make his work a unifying influence in human society. 'The Wagon' has a mystic undertone that is present in all ancient poetry. 'The Highwayman' is one of his best narratives, and has the virtue of brevity. 'The Song Tree' (found like a grain of wheat in the chaff of *Lord of Misrule)* should be printed at the end of Noyes's twenty-eight volumes as a reflection of what poetry has meant to him, and what he would have it mean to others.

These, with other readable lyrics in the four volumes of his *Collected Poems* (1910-1927), were mostly written when Noyes was ranked among the 'younger poets.' Then he came to America, took to the lecture platform, became professor of poetry at Princeton—and lost the greater part of his audience, because his verse had lost its singing quality.

Long Narratives

Among his long and laboured works *Sherwood,* perhaps the best of the lot, is a dramatized version of Robin Hood legends. *A Forest of Wild Thyme* reintroduces us to Miss Muffet, Little Boy Blue, the Sparrow that killed Cock Robin, and other half-forgotten characters of nursery days. *'Tales of the Mermaid Tavern'* tries to interest us in the imaginary conversations of Raleigh, Shakespeare, and other famous Elizabethans. *Drake* is the story of that sea dog told in blank verse, with occasional lyrics to relieve the monotony, and preceded by a tediously long Preface, all Exordium, and a First Book, which only delay the start. The most ambitious work ever attempted by a modern poet is *The Torch-bearers,* a three-book narrative which attempts to tell of science and scientists through the ages, only to prove that the subject is not for poetry.

There was a time when Southey wrote long romances in rhyme because verse narrative was then the literary fashion, and a later time when readers thought Tennyson's *Enoch Arden* a good novel; but any poet who would hold a present-day audience should deeply impress on his mind the legend that visitors saw graved on the door of Cotton Mather's study: 'Be short.'

A. E. Housman (1859-1936)

Housman is one of the most individualistic of contemporary poets, being in this respect comparable only with Conrad the novelist. From his verse we learn, first, that he regarded humanity as an inconsequential part of the mighty life of nature, with its rhythmic flow of life and death, like the tides that endlessly come and go; and second, that as a Stoic kind of philosopher he must endure his lot bravely, without complaint, as a hopeless atom of helpless mankind:

> They say my verse is sad: no wonder;
> Its narrow measure spans
> Tears of eternity, and sorrow,
> Not mine, but man's.

From his friends and a few published letters we learn that Housman was a professor of Latin, a shy man, reserved in manner, solitary of habit, whose scholarly work was to edit old manuscripts that would be read by nobody except, perhaps, another Latin professor. For recreation he would walk alone in the fields, thinking of nothing in particular, until, as he said, 'there would flow into my mind with sudden and unaccountable emotion a line or two of verse, accompanied by a vague notion of the poem of which they would be a part'. Over these lines, which elder poets might have regarded as a gift from heaven, he laboured from time to time; not any time but only when, as he said, 'the spring bubbled up again'. One of two results followed: either he threw the lines away or he revised them again and again, cutting out every superfluous word, reducing his poem to the unadorned simplicity of a diamond or a violet. He was a fastidious craftsman, severely critical of his own work, which he collected in two tiny volumes, *A Shropshire Lad* (1896) and *Last Poems* (1923). After his death his brother Laurence, a dramatist and novelist, published *More Poems* (1936), containing work that Housman had rejected.

With this introduction, open *A Shropshire Lad* to read and remember whatever appeals to your own taste. The poems are all

Sad Songs

of the 'local' kind, reflecting a corner of rural England

where the poet spent his boyhood; hence the aura of nostalgia that envelops them, as of longing for something that is gone forever. Each poem is a finished work of literary art; and a few—such as 'On Wenlock Edge', 'Into My Heart', and the lyric beginning 'When I was one and twenty'—are rightly called 'classic', because they show the power of simple words to stir a responsive emotion, which is the magic of all enduring verse. Though the poems deal with youth exclusively, they reflect nothing of joy, faith, hope, high endeavour, or any other of the interests with which that period is forever associated. It is not a youth who speaks to us in the perfect lines, but a man who evidently had no natural youth and can only regret the loss.

In the second volume his mood deepens into a settled resignation, as of one who must live on aimlessly, thinking that life is hardly worth the living. Cavalier poets, as you may remember, cultivated a melancholy mood when their world of Stuart royalty was falling to pieces; but because their melancholy was brightened by hope their best lyrics were gay rather than sombre. Housman could see nothing to hope for in this latter day of democracy; even its triumph over tyranny in the First World War passed unnoticed. Looking into the glass, he mistook his own face for that of mankind; and what some critics have called his realism is, from another viewpoint, a romantic denial of human nature and human history.

George Bernard Shaw (1856-1950)

'I write plays with the deliberate purpose to convert the nation to my opinions', said Shaw, another medicine man who would use the stage, as Wells used the novel, to reform society. The essential difference between their chosen 'tools' is that the novel is a story designed to be read by an individual in solitude, and the drama is a social spectacle designed to be acted in a crowded theatre. Hence the debatable question, Is the drama a form of literature?

Assuming for the moment that the right answer is affirmative, another question follows: Was Shaw a dramatist or a showman? In view of clashing opinions, the only valid answer at present is that he fathered a new type, called the play of ideas, and that for some thirty-odd years he was the most talked about personage in the dramatic world. That he wrote much drivel which he thought was excellent drama is generally admitted; but he also wrote several plays that others thought excellent, and these are the most debatable of all because his characters are only puppets to voice his ideas, and because he so often spoils a good dramatic scene by his irrepressible posturing and clowning. Our first purpose here is to understand, if possible, a playwright whose work is sometimes puzzling and at times repellent, by quoting his own estimate of himself and by examining one play that reveals his dramatic method.

The Man and His Method. Shaw was born in Dublin, of parents who were originally of English stock. As he said, with his incurable bent for standing truth on its head, 'I am a typical Irishman. My family came from Yorkshire'. His mother, an amateur singer, supported the family by giving music lessons. Of what he called 'the most completely wasted part of my life' he wrote: 'I never learned anything at school, but took refuge in total idleness. My parents went their own way and let me go mine. Thus the habit of freedom, which most Englishmen never acquire and never let their children acquire, came to me naturally.'

Underwood & Underwood

George Bernard Shaw

Leaving a useless school at fifteen, he worked for a few years as clerk in a land-agent's office. Next, he followed his mother to London, where he now and then earned a few shillings, but never a living, by writing socialistic pamphlets and advertisements for a patent medicine. After trying a few novels, which he could not sell to a publisher, he got successive jobs as music critic on one newspaper, as art critic and drama critic on another. Of music he knew a little, of art or drama nothing; but he had a naturally keen intellect, a vast conceit, and what the Irish call a 'gift of gab'. Having learned as a drama critic the stage tricks that have been used over and over again since Roman days, he proceeded to show what a modern play should be by writing one himself. His first comedy, *Widowers' Houses* (1893), made a mild 'hit' by its novelty, and he was off on a dramatic career.

Shaw was then thirty-six years old, a man of surprises who had really learned nothing and thought he knew everything worth knowing. The 'freedom' of which he boasted was that of the Prodigal Son—to disinherit himself from the past with all its culture and become anti-government, anti-Church, anti-State, anti-everything that Englishmen honoured or revered. His forty-odd plays were mostly 'against' the established order, and written, as he declared, with intent to make Englishmen drop their outworn beliefs and accept his own, which were invariably of the opposite kind. His motive, as voiced in one or another of the interminable prefaces that explained his plays, was to knock all 'romantic notions' out of English life and literature—a thing which might be more easily done if romance were not so deeply ingrained in human nature.

Of himself he said, 'They tell me that so-and-so is no charlatan. Well, I am. Like all dramatists, I am a natural born mountebank.'

Self-drawn Portrait

And of his superior talent, 'I know of no man, with the possible exception of Homer, for whose intelligence, in comparison with my own, I have more contempt than for Shakespeare.' His contempt for Americans, whom he had never met, became wrathful when his *Simpleton of the Unexpected Isles,* staged here in 1935, was criticized as shallow talk masquerading as drama, and he answered from across the sea: 'Any reporter who has become stage-struck by seeing a dozen crude melodramas thinks himself qualified to deal with Sophocles, Shakespeare, Goethe, Ibsen and Tolstoi, to say nothing of myself.'

There is more to this self-drawn portrait, much more of the same kind; but in that last word 'myself' is the measure of Shaw's world. In explaining why he drew such topsy-turvy pictures of historic characters he said, 'I deal with all periods but I never study any period but the present. I have no clue to any personage save that part of him which is myself. I represent historical characters as saying the things they would have said if they had known what they were doing.' Made confident by such inner enlightenment, he portrayed Caesar, in *Caesar and Cleopatra* (1901), as a jester who had the sense to use the stupidity of other people for his own advantage, and so became a great man in the silly opinion of historians.

Typical Shaw Plays. American readers might well begin with *The Devil's Disciple,* which was written for our instruction and staged only in this country. The time of the play is 1777, during our War of Independence, and the theme is an incident of Burgoyne's invasion. One might naturally think that any dramatist who deals with a foreign country would at least consult a map and a primer of history; but Shaw gets his ideas of geography as well as of historical characters from his own head, and we must take him as he is.

The Devil's Disciple

The scene is located in New Hampshire, then a wilderness of forests and mountains, through which Burgoyne leads his army to Boston, and from that city down the Hudson to Albany. As well might Shaw, in staging a French invasion of England, have portrayed the enemy as marching around the English Channel to Glasgow and down the Clyde to London. Incidentally, Burgoyne is dramatized as leading a campaign of brutality and terror; which is bearing false witness against the dead because, as it happened, 'Gentleman Johnny' Burgoyne was especially careful to respect the rights of civilians. Here is an outline of the plot:

The evil genius of the play is an American mother of Puritan stock, a repellent creature, who has won 'a large reputation for piety' by making herself as disagreeable as possible. Her son Dick, hero of the action, is a ne'er-do-well who escapes the maternal tyranny and hypocrisy by running away to become a smuggler, an outcast, a willing disciple of the devil.

One of Burgoyne's victims is a clergyman, condemned to be hanged because he has warned American rebels of the British approach. Dick makes use of an old stage trick to enter the jail and take the clergyman's place. He is being led out to death when he is saved from the gallows by another stage trick, a reprieve at the last moment. The moral of the play is dramatized in the final scene, when it is proposed that Dick shall take the clergyman's place in the pulpit also, because only a disciple of the devil knows how to preach true religion.

Why did Shaw write such melodramatic stuff, brightened by-clever dialogue and made thrilling by old stage tricks? Because he had a violent prejudice against every form of established religion and, in his own words, used the stage to 'convert a misguided people'. That is not a high dramatic motive, but it is the only one he used from first to last. In a long preface to *The Doctor's Dilemma* (1906), for example, he jeers at physicians for their ignorance and quackery; or in two plays, *Candida* and *John Bull's Other Island* (1907), he flouts stage conventions; or in three plays, *Divorce, Getting Married,* and *You Never Can Tell,* he airs his low opinion of social traditions. And so on through a long list, the more a play changes its name the more it remains the same thing—a lusty beating of whatever the author happens to dislike. That is why he creates not characters but only puppets to repeat his opinions, and defines the play as 'anything that holds the attention of an audience for two and a half hours on the stage of a theatre'.

Suggestions for Reading

To those who read dramatic literature for pleasure three Shaw plays can safely be recommended. *Arms and the Man,* an amusing satire on military heroes, became more amusing when Oscar Straus changed it into *The Chocolate Soldier,* a musical comedy. *Fanny's First Play,* a favourite with drama-study groups, keeps two comedies running by the old stage device of a play within a play. *Pygmalion* dramatizes the Greek myth of a sculptor who fell in love with an ivory statue, which at his prayer was changed into a living woman. With his propensity for making a burlesque of whatever subject he touched Shaw ignored the original theme, the love of beauty, and turned a girl of the slums into a woman of fashionable society by giving her a few lessons in correct speaking.

Alone among his many plays *Pygmalion* drew large audiences when it was transformed into what the English call a cinema play and we call a movie.

The longest plays, a half score of them, were designed to give us new conceptions of history or of the human race. *Saint Joan* (1923), best of the lot, portrays the Maid of Orleans as an ordinary country girl whose common sense was in tragic contrast with the stupidity of her enemies. *Back to Methuselah* (1922) puts a few puppets on the stage to talk for six mortal hours about Shaw's borrowed notion of what philosophers were then calling 'creative evolution'. *Charles the Second* (1939) employs several different puppets, including Nell Gwyn and George Fox, to prove by their talk that the merry Stuart monarch was not so bad as historians have painted him. Like the shorter plays, they challenge us by their novelty alone. If after reading any two of them, or any twenty, you conclude either that Shaw was a great dramatist or that he was a clever sensation-monger, do not misdoubt your own taste, because in either case there are critics in good standing who will agree with you.

The Celtic Revival

The term Celtic Revival applies to a school of writers who of late years have been calling attention to a wealth of unused literary material in Ireland, as Kipling had done for India and Barrie for Scotland. The school probably originated in a lecture by Stopford Brooke, a famous literary historian, on 'The Need of Getting Irish Literature into the English Language'. Its changing centres have been the Irish Literary Society of London, the National Literary Society of Dublin, the Irish Literary Theatre, and the later Abbey Theatre (1904). Among its exemplars are Hyde, Lady Gregory, Yeats, and Katharine Tynan, to name only four of its many scholars, poets, dramatists, and storytellers.

The original purpose of the revival was to awaken interest in what was called ancient bardic literature.This was a misnomer, because the bards had no written literature; the first rule of their schools was that every tale in verse or

Bardic Tales

prose must be committed to memory verbatim, and never under any circumstance committed to manuscript. The bardic tales were first recorded in Latin by missionary monks, who collected, it is said, enough to fill over a thousand volumes, few of which have ever been printed. Their chaotic quality may be judged by the contents of one volume, wherein the many tales are grouped under nine heads: Destructions, Battles, Voyages, Caves, Tragedies, Courtships, Loves, Elopements, and Migrations.

One series of tales, taken at random from any volume, may deal with the bard Oisin (Ossian), who got his themes from a whisper of leaves and his melody from the cry of departing birds; another series, with the warrior Cuchulain (variously spelled), who after killing a multitude of enemies cooled off by taking three baths, the first in boiling water, which was so overheated by this temper that it burst the tub; a third series, with the mysteriously sorrowing Deirdre, who is vaguely suggestive of the Niobe of Greek legend. Whatever the subject, bardic tales are all alike in transporting us into a world of enchantment where Nature is a whispering gallery, and the very air is magical, and death is but a transition to a realm of beauty where people are forever young and the time is always morning.

It is possible that these thousands of tales were fragments of a great epic that once had a central theme and dramatic unity. As taken down by the monks they were jumbled into a literary crazy quilt with plenty of gorgeous colour but no design or pattern. Until some genius does for them what Homer did for Greek mythology, or Malory for the Arthurian legends, they can never have more than a fleeting interest to modern readers.

Such was evidently one of the first hard lessons learned by writers of the new school. Taught by failure that the confused shadows of a dead mythology cannot be made lifelike, they turned to the abundant poetic and dramatic material cherished by living people of the Irish countryside, and in this field alone has their work any promise of enduring value.

Forerunners. A way had been opened for the revival by William Allingham, of Ballyshannon, in Donegal, whose six volumes of lyrics and ballads included *The Fairies* (1883), which made him spokesman for the Little People, as fairies are called in Ireland:

Wee folk, good folk,
Trooping all together;
Green jacket, red cap,
And white owl's feather.

Another and greater forerunner was Douglas Hyde, who was familiar with the ancient Gaelic language, and whose scholarship, as revealed in his book, *A Literary History of Ireland* (1899), was honoured by his selection as president of the new Irish Republic. Men of Irish birth who before him had won high rank in literature—Goldsmith, Sheridan, Burke—had always written in the latest English style; but he who would reflect the thoughts and emotions of the Irish common people, said Hyde, should use their 'fascinating turn of speech'. Even a slight acquaintance reveals that their speech is happily different from that of the 'stage' Irishman, as popularized in the novels of Samuel Lover, for example, or in the soldier stories of Kipling, or in the melodramas of Dion Boucicault. To make plain his idea, Hyde published his *Songs of Connacht* (1903) in double column, Gaelic in one, and in the other English as it is really spoken by his countrymen.This was the first notable appearance of Anglo-Irish, as it is now called, a speech 'as full of flavor as a nut or an apple', which Yeats ignored in his verse and Synge brought to perfection in his drama.

Anglo-Irish

William Butler Yeats (1865-1939)

Because of his varied work as editor, essayist, poet, playwright, and co-founder with Lady Gregory of the Abbey Theatre as 'the centre of Irish literature', Yeats is honoured as leader of the Celtic revival, more so in this country than in his own. The surprising thing about such leadership is that he was always a follower, first of Shelley and Swinburne, next of the mystic Blake, then of French symbolists, finally of theosophy or some other outlandish doctrine which turned him aside from his original purpose.

That purpose was, he said, 'always to write out of the heart of the Irish common people', and for it he was well fitted by natural gifts as well as by environment. For he was born near Dublin and educated in that city, and spent long vacations in the west country, where legend and folklore were as much a part of life as the curlew's call or the pungence of turf smoke. Unhappily, when he put his countrymen into literature he represented their cherished traditions as a mixture of Celtic, Norse, Hindu, and mongrel elements, saying, 'I have taken no pains to separate my own beliefs from those of the peasantry.' In another preface, to *Wild Swans at Coole* (1917), he speaks loftily of 'the transmagoria through which alone I can express my convictions about the world'. By that time the 'transmagoria' had become an affectation, and the poet was so lost in the poseur that even his friend Hyde cried out, sadly, 'Why can't he be natural?'

© Elliot & Fry

William Butler Yeats

Some such review of Yeats's career, however imperfect, is needed in order to clarify the different impressions made by his earlier and later work: one, of a natural-born singer, gifted and of large promise; the other, of a poet who has lost his way by following too many masters, all foreign, each as fugitive as a will-o'-the-wisp.

Like others of the revival school Yeats tried his hand at retelling Celtic mythology, as in *The Seven Woods* (1903), or in 'The Wanderings of Oisin' (in the volume with that title), or in 'The Madness of King Goll', or, more romantically, in 'Bale and Aillin'. The last-named is recommended, not because it is very good but because it may acquaint English readers with a tale that was endlessly told and retold in bardic schools—the tale of two separated lovers, each of whom dies on hearing that the other is dead, and so hasten to their reunion. To this old pagan tale someone added an epilogue: the lovers were buried at opposite ends of the same 'chapel'; from one grave sprang a red rose, from the other a white, and the climbing vines met and blossomed together.

French poets were so charmed by this ending that they must add it to the Celtic tale of Tristram and Iseult, the most widely poetized love story ever told or written, which crossed the world to India and back, suffering many changes in going or coming, until it was dramatized by Shakespeare as the Italian story *Romeo avid Juliet,* or was turned into the Wagnerian opera *Tristan und Isolde.*

The many plays of Yeats, which had an ephemeral interest because of their novelty, have already vanished from the stage; but a few of them, notably the *Land of Heart's Desire* and *The Shadowy Waters,* still charm drama-study groups by their poetic scenes. Of his lyrics and ballads, which have very uneven merit, one can only say to a reader, Dip into his first little volume, *The Wind among the Reeds* (1899) or into his *Collected Poems* (1933) to linger over 'The Lake Isle of Innisfree', 'Hour Glass', 'Ballad of the Fox Hunter', and any others that may appeal to your own poetic taste. By such minor poems, simple and melodious,Yeats will be longest remembered.

Representative Singers. A feature of Celtic mythology which still appeals to Irish country folk is that the ancient bards and warriors do not die; they only sleep until their songs or swords will again be needed. The common origin of Irish and Welsh folklore is suggested by the fact that the bard Merlin and the warrior Artva of the Arthurian legends are also represented as waiting, one in a crystal prison, the other in enchanted Avalon, for the call that shall again bring them forth to serve their country.

One of the first to share this ancient Celtic idea with modern readers was Katharine Tynan (Mrs Hinkson, 1863-1931) in her 'Waiting', which portrays Finn and his warriors sleeping in a cave of the Donegal hills until the harp summons

Katharine Tynan

them to battle once more for Irish freedom. Other writers of the revival who had larger audiences in Britain and America—Yeats, Lady Gregory, Synge, Lord Dunsany, and the rest—found small favour in their own land because, it was said, they misrepresented the Irish people. That is why many a play which they thought artistic raised a ruction in the Abbey Theatre. Katharine Tynan, who won instant favour by her 'Waiting', was by Irish folk regarded as 'one of them', for the odd reason that in some of her early books of verse, she came under the curse that afflicts almost every Irish writer, soon or late, by making him take sides in a political squabble. Other and better volumes, such as *The Wind in the Trees* (1898) and *Collected Poems* (1931), reflect a very wide range, from balladry to religion and from the sunshine of peace to the dark shadows of the First World War.

Russell

There was such lovable oddity in George W. Russell (1867-1935) that his admirers hardly knew what next to expect from a voluminous writer who modestly signed Æ to his published work. When he founded the Irish Theosophical Society of Dublin, for example, most Irishmen were as puzzled as if he had opened a school for the study of local herpetology in a country that has no snakes. Before that he was known as 'the Irish mystic', his mysticism being largely Oriental and wholly pagan in spirit. In it was a kind of radiant clarity, as of light from a hidden lamp, and a deep serenity which sprang from his conviction that there is in nature a divinity of which man's life is a part. Such is the tenor of *Homeward* (1894), a tiny book of verse wherein we meet him as a pilgrim passing through a world of shadows and singing on his way to the real or heavenly country. In another little volume, *Collected Poems* (1913), he published, as he modestly said, 'only such poetry as I would like my friends to read'. Open it to 'Dust', or to the lyric beginning 'And one thing after another', if you would know why Æ won and still holds an appreciative audience.

Colum

Of several other books of revival verse, two of the most notable are *The Four Winds of Eirinn* (1902), by Ethna Carberry, and *Songs of the Glens of Antrim* (1921), by Moira O'Neill, which reflect the singing quality of Irish folk songs without a trace of the sentimentality found in the older and more famous *Irish Melodies* (1834) of Thomas Moore, the friend of Byron. The most beautifully symbolic single poem is 'An Old Woman of the Roads', which appeared in Padraic Colum's first book of verse, *Wild Earth* (1909). The speaker is one who must wander from door to door, hiding deep in her heart the longing for what every woman wants—a little home of her own, with its fireplace and chair and clock and pretty dishes on a shelf. Not till we have read the six stanzas a second time, with understanding, do we discover that here is the voice of Ireland, pleading for a nation and a government of its own—a plea that has since been answered. The author is better known to drama-study groups by his *Fiddler's House* (1907), a three-act play portraying with skill and humour an Irish foil for the Woman of the Road. The hero is a young man, of vagabond spirit, who prefers to wander carefree through a world of variety rather than be tied down, as he says, to a bit of land and a house.

John Millington Synge (1871-1909)

Synge appeared on the Irish stage like a response to the saying of Ruskin, that what the literary world needs is a man who can see clearly and write what he sees. After vainly trying to interest readers in Celtic mythology, he was living at loose ends in Paris when he met Yeats, who advised him to go to a remote corner of Ireland and put the life of its people into literature. Taking the advice he settled among fisherfolk of the lonely Aran Islands, where he wrote six plays before his untimely death. Though none of them is ranked as a great play, they are in three respects the most interesting produced by the Celtic revival.

First of all, they deal at first hand with life as men and women now live it on the Irish sea coast. And life, whether in a crowded city or a fishing village, is everywhere a complex thing, having both tears and laughter, nobility and savagery, Christian ideals and heathen habits. Every aspect of life was to Synge a challenge, its folly no less than its virtue; but somehow he contrived to make its bewildering complexity leave a total impression of what he called the two essentials of drama—reality and joy.

Next, in contrast with the problem plays of Galsworthy and the Shavian play of ideas, a Synge play teaches no lesson, has no moral, calls for no reform. To him the drama was a scene taken from life by one who sought truth for its own sake. Whether staging a comedy or a tragedy, therefore, Synge was objective, impersonal, detached, keeping himself and his opinions wholly out of the picture. His whole dramatic credo was voiced in one terse sentence: 'The drama, like a symphony, does not teach or prove anything.

Finally, the language of the plays is the perfection of AngloIrish in that Synge took it from the lips of living men, as he took his plots from tales he had heard told by the fireside or at a county fair. Getting his language, as he said, 'from herds and fishermen, from beggars and ballad singers near Dublin, and from servant girls in the kitchen', he added a rhythm all his own, making his prose dialogue frequently have the emotional effect of natural poetry.

Typical Plays. One overlooked feature of every Synge play is a dimly sensed undertone of fear, not a fear of danger or hardship that the young can bravely meet or endure, but an old-age fear of weakness or want or helplessness. He is thus in harmony with bardic literature, wherein the object of all human endeavour is security, an end of which the old think constantly and the young think not at all. Almost invariably the old tales of adventurous youth hint of a time to come when youth is fled and man is left with only memories to comfort him. Such was the underlying theme of Synge in his romantic tragedy *Deirdre of the Sorrows.* Though it runs through all Celtic literature, Yeats glimpsed it but once and reflected it in the singing stanza:

> He hears the wind in the chimney above,
> As he bends to the fire and shakes with cold;
> While his heart still dreams of battle and love
> And the cry of hounds on the hills of old.

The best-known Synge play, and probably the most enduring, is *The Playboy of the Western World,* which added a picturesque word to our English vocabulary. Following is an outline of the plot, up to the climax:

The leading character, Christie Mahon, is a dull, witless, no-account lad who in a fit of temper hits his da (father) on the head with a spade, and leaves him for dead in the field. Pursued by imaginary terrors of the law, he flees across country to find refuge in a remote village of strangers. At a vague rumour that he has slain a tyrant, the women make a hero of him. When some men object, they are silenced by the warning that Christie, for all his quiet ways, is really a terrible fellow with a touch of madness that gives him the fury of an enraged lion and the strength of ten men. At that one of the scoffers steals away, saying, 'It's a fright, surely. I knew a man was kicked in the head by a red mare, and he went about killing horses a great while, till he ate the inside of a clock and died after.'

By this time Christie imagines himself to be of heroic stature, believing all that is whispered about him. Easily he wins the heart of the landlord's daughter, who deserts the young man to whom she was engaged, saying, 'Wouldn't it be a bitter thing for a girl to go marrying the like of Shaneen, and he a middling kind of scarecrow with no savagery or fine words in him at all?'

To the village comes old man Mahon, head bandaged, shillelagh in hand, following the trail of his runaway son. When told by the women that Christie is a jewel of a man, and about to wed the landlord's daughter, he breaks out: 'What, that man marry a decent and a moneyed girl! Is it mad yous are? Is it in a crazy house for females that I'm landed now?'

So the play runs on from one absurdity to another, with convincing realism because the simple-minded villagers believe what they hear, and trust their imagination rather than their common sense. It is unique among comedies in being humorous from beginning to end but without a single humorous character.

Very different in its appeal is *Riders to the Sea,* a one-act tragedy as simple as a cross over a soldier's grave, and as deeply impressive. There is no plot, and no need of one. We are present at a tragic hour when the fisherfolk look upon life and death.

The scene is a cottage kitchen, its walls hung with fishing gear. Our eyes question a few white boards standing in a corner, as much a part of the furniture as the table or the fireplace. We do not know that they are ready against the day when the body of a loved one may be washed ashore and there will be no time to get a coffin from the mainland.

The characters are old Maura, her two daughters, and her youngest son Bartley. Five other sons have been lost at sea. After a little home talk Bartley says goodbye and takes a roundabout course to the harbour. He is out of sight when Maura hurries to the hilltop to get a last glimpse of him. In her hand is a cane, left by one of her sons, to help her feeble steps up the stony path. All the sorrows of age are voiced in her words: 'In the big world the old people do be leaving things after them for their children; but in this place it is the young do be leaving things for them that do be old.'

Maura is again busy in the cottage when the muted roar of surf tells of a rising storm. Then another sound to make the heart stand still, the crunch, crunch of feet that approach heavily. Silently men enter, bearing something covered with a bit of sail—the body of drowned Bartley.

'The tragic poet', said Aristotle, 'purifies the minds of his audience by the emotion of pity.' Synge does that for us here, and something more. Alone among modern dramatists he portrays the victory of sorrow long endured. Maura will no longer be sorrowful when the surf is moaning and other women are keening the lost. Her sorrow will go out to them instead of hiding deep in her own heart. All her life long she has feared the sea. In place of fear now is peace, the peace of her sons, which can never again be troubled. There is only triumph in her final word: 'They are all gone now, and there isn't anything more the sea can do to me.'

Bibliography. From a library of books dealing with contemporary literature we have selected here a few that may attract the student, rather than a multitude that will of a certainty repel him.

History and Criticism. Cunliffe, English Literature in the Twentieth Century (Macmillan, 1933); Williams, Modern English Writers (Knopf, 1919); Beach, The Twentieth Century Novel (Appleton-Century); Phelps,

Advance of English Poetry in the Twentieth Century (Dodd, Mead); Morton, Renaissance of Irish Poetry (Washburn); Dickinson, Contemporary Drama of England (Little, Brown); Cunliffe, Modern English Playwrights (Harper); Malone, The Irish Drama (Constable).

Texts. Fiction. Pocket Books, Blue Ribbon Books, Triangle Books, Everyman Library, and other inexpensive editions. Poetry. Rittenhouse, Little Book of Modern British Verse (Houghton); Untermeyer, Modern British Poetry (Harcourt); Oxford Book of Verse, latest edition (Oxford University Press); Cooper, Poems of Today (Ginn and Company); Anthologies, several lately published. Drama. Whitman, Representative Modern Dramas (Macmillan); Watson, Contemporary English and Irish Plays (Scribner); Separate plays by Barrie and by Galsworthy (Scribner); Synge plays (Random House).

GENERAL BIBLIOGRAPHY

Every chapter in this book includes two lists, one of selected readings, the other of special works treating of the history and literature of the period under consideration. The following lists include the books most useful for general reference work and for supplementary reading.

A knowledge of history is of great advantage in the study of literature. In each of the preceding chapters we have given a brief summary of historical events and social conditions, but the student should do more than simply read these summaries. He should review rapidly the whole history of each period by means of a good textbook. Montgomery's *English History* and Cheyney's *Short History of England* are recommended, but any other reliable text-book will serve the purpose.

For literary texts and selections for reading a few general collections, such as are given below, are useful; but the important works of each author may now be obtained in excellent and inexpensive school editions. At the beginning of the course the teacher, or the home student, should write for the latest catalogue of such publications as the Standard English Classics, Everyman's Library, etc., which offer a very wide range of reading at small cost. Nearly every publishing house issues a series of good English books for school use, and the list is constantly increasing.

History

Text-books: Montgomery's English History; Cheyney's Short History of England (Ginn and Company).

General Works : Green's Short History of the English People, 1 vol., or A History of the English People, 4 vols. (American Book Co.).

Traill's Social England, 6 vols. (Putnam).

Bright's History of England, 5 vols., and Gardiner's Students' History of England (Longmans).

Gibbins's Industrial History of England, and Mitchell's English Lands, Letters, and Kings, 5 vols. (Scribner).

Oxford Manuals of English History, Handbooks of English History, and Kendall's Source Book of English History (Macmillan).

Lingard's History of England until 1688 (revised, 10 vols., 1855) is the standard Catholic history.

Other histories of England are by Knight, Froude, Macaulay, etc. Special works on the history of each period are recommended in the preceding chapters.

History of Literature

Jusserand's Literary History of the English People, 2 vols. (Putnam).

Ten Brink's Early English Literature, 3 vols. (Holt).

Courthope's History of English Poetry (Macmillan).

The Cambridge History of English Literature, many vols., incomplete (Putnam).

Handbooks of English Literature, 9 vols. (Macmillan).

Garnett and Gosse's Illustrated History of English Literature, 4 vols. (Macmillan).

Morley's English Writers, 11 vols. (Cassell), extends through Elizabethan literature. It is rather complex and not up to date, but has many quotations from authors studied.

Taine's English Literature (many editions), is brilliant and interesting, but unreliable.

Literary Criticism

Lowell's Literary Essays.

Hazlitt's Lectures on the English Poets.

Mackail's The Springs of Helicon (a study of English poetry from Chaucer to Milton).

Dowden's Studies in Literature, and Dowden's Transcripts and Studies.

Minto's Characteristics of English Poets.

Matthew Arnold's Essays in Criticism.

Stevenson's Familiar Studies in Men and Books.

Leslie Stephen's Hours in a Library.

Birrell's Obiter Dicta.

Hales's Folia Litteraria.

Pater's Appreciations.

Note. Special works on criticism, the drama, the novel, etc., will be found in the Bibliographies on pp. 9, 181, etc.

Texts and Helps (inexpensive school editions).

Standard English Classics, and Athenæum Press Series (Ginn and Company).

Everyman's Library (Dutton).

Pocket Classics, Golden Treasury Series, etc. (Macmillan).

Belles Lettres Series (Heath).

English Readings Series (Holt).

Riverside Literature Series (Houghton, Mifflin).

Canterbury Classics (Rand, McNally).

Academy Classics (Allyn & Bacon).

Cambridge Literature Series (Sanborn).

Silver Series (Silver, Burdett).

Student's Series (Sibley).

Lakeside Classics (Ainsworth).

Lake English Classics (Scott, Foresman).

Maynard's English Classics (Merrill).

Eclectic English Classics (American Book Co.).

Caxton Classics (Scribner).
The King's Classics (Luce).
The World's Classics (Clarendon Press).
Little Masterpieces Series (Doubleday, Page).
Arber's English Reprints (Macmillan).
New Mediæval Library (Duffield).
Arthurian Romances Series (Nutt).
Morley's Universal Library (Routledge).
Cassell's National Library (Cassell).
Bohn Libraries (Macmillan).
Temple Dramatists (Macmillan).
Mermaid Series of English Dramatists (Scribner).

Note. We have included in the above list all the editions of which we have any personal knowledge, but there are doubtless others that have escaped attention.

Biography

Dictionary of National Biography, 63 vols. (Macmillan), is the standard.

English Men of Letters Series (Macmillan).
Great Writers Series (Scribner).
Beacon Biographies (Houghton, Mifflin).
Westminster Biographies (Small, Maynard).
Hinchman and Gummere's Lives of Great English Writers (Houghton, Mifflin) is a good single volume, containing thirty-eight biographies.

Note. For the best biographies of individual writers, see the Bibliographies at the ends of the preceding chapters.

Selections

Manly's English Poetry and Manly's English Prose (Ginn and Company) are the best single-volume collections, covering the whole field of English literature.

Pancoast's Standard English Poetry, and Pancoast's Standard English Prose (Holt).

Oxford Book of English Verse, and Oxford Treasury of English Literature, 3 vols. (Clarendon Press).

Page's British Poets of the Nineteenth Century (Sanborn).

Stedman's Victorian Anthology (Houghton, Mifflin).

Ward's English Poets, 4 vols.; Craik's English Prose Selections, 5 vols.; Chambers's Encyclopedia of English Literature, etc.

Miscellaneous

The Classic Myths in English Literature (Ginn and Company).

Adams's Dictionary of English Literature.

Ryland's Chronological Outlines of English Literature.

Brewer's Reader's Handbook.

Botta's Handbook of Universal Literature.

Ploetz's Epitome of Universal History.

Hutton's Literary Landmarks of London.

Heydrick's How to Study Literature.

For works on the English language see Bibliography of the Norman period, p. 65.